Tweedell

MOLECULAR AND CELLULAR ASPECTS OF *Development*

Molecular and Cellular Aspects of

DEVELOPMENT

EDITED AND WITH INTRODUCTIONS BY

Eugene Bell

MASSACHUSETTS INSTITUTE OF TECHNOLOGY

 HARPER & ROW, PUBLISHERS, *New York, Evanston, and London*

✿ *Contents* ✿

4. ROLE OF THE NUCLEUS

5. CHROMOSOME DIFFERENTIATION

6. GENETIC CONTROL OF DIFFERENTIATION

7. ISOZYMES

✵ *List of Contributors* ✵

Number in parentheses indicates page on which article begins.

ABBOTT, J. Department of Anatomy, School of Medicine, University of Pennsylvania, Philadelphia (134)

ADA, G. L. The Walter and Eliza Hall Institute, University of Melbourne, Melbourne, Australia (360)

AUERBACH, ROBERT Department of Zoology, University of Wisconsin, Madison (230)

AUSTIN, CAROLINE M. The Walter and Eliza Hall Institute, University of Melbourne, Melbourne, Australia (360)

BAGLIONI, CORRADO International Laboratory of Genetics and Biophysics, Naples, Italy (236)

BEERMANN, WOLFGANG Max-Planck-Institut für Biologie, Tübingen, Germany (204)

BELL, EUGENE Department of Biology, Massachusetts Institute of Technology, Cambridge (340, 343, 410)

BOLLE, A. Biophysics Laboratory, University of Geneva, Geneva, Switzerland (245)

BONNER, JOHN TYLER Department of Biology, Princeton University, Princeton, N.J. (40)

BRIGGS, ROBERT Department of Zoology, University of Indiana, Bloomington (171)

BROWN, DONALD D. Department of Embryology, Carnegie Institution of Washington, Baltimore, Md. (333)

CHEVALLEY, R. Institut de Biologie Moléculaire, Geneva, Switzerland (245)

COHEN, STANLEY Department of Biochemistry, Vanderbilt University, Nashville, Tenn. (460)

DARNELL, JAMES E., JR. Departments of Biochemistry and Cell Biology, Albert Einstein College of Medicine, Yeshiva University, New York, N.Y. (340)

DE LA TOUR, E. BOY Institut de Biologie Moléculaire, Geneva, Switzerland (245)

DENHARDT, G. H. Formerly Division of Biology, California Institute of Technology, Pasadena (?45)

EBERT, JAMES D. Department of Embryology, Carnegie Institution of Washington, Baltimore, Md. (351)

EDGAR, R. S. Division of Biology, California Institute of Technology, Pasadena (245)

EPSTEIN, R. H. Biophysics Laboratory, University of Geneva, Geneva, Switzerland (245)

GALL, JOSEPH G. Department of Biology, Yale University, New Haven, Conn. (213)

GLIMCHER, MELVIN J. Massachusetts General Hospital, Boston (427)

GROBSTEIN, CLIFFORD Department of Biological Sciences, Stanford University, Stanford, Calif. (101, 381)

GROSS, JEROME Massachusetts General Hospital, Boston (416)

GROSS, PAUL R. Department of Biology, Brown University, Providence, R.I. (316)

GURDON, J. B. Department of Zoology, Oxford University, Oxford, England (333)

HAEMMERLING, J. Max Planck Institute for Marine Biology, Wilhelmshaven, Germany (194)

HODGE, ALAN J. Division of Biology, California Institute of Technology, Pasadena (427)

HOLTFRETER, JOHANNES Department of Anatomy, The University of Rochester, Rochester, N.Y. (3)

HOLTZER, HOWARD Department of Anatomy, University of Pennsylvania, Philadelphia (134)

ix

HOLTZER, SIBYL Department of Anatomy, University of Pennsylvania, Philadelphia (134)

HOMMES, FRITS A. Strangeways Research Laboratory, Cambridge, England (95)

HOTTA, YASUO Botany Department, University of Illinois, Urbana (306)

HUMPHREYS, TOM Department of Biology, Massachusetts Institute of Technology, Cambridge (78, 410)

KELLENBERGER, E. Laboratoire de Biophysique de l'Institut de Biologie moléculaire, University of Geneva, Geneva, Switzerland (245)

KING, THOMAS J. The Institute for Cancer Research, Philadelphia, Pennsylvania (171)

KIRK, DAVID L. Department of Zoology, University of Chicago, Chicago, Ill. (296)

KONIGSBERG, IRWIN R. Department of Embryology, Carnegie Institution of Washington, Baltimore, Md. (116)

LASH, JAMES W. Department of Anatomy, School of Medicine, University of Pennsylvania, Philadelphia (95, 134)

LERNER, A. MARTIN Department of Biology, Wayne Medical School, Wayne State University, Detroit, Mich. (340)

LEVI-MONTALCINI, RITA Department of Zoology, Washington University, St. Louis, Miss. (471)

LIELAUSIS, A. Division of Biology, California Institute of Technology, Pasadena (245)

MALKIN, LEONARD I. Department of Biology, Brown University, Providence, R.I. (316)

MAPES, MARION O. Department of Botany, Cornell University, Ithaca, N.Y. (142, 155)

MARCUS, PHILIP I. Department of Microbiology, Albert Einstein College of Medicine, Yeshiva University, New York, N.Y. (507)

MARKERT, CLEMENT L. Department of Biology, The Johns Hopkins University, Baltimore, Md. (267)

MEARS, KATHRYN Formerly Department of Botany, Cornell University, Ithaca, N.Y. (155)

MILLER, CARLOS O. Botany Department, Indiana University, Bloomington (481)

MOORE, RICHARD O. Department of Biological Chemistry, Harvard Medical School, Boston, Mass. (280)

MOSCONA, AARON Department of Zoology, University of Chicago, Chicago, Ill. (55, 296)

MOYER, WAYNE A. Coordinator of Secondary Science, East Brunswick Public Schools, East Brunswick, N.J. (316)

NEMER, MARTIN The Institute for Cancer Research, Philadelphia, Pennsylvania (323)

NOSSAL, G. J. V. The Walter and Eliza Hall Institute, Parkville, Victoria, Australia (360)

PENMAN, SHELDON Department of Biology, Massachusetts Institute of Technology, Cambridge (410)

PORTER, KEITH R. Biological Laboratories, Harvard University, Cambridge, Mass. (391)

ROSSETTI, FIAMMETTA Formerly Department of Zoology, University of Chicago, Chicago, Ill. (435)

ROTH, THOMAS F. Department of Biology, University of California, San Diego (391)

RUBIN, HARRY Department of Molecular Biology, University of California, Berkeley (496)

RUTTER, WILLIAM J. Division of Biochemistry, University of Illinois, Urbana (381)

SAVAGE, L. J. Department of Statistics, Yale University, New Haven, Conn. (40)

SCHMITT, FRANCIS O. Department of Biology, Massachusetts Institute of Technology, Cambridge (427)

SCOTT, ROBERT B. Department of Biology, Massachusetts Institute of Technology, Cambridge (343)

SKOOG, FOLKE Department of Botany, University of Wisconsin, Madison (481)

SMITH, JOAN Formerly Department of Botany, Cornell University, Ithaca, N.Y. (142)

SPARKS, CHARLES E. Department of Biology, Massachusetts Institute of Technology, Cambridge (236)

STEINBERG, C. M. Biology Division, Oak Ridge National Laboratory, Oak Ridge, Tenn. (245)

STEINBERG, MALCOLM S. Department of Biology, Johns Hopkins University, Baltimore, Md. (64, 76)

STERN, HERBERT Botany Department, University of Illinois, Urbana (306)

STEVENS, LEROY C.   The Jackson Memorial Laboratory, Bar Harbor, Me. (160)

STEWARD, F. C.   Department of Botany, Cornell University, Ithaca, N.Y. (142, 155)

SUSMAN, M.   Genetics Department, University of Wisconsin, Madison (245)

SZENBERG, A.   The Walter and Eliza Hall Institute, Department of Medicine, University of Melbourne, Melbourne, Australia (360)

TEMIN, HOWARD M.   McArdle Laboratory, University of Wisconsin, Madison (496)

TOWNES, PHILIP L.   Department of Anatomy, School of Medicine, University of Rochester, Rochester, N.Y. (3)

VILLEE, CLAUDE A.   Department of Biological Chemistry, Harvard Medical School, Boston, Mass. (280)

WALKER, JAMES B.   Department of Biology, Rice University, Houston, Tex. (285)

WEISS, PAUL   Graduate School of Biomedical Sciences, University of Texas, Houston (435)

WESSELLS, NORMAN K.   Department of Biological Sciences, Stanford University, Stanford, Calif. (381)

WIGGLESWORTH, V. B.   Department of Biology, University of Cambridge, Cambridge, England (447)

WILT, FRED H.   Department of Zoology, University of California, Berkeley (373)

ZILLIKEN, F.   Department of Biochemistry, School of Medicine, Nijmegen, The Netherlands (95)

✤ *Preface* ✤

Developmental biology—with its central issue, cellular differentiation—is a field upon which many disciplines have begun to converge. It is consequently a field which is being redefined by both old and new developmental biologists. It consists more now of a collection of related problems than of a unified continuous subject matter. This volume represents an attempt to focus on some of the problems through selections of key papers in fourteen different but closely allied areas. Each chapter of the book begins with a discussion of questions pertinent to it but is not intended as a comprehensive review; rather a device for summarizing the status of some of the problems and directing attention to others.

I have used the collection of papers for a first course in developmental biology at M.I.T.; but it is not meant to substitute for either descriptive embryology or classical experimental morphology. Some of both may be required for preparation which precedes or accompanies use of this book.

The book is intended, too, for graduate students and advanced scientists who wish to survey central contributions to cellular and molecular aspects of development.

The author wishes to thank Professor Mac V. Edds and Professor Tom Humphreys for reading his manuscript with great care and for making valuable suggestions. He also is indebted to his devoted secretary, Miss Esther Theodorou, and to a most efficient proofreader, Miss Lowell Ayers.

E. B.

Cambridge, Massachusetts
1965

MOLECULAR AND CELLULAR ASPECTS OF *Development*

1

Cell Association

No matter how cells are impelled to move—by internal or external stimuli, whether their movements are random or directed—most cells come to rest in an organized tissue fabric. They are integrated in the fabric into a functional whole. The cell movements of gastrulation and organogenesis, aggregation of slime mold amoebae, migration of pigment cells from neural crest, fertilization, congregation of lymphocytes at foci of infection, and reaggregation of dissociated cells are situations in which cells move and then come to a halt in their appointed places.

In nature and in experiments, cells which organize into tissues, organs, or organisms arrive at their destinations by random movements or their course may be regularly influenced by chemicals or by formed guides in the substrate. Most sperm, aggregating sponge cells, and dissociated embryonic cells move randomly. On the other hand, it is certain that response to a gradient of a chemical is an important factor in the aggregation of slime mold cells. The existence of a chemotactic substance (acrasin) which attracts amoebae to growing aggregation centers was first shown by *Bonner (1947)*.* Its chemical composition and its metabolic mode of action are unknown, but some details concerning its character and its active life span have been reported (Shaffer 1956; Sussman, Lee, and Kerr 1956). In the fertilization of the egg of *Campanularia* (Miller 1964), a chemical agent may be responsible for directing sperm movements. In the ferns malic acid or other organic compounds can assist the sperm in "finding" the bracken egg (Pfeffer 1884; Rothschild 1952).

There are no examples of chemotactic responses occurring in cells during development although the possibility that tissue cells lay down chemical trails (Rosenberg 1960) which might play a role in the morphogenetic organization of cell populations has been raised (Weiss 1961).

The term, "contact guidance," (Weiss 1941) has been used to describe the effect of a structured substrate on cell movements. For example the grooves in fish scales provide roadways along which cells will confine themselves; similarly the aligned macromolecules of a stretched gel serve to channel the movements of cells; also an organized tissue substrate can serve to guide the regenerating nerve fiber (Weiss 1955). It is not known, however, whether pigment cells or other moving embryonic cells reach specific terminals by contact guidance, by chemotaxis, by random movements or by combinations of these devices.

Why do cells stop moving? Some aggregating cells probably come to rest in a tissue or higher order structure as a result of descending a free energy trough

---

* Italicized references indicate articles which appear in this book.

1

(*Steinberg 1963*). Abercrombie and Heaysman (1954) found that fibroblasts grown on glass continue to move over the surface as long as no contact is made with neighboring cells. In migrating fibroblasts directional movements are attributed to the maintenance of the ruffled membrane which is called the "undulating locomotory organ" (Abercrombie 1961). When cell contact is established, movement ceases. Abercrombie called the phenomenon "contact inhibition." It is not known to what extent contact inhibition operates in the embryo.

Since the important observations of Holtfreter (1939) and *Townes and Holtfreter (1955)*, it has been realized (Weiss 1941) that a fuller understanding of cell surface properties is essential for further analyses of cell movements and cell associations. Although little is known about the characteristics of the cell surface upon which sorting out to form transitory or permanent association is based, much has been learned about the epiphenomena of cell associations. Some of the rules which govern the association of cells have been discovered. Through some mechanism of recognition, dissociated cells from mixed tissues ultimately sort out into homogeneous subpopulations. Even mixtures of embryonic cells from widely different organisms may result in subpopulations which are histogenetically consistent (*Moscona 1957*). Sorting out in accordance with tissue type need not be based upon qualitative differences in the cell surface binding apparatus (*Steinberg 1963*).

The first opportunity to characterize biochemically cell surface components which play a part in holding cells together has arisen through the work of *Humphreys (1963)*, who isolated from two species of sponges, species-specific factors required for cell aggregation.

There has been much speculation on the physical-chemical character of the binding between cells. This subject has been briefly reviewed recently by Curtis (1962) and by Rosenberg (1964), who also examined interfacial dynamics in a model system.

Some cells become more closely apposed than others, and some develop special surface modifications designed to keep them in a permanent relation with one another. True intercellular bridges as well as desmosomes and other adaptions are discussed by Fawcett (1958, 1961). In electron micrographs, cells seem generally to be separated by a space of about 100 to 200 angstroms. Nothing is known about what fills the space.

REFERENCES

1. Abercrombie, M. (1961). The bases of the locomotory behavior of fibroblasts. *Exptl. Cell Res. Suppl.* **8**:188–198.

2. Abercrombie, M., and J. E. M. Heaysman (1954). Social behavior of cells in tissue culture. II. "Monolayering" of fibroblasts. *Exptl. Cell Res.* **6**:293–306.

3. Curtis, A. S. G. (1962). Cell contact and adhesion. *Biol. Rev.* **37**:82–129.

4. Fawcett, D. W. (1958). Structural specializations of the cell surface. In S. Palay (ed.), *Frontiers of Cytology*, Yale Univ. Press, New Haven.

5. Fawcett, D. W. (1961). Intercellular bridges. *Exptl. Cell Res. Suppl.* **8**:174–187.

6. Holtfreter, J. (1939). Gewebeaffinitat, ein Mittel der embryonalen formbildung. *Archiv für experimentelle Zell Forschung.* **23**:169–209. Also in B. H. Willier and J. M. Oppenheimer (eds.), *Foundations of Experimental Embryology*, Prentice-Hall, Englewood Cliffs, New Jersey (1964).

7. Miller, R. (1964). Isolation of the chemotactant of *Campanularia* (*Laomedea*) *palceo calceolifera. Biol. Bull.* **127**:381.

8. Pfeffer, W. (1884). Locomotorische richtungsbeweguhgen durch chemische reize. *Ultersuch. Bot. Inst. Tubengen* **1**:364–482.

9. Rosenberg, M. (1960). Microexudates from cells grown in tissue culture. *Biophys. J.* **1**:137–159.

10. Rosenberg, M. (1964). Cell surface interactions and interfacial dynamics. In P. Emmelot and O. Mühlbock (eds.), *Cellular Control Mechanisms and Cancer*, Elsevier, Amsterdam.

11. Rothschild, L. (1952). The behavior of sper-

matozoa in the neighborhood of eggs. *Inter. Rev. Cytology* **1**:257–263.

12. Shaffer, B. M. (1956). Properties of acrasin. *Science* **123**:1172–1173.

13. Sussman, M., F. Lee, and N. S. Kerr (1956). Fractionation of acrasin, a specific chemotactic agent for slime mold aggregation. *Science* **123**:1171–1172.

14. Weiss, P. (1941). Nerve patterns: the mechanics of nerve growth. *Growth* **5**:163–203 (suppl.).

15. Weiss, P. (1955). Nervous system (neurogenesis). In B. H. Willier, P. A. Weiss, and V. Hamburger (eds.), *Analysis of Development*, Saunders, Philadelphia.

16. Weiss, P. (1961). Guiding principles in cell locomotion and cell aggregation. *Exptl. Cell Res. Suppl.* **8**:260–281.

Directed Movements and Selective Adhesion of Embryonic Amphibian Cells[1]

PHILIP L. TOWNES

JOHANNES HOLTFRETER

INTRODUCTION

One of the most striking features of early vertebrate development is the transformation of a spherical egg into a body of about equal size in which groups of cells have shifted into specific arrangements which foreshadow the tissue pattern of the adult organism. This transition occurs principally between the blastula and neurula stages. Throughout the history of embryology, these shiftings of cell associations and their subsequent segregation into germ layers and tissues have been of foremost interest to students of embryogenesis.

It was these transformations which prompted His (1874) to propose his famous, though no longer acceptable, interpretation of embryological phenomena in mechanistic terms. Roux (1894, 1896), in an attempt to relate tissue formation to the kinetic properties of individual cells, teased early amphibian embryos apart and recorded the movements and re-aggregations of the free cells in a medium of diluted egg white. Roux claimed to have found evidence that the cells produce diffusible substances which either attract or repel other cells in the immediate vicinity and which he considered to be essential agents for bringing about normal tissue aggregations and segregations. These claims about cytotropisms remained unchallenged for many years. When, finally, Voigtländer (1932) and Kuhl (1937) subjected them to a careful reinvestigation, they could not be confirmed. These workers found that no attraction nor repulsion between the separated cells could be detected and that the path of the individual motile cells is entirely at random; but when two or more cells meet by chance, they tend to unite, even if they are derived from different species or germ layers. Kuhl concluded that the phenomena were largely "pathological" and as such unsuited to serve as a basis for interpreting normal histogenesis.

A more optimistic attitude was adopted by Holtfreter (1938, 1939, 1943a, b, c, 1944, 1947a, b, 1948), who found that isolation of embryonic amphibian cells in an appropriate medium need not in itself interfere with their viability or differentiation, and that the method of isolating embryonic tissues or their cellular constituents, combined with the method of reuniting them in new combinations, offers valuable opportunities for a study of the factors involved in organogenesis. From his studies we may extract the following points relevant to our discussion.

[1] Reprinted by publisher's permission from *The Journal of Experimental Zoology*, volume 128, pp. 53–120.

Revision of a thesis submitted in partial fulfillment of the requirements for the degree of Doctor of Philosophy, Department of Biology, The University of Rochester.

1. The cellular mass movements of gastrulation-neurulation are controlled both by cell-specific and more or less stage-specific kinetic tendencies of the axially polarized cells as well as by inside-outside gradients of a rather obscure nature between the embryo or the complex cell aggregate and the ambient aqueous medium.

2. While, experimentally, individual cells from the various germ layers may exhibit tissue-specific tendencies of invagination, spreading or stretching, their movements are normally coördinated by means of a special structure, the surface coat, which unites the peripheral cells into a layer of interdependent units.

3. Although in a culture of dispersed cells from early amphibian stages any of the cells may unite indiscriminately with any other cell, the cells later separate and sort out according to tissue specificity. Holtfreter studied these phenomena in both composite explants (1939, 1944) and aggregates consisting of isolated and intermingled cells of different prospective fate (1943c). He concluded that the variety of tissue segregations, delaminations, dispersals and recombinations occurring in normal embryos could, at least largely, be attributed to stage-conditioned positive or negative "affinities" of the cells involved.

Weiss (1941, 1947, 1950) and Tyler (1946) suggested that selective cell adhesion involves the reaction of specific molecules at the cellular interfaces in a manner analogous to an antigen-antibody complex.

The following studies are intended to further elucidate the significance of the coat, of directed cell movements and selective cell adhesion in the processes of invagination, segregation, and differentiation during early morphogenesis.

MATERIALS AND METHODS

The experimental work was performed on several species of Amphibia: *Amblystoma punctatum*, *Amblystoma tigrinum*, *Triturus torosus*, *Pleurodeles waltlii* and *Rana pipiens*. The eggs of the first three species were collected from sites of natural breeding in California, Tennessee, Missouri, New Hampshire and New York.[2] Fertilized eggs of *Rana pipiens* were obtained through induced ovulation and inseminated after the method of Rugh (1934). *Pleurodeles waltlii* was induced to deposit fertilized eggs in aquaria through low-temperature conditioning (10°C. for 10 days) followed by injection of sheep anterior pituitary extract (Gonadophysin, G. D. Searle Co.). Most of the experiments were performed on explanted material of *Amblystoma punctatum*. The other species mentioned, and heteroplastic combinations between them, gave essentially the same results.

In view of the fact that the explants are highly susceptible to bacterial infection, it was necessary to employ aseptic procedures whenever feasible. The egg clusters were briefly treated with a strong solution of KOH (0.5 to 1%). This treatment has the advantage that its sterilizing effectiveness can be estimated immediately. The jelly protects the eggs for a while from being injured. If injury does occur, it can be readily noticed because of the ensuing decomposition of the eggs. Before this happens, the clusters were transferred to sterile tap water of an acid range and then washed several times. To destroy the microbes attached to the surface of the cluster, without damaging the eggs themselves, it has been found useful to observe the effect of the alkali on some eggs deprived of their protective jelly. When the latter begin to decompose, it is essential to transfer the egg clusters to a more acid medium.

The eggs were then removed from their jelly and kept for 1–3 hours in sterile tap water containing 0.5% sodium sulfadiazine and traces of streptomycin (about 20 gamma per liter; Wilde, 1948). Thereafter, the fertilization membrane was removed and, after more washings, the eggs were operated on in isotonic salt solution. The loss of explants through infection was reduced to almost zero.

Methods of Operation. Most of the experiments were performed on neurula material. The desired embryonic areas were excised

---

[2] The authors are grateful to Dr. W. W. Ballard, Dartmouth College, and Dr. V. C. Twitty, Stanford University, for egg shipments to this laboratory.

with glass needles. In some of the experiments these fragments were simply recombined in various combinations; in others, they were briefly subjected to KOH, added dropwise to the culture medium, until pH 9.6 to 9.8 was reached. This caused disaggregation of the tissues into single cells (Holtfreter, 1943a, c). The isolated cells from two or more types of tissue were then mixed with the aid of glass needles, and the alkaline medium gradually replaced by fresh solution of pH 8.0. At this lower pH the cells reaggregated.

The procedure of raising and lowering the pH requires delicate handling. If the pH rises above 10.0, excessive amounts of slime are released and some of the cells burst; re-aggregation is then difficult or impossible. However, if the limits of pH tolerance are not exceeded, the isolated cells immediately regain adhesiveness and show no signs of injury. All following experiments deal with such non-injured cell material.

Contrary to the aims of orthodox tissue culture, care was taken to avoid "outgrowth" of the explants over external surfaces. This could easily be prevented by covering the bottom of the culture dish with a thin layer of 1% agar. The culture media were Holtfreter's Solution (Holtfreter, 1931) or Niu and Twitty's modification of White's Solution as reported by Flickinger (1949). The latter solution was found to be advantageous in disaggregation experiments because it is highly buffered, thereby making readjustment of pH after alkali treatment less difficult. Control embryos developed normally in this solution.

The cultured explants were examined microscopically at close intervals; concurrently representative cases were fixed for cytological study. Several thousand experimental recombinations were performed, of which 550 were studied in serial sections.

EXPERIMENTAL RESULTS

General Aspects of the Processes of Cellular Disaggregation and Reaggregation

The gross aspects of cellular disaggregation and re-aggregation are illustrated in Fig. 1–9, which depict this process in successive stages in a neurula which was briefly treated with alkali. Within a few minutes after a pH of 9.8 has been reached, the coated surface breaks apart. This results in the protrusion of single peripheral cells which round up and isolate themselves. Complete disaggregation occurs within some 5 minutes, at which time the neurula has been reduced to a mound of disconnected cells which are partly scattered over the bottom of the culture dish (Fig. 5). When the pH of the medium is restored to the normal level (pH 8.0), the cells regain adhesiveness and form an increasingly compact mass (Figs. 6–9).

Microscopic examination reveals that re-aggregation is entirely indiscriminate; i.e., any type of cell will unite with any other cell type. At this stage, therefore, cellular adhesion is non-selective. Locomotion of the free amoeboid cells plays a minor role in this process because the cells move too slowly and irregularly. Re-aggregation is mainly due to those cells which are already in point-contact with each other, and which progressively increase their areas of mutual contact until all intercellular spaces disappear.

Figures 7–9 record at hourly intervals the manner in which the cell heap regains compactness through the re-incorporation of the dispersed cells into the main body. Those cells which have not been dislodged markedly, simply re-attach themselves to the underlying cells of the broken-up neurula. The more scattered cells of the periphery undergo more spectacular morphogenetic movements. The configuration of a suspension of densely packed free elements changes first into that of a flat plate of cells; then, through further cellular condensations and re-arrangements, the peripheral cell plates are drawn into the main aggregate which eventually forms a smooth spherical body.

The most peripherally scattered cells which have lost contact with those of the central mass may fail to become re-incorporated. They tend to form spherical aggregates of their own, the number and size of which depends upon the density of the cell suspension. The loss of these cells can be prevented by simply sweeping them into contact with

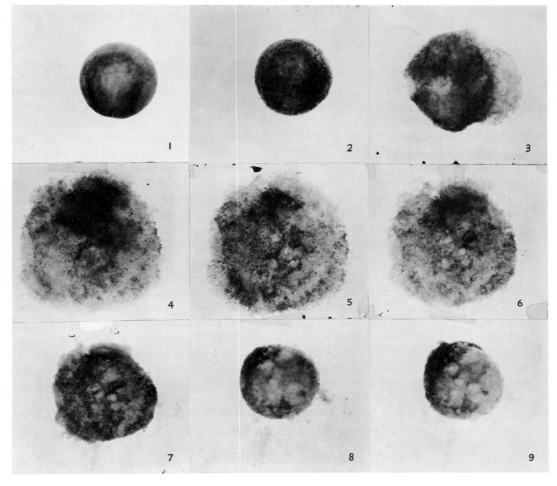

Figs. 1–9. A neurula of *Amblystoma tigrinum*, when subjected to alkali treatment, disintegrates into free cells (Figs. 1–5). Following re-adjustment of pH, the cells re-aggregate into a compact body (Figs. 6–9).

the main cell mass. It will be noticed—and we could substantiate this by time-lapse microphotographs—that these phenomena are much the same as those observed in the process of re-aggregation of mechanically dispersed cells from adult sponges (Wilson, 1908; Galtsoff, 1925, *et al.*).

Numerous observations made in the course of this study indicate that a temporary disaggregation of a neurula by means of alkali does not seem to change the developmental fate of the re-aggregated cells, especially not the fate of the prospective epidermal and neural cells. In other words, induction effects of an alkali treatment have not been observed

in neurula material as contrasting to the observations made on temporarily disaggregated gastrula material (Holtfreter, 1945; Yamada, 1950). We may therefore disregard the problem of induction in most of the following considerations.

A temporary disaggregation of a neurula does not necessarily lead to grave anatomical malformations such as have been observed in alkali-treated gastrulae (Holtfreter, 1948). On the contrary, when neurulae, within their fertilization membranes, were subjected to a thorough disaggregation of the ectodermal cells and then returned to normal pH conditions, the disaggregated mass of cells reconstituted itself into an intact neurula and then developed into a practically normal embryo (unpublished).

Figure 9 does not show such a return to a normal tissue configuration, simply because the dispersal of the cells from the different germ layers was carried to the extreme, namely to a total disaggregation of all cells of the decapsulated neurula. The purpose of Figs. 1–9 is to demonstrate that these completely dissociated cells can re-aggregate into a single mass without being pushed together by the investigator.

Combination of Different Embryonic Cell Types in Explants

All of the following experiments were performed with the aim of studying the kinetic and morphogenetic phenomena subsequent to the combination of two or more well defined cell types. Two main procedures were adopted: (1) Different germ layers or primordia were excised and then simply united in different combinations. (2) Such different fragments were first disaggregated by means of alkali; the resulting free cells were thoroughly intermingled and then allowed to re-aggregate into a solid body (re-aggregates). We shall first discuss the experiments on the material from early neurulae (Harrison stages 13–14). The presentation will proceed from simple to more complex combinations.

A. Ectodermal Derivatives

1. Combination of Fragments of Medullary Plate and Prospective Epidermis. The anterior part of the medullary plate, not including the neural fold, and a piece of the prospective belly epidermis were removed and placed together with their uncoated surfaces in contact. The approximate areas excised are shown in Fig. 10. It may be added that in all subsequent experiments the part of the neural plate used corresponds to the area outlined in this figure.

Immediate adhesion between the two tissues resulted and, within the first few hours, the medullary plate became partly enveloped by epidermis. At the same time the plate underwent an infolding similar to that which leads

to the formation of the neural tube in normal development. About 10 hours later, the neural tissue, now entirely covered by epidermis, commenced to separate from the latter; this separation resulted in the formation of a space between the two tissues. After 15–20 hours the neural tissue was no longer in contact with the epidermis. This self-segregation of the tissues occurred at the same time as the detachment of the neural tube in control embryos; it is clearly the result of a newly arising lack of affinity between the tissues. Neither archenteron roof nor mesenchyme are required for the infolding nor for the separation of the neural tube from the epidermis (see also, Holtfreter, 1939, 1945; Barth, 1941).

Sections (46 cases) revealed that differentiation of the explants was fairly typical since specific brain regions became recognizable. In all cases only a single continuous neurocoel was present. It was not our aim, as was that of Ter Horst (1948), Mangold and von Woellwarth (1950) and others, to study the capabilities of organotypical self-differentiation of the isolated different sections of the neural plate. Instead, these experiments were intended to assist in interpreting the results obtained with disaggregated cells in which the continuity of the epithelial layers was disrupted.

2. Recombination of Dissociated Epidermal and Medullary Cells. As in the preceding experiment, neural plate and ventral epidermis from an early neurula were removed. Following the procedure outlined on page 5 and illustrated in Fig. 10, the tissues were disaggregated and the resulting single cells re-aggregated so as to form a completely mixed composite body.

Since it is difficult to distinguish between the two intermingled cell types it was necessary to resort to heteroplastic combinations. The ectodermal cells of *Amblystoma punctatum* differ markedly from those of *Triturus torosus* in their degree of pigmentation; therefore isolated cells from the medullary plate of one species were aggregated with epidermal cells from the other species in reciprocal combinations. Xenoplastic combinations with

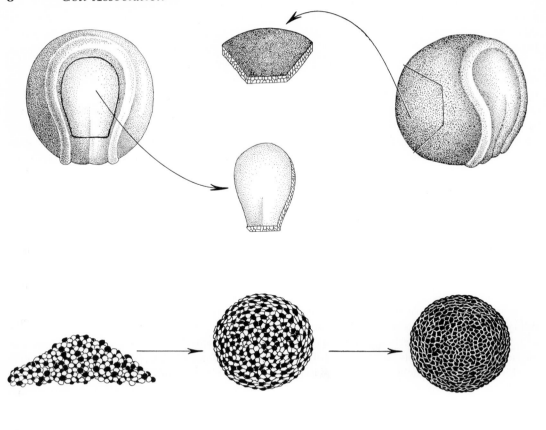

DISAGGREGATION   **REAGGREGATION**   **CELLULAR SEGREGATION**

Fig. 10. A piece of the medullary plate and a piece of prospective epidermis are excised and disaggregated by means of alkali. The free cells are intermingled (epidermal cells indicated in black). Under re-adjusted conditions, the cells re-aggregate and subsequently segregate so that the surface of the explant becomes entirely epidermal.

Rana pipiens were also attempted, but their culture was limited to 48 hours or less, due to incompatability between the tissues. Within this period, it was seen, however, that the combined cells at first united indiscriminately and then exhibited the same shiftings that were found in homo- and heteroplastic combinations of equal age. Only the latter will be considered in the following paragraphs.

The heteroplastically intermingled epidermal and medullary cells united without delay so that within an hour all of the cells were incorporated into a single mass which was at first flat, and then, within 10–12 hours, rounded-up as indicated in Fig. 10. The surface of the aggregate showed a mosaic of epidermal and neural cells in a random ar-

rangement, giving it an overall coloration intermediate to the brown and yellow tinges characteristic of the two donors. Shortly after aggregation was complete, the different cell types began the process of sorting out. At 20 hours the surface of the living aggregate acquired the smoothness of a typical homogeneous epidermis and showed the coloration of the epidermal donor. Thereafter the explants underwent a progressive swelling which commenced on the fourth day after operation and continued throughout the culture period. At the same time the surface epithelium acquired the transparency of normal epidermis and frequently was underlain by a few pigment cells probably derived from the neural plate.

Some 90 cases have been studied cytologi-

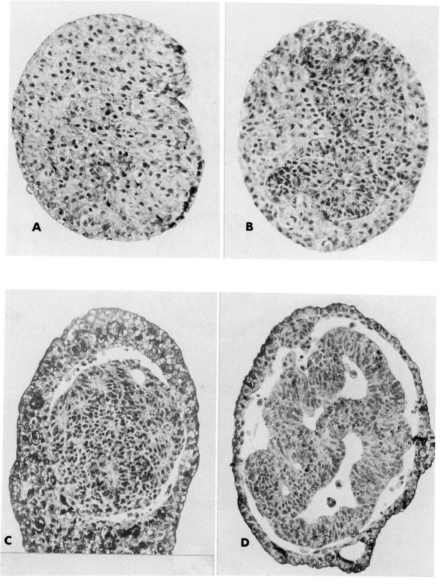

Fig. 11. Successive stages of sorting out occurring in aggregates of intermingled prospective epidermal and neural cells. The photographs correspond to the diagrams of Fig. 12a-d.

cally. They were fixed at close intervals from three hours to 12 days, with particular emphasis on the first 48 hours, since it is within this period that the major events of cellular sorting out and tissue formation occur.

The results of these and subsequent experiments are illustrated in the semi-diagrams of Figs. 12–26. These drawings neglect individual variations in size, shape and tissue pattern of the explants and show fewer cells than were present in the aggregates; but the essential trends of cellular re-arrangement observable in the sections are rather faithfully represented. The photomicrographs of Fig. 11 a–d correspond to the schematic drawings of Fig. 12 a–d.

MED. PLATE + EPIDERMIS   MED. PLATE + EPID. + FOLD   MED. PLATE ON ENDODERM

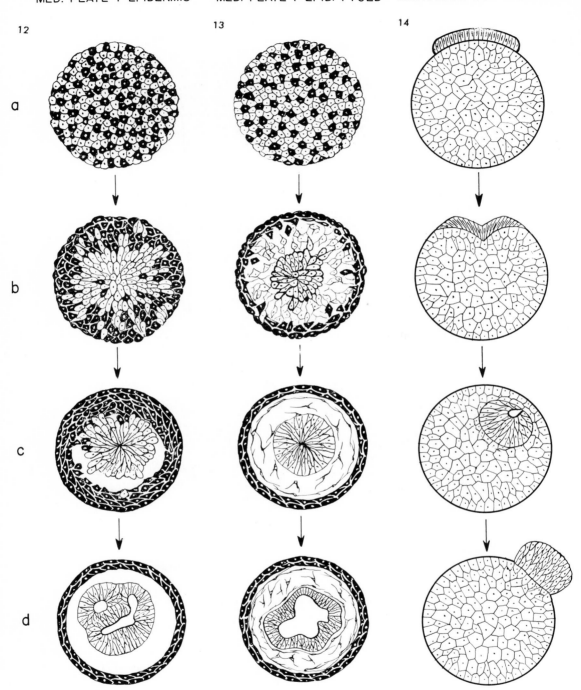

Figs. 12–14. Diagrammatic sections through successive stages of composite re-aggregates. Fig. 12. Randomly arranged cells of epidermis (black) and medullary plate (white) move in opposite directions and re-establish homogeneous tissues. Fig. 13. Same as Fig. 12, except that cells from the neural fold were added. The latter move to occupy the space between neural tissue and epidermal covering. Fig. 14. A piece of medullary plate or of larval forebrain first moves into, then out of, a matrix of endoderm.

During the first 10 hours, the sections show closely packed, isodiametric and randomly arranged epidermal and medullary cells (Fig. 12 a). Within the following few hours, a remarkable regrouping begins: all of the scattered prospective epidermal cells accumulate in increasing numbers at the periphery while the medullary cells move toward the center of the explant, where they unite into a progressively larger and more homogeneous cell mass (Fig. 12 b). The boundary between the two types of cells is indistinct and jagged. Small groups of medullary cells still occupy a surface position and a number of epidermal cells may be found scattered in central locations. The centripetal migration tendency (immigration or invagination) of the prospective neural cells is reflected in their proximo-distal elongation and in the formation of pit-like depressions at the periphery (Fig. 11 b). In contrast, the outermost layer of epidermal cells begins to undergo a cell-specific tangential flattening. It seems that the inward movement of the medullary cells is slightly more rapid than the outward movement of the epidermal cells since relatively more epidermal cells are found amidst the neural core than medullary cells at the periphery.

Within 14 to 20 hours after operation the sorting out becomes complete, resulting in the formation of a central homogeneous mass of medullary cells. The process of segregation continues with the appearance of a distinct and smooth line of demarcation between the neural core and the epidermal covering. Soon afterward (22–24 hours), the line changes into a cleft which demonstrates that the two types of cells are no longer adhesive (Figs. 11 c, 12 c). The cleft widens and gradually encircles the entire medullary cell mass so that there is no longer any contact between the two cell types. With the expansion of the cleft into a cavity, lumina—rarely more than five or six—appear within the medullary tissue (Figs. 11 d, 12 d). During the next days the epidermis undergoes a progressive expansion and thinning until, after about 4 days, a typical uniformly thin epithelium is established.

Problems of organogenesis and regional differentiation of the neural system may be briefly considered at this point. Little organogenesis results from the recombination of disaggregated medullary and epidermal cells as compared with whole fragments, even though the medullary cells form typical nuclear and fibrous layers around the lumina with differentiation into neurones. Unlike the results obtained from isolation, transplantation and defect experiments on the anterior part of the neural plate (Adelmann, 1936; Ter Horst, 1948; Mangold and von Woellwarth, 1950), the present, more thoroughly disarranged material failed to differentiate into typical brain regions. Since the area excised as indicated in Fig. 10 did not contain the eye primordia, eyes did not usually develop.

As pointed out above, the temporary disintegration of a whole neurula need not lead to abnormal organ and tissue patterns of the reunited cells. The present conditions differ from those of the previous experiments in that the tissues were removed from the rest of the neurula and were thoroughly intermingled. The absence of typical regional organogenesis in the present re-aggregates may be ascribed (1) to the absence of a continued determinative influence of the archenteron roof, and (2) to the fact that the neural plate, at the time of operation, may be considered as determined in a local, though rather vaguely circumscribed sense, and that a haphazard shuffling of its cells cannot be corrected by way of regulation to restore typical organ pattern. At any rate, these results show that this medullary material (Fig. 10) does not represent a single embryonic field which is capable of reconstituting itself after a thorough disarrangement of its constituent cells.

Whatever relations may exist between the field properties of the induced parts of the neural plate and their subsequent shaping by the underlying mesoderm, the present data bring out clearly two other principles, namely cell-specific movements and adhesions. Their combined effects result in tissue segregation. Two conclusions are indicated by these results: (1) The medullary cells need not constitute a continuous coated epithelium in order to invaginate. Each individual cell has this tendency. (2) A central lumen which normally results from the infolding of the plate, can be formed equally well by way of secondary cavitation.

3. Recombination of Dissociated Cells from Medullary Plate, Neural Fold and Prospective Epidermis. The material consisted of a single sheet of ectoderm comprising the anterior portion of the plate plus adjacent neural fold and lateral epidermis which was isolated from early neurulae of *A. punctatum.* Disaggregation and re-aggregation as before (20 sectioned cases).

The sorting out of medullary and epidermal cells progressed as in the preceding experiment, with inward movement of the former and outward movement of the latter. The cells derived from the neural fold became located between the accumulating mass of centrally located medullary cells and the re-established layer of peripheral epidermis (Figs. 13 a–d). The end result was a perfectly neat segregation of the three types of tissues which attained a concentric arrangement similar to that in normal embryos.

The addition of neural fold material did not lead to neural organ patterns superior to those of the preceding experiment. According to prospective significance, the cephalic neural fold gave rise to mesenchyme, melanophores, small ganglionic cell clusters and a corium underlying the epidermal covering. Contrary to prospective significance, no cartilage was differentiated. This may be attributed to the absence of pharyngeal endoderm which, according to several authors, is necessary to transform cephalic mesectoderm into cartilage (Hörstadius and Sellman, 1946).

As in the preceding experiment, the newly established core of medullary cells formed a variable number of neurocoels by way of cavitation, and the tissue underwent differentiation into mantle and marginal layers. The neurocoels tended to become excessively expanded, and their configuration provided no criteria to compare them with normal divisions of the brain. However, some abortive eye-like formations consisting of accumulations of retinal and tapetal cells were found.

The essentially new problem in this experiment is to find an explanation for the re-

arrangement of the cellular derivatives of the neural fold in such a way that they finally settle between epidermis and neural tissue.

B. Ectodermal and Endodermal Derivatives

1. Combination of Medullary Plate and Endoderm from a Neurula. The isolated anterior part of the neural plate and a mass of ventral endoderm of early neurulae were combined. The two tissues adhered to each other without delay, but the originally flat piece of neural plate curled up rapidly, thus anticipating its normal infolding process.

The plate subsequently flattened out again, increased its contact surface with the endoderm and then sank as a contracted mass into the endoderm. After about 10 hours most of the medullary tissue had disappeared from the surface and, some 10 hours later, it had been engulfed entirely by the endodermal matrix (Fig. 14 a–c).

In contrast to the movements of medullary cells into an epidermal matrix (p. 9), or of mesodermal cells into the very center of an endodermal mass (p. 21), here inward movement was less complete. The invaginated dark cell mass could be seen shining through a thin layer of endoderm cells which formed a daisy-like pattern, observed in other instances of invagination and wound healing (Holtfreter, 1943a, 1944).

After 30 hours the rounded medullary fragment began to reverse its direction of movement and return to the surface (Fig. 14 d). The whole mass re-appeared within 40–45 hours. Obviously, the initial incorporation and subsequent expulsion reflect changes in affinity between the two types of tissues.

Examination of the sectioned material (28 cases) revealed more details concerning cellular arrangement and lumen formation. When the piece of medullary plate had slipped halfway into the endodermal matrix, it exhibited the U-shape infolding, and elongation of its cells, characteristic of normal neurulation (Lehmann, 1926; Boerema, 1929; Gillette, 1944). But when invagination was complete, the neurocoel disappeared entirely, soon after it had been formed by way of infolding. Explants fixed at successive intervals showed a progressive fusion of the walls of the neurocoel until only the accumulation of pigment indicated a former cavity. Eventually the invaginated plate material formed a solid mass of cells that returned without change to the periphery of the endodermal matrix.

Apparently, the surface coat which is responsible for the maintenance of invaginated cavities in general (Holtfreter, 1944, 1948) becomes dissipated under the present conditions, just as the coat of the mesodermal primordia disappears during the course of normal invagination. This disappearance of a neurocoel differs from the results of the preceding experiments where the experimental conditions led to the re-establishment of neurocoels within a compact mass of prospective neural cells. It is obviously the abnormal endodermal environment which inhibits the formation of neurocoels.

With the loss of an inner cavity, the medullary cells more or less lose their radial arrangement but they continue differentiating into neural elements. The finally expelled cell mass remains slightly attached to the endoderm with its fibrous layer, whereas the nuclear layer, showing a ragged surface, is turned toward the external medium. Within 9 days of culture there occurred no infiltration of nerve fibres into the underlying aggregation of large and undifferentiated endodermal cells.

The time required for complete invagination into the alien matrix of endoderm is about the same (some 20 hours) as that for transformation of the neural plate into a tube in control embryos. Thus the kind of histological environment does not seem to influence specifically the rate of invagination. However, the endodermal environment proves to be unsuited in that it prevents neurocoel formation and does not permit a prolonged sojourn of neural material within this cell mass or the outgrowth of nerves into it.

The following experiments show that endoderm from a wide range of stages can equally well serve as a matrix for the invagination of medullary material.

a. Lack of stage specificity of the endo-

dermal substratum: When fragments of medullary plate were combined with isolated endoderm from blastula and gastrula stages (17 sectioned cases), it was found that the time sequence of events—invagination followed by expulsion—was the same as described above with reference to endoderm from the neurula.

In another experimental series (9 cases), medullary plate was combined with endoderm from advanced stages, namely from stages 13, 14, 19, 22 and 33. In this series, the endoderm was not isolated but simply denuded by removing the overlying epidermis and mesoderm of the lateral trunk region. A piece of medullary plate was then placed upon the smooth endodermal surface. Hosts older than stage 33 proved to be unsuited for this experiment because the graft would not adhere to the endodermal surface. This lack of adhesiveness possibly illustrates the change of affinity which has been mentioned above.

When the piece of medullary plate did adhere to the denuded, aged endoderm, it underwent the processes of initial invagination and subsequent expulsion as described above. Only when the advanced host stages 22 and 33 were used, complete invagination was rarely achieved. There was also some slight delay in the initial attachment of the medullary material to the endoderm of these older embryos.

It follows from these observations that the age of the endodermal substratum does not affect the movements of the medullary material. At any rate, it is not just the endoderm of a neurula which permits invagination of a piece of medullary plate.

As a further instance of the unspecificity of the substratum and its developmental stage, a fragment of medullary plate readily invaginates into the interior of a morula. In these instances (15 cases) the graft slipped in between the large cells of the animal pole region to become permanently lodged within the underlying endoderm.

b. Lack of stage specificity of the invagination tendency: The preceding experiments demonstrate that it is not the specificity of a certain germ layer nor the age of the cellular substratum which control the movement of medullary tissue into the depth. The following experiments were performed in order to examine whether or not the tendency for invagination is specific only for the medullary plate stage.

Excised fragments of larval forebrain (stages 23–30) were brought into contact with isolated endoderm from a neurula (9 sectioned cases). The fragments adhered immediately, though not very firmly to the much younger endoderm. Within 15 minutes, adhesion was sufficient to resist mechanical separation of the tissues. The brain fragment moved into the endodermal substratum and, within 20 to 33 hours, entirely disappeared from view. During the second day, it returned to the surface where it remained for two days, barely attached to the endoderm.

Thus, with respect to directed movements, the larval forebrain behaved essentially like medullary plate. These processes were executed at practically the same time intervals in all of the experimental modifications investigated.

Whereas in the preceding instances the neural material moved inward either by way of infolding (invagination) of a plate of cells or by way of immigration of scattered cells, the piece of larval brain slips into the endoderm as a solid lump of cells ("ingression") and there is no interdigitation between the neural and endodermal cells. One might wish to find a common mechanism for these three modifications of inward movement.

Additional experiments (9 cases), in which larval brain was combined with endoderm beyond the neurula stage (stages 19–22), merely confirmed this conclusion: within the range of the stages investigated, neither the age of the embedding endoderm nor that of the neural graft influence either the mode or the time sequence of invagination and subsequent expulsion. If invagination were simply a function of the state of differentiation of the two tissues, one would expect that the neural tissue from older donors, which has already undergone invagination and segregation, would fail to adhere to younger endoderm and to invaginate and segregate itself once

more. Instead, the results show that neural tissue and endoderm from a wide range of stages have the tendency to establish at first a maximal mutual contact for a definite period, and then to separate, irrespective of the age of either component. Normal neurulation seems to result from a fortunate coincidence of invagination tendency and a favorable matrix.

These findings warrant a revision of the theoretical schemes devised to account for the change of affinity between different tissues. Apparently in cellular adhesiveness, two principles are involved: a non-specific adhesiveness that is found in early embryonic stages and persists in older material, and a cell-specific adhesiveness that develops after the different cell types have been in contact for a definite period. This would imply that selective cell adhesion is only partly the result of aging of the cells concerned. It is also the result of mutual interactions between the combined cells of different germ layers.

In the following experiments we return to the earlier problem of the significance of the coat in invagination and of the effects which different tissue environments exert upon the shaping of tissue patterns.

2. Combination of Endoderm with Neural Plate and Neural Fold. When the neural fold was added to combinations of isolated, non-disaggregated medullary plate and endoderm (6 cases), the medullary plate invaginated into the endoderm and most of the neural fold material remained close to the surface differentiating into epidermis at the periphery and into mesenchyme underneath and between neural tissue and endoderm (Fig. 15 a–d). The mesenchyme acted as true binding material connecting neural tissue with epidermis as well as with endoderm. No expulsion of neural tissue occurred. The presence of epidermis-covered mesenchyme permitted the neural tissue to maintain a central lumen. Here again, regional specification of the neural formations has not been observed.

3. Combination of Dissociated Medullary Plate and Endodermal Cells. Anterior medullary plate and ventral endoderm of the early neurula (stage 13) were isolated, dis-

MED. PLATE + FOLD ON
ENDODERM   MED. PLATE + ENDODERM   MED. PLATE + FOLD + ENDODERM

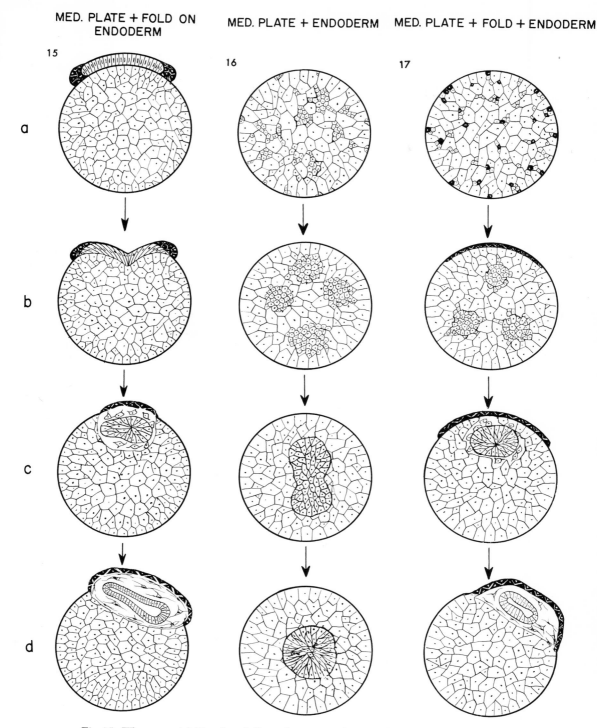

Fig. 15. When neural fold and medullary plate are combined with endoderm, invagination
of the medullary material is incomplete and the developing epidermis and mesectoderm
prevent isolation of the neural tissue.   Fig. 16. When dissociated cells of medullary plate
and endoderm are mixed, the former move centripetally to produce a core of neural tissue
lacking a neurocoel.   Fig. 17. The addition of neural fold produces epidermis and mesenchyme, which prevent central allocation of the neural tissue and promote neurocoel formation.

aggregated and re-aggregated. The difference in size between the two cell types promotes some clustering of the medullary cells; however, once aggregation has started, this preliminary grouping ceases.

Within 3 hours after operation the aggregate becomes a smooth, more or less spherical mosaic of endodermal and neural cells. The latter invaginate rapidly so that, after 14 hours, few if any remain at the surface. The surface aspects change very little after the first 20 hours, except for an occasional thinning of the endoderm overlying the neural tissue. In some, though infrequent, instances the endoderm may recede, exposing the neural mass to the medium.

The dynamics of the segregation process are more clearly revealed in sections (37 cases). Five hours after re-aggregation one finds single medullary cells or small clusters of them interspersed in the gross texture of the endoderm cells (Fig. 16 a). The peripheral medullary cells are still invaginating, as may be deduced from their formation of pits and from their elongation perpendicular to the surface.

Intrinsic cell polarity controls the direction of movement. According to observations of Holtfreter (1947) on isolated cells, it is the inner, non-coated portion of the elongated medullary cell which forms the anterior pole in amoeboid locomotion. In the individually scattered medullary cells within the present aggregates, it is this cell pole which can be seen to turn toward the center of the aggregate while the originally coated and still heavily pigmented distal pole becomes turned distally. Thus the centripetal cell movement seems to be due to a response of the kinetically most active proximal cell portion to an inside-outside gradient of some kind existing within the aggregate. It is, however, difficult to apply the notions gained from the study of isolated cells directly to the solid clusters of medullary cells which likewise move into the depth within the first 5 to 24 hours (Fig. 16 b, c).

After 24 hours not more than two medullary clusters were found, and by 40 hours all of the originally dispersed cells became united into a single central mass which was clearly demarcated from the surrounding endoderm by differences in cellular shape, size and orientation with a distinct line of pigment at the outside of the medullary cell mass. As in the case of the combination of dissociated medullary and epidermal cells, a neat sorting out of the two cell types takes place.

The centrally assembled prospective neural cells formed a homogeneous tissue which failed to undergo regionally specific differentiation. Within this mass, the cells became arranged in irregular whorl-like patterns—an abortive attempt at organizing themselves. As in the preceding experiments, the embedding endoderm proved to lack the proper conditions for the formation of neurocoels which occurred when reconstitution of neural tissue took place within an epidermal covering (p. 11).

In contrast to the experiments with whole pieces of medullary plate (p. 12), the neural tissue did not return to the surface of the embedding endoderm during the culture period of 10 days. To attribute this to the absence of a continuous coat is not convincing in view of the fact that a piece of forebrain, lacking a coated surface, does move back to the endodermal surface. Further studies must elucidate this problem.

4. Combination of Dissociated Cells from Medullary Plate, Neural Fold and Endoderm. When neural fold material is added to the cell mixtures considered in the preceding paragraph, the neural cells invaginate as described above. At 20 hours the surface of the aggregate consists of patches of endodermal and ectodermal cells. The latter spread and fuse with each other until, on the fifth day, there is usually a single cap of epidermis which becomes elevated and finally underlain by pigment cells.

In sections (6 cases), segregation of neural and endodermal cells proceeds as described previously, when neural fold was not included. During this process the neural tissue becomes surrounded by the differentiating mesenchyme, which is evidently responsible for the fact that well formed, though irregularly shaped lumina arise in the neural tissue. The final distribution is principally the same as that which results from a combination of corresponding intact fragments (compare Figs. 17 and 13).

These data give further support to the notions gained from the preceding experiments. They show clearly that in the process of sorting out, the different cell types exhibit a cell-specific tendency to arrange themselves in a definite tissue pattern which corresponds to that in normal development.

5. Combination of Fragments of Prospective Epidermis and Endoderm. Fragments of prospective epidermis and ventral endoderm from the gastrula and neurula (stages 10 and 13) were combined. The results obtained were consistent irrespective of the different age of the tissues employed (13 sectioned cases). Detailed description of this experiment is not necessary because similar tissue combinations have been described by Holtfreter (1939, 1944) whose results we could confirm.

A piece of prospective gastrula or neurula epidermis whose inner surface has been brought into contact with non-coated endoderm, adheres to the latter and then spreads peripherally. This movement is carried out, not because of the contractile strength of the coat (Lewis, 1947), but in spite of it; it results from an active amoeboid spreading of the whole sheet of epidermal cells. The basal part of the endodermal ball which touches the agar-plated culture dish does not become covered by the spreading ectoderm. Similarly, in whole embryos which are kept in standard solution on a glass surface, the epidermis which touches the glass, tends to recede from the embryo and to spread sheet-like over the glass; but such extra-embryonic spreading will not take place when the medium is simply water or when the embryo rests upon agar.

For about 24 hours the epidermal cap continues spreading and flattening centrifugally over the body of endoderm. Then epiboly ceases and, after 4 days, the epidermis reverts to the opposite movement of contracting and receding from the endoderm. This signals the onset of a state of disaffinity between the two tissues. For the following 2 days the epidermal cap becomes progressively thicker,

more wrinkled and less attached to the endoderm. However, complete self-isolation of the two tissue components, such as has been reported by Holtfreter (1939), was not observed within the culture period of 10 days, although there remained only sporadic points of mutual adhesion. Holtfreter cultured his preparations for a longer period.

6. Combination of Dissociated Prospective Epidermal with Endodermal Cells. When the same tissues as used in the preceding experiment were briefly subjected to alkali and then allowed to re-aggregate haphazardly, they formed a firm, compact mass within 2–3 hours (Fig. 18 a). The surface of the mass was at first a mosaic of epidermal and endodermal cells except that the unequal size of the two cell types promoted some clustering of the epidermal cells. The peripheral epidermal cells immediately began to spread over the endodermal cells indicating that the former have a stronger spreading tendency than the latter. The internally buried epidermal cells remained isodiametrical.

As seen in sections (14 fixed cases), the cellular sorting out proceeds rapidly so that, after 12 hours, all of the internally located epidermal cells become linked up with the peripheral ones by radiating cellular connections. Within the next 10 hours or so, all epidermal cells have moved to the periphery, where they spread and unite to form an epidermal covering. If the number of epidermal cells is insufficient to cover the whole endoderm, or if the contact between aggregate and culture dish prevents epidermal spreading over the basal portion of endoderm, the condition illustrated in Fig. 18 c results, namely an epidermal "capping." From the fourth day on, the cap contracts and detaches itself progressively from the endoderm as a wrinkled mass (Fig. 18 d). Complete self-isolation of the two tissues seems to be only a matter of a sufficiently long culture period.

To conclude: the initial indiscriminate union between dissociated and intermingled prospective endodermal and epidermal cells is soon followed by their sorting out through directed cell movements and selective adhesions leading to the formation of homogene-

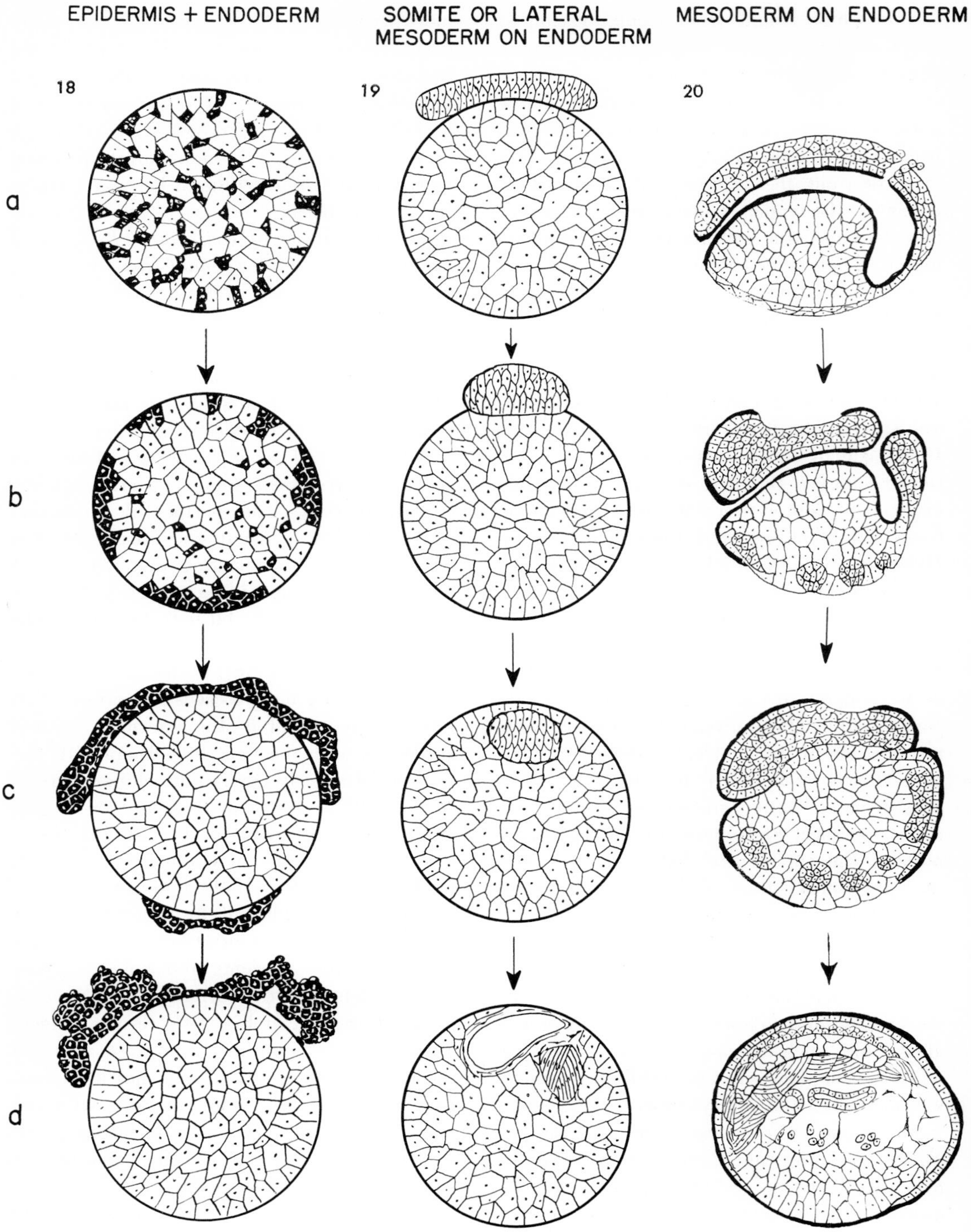

EPIDERMIS + ENDODERM SOMITE OR LATERAL MESODERM ON ENDODERM MESODERM ON ENDODERM

Fig. 18. The recombination of dissociated epidermal and endodermal cells leads to a sorting out and self-isolation of homologous tissues. Fig. 19. Combination of a fragment of the mesoderm mantle with trunk endoderm results in the incorporation of the mesoderm into endoderm. Fig. 20. Removal of the whole ectoderm of a neurula or older stages leads to a movement of mesoderm into endoderm and a spreading of the coated endoderm of the archenteron over the denuded embryo (coated surfaces indicated by a heavy black line).

ous layers of superficial epidermis and internal endoderm. Both the ectoderm and endoderm are obviously capable of establishing peripheral epithelia, but when competing with each other, the ectodermal cells display a stronger tendency than the endodermal cells to move peripherally and to spread as a surface epithelium. However, a permanent association of the two layers appears to be impossible for the lack of connective tissue.

C. Mesoderm and Endoderm Derivatives

1. Combination of Fragments of Prospective Notochord and Endoderm. Prospective notochord and ventral endoderm were excised from neurulae (stage 15) and placed in contact. Firm adhesion occurred within 5 minutes. The notochordal tissue invaginated much faster than did neural tissue, namely within 2–3 hours. A thin layer of endodermal cells shifted over the graft, thereby exhibiting the characteristic daisy pattern.

Sectioned material fixed after 24 hours (9 cases) showed the notochordal tissue as a round compact mass lying close to the surface and being sharply delimited from the endoderm. Typical vacuolization and a distinct sheath became evident on the third day. During the next few days the notochord elongated and in so doing, a terminal tip would sometimes break through the endoderm. The two tissues remained in close contact for as long as 9 days, during which time the notochord differentiated normally except for the fact that its elongation was not as extensive as in intact embryos. Thus, in contrast to the preceding combination, no disaffinity arose between notochord and endoderm during the period under examination.

2. Combination of Fragments of Prospective Somites or Lateral Mesoderm with Endoderm. Prospective somites or lateral mesoderm from a neurula when placed on ventral endoderm were found to behave much like prospective notochord (Figs. 19 a–d). The mesoderm upon isolation contracted and proceeded to invaginate into the endoderm within a few hours. Differentiation of these tissues (11 cases) was according to prospective fate: the dorsal mesoderm formed typical somites,

while the hypomere produced coelomic cavities within the endoderm. These aggregates showed no sign of self-isolation of the different tissue components for as long as 10 days.

3. Combination of the Total Mesoderm and Endoderm of a Neurula. The experiments reported above demonstrate that different parts of the mesoderm mantle will invaginate into isolated endoderm and undergo typical differentiation. We shall presently consider the kinetic behavior of the entire mesoderm mantle of a late neurula (stage 20) when left in contact with the denuded endoderm. To obtain such preparations the entire epidermis and neural plate were removed (Fig. 20 a). At stage 20 the mesoderm is clearly demarcated which permits this operation without injury to the archenteron roof (12 sectioned cases).

Following removal of the ectodermal surface layer, the chorda mesoderm mantle contracts and moves into the underlying endoderm. Its dorsal portion invaginates as a compact mass, whereas its latero-ventral portion breaks up into patches which slip independently into the endodermal matrix (Fig. 20 b, c). After 10 hours, only endoderm is present on the surface, while the still undifferentiated entire mesoderm collects as a single centrally located mass of cells. This mass undergoes histotypical differentiation into notochord, somites, pronephros, coelomic cavities, blood cells, etc., which are rather haphazardly arranged (Fig. 20 d). A more typical bilateral and antero-posterior alignment of the axial mesoderm occurs when older embryos (stage 28) are deprived of their ectodermal covering.

It should be pointed out that the endoderm does not merely play a passive role in the process of transportation of the mesoderm into the depth. Any kind of invagination involves movements both of the invading and the embedding cell material. Under the present conditions, the coated endoderm of the archenteron (indicated by a heavy black line) moves out through the slit-shaped blastopore, or through an accidental hole in the archenteron roof, and spreads actively over the denuded mesoderm and uncoated endoderm (Fig. 20 b, c). The whole preparation thus becomes turned inside out; i.e., the coated endoderm of the archenteron eventually becomes the external covering of the entire preparation. Such inversions and epibolic expansions of coated over non-coated endoderm (and mesoderm) have been described before (Holtfreter, 1943a, 1944).

The general configuration attained in this experiment resembles that of a total exogastrula in which an endodermal instead of an epidermal epithelium forms the envelope of the mesodermal tissues. Here, however, the inversion of the two germ layers takes place *after* they had already achieved normal topographic arrangement. These observations permit two general conclusions: (1) An ectodermal covering seems to be the necessary prerequisite for the normal shifting of the mesoderm over the endoderm as well as for the maintenance of the mesodermal sheet; in the absence of an ectodermal covering, any part of the mesoderm will exhibit the "abnormal" behavior of slipping into the interior of an adjacent endodermal cell mass. (2) The tendency of the mesoderm to invaginate is not restricted to a certain stage, which is normally the gastrula, but it is present, though normally not used, in neurula and probably older stages.

4. Combination of Dissociated Cells from the Chorda Mesoderm and Endoderm of the Neurula. The entire complex of endoderm-mesoderm tissues employed above was dis-aggregated, mixed-up and allowed to re-aggregate. As in all previous re-aggregations, initial union of the cells was at random and a spherical compact mass resulted in a few hours (Fig. 21 a). The mesoderm cells exhibited a pronounced invagination tendency so that after the first 5 hours they were no longer visible at the surface. In addition to the large endodermal cells from the trunk region, a number of much smaller prospective foregut cells collected on the surface in small patches. After 20 hours these patches became more conspicuous for they began to differentiate into protruding bulges of epithelium. The prospective ventral endoderm could also form peripheral membranous epithelia. In later stages of culture (10 days) many of the

explants exhibited cardiac pulsations which were easily detected if they occurred underneath the flexible foregut endoderm.

In the sectioned material (39 cases) it is apparent that at 9 hours all of the mesodermal cells have left the surface and are scattered throughout the endoderm in the form of single cells or aggregates of various sizes. Within the next 3 hours the number of aggregates decreases and their mass increases. At 35–44 hours, only two mesodermal aggregates are found (Fig. 21 b), and after 50 hours they have united to form a single central mass (Fig. 21 c). Notochordal and somite differentiation becomes recognizable after 90 hours, while much of the remainder of the mesoderm is still relatively undifferentiated.

On the fifth day of culture the somites exhibit characteristic segmentation while notochordal tissue becomes vacuolated. A number of mesenchyme lined cavities also appear and can be designated as coelomic cavities, particularly since the pronephros is associated with them. Large numbers of loose cells—probably early blood elements—are found in the cavities. In addition, spaces not lined by mesenchyme develop within the endoderm, due to cavitation. Pronephros becomes well differentiated on the sixth day. The pronephric tissue is usually a single, continuous, twisted tube, but in some instances additional tubes are present which are not continuous with the main tube. In older preparations one finds well-differentiated gut epithelia, which are peripherally located and usually underlain by mesenchyme as shown in Fig. 21 d. The heart fragments which were noticed because of rhythmical contractions could not be clearly identified in sections. A bilateral and axial disposition of the re-established tissues fails to develop in such aggregates.

D. Ectoderm and Mesoderm Derivatives

1. Combination of Dissociated Cells from the Latero-Ventral Epidermis with Mesoderm. Latero-ventral epidermis and underlying mesoderm were removed from neurulae (stages 13–14) and dissociated into single cells which were recombined. As a result of

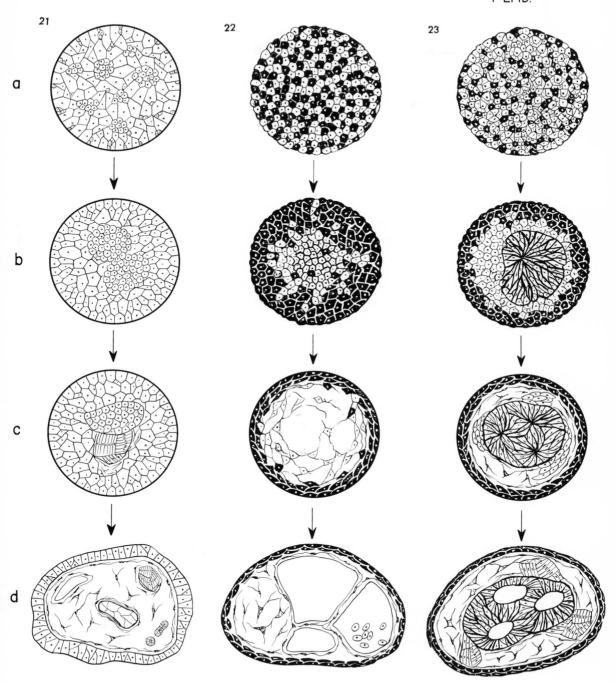

MESODERM + ENDODERM   **EPIDERMIS + MESODERM**   **MED. PLATE + ARCH. ROOF + EPID.**

Fig. 21. Combination of dissociated mesoderm and endoderm cells results in centripetal migration of the mesoderm cells. Fig. 22. Outward movement of epidermal cells and inward movement of mesodermal cells, the latter eventually forming mesenchyme, coelomic cavities and blood cells. Fig. 23. Sorting out of randomly arranged cells from medullary plate, epidermis and axial mesoderm resulting in the formation of centrally located neural tissue which is surrounded by somites, mesenchyme and epidermis.

directed cell movements within the aggregate, an epidermal surface was established after 10 hours while the mesodermal cells slipped inside. For the most part, the latter left the surface before the aggregate became compact. The explant swelled markedly and changed from a solid ball to a vesicle covered by a transparent epidermis. Melanophores sometimes appeared after 7 days; their origin is problematical. Since the neural fold was not included, it appears that they have arisen from the area immediately ventral to the neural fold, or by induction. Rhythmical contractions suggesting the presence of heart fragments were frequently observed.

In sections (18 cases) the results were as follows: Cell segregation, effected through the inward and outward movements of the mesodermal and epidermal cells respectively, eliminates the mosaic condition (Fig. 22 b) within the first 10–15 hours. The explants are then composed of a solid core of mesoderm surrounded by a thick shell of epidermis. During the following 10 days the mesoderm which initially consisted of tightly packed isodiametric cells, becomes differentiated into blood elements, vessels, mesenchyme and corium, the latter underlying the thinned-out epidermis (Fig. 22 c, d). Occasionally, a few pronephric tubules may be seen; however, in most cases the presumptive pronephros was not included in the tissues excised.

To conclude: the opposite movements of the re-aggregated mesodermal and epidermal cells result in a segregation of the two cell types and in the formation of a vesicle such as develops when the same ventro-lateral material is simply explanted as a fragment.

2. Combination of Dissociated Cells from the Medullary Plate, Archenteron Roof and Epidermis. Excised anterior part of the medullary plate together with underlying archenteron roof and a piece of ventral epidermis were dissociated and the free cells reaggregated after mixing (21 sectioned cases). Shortly after removal of the alkali, all cell types firmly adhere to one another (Fig. 23 a). During the first 20 hours the surface of the explant becomes completely epidermal. This condition is brought about through the inward movement of the mesodermal and neural cells as well as the outward movement of the epidermal cells. This results in the three-layered configuration of a central ball of neural tissue, surrounded by a mantle of mesoderm, which in turn is enveloped by a shell of epidermis (Fig. 23 c). Obviously, although both the neural and mesodermal cells have an invagination tendency, it is more pronounced in the former than in the latter.

During the following 4–5 days the epidermal surface commences to bulge out owing to subjacent mesenchymal differentiation. Within 8–10 days the neural mass develops a number of neurocoels—as many as six may be present in a single complex—which makes it appear brain-like (Fig. 23 d). Identification of distinct brain divisions is not possible, but cytological differentiation proceeds well, with fibers being produced. Abortive eye cups, or secondary induction products, e.g., frontal glands, small ear vesicles or nasal placodes may appear.

The mesoderm forms scattered mesenchyme, irregular masses of somites, and notochord tissue, generally closely associated with the neural tissue. Although there is usually a continuous single notochord, isolated fragments of it are occasionally found trapped in the neural tissue. The mesodermal tissues, though differentiating normally, fail to adopt a typical bilateral and axial arrangement. This may be partly the reason for the absence of typical organization in the adjacent neural tissue.

E. Ectoderm, Mesoderm and Endoderm Derivatives

1. Combined Fragments of Medullary Plate, Chorda Mesoderm and Endoderm. Head plate plus underlying chorda mesoderm were combined with ventral endoderm of the early neurula. The grafts invaginate into the endoderm within the first 2–3 hours and, in so doing, become folded into a "U" configuration (Fig. 24 a–c). After 12 hours, invagination is complete but during the subsequent 12 hours the movement is reversed. This results in the reconstitution of the open-book-shaped plate, a condition which is attained after 42 hours and remains for at least 6 days (Fig.

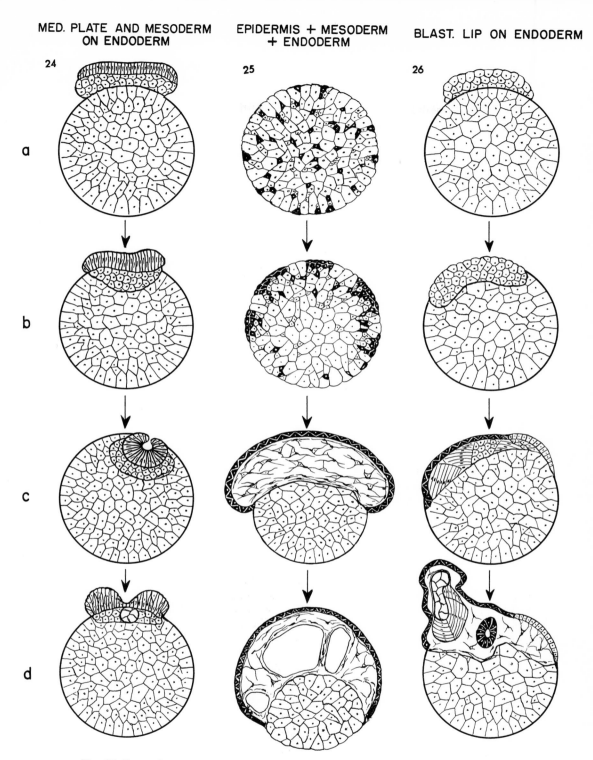

MED. PLATE AND MESODERM ON ENDODERM   EPIDERMIS + MESODERM + ENDODERM   BLAST. LIP ON ENDODERM

Fig. 24. Incomplete invagination of medullary plate and axial mesoderm when placed on trunk endoderm. Fig. 25. Cell segregation and tissue formation which occur in re-aggregated cell mixtures of epidermal. mesodermal and endodermal cells. Fig. 26. A fragment of the blastoporal lip only partially invaginates into a socket of endoderm. It forms a peripheral epithelium of epidermis (black) and fore-gut endoderm; underneath axial tissues and a neural tube.

24 d). Notochord and somites differentiate quite typically.

It is rather surprising that the graft is expelled in spite of the presence of mesoderm which, when grafted alone, does not experience this fate. The mesoderm remains firmly attached both to the endoderm and neural tissue. Evidently it is the emerging disaffinity between neural tissue and endoderm which drives the graft to the surface. The strong adhesion between chorda mesoderm and neural tissue, in conjunction with the absence of epidermis, causes the neural material to form a spina bifida instead of a tube.

2. Combination of Dissociated Cells from the Latero-Ventral Mesoderm, Epidermis and Ventral Endoderm. The ventral and lateral epidermis plus underlying mesoderm and trunk endoderm were removed as a whole (stage 13–14), disaggregated and allowed to re-aggregate. The amount of endoderm which was included varied from the whole ventral mass to small fractions of it. Depending on the relative amount of endoderm, one of two things happened: If the entire endoderm was used, the epidermis and mesoderm were unable to completely cover it; with smaller amounts of endoderm it became entirely covered. Our discussion will be limited to the first condition (20 sectioned cases).

Within 10 hours after re-aggregation all of the epidermal cells accumulate peripherally. Although several patches of epidermis may be present initially, they soon fuse to form a single cap. The endoderm facing the bottom of the culture dish remains uncovered by epidermis. While some mesoderm may be buried in the endoderm, it becomes mainly located between epidermis and endoderm (Fig. 25 a–d). Mesenchyme, pronephros, blood cells, and mesothelium appear in late stages of culture. A small number of trapped cells may be found: single endodermal cells in the mesenchyme, or a few mesodermal cells in the endoderm. The epidermis is nowhere in direct contact with endoderm.

The final tissue configuration is essentially like that of the normal embryo. Its formation and maintenance were possible because (a) the presence of ectoderm prevented the meso-derm from accumulating in the center of the endoderm; (b) the presence of mesoderm prevented the ectoderm from self-isolation.

3. Combination of Endoderm with Prospective Chorda Mesoderm from an Early Gastrula. Heretofore we have been concerned with tissues and cells of neurulae and older stages which at the time of recombination were for the most part determined and had already undergone the morphogenetic movements of gastrulation. It was the more surprising that under these conditions several of the tissues again executed the movements characteristic of the gastrula stage. The following experiments deal with material from the early gastrula, the developmental fate of which is not at all locally determined. The material used consisted of most of the prospective areas of chorda mesoderm and cephalic endoderm located dorsal to the sickle-shaped blastopore.

The blastoporal graft adheres firmly to the non-coated endoderm and soon sinks into the latter to form a flush surface with it (Fig. 26 b). However, complete invagination is not achieved, evidently because many of the prospective chorda mesoderm cells are converted regulatively into epidermis and form a peripheral cap which acts like the epidermis in the preceding experiments, preventing the mesodermal tissues from moving into the center of the endoderm.

Sections (17 cases) show that in accordance with the results of previous workers (reviewed by Holtfreter, 1938), the grafted blastoporal material produced regulatively not only epidermis but also some neural tissue and pigment cells. If the graft contained prospective foregut endoderm, this coated material did not invaginate into the uncoated trunk endoderm but spread over the latter and competed with the epidermis to form an epithelial covering over the mesoderm. The mesodermal differentiations consisted of notochord, somites, mesenchyme and pronephric tubules which sometimes grew out into blunt projections (Fig. 26 d). Antero-posterior elongation and bilateral disposition of the axial tissues were not as perfect as might have been expected.

It is well known that if such blastoporal

material is grafted into or underneath the ventral ectoderm of a whole gastrula, it invaginates and establishes a complete axial system, partly out of its own substance, partly by way of recruiting into this system induced host cells (Spemann and Mangold, 1924; Mayer, 1935, *et al.*). Even explanted blastoporal primordia undergo complicated re-arrangements of their cells and then segregate into axial tissues which tend to exhibit a bilaterally symmetric and antero-posterior configuration (Holtfreter, 1938). This occurred only if the explants became attached to a surface, such as glass; non-attached explants remained balled-up and failed to achieve a typical axial tissue arrangement. The occurrence of similar irregularities in the present preparations may be ascribed mainly to the fact that the epidermal-endodermal covering was both too fragmentary and unsuited to allow for an axial arrangement of the chorda mesoderm.

4. Recombination of Dissociated Cells from Several Dorsal Blastoporal Lips. The free cells from several blastoporal explants—six in most cases—were mixed and recombined. Preparations of this kind have been made and briefly discussed by Holtfreter (1943c).

Due to the presence of cephalic endoderm and the formation of epidermis by way of regulation, the cells determined to become mesodermal move away from the surface of the initially globular re-aggregates. This process of sorting out cannot be followed histologically as closely as was possible with the more distinctly characterized cells from neurulae. It is quite likely that the transformation of prospective mesoderm into epidermis occurs only at the periphery of the explant, not involving any centrifugal cell movements.

What can be observed in sections (22 cases) is this: After 48 hours the surface of the re-aggregates consists of a mosaic of endodermal and epidermal tissue patches. Subsequently, the epidermal patches, having a greater spreading tendency than the endodermal cells, tend to fuse into larger patches; but not enough epidermis is formed to cover the whole explant. It need hardly be mentioned that the peripheral foregut epithelium has its ciliated or otherwise active surface turned outside, such as has been observed in many corresponding situations, e.g., in exogastrulae.

The mesodermal tissues collect as a single mass underneath the peripheral endodermal-epidermal epithelium and then differentiate into the same kind of cells as were listed in the preceding experiment on non-dissociated material. Of special interest is the fact that the notochord usually occurred not in the form of many scattered bits, but as a single mass which however failed to exhibit pronounced elongation, and possessed abnormal branchings. Notochord was as a rule associated with quite typically segmented somites whose myoblasts elongated tangentially to the notochord. The regulatively formed neural tissue also tended to appear associated with notochord; it became subject to the molding influences of both notochord and somites which have been pointed out by previous workers (see Lehmann, 1945). The pronephric tubules appeared preferentially next to mesothelium-lined (coelomic) cavities which were scattered throughout the explant. One major continuous pronephric tubule always developed and occasionally one or two small accessory pronephric islets were found. As compared with the corresponding non-disaggregated material the degree of tissue reorganization was somewhat less perfect: no indications of antero-posterior or bilateral axiality were noticeable. Considering the fact that these preparations consisted of the cell material from several, thoroughly mixed blastoporal isolates, the reorganizations obtained are remarkable enough to deserve further inquiries.

In an attempt to interpret the results, several factors must be taken into account. The two organizing factors which became so clearly revealed in the preceding experiments with older cell material, namely directed locomotion of cytologically determined cells and selective cell adhesions, were obviously also operative here. The least that can be attributed to them is the segregation between endodermal and mesodermal tissues.

The question of how the tissues within the prospective mesoderm became segregated leads to the problem of embryonic fields.

Numerous workers have found that the prospective chorda mesoderm of the early gastrula is not locally determined but has the regulative capacities of a field. The present data suggest that the cells from several blastoporal lips, when mixed tend to establish a new, supranormal, and yet integrated embryonic field. The mixed and re-aggregated cells of six such fields, instead of forming six notochords and twelve pronephric tubules, form much less of these tissue units, usually a single though abnormally shaped notochord. In view of these results and those of other workers we may conclude that inductive cell determinations occurring amongst the components of the centrally accumulated mass of mesoderm have played an equally important role in the process of tissue-patterning as did purely cell kinetic processes. The latter are one of the consequences of inductive cell transformations.

General Considerations and Conclusions

Two general conclusions emerge from the foregoing experiments. (1) The different cell types of the amphibian embryo, whether present as single cells, cell sheets, or globular cell masses, exhibit tissue-specific tendencies of moving either centrifugally or centripetally within a composite cell aggregate. (2) Directed movements are followed by the phenomenon of cell-specificity of adhesion. The combined effects of these processes necessarily result in segregations and recombinations of tissue primordia or individual cells.

Analysis is difficult if the cell types cannot be clearly distinguished from each other, or if in the course of experimentation the cells enter into new pathways of differentiation. In other words, such experiments must be carried out with well defined types of cells that are no longer responsive, or not exposed to inductive or other determinative influences of their new environment.

Difficulties of this kind turned up in the experiments on mechanically dissociated and re-associated cells of sponges (Wilson, 1908; Galtsoff, 1925; Brondsted, 1936, *et al.*). There, as in our experiments, the re-aggregates formed typical tissue patterns, but the prin-

ciples of directed cell movements and cellular transformation could not be clearly defined as separate agencies to bring about the organismic reconstitutions.

We have encountered similar complications in the experiments with the cytologically undetermined gastrula material. But in most of our experiments the possible interference of induction was avoided by using more definitely determined material from older stages and by dealing with cell types which, according to their germ layer derivation, are clearly distinguishable both in living and sectioned preparations. This made it possible to trace exactly the locomotions and subsequent differentiations of the cells employed in the various combinations. Let us examine in more detail the different aspects of the problems raised here.

Unsupported Hypotheses on Morphogenesis

Many of the data obtained from this study do not support some of the hypotheses of earlier workers regarding the mechanisms of gastrulation-neurulation. There are three hypotheses which warrant consideration in this regard.

1. The notion of His (1874) that embryonic infoldings or outfoldings are caused by locally increased cell proliferations has already been refuted by numerous investigations on the mitotic activity of embryonic areas in various animals (see Holtfreter, 1943b; Gillette, 1944). The extensive studies on localized vital staining further invalidate this notion. In agreement with previous reasonings, this argument may be added: the invaginations or spreadings in normal or experimental tissue combinations occur within 10–15 hours (amphibians), when hardly any cell divisions and certainly no mass increment occur. Clearly, the principle of growth is no more involved in these processes than it is in the filling of a sports arena by people. It is an anachronistic trend of many embryologists to speak of ingrowth, outgrowth or overgrowth when referring to gastrulation movements.

2. Other speculative minds ascribed infoldings to imaginary pushing forces of the sur-

rounding epithelium (Bütschli, 1915; Giersberg, 1924) or to localized water intake (Glaser, 1914, 1916; Spek, 1931). The findings of subsequent investigators (Brown, Hamburger and Schmitt, 1941; Holtfreter, 1944) as well as the results of this study provide no factual evidence for these suppositions.

3. More recently, Lewis (1947, 1949) has interpreted the gastrulation-neurulation processes as resulting from localized contractions of a rather ill-defined superficial gel-layer. This concept cannot be reconciled with the experimental data of Holtfreter (1944, 1948), Devillers (1948, 1950) and Trinkaus (1949, 1951). The present experiments furnish numerous additional data which disqualify the assertions of Lewis. They demonstrate that the inward movement of one cell type underneath or into a layer of other cells has nothing to do with the contraction of a superficial gel-layer. This layer can hardly be interpreted as anything else but the coat.

It is true that under normal conditions the coat is in a state of elastic tension, comparable to that of an expanded rubber film. The coat does contract when released from tension, for example, when fragments of neural plate or blastoporal region are isolated. The fragments immediately curl into concave bodies (Holtfreter, 1943a, b). But owing to the antagonistic forces of lateral cell adhesion, such precociously involuted fragments soon flatten out again. It is inconceivable that epiboly or the formation of such deep cavities as the archenteron could result from curlings due to the contraction of any kind of surface structure. At any rate, single cells, or uncoated cell masses, move into the depth just as well as does a layer of coated cells.

In the areas of medullary plate or blastoporal region, the coat unites the invaginating cells peripherally but it does not provide the motive power for invagination. On the contrary, the coat counteracts invagination and favors (in an apparently paradoxical way) epibolic spreading. This is strikingly illustrated by the fact that a piece of epidermis which has been deprived of its upper coated cell layer, will slip underneath the surrounding coated epidermis or into a mass of denuded endoderm (Holtfreter, 1943a, 1944). Similarly, as shown here and in previous experiments, coated endoderm tends to spread over uncoated endoderm, or mesoderm, whereas uncoated endoderm or mesoderm will invaginate into uncoated endoderm. Hence the initial decrease of surface area (contraction of the coat), as observed in the infoldings of medullary plate, blastoporal region, etc., is the result and not the cause of invagination. These and many other data (see below) point to the conclusion that invagination as well as epithelial spreading result from an active locomotion of cells or tissues and that the coat merely assists in integrating these collective cell movements.

Dalcq and Pasteels (Dalcq, 1941) have postulated that invagination of the blastoporal material is caused by an interplay of two hypothetical concentration gradients. It would require much imagination to find support of this hypothesis in the present results.

Classification of Cell Movements. In his fundamental analysis of the morphogenetic cell movements of the amphibian embryo, Vogt (1929) distinguished between epiboly, invagination, convergence, divergence and axial elongation. Our experiments have contributed little to an elucidation of the last three phenomena. On the other hand, they indicate the presence of another tendency, namely that of an outward movement of cells which is different from evagination and which may be designated as emigration. Epiboly which is normally associated with the coated ectoderm, can be exhibited also by coated endoderm; so the less committal term "spreading" will be applied to this common phenomenon.

To designate inward movements, a diversity of words have been used in the literature: invagination, involution, infolding, immigration, invasion, ingression, and ingrowth. These terms come in handy for descriptive purposes but they have no explanatory value. Evidence shows that the cells of one and the same primordium can, under different experimental conditions, display any one of the processes designated by the above terms (except ingrowth). It seems justified therefore to make no special efforts to distinguish between the various terms and speak of invagination when referring to any kind of inward shiftings.

Tissue Specificity of Morphogenetic Movements

The present experiments were aimed at studying both the cell-inherent kinetic tendencies of embryonic primordia and the environmental conditions which favor or impede their expression. That the phenomena of spreading or of axial elongation and segregation are actually due to tissue-inherent tendencies has been shown previously by culturing isolated pieces of ectoderm, endoderm, or blastoporal lip on an unspecific surface, for example, on glass (Holtfreter, 1938, 1944). Without an organic or inorganic surface to adhere to, the primordia cannot spread, and axial stretching remains abortive. Nor can invagination occur in the absence of an embedding matrix of other cells. The present data throw some light upon the question of why the primordia in an intact embryo move about and segregate as they do normally.

In the following discussion the kinetic manifestations of the different primordia will be treated separately.

1. Prospective Coated Epidermis of Gastrula or Neurula Stages Never Moved into the Depth of Other Tissues (Inductions Excluded). Instead, it spread over mesoderm, uncoated endoderm or medullary tissue. When competing with coated endoderm, the ectoderm exhibited a relatively stronger spreading tendency than the endoderm. When individual ectodermal cells were interspersed in between either endodermal, mesodermal or medullary plate cells, they moved to the surface of the aggregate and then established, by way of spreading, a continuous surface epithelium.

Centrifugal emigration of scattered cells, or of nucleated cytoplasm, to a peripheral position is a familiar phenomenon in arthropod eggs. In a less conspicuous way, it occurs also in normal amphibian embryos, namely, when the multilayered ectoderm changes into a thinned-out epidermis (Holtfreter, 1943b; Gillette, 1944). After the initially buried epidermal cells have attained a surface position, they secrete a coat and it appears that concomitantly they acquire a pronounced tendency for epibolic spreading.

2. Endoderm. It seems strange at first sight that the endoderm cells also have the tendency of centrifugal locomotion and surface spreading. This tendency is manifested in preparations which consist only of endoderm and mesoderm but it is inhibited when the surface is already occupied by ectoderm. Coated endoderm has a definitely stronger spreading tendency than uncoated endoderm. The experimental data appear less strange in view of the fact that in normal development endodermal expansions also occur, viz., in the dorsad movement of the walls of the archenteron and in the subsequent increase of surface area in the elongating gut. In whole embryos it is the relatively stronger spreading tendency of the ectoderm which prevents the endoderm from expanding into a peripheral epithelium.

This implies that an internal archenteron cannot be established, and not even be maintained, in the absence of an epidermal covering. Inhibition of ectodermal epiboly produces exogastrulae whose endoderm forms the outer envelope of the mesoderm. Removal of the whole ectoderm at neurula or even older stages causes a complete inversion of the remaining two germ layers, largely brought about by an outward movement and spreading of the coated endoderm of the archenteron over the denuded surface of the embryo (p. 19). If a wound is inflicted on an advanced embryo, reaching into the archenteron, the coated epithelium of the latter moves outward through the hole until it meets the epidermis. Since coated endoderm and epidermis cannot spread over each other, such a fistula remains forever open.

a. Invagination of the blastopore: Although the above as well as previous data demonstrate that the spreading of coated endoderm is counteracted by the relatively stronger spreading power of coated ectoderm, it follows by no means that invagination of the blastoporal endoderm results from a pushing action of the expanding ectoderm of the gastrula. In the complete absence of this ectoderm, a fragment of the blastoporal lip will move into a socket of uncoated endoderm, although the coated endodermal portion of the graft tends to spread over the socket (p. 24). But a ball of uncoated endoderm moves entirely into a layer of uncoated endoderm. This alternative exhibition of the opposite movements of spreading and invagination by the endoderm requires an explanation. The following one may be offered.

In blastoporal invagination, the factors making for invagination must evidently overcome those making for peripheral spreading of the endoderm. Since spreading tendency can be associated with the presence of a coat, and invagination with uncoated cell surfaces, it seems that the endoderm of the blastoporal lip moves inward due to a response of the inner, motile cell surfaces to some "cytotatic" or other directional influence of the inner milieu. The coated outer surface yields passively to the pulling force of the actually observed inward movement of the cells. Soon after invagination has begun, the adjacent marginal mesoderm becomes involved; its pronounced invagination tendency no doubt contributes considerably to the completion of the formation of the archenteron.

b. Evaginations: No special endodermal differentiations were recorded because in most of these experiments the bulky endoderm of the prospective trunk region was used. Even in normal embryos, this material fails to attain differentiation and degenerates eventually (Holtfreter, 1933). The primordia of foregut or stomach which did differentiate in mesoderm-endoderm aggregates, formed a peripheral epithelium, the secreting or ciliated side of which was turned outside. If gastric glands developed in this everted epithelium, they would sink into the underlying mesenchyme. To follow the time-honored terminology, here one must speak of an invagination and not, as in normal development, of an evagination of the glands. (For illustrations of this phenomenon, see Holtfreter, 1933, 1938).

The data indicate that invagination and evagination are actually controlled by the same principles and that these two terms merely refer to topographic relationships and not to different mechanisms. Both the ecto- and endoderm are surface epithelia which protect the mesoderm from the vicissitudes of the external medium. The tubular glands which develop from both kinds of epithelia represent in either case shiftings away from the extra-organismic medium.

3. Medullary Plate. In combination with either prospective epidermis, endoderm or both, fragments or individual cells of the medullary plate invariably moved into the core of the aggregate, where they formed a homogeneous neural tissue. The same occurred when mesenchyme from the neural fold or from the mesoderm mantle was added to the above combinations.

It is obvious that the tendency for inward movement is present in each medullary cell and that to manifest it, a matrix as atypical as a mass of epidermal or endodermal cells is sufficient. Hence neither the surface coat, the expanding epidermis, nor the mesodermal substratum can be made specifically responsible for the infolding of the medullary plate in whole embryos. We hasten to add, however, that the coat and the various embedding tissues do play an important role in normal embryogenesis, namely, in the subsequent shaping of the invaginated medullary material.

Some of these environmental (not "inductive") influences are concerned with the formation of a characteristically shaped *central lumen of the neural tube*. In the invaginating whole neural plate, or in fragments of it, the contractile coat remains intact. Although not causing invagination, the coat nevertheless contracts, retains its distal non-adhesiveness and becomes significantly engaged in the formation and maintenance of the central lumen.

The above data show that central lumina can be formed in the absence of a continuous coat, namely, by way of secondary cavitation within a compact mass of prospective neural tissue. Subsurface formation of a neurocoel has been observed before in experiments in which the ectodermal layer was too thick to become entirely neuralized by the underlying inductors. This type of secondary neurocoel formation is the norm in teleost development. Under the term of polymyely, similar secondary cavitations have been described in experimentally injured brains and in tissue cultures.

Evidently, secondary lumen formation is caused by the exudation of a liquid which increasingly separates the initially contacting cells. Localized liquid formation presupposes an alignment of axially organized cells around their future lumen. Such a preparatory cell arrangement could actually be observed in our aggregates containing centrally accumulated medullary tissue. The difference between lumen formation through infolding and through secondary cavitation is not as great as it appears if one considers the fact that the infolded lumina are likewise kept open thanks to a continuous secretion of a liquid from the walls of the lumen.

Prospective neural tissue, like epidermis and gut epithelium, seems to be capable of transferring water from the outside to a central lumen. In epidermis-covered explants of neural tissue this process may result in an excessive blowing-up of the neurocoel cavities (p. 12). The opposite occurred in preparations in which the invaginated medullary cells became covered by endoderm and lacked a mesenchymatic mantle. Here the infolded lumen disappeared and no new lumina developed by way of cavitation (pp. 13, 16). In a still undisclosed way, a purely endodermal environment seems to prevent the transfer of water to the medullary tissue. Normal embryogenesis does not have to cope with this situation.

a. Lumen formation through infolding versus secondary cavitation or delamination: There is the well-known phenomenon that, varying with the taxonomic group, the same kind of internal cavity can be established either by way of infolding or through secondary cavitation. Examples: archenteron, coelom, neural tube, lens, otocyst, and various structures in invertebrates. These alternative modes of lumen formation are distributed so erratically amongst the taxonomic

types that they cannot serve as a basis for establishing phylogenetic relationships. The present data underline the insignificance of the different kinetic devices used to achieve the same result. One and the same primordium, such as the cells of the medullary plate, can resort to the normally not employed device of secondary cavitation if they attain an internal position without infolding. Similarly, in certain instances of tumor growth, e.g., in carcinoma of the mammary gland, follicles are produced through secondary cavitation rather than from outgrowth of the duct system as occurs normally.

It appears that in a general sense internal epithelial lumina can be established or retained only if there is a gradient of some sort between the intra- and extraorganismic milieu. The medullary plate of an embryo remains a flat layer (spina bifida) in the absence of an epidermal covering. On the other hand, a piece of prospective epidermis which is grafted into the mesenchyme, or into the coelom of older amphibian larvae, either loses its coat and disintegrates into scattered cells or it forms, by way of rounding-up and secretion, a vesicle, whose coated surface is turned inside as in all invaginated epithelia (Harris, 1942). Likewise, the formation of an internal gut lumen presupposes the existence of another epithelium (epidermis) which shields the endoderm from the external medium. Therefore, the decision of ectoderm or endoderm to form either an external layer or an internal cavity depends upon the topographic relationship of these epithelia to the external medium. None of the germ layers can form tubes or cavities in the absence of enveloping tissues.

b. Regional organization of the neural system: This problem is far too complex and the data we can offer to solve it are too fragmentary to justify a lengthy discussion. It may be mentioned, however, that the present results confirm the often stated notion that the shape of the neurocoel and the bilateral and anteroposterior organization of the neural system are largely dependent upon continued formative influences of the various tissues of the archenteron roof. Consequently, little regional organization was obtained in combinations in which the tissues of the archenteron roof were absent or had been deranged together with those of the medullary plate. The multiplicity of atypically shaped neurocoels as observed in these combinations would probably not have occurred if the disarranged and re-associated cells of the medullary plate had been subsequently exposed to the formative influences of a normal archenteron roof. Nevertheless the method of reshuffling the cells of a disaggregated primordium represents a new and promising approach to investigating the baffling problem of embryonic fields. A diversity of experiments along these lines are in progress.

4. Mesodermal Primordia. In any of the combinations employed, cells determined to form mesodermal tissues moved into internal sites, irrespective of whether the embedding material consisted of ectoderm or endoderm and of whether the mesoderm represented scattered cells or solid cell masses. The mesectoderm from the neural crest behaved similarly. However, the final allocation of the sorted-out mesoderm varied with the kind of tissue association. If combined only with endoderm or ectoderm, the mesoderm took up a *central position;* but if ectoderm cells were added to the endoderm, or if medullary cells were added to the ectoderm, the mesodermal cells occupied an *intermediary position* between the centrally accumulating endoderm, or neural tissue, and the peripherally established epidermal layer. To attain this intermediary position in an initially mixed-up cell aggregate, the centrally dispersed mesoderm cells must have moved centrifugally and the peripherally scattered mesoderm cells must have moved centripetally.

Evidently the direction of movement of the mesoderm in these combinations is controlled by the presence or absence of an epidermal covering. The behavior of the mesoderm is only partly similar to that of the endoderm. The cells from both germ layers tend to invaginate in the presence of ectoderm, but when endoderm alone is combined with mesoderm, the latter invariably moves into the former indicating a comparatively stronger invagination tendency and the absence of a spreading tendency within the mesodermal primordia.

With reference to normal embryogenesis, these data show that the formation of a mesoderm mantle over an endodermal core requires the presence of an epidermal covering. Even after it has attained its intermediary allocation, the mesoderm cannot maintain it without a protective epidermal covering. When the latter is removed in advanced stages, the whole mesoderm mantle breaks up into patches which then move into the underlying endoderm (p. 19).

Investigation of the factors involved in the *regional and bilateral organization* of the mesodermal primordia transgresses the scope of this paper. Let us mention, however, that although the mesoderm can achieve tissue segregation and histotypical differentiation inside an endodermal envelope, it fails under these conditions to exhibit typical caudal stretching and bilateral arrangement of its components. Evidently such an envelope cannot substitute for the epidermis to allow for a manifestation of the inherent tendencies of the mesoderm to establish a typically organized axial system.

The intermingled cells of disaggregated blastoporal lips showed a more pronounced capability of regulating into an axial system than did those of the archenteron roof. This agrees with the current notion that the parts of the mesoderm become more definitely determined during the period of gastrulation. To state it differently: whereas the tissue segregations within the mesoderm, as observed in the experiments with neurula and older stages, can mainly, if not entirely, be attributed to directed cell movements, the more perfect reconstitutions as obtained in disarranged blastoporal lips are at least partly due to inductive interactions amongst the parts of the lips, each lip representing initially an "embryonic field." It should be pointed out in this connection that histological regulations or reconstitutions of any kind probably always involve considerable shiftings of cytoplasm or cells resulting in the reconstitution of a new organismic field.

Factors Determining Morphogenetic Cell Movements

The above data, as stated in histological terms, raise problems on cellular and physico-chemical levels. Unfortunately, no satisfactory answer can be given to the question of what makes the cells move either inward or outward under normal or experimental conditions. As a basis for further investigations let us point out the crucial phenomena and the problems that arise from them.

The *tendency for directed cell movements* has been shown to be tissue-specific whereas the environmental factors enabling the execution of these movements are far from specific. Consider the spreading tendency. The literature on tissue cultures provides ample evidence that a spreading of all sorts of epithelia can take place on such atypical surfaces as glass or clotted blood plasma. Under these conditions, epithelia like those of the gut, of endodermal glands, or of the kidney, will form membranes rather than tubular cavities. These epithelia may exhibit inward movement and tubular configuration in the presence of a substratum which need not be specific but simply allows the cells to move away from the interfacial conditions between substratum and external environment. Examples: medullary tissue, or mesoderm, migrating into such atypical substrata as endoderm or ectoderm, or explanted kidney epithelium moving into the fibrin matrix of a clot of blood plasma (Rienhoff, 1922) to form tubules. Grobstein (1953) observed in the case of salivary glands from mouse embryos that the type of mesenchymatic matrix influences the extent of tubular ramification of these glands.

While the enhancing and specifying influences of the tissue environment upon shape and perfection of any invaginated epithelial structures is acknowledged, there remains the more general problem of why certain tissues tend to spread or to invaginate at all. What does cellular kinetic "tendency" mean in a more concrete sense?

The *studies on isolated cells* provide some important though not sufficient clues for an understanding of morphogenetic mass movements. There is no doubt that the isolated cells of the different germ layers here investigated do exhibit tissue-specific locomotion and that their direction of locomotion is controlled by an inherent cellular axial polarity. For instance, singly isolated cells of prospective epidermis flatten and spread on a contact surface while those from the medullary plate or the blastoporal lip do the opposite: they elongate along their proximo-distal axis and migrate, with their non-coated inner cell pole leading the way, a tendency which normally leads to invagination (Holtfreter, 1947a, b).

The ectodermal primordia of neural system, lens, nose, or ear vesicle, *acquire the tendency to invaginate as a consequence of induction*. In the case of the medullary plate, it could be shown that the cylindrical elongation of the constituent cells, as seen in sections, is due to a newly arising stretching tendency of each cell and not, as has been suggested by Schmitt (1941), to contact influences between neighboring cells (Holtfreter, 1947). Evidently, induction involves the elaboration of structural properties of the cell membrane which are absent in pre-induction stages and which cause the induced cells to elongate and to invaginate instead of spreading as does the non-induced epidermal portion of the ectoderm. It should be mentioned, however, that cell elongation and invagination tendency are not necessarily linked up with induction. For instance the blastoporal endomesoderm exhibits these phenomena in the absence of adjacent inductors.

Amoeboid motility in any cell type of the amphibian embryo is produced by an axially organized succession of alternating expansions and contractions of the cell surface which need not be associated with gel-sol transformations of the inner cytoplasm (Holtfreter, 1947a, b). If, as in isolated epidermal cells, this three-steps-forward, two-steps-backward succession of movements is executed by the entire peripheral margin of the attached cell, the net result is centrifugal spreading of the cell. If the extension movements are confined to only the "anterior" part of the cell, as in medullary and other non-spreading cells, they cause unidirectional locomotion or, if the cell body remains sessile, the projection of localized, sometimes highly extended amoeboid processes, as in a neurone.

To what extent can the observations on isolated cells further an understanding of the mechanisms operating in the *directed cell movements* in complex tissue combinations? Definitely more than has been conceded by Vogt (1913), Kuhl (1937) or Bonner (1952).

One can interpret ectodermal epiboly as due to the summative effect of the spreading tendency of each of the constituent cells of the cell sheet. In gastrulation and wound healing, the extent of epidermal spreading seems to be simply a matter of readily available, non-coated cell surfaces which controls the manifestation of the ever-present spreading tendency of the individual cells.

Difficulties of interpretation arise in the case of invagination movements. To be sure, the penetration of the blastoporal endoderm into the inner endodermal cell mass of the gastrula seems to involve the same principles which direct the locomotion of the isolated cells from this region. The interdigitations between blastoporal cells and the inner endoderm support this view. Also, the immigration of individual cells of mesoderm or neural plate into a non-specific cellular matrix can be largely attributed to the mechanism of amoeboid locomotion. Most likely, this inward movement of scattered cells into a densely packed layer of other cells proceeds without the formation of hyaline pseudopodia and of gel-sol transformations.

The above interpretations fail, however, to explain the inward movement of large cell masses. The neural plate, a piece of forebrain, or a lump of mesoderm consisting of hundreds of cells, glides into the depth of a cellular matrix with a perfectly smooth periphery. This excludes intervention of the extension-contraction mechanism of the cell membrane which makes for the locomotion of isolated cells. And yet, compact cell masses showing no amoeboid locomotion of their peripheral cells, move inward just as readily as do individual cells.

The riddle of this situation comes somewhat closer to a solution if it is realized that the shifting of a tissue into or underneath another tissue always involves reciprocal accommodating cell movements of the latter. When a lump of neural or mesoderm cells is placed upon the smooth surface of endoderm, the loosely connected cells of the endoderm actively move around the graft, comparable to the phagocytic movement of an amoeba around a food particle. It appears that while in some instances the amoeboid movements of both the invading and embedding cells are equally instrumental in bringing about inward shiftings, in other instances it is mainly or entirely the engulfing tendency of the embedding cells which achieves the same end result.

These considerations do not tell us why, in embryos or in composite aggregates, certain cell types move inward and others outward. It seems necessary to assume the *existence of a concentration gradient of some sort between inner and outer milieu of the aggregate towards which the different cell types react differently*. To indicate the general nature of this problem, the experiments of Roudabush (1933) may be mentioned. They showed that when a Hydra is turned inside-out, a normal Hydra can be reconstituted due to an "amoeboid" inward movement of the everted endodermal cells and an outward movement of the ectodermal cells. Probably similar directed cell migrations are involved in the reconstitution of dissociated sponges.

By way of analogy one may compare invagination with amoeboid phagocytosis or with the incorporation of an oil drop of a relatively high surface tension into the denuded egg of a sea urchin having a low surface tension (Kopac and Chambers, 1936). Similarly, epibolic spread might be interpreted by assuming that the interfacial tension between coated epithelia and the ambient aqueous medium is lower than that between uncoated cells and this medium. Rhumbler (1899, 1902, 1927) and Holtfreter (1943b) have elaborated upon such speculations. They suggested that if the blastocoel, or the interior of a cell aggregate in general, contains surface tension-lowering substances, invagination may be due to a kind of cytotactic reaction of the proximal cell surfaces to a gradient of interfacial tension between inside and outside of the embryo. The cells or cell masses would move toward the surface tension-lowering gradient comparable to the engulfing of certain kinds of oil drops by a sea urchin egg.

As has been emphasized by Rhumbler (*op. cit.*), the forces of molecular interfacial tension cannot be ruled out in the kinetics of embryonic cells whose surface is of a semiliquid nature. Yet the well-attested structural properties of the cell membrane would necessarily resist a free display of these forces since the latter presuppose freely mobile molecules. Further work is required to clarify the significance of interfacial tension in morphogenesis and to define the factors which direct the tissue-specific movements here recorded.

Cellular Adhesiveness

The phenomenon of cellular adhesion is the prerequisite for the evolution and ontogenesis of multicellular organisms. In early cleavage stages this phenomenon may be almost absent, as in the eggs of mammals, or echinoderms, where the blastomeres round up and retain hardly any contact with each other. Their falling apart is largely prevented by the tightly applied hyaline layer (echinoderms) or by the egg membranes. In the case of the amphibian egg, the syncytial coat is at least as important as is intercellular adhesion to hold the blastomeres together. In all these instances the function of the external coverings as a mechanism to insure cohesion of the blastomeres is progressively replaced by an increasing adhesiveness of the adjacent cell walls. At the gastrula stage, the cells of the peripheral layers have attained mutual adhesion, whereas the cells of the inner endoderm are still lacking it.

In any of the above recombinations, the different cell types at first adhered to each other irrespective of germ layer derivation and of differences of species. The cells tended to form a tightly packed globular aggregate which reflects their tendency to establish maximal mutual contact and to reduce their inter-

face with the ambient aqueous medium to a minimum. However, this initial adhesiveness is static only if the aggregate consists of one kind of cells. In heterologous combinations, subsequent sorting-out movements lead to new cell arrangements. This suggests that the molecular bonds making for indiscriminate cell adhesions are somewhat unstable.

The Question of an Extracellular Cementing Matrix. There is no evidence that embryonic amphibian cells migrating on glass secrete a sticky substance that facilitates locomotion as in the case of the amoebae (Jennings, 1904) and amoebocytes of invertebrates (Fauré-Fremiet, 1929). There is no indication either that Weiss' (1945) observations on tissues cultured in clotted blood plasma are pertinent with regards to cellular movements and adhesions in early embryos because the latter do not seem to possess extracellular matrices comparable to a fibrin coagulate.

The question of whether or not the embryonic cells adhere to each other with their "naked" surfaces or by means of an intercellular cement appears to be largely a matter of definition. The presence of such a cement seems to be well documented in the case of various epithelia or endothelia in adult organisms (Gray, 1926; Chambers, 1940). Clearly, the peripheral coat represents an exudation product of this kind; but the coat is non-adhesive at its outer surface and it does not extend down to the cellular interfaces which appear to touch each other directly (Holtfreter, 1943a; Dollander, 1951). Nor does the free mobility of isolated cells along each other's surfaces indicate the intervention of an adhesive cement (Holtfreter, 1947a). On the other hand, it has been observed that the same external conditions which cause dissipation of the coat, also destroy mutual adhesiveness of the non-coated cells. This suggests a constitutional similarity between the well-defined coat and the microscopically non-detectable cement which holds the inner cells together.

It should be pointed out that whereas the cell-disaggregating effect of alkali, citrate or oxalate is reversible, that of proteases is irreversible (Townes, 1953). This shows that calcium ions and proteins are involved in adhesion, but it is a matter of taste to consider the proteolytically susceptible material as an intercellular cement or as part of the living cell membrane.

Morphogenetic movements and cellular adhesiveness obey quite different controlling factors although both result from specific properties of the cell membrane. Prospective neural tissue invaginates while losing adhesion to ectoderm or endoderm, whereas mesoderm invaginates while retaining adhesiveness to the embedding tissues. Not only in the latter instance, but in cellular locomotion in general, the crux of the matter is that a cell migrates in spite of being adhesive to an organic or inorganic surface of contact. In morphogenesis, the forces controlling directed movements must overcome those of cell adhesion. It becomes evident once more that the molecular bonds involved in these early, temporary and indiscriminate cell adhesions are extremely labile and as such not comparable to the bonds involved in antigen-antibody reactions.

Tissue and Stage Specificity of Cell Adhesion. The situation becomes more involved because of two sets of experimental data: (1) The indiscriminate adhesiveness of early embryonic cells changes subsequently into tissue-specific selective adhesiveness; (2) this change cannot readily be correlated with the stages of cellular differentiation.

As to the first point, the present as well as previous data show that initially intermingled different cell types, after they have undergone sorting-out by way of directed movements, stick together permanently to form homogeneous tissues which segregate themselves from adjacent, other types of tissues. Whether this segregation results from a process of "pinching off" or through cleft formation seems to be irrelevant. One and the same tissue may follow either of these procedures according to the environmental conditions; for example, prospective neural tissue separates from epidermis or endoderm under any circumstances —obviously due to an arising disaffinity between these tissues. On the other hand, meso-

dermal tissues retain a permanent adhesiveness to ecto- and endodermal tissues. New cellular affinities arise in the course of development (Holtfreter, 1939).

As to point two, the above experiments dealing with the combination of primordia of different developmental stages (p. 14) show that the alternative between indiscriminate and selective adhesiveness is not simply determined by developmental stage. A piece of forebrain, or of mesoderm, which has already undergone invagination and segregation will, under experimental conditions, once more adhere to a layer of early ectoderm or endoderm and move into these layers. Invagination and subsequent segregation of these tissues of different age require about the same time interval as is observed in corresponding tissue combinations of an earlier stage. Hence it appears that the factors making for indiscriminate and selective cell adhesion may be present simultaneously and that it requires a prolonged contact between heterologous tissues to bring forth the selective component of adhesion.

There is another point worth mentioning though it is partly implicit in the above statements. It is the fact that adhesiveness between different tissues may vary in *degree*. Dissection of a fresh neurula shows for instance that the prechordal mesoderm is much less firmly attached to the medullary plate than is the notochordal tissue. Alkali treatment of advanced embryonic stages does not produce the ready cell dissociations as it does in earlier stages.

Hypotheses Concerning the Molecular Factors Engaged in Cellular Adhesion. The hypothesis of Weiss (1941, 1947, 1950) which interprets selective cell adhesion in terms of an interlocking of complex molecules possessing complementary configurations is based on Pauling's theory that the strength of a chemical bond is proportional to the complementariness or fit of the molecules. Weiss has diagrammatically portrayed some of the possible molecular configurations that might account for selective cell adhesion. While it should be realized that no precise data as to the configuration of the cell-binding ele-

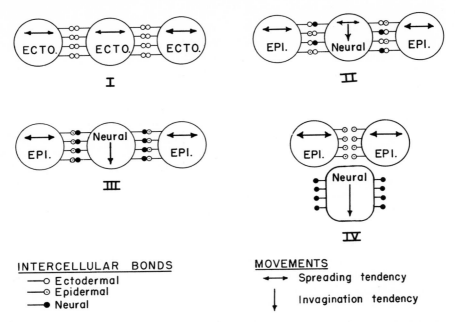

INTERCELLULAR BONDS
—○ Ectodermal
—○ Epidermal
—● Neural

MOVEMENTS
⟷ Spreading tendency
↓ Invagination tendency

Fig. 27. Schematic representation of changes in intercellular bonds and migration tendency leading to segregation of medullary and epidermal cells (or tissues). Stage I. Early condition of ectodermal cells having a moderate spreading tendency and non-specific intercellular bonds. Stage II. Partial conversion of ectodermal into epidermal and neural types. Stage III. Completion of bond modifications and emergence of cell-specific migration tendencies. Stage IV. Invagination and segregation result from these cellular modifications. In artificial aggregates of neural and epidermal cells, the cells may be considered to have been returned to the condition of stage III from which stage IV is once again attained.

ments are available, Weiss' hypothesis sounds persuasive. Nevertheless, the non-static nature of cell adhesions, as pointed out above, leaves room for other hypotheses envisaging a more complex and less rigid lock and key mechanism.

In a more specific way, Tyler (1946) attempted to explain cell affinity in terms of an antigen-antibody complex. He proposed that the molecules at the cell surface react with molecules of adjacent cells surfaces in a manner analogous to the union of an antigen with its antibody. However, according to the more generally accepted concepts of immunological reactions, combinations of this type would not appropriately be considered as antigen-antibody complexes. Obviously in the present case, no foreign element is introduced which could elicit formation of an antibody, a condition which is essential for an antigen-antibody reaction. The auto-antibody concept, by not sharing this basic requirement, may

be applied to describe the combination or chemical interaction of any complex molecular species, not only linkages between interfacial cell surfaces, but innumerable others even as remote as the recombination of dissociated hemoglobins. Under these circumstances, referring to the molecular species responsible for cell adhesion as antigens yields little clarification of the essential problem.

In view of the rather complicated nature of the phenomena observed and of our ignorance concerning the physico-chemical factors involved, one could think of a diversity of symbolistic schemes which might tentatively cover the actual situation without, however, explaining it. One of the possible interpretive illustrations which suggests itself is that of Fig. 27. In these diagrams it is attempted to combine the changes of adhesiveness with the *simultaneously* occurring directed cell movements, as exemplified in the combination of prospective epidermal and neural cells. Only a few words need be added to these self-explanatory diagrams.

While the cells of different prospective fate either spread or invaginate due to cell-specific migration tendencies which are evidently directed by inside-outside gradients within the aggregate, their mutual adhesiveness is only temporary and not very firm. Hence the prospective neural cell of Fig. 27 can readily slip into the depth, whereas the prospective epidermal cells continue spreading (indicated in arrows). By the use of different symbols for the bonds of cellular adhesion, it is indicated that the originally indiscriminate adhesiveness of the early ectoderm (stage I) changes into cell-specific adhesiveness of respectively epidermal and neural cells (stages II and III), making for a separation of the two cell types or tissues.

While the experiments reported clearly indicate that changes in adhesiveness occur, the precise mechanism for them are unknown. Two possibilities are evident: (1) Bonds arise *de novo* in the course of cell differentiation which are responsible for selective adhesion, while pre-existing bonds are retained and are responsible for indiscriminate adhesion. In normal segregation the latter ultimately yield to the increasing tendency for cell movement, and segregation occurs. In experimental cell mixtures, through re-association of differentiated cells, these indiscriminate bonds are once more called into play and yield again. (2) The early bond type (indiscriminate) becomes *modified* according to cell type to the extent that the degree of adhesion varies with the cell type involved. The modification is however not so extreme that indiscriminate adhesions can no longer occur. Again, in conjunction with different degrees of adhesion, changes in tendency for cell movement lead to normal segregation (stages I–IV), while in experimental re-association the condition of less effective cell union is re-introduced (stage III) and segregation occurs once more. Either of these mechanisms may be responsible for the changes of adhesion observed.

At present, it would be futile to speculate further upon the possible subcellular factors that are engaged in cellular adhesiveness. It should be pointed out, however, that this principle is of universal significance in morphogenesis, and that, in connection with directed cell movements, it is deserving of more attention than it has received.

SUMMARY

1. With the aim of elucidating the factors which are engaged in the morphogenetic movements and tissue segregations of the amphibian embryo, tissues of known prospective fate from embryos between gastrula and late neurula stages were excised and united with each other in different combinations. The excised tissues were either simply combined in various permutations or they were at first disaggregated into single cells by the addition of alkali, whereupon the cells of one primordium were intermingled with those of another primordium. When returned to optimal pH conditions, the cells united to form a compact body.

2. The mixed-up individual cells perform, according to their cell type, the same kinds of directed movements as do the corresponding tissue fragments. These movements are essentially of two kinds: (a) inward movements, as manifested by the cells from the neural plate, or the mesoderm, which have been combined with either epidermal or endodermal cells; (b) outward movements and peripheral spreading, as manifested by epidermal and, to a lesser extent, by endodermal cells or tissue fragments under the same conditions. It may be concluded that the normal pattern of gastrulation-neurulation movements is primarily due to different migration tendencies inherent in each cell type; that the contractile surface film of the embryo ("coat") merely coordinates but does not—as suggested by Lewis—cause or direct either invagination or epiboly; that the inward movement of single cells or cell sheets does not result from localized "growth" (His), from localized water uptake (Spek, Glaser) or from a pushing effect of the surrounding ectoderm (Giersberg). The migratory cells merely require a rather unspecific cellular substratum to move away from the periphery. The outward movement of

epidermal cells in a composite explant can be likewise ascribed to cell-inherent migratory tendencies.

3. The tendency of neurogenic cells to move inward is not confined to material from the neurula stage, but is still present in the explanted and properly combined pieces of brain from larvae. This tendency is absent in the prospective medullary plate prior to induction. Both endodermal or ectodermal cells represent an adequate embedding substratum for the invading neurogenic material.

4. A neurocoel can be formed (a) as a result of the infolding of any portion of the coated medullary plate, or (b) through secondary cavitation of a compact mass formed by individually immigrated neurogenic cells.

5. In consequence of directed movements, the different cell types in a composite aggregate are sorted out into distinct homogeneous layers, the stratification of which corresponds to the normal germ layer arrangement. The tissue segregation becomes complete because of the emergence of a selectivity of cell adhesion: homologous cells when they meet remain permanently united to form functional tissues, whereas a cleft develops between certain non-homologous tissues (e.g., between neural or endodermal tissues and adjacent epidermis). As in normal embryogenesis, the mesodermal elements take up an intermediate position connecting the inner with the outer epithelia.

6. Regional organ characteristics such as may develop in combinations of non-dissociated fragments hardly ever occur although the reconstituted part-embryos display rather typical cyto- and histodifferentiation. One may conclude that the districts of medullary plate and axial mesoderm are to a certain extent locally determined and that the disaggregated and intermingled cells of these primordia are incapable of reestablishing these patterns. Corresponding experiments on gastrula material yielded more typical neural and mesodermal structures reflecting a higher degree of regulative capacity in these younger stages.

7. It would appear that the principles of cell-specific movements, selective adhesions and cavitation, as manifested in the present experiments, help to elucidate the factors instrumental in the normal formation of germ layers and their further segregation. An interpretation of these phenomena in cytological and physicochemical terms is attempted.

LITERATURE CITED

Adams, A. E. 1924. An experimental study of the development of the mouth in the amphibian embryo. *J. Exp. Zool., 40:* 311–379.

Adelmann, H. B. 1936. The problem of cyclopia. *Quart. Rev. Biol., 11:* 161–182.

Barth, L. G. 1941. Neural differentiation without organizer. *J. Exp. Zool., 87:* 371–382.

Boerema, I. 1929. Die Dynamik des Medullarrohrschlusses. *Arch. Entw. mech., 115:* 601–615.

Bonner, J. T. 1952. *Morphogenesis—An Essay on Development.* Princeton Univ. Press.

Brøndsted, H. V. 1936. Entwicklungs-physiologische Studien über *Spongilla lacustris* (L.). *Acta Zool., 17:* 75–172.

Brown, M. G., V. Hamburger and F. O. Schmitt. 1941. Density studies on amphibian embryos with special reference to the mechanism of organizer action. *J. Exp. Zool., 88:* 353–372.

Bütschli, O. 1915. Bemerkungen zur mechanischen Erklärung der Gastrula-Invagination. *Sitz. Ber. Ak. Wiss. Heidelberg, 4.*

Chambers, R. 1940. The relation of extraneous coats to the organization and permeability of cellular membranes. *Cold Spring Harbor Symp. Quant. Biol., 8:* 144–153.

Dalcq, A. 1941. *L'Oeuf et son dynamisme organisateur.* A. Michel, Paris.

Devillers, Ch. 1948. Mécanique gastruléene de l'oeuf de Truite (Salmo). *C. R. de l'Acad. des Sci., 226:* 1310–1312.

——— 1950. Mécanisme de l'épibolie gastruléene. *C. R. de l'Acad. des Sci., 230:* 2232–2234.

Dollander, A. 1951. Observations concernant la structure de cortex de l'oeuf de certains amphibiens urodèles mise en evidence du "coat" de Holtfreter. *C. R. de l'Assoc. d'Anatomistes, 38:* 1–6.

Fauré-Fremiet, E. 1929. Caractères physicochimiques des choanoleucocytes de quelques Invertébrés. *Protopl., 6:* 521–609.

Flickinger, R. A., Jr. 1949. A study of the metabolism of amphibian neural crest cells during their migration and pigmentation. *J. Exp. Zool., 112:* 465–483.

Galtsoff, P. S. 1925. Regeneration after dissociation (An experimental study on sponges). *J. Exp. Zool., 42:* 183–222.

Giersberg, H. 1924. Beiträge zur Entwicklungsphysiologie der Amphibien. II. Neurulation bei Rana und Triton. *Arch. Entw. mech., 103:* 387–424.

Gillette, R. 1944. Cell number and cell size in

the ectoderm during neurulation (*Amblystoma maculatum*). *J. Exp. Zool.*, 96: 201–222.

Glaser, O. C. 1914. On the mechanism of morphological differentiation in the nervous system. *I. Anat. Rec.*, 8: 525–551.

——— 1916. The theory of autogenous folding in embryogenesis. *Science*, 44: 505.

Gray, J. 1926. The properties of an intercellular matrix and its relation to electrolytes. *Brit. J. Exp. Biol.*, 3: 167–187.

Grobstein, C. 1953. Inductive epithelio-mesenchymal interaction in cultured organ rudiments of the mouse. *Science*, 118: 52–55.

Harris, M. 1942. Differentiation and growth of gastrular anlagen implanted homoplastically into tadpoles of *Hyla regilla*. *Univ. Calif. Publ. Zool.*, 51: 41–86.

His, W. 1874. *Unsere Körperform und das physiologische Problem ihrer Entstehung.* Leipzig.

Holtfreter, J. 1931. Über die Aufzucht isolierter Teile des Amphibienkeimes. *Arch. Entw. mech.*, 124: 404–466.

——— 1933. Die totale Exogastrulation, eine Selbstablösung des Ektoderms vom Entomesoderm. *Arch. Entw. mech.*, 129: 669–793.

——— 1938. Differenzierungspotenzen isolierter Teile der Urodelengastrula. *Arch. Entw. mech.*, 138: 522–565.

——— 1939. Gewebeaffinität, ein Mittel der embryonalen Formbildung. *Arch. Exp. Zellf.*, 23: 169–209.

——— 1943a. Properties and function of the surface coat in amphibian embryos. *J. Exp. Zool.*, 93: 251–323.

——— 1943b. A study of the mechanics of gastrulation; Part I. *J. Exp. Zool.*, 94: 261–318.

——— 1943c. Experimental studies on the development of the pronephros. *Rev. Canad. de Biol.*, 3: 220–249.

——— 1944. A study of the mechanics of gastrulation; Part II. *J. Exp. Zool.*, 95: 171–212.

——— 1945. Neuralization and epidermization of the gastrula ectoderm. *J. Exp. Zool.*, 98: 161–209.

——— 1947a. Observations on the migration, aggregation and phagocytosis of embryonic cells. *J. Morph.*, 80: 25–56.

——— 1947b. Changes of structure and kinetics of differentiating embryonic cells. *J. Morph.*, 80: 57–92.

——— 1948. Significance of the cell membrane in embryonic processes. *Annals N. Y. Acad. Sci.*, 49: 709–760.

Hörstadius, S., and S. Sellman. 1945. Experimentelle Untersuchungen über die Determination des knorpeligen Kopfskelettes bei Urodelen. *Nov. Acta Soc. Scient. Uppsala. Ser. 4*, 13: 1–170.

Jennings, H. S. 1904. *Contributions to the study of the behavior of lower organisms.* Publ. Carnegie Inst. Wash.

Kopac, M., and R. Chambers. 1937. The coalescence of living cells with oil drops. Part I. *J. Cell. and Comp. Physiol.*, 9: 331–344. Part II. *J. Cell. and Comp. Physiol.*, 9: 345–362.

Kuhl, W. 1937. Untersuchungen über das Verhalten künstlich getrennter Furchungszellen und Zellaggregate einiger Amphibienarten mit Hilfe des Zeitrafferfilms. *Arch. Entw. mech.*, 136: 592–671.

Lehmann, F. E. 1926. Entwicklungsstörungen in der Medullaranlage von Triton, erzeugt durch Unterlagerungsdefekte. *Arch. Entw. mech.*, 108: 243–282.

——— 1945. *Einführung in die physiologische Embryologie.* Verlag Birkhäuser, Basel.

Lewis, W. H. 1947. Mechanics of invagination. *Anat. Rec.*, 97: 139–156.

——— 1949. Gel layers of cells and eggs and their role in early development. *Lect. Ser. Roscoe B. Jackson Mem. Lab.*, 59–77.

Mayer, B. 1935. Über das Regulations- und Induktionsvermögen der halbseitigen oberen Urmundlippe von Triton. *Arch. Entw. mech.*, 133: 518–581.

Mangold, O. 1936. Experimente zur Analyse der Zusammenarbeit der Keimblätter. *Naturwiss.*, 24: 753–760.

Mangold, O., and C. von Woellwarth. 1950. Das Gehirn von Triton. Ein experimenteller Beitrag zur Analyse seiner Determination. *Naturwiss.*, 37: 365–372.

Rhumbler, L. 1899. Physikalische Analyse von Lebenserscheinungen der Zelle. *Arch. Entw. mech.*, 9: 63–102.

——— 1902. Zur Mechanik des Gastrulationsvorganges, insbesondere der Invagination. *Arch. Entw. mech.*, 14: 401–476.

——— 1927. Versuch einer physikalischen Analyse der Attraktion gleichnamiger Zonenoberflächen bei äquivalent zonierten Furchungs- und Epithelzellen. *Arch. Entw. mech.*, 111: 1–28.

Rienhoff, W. F. 1922. Development and growth of the metanephros or permanent kidney in chick embryos. *Johns Hopkins Hosp. Bull.*, 33: 392–406.

Roux, W. 1894. Über den Cytotropismus der Furchungszellen des Grasfrosches (*Rana fusca*). *Arch. Entw. mech.*, 1: 43–68.

——— 1896. Über die Selbstordnung (Cytotaxis) sich "berührender" Furchungszellen des Froscheies durch Zellzusammenfügung und Zellengleiten. *Arch. Entw. mech.*, 3: 381–468.

Roudabush, R. L. 1933. Phenomenon of regeneration in everted Hydra. *Biol. Bull.*, 64: 253–258.

Rugh, R. 1934. Induced ovulation and artificial fertilization in the frog. *Biol. Bull.*, 66: 22–29.

Schmitt, F. O. 1941. Some protein patterns in cells. *Growth*, 3: 1–20.

Spek, J. 1931. Allgemeine Physiologie der Entwicklung und Formbildung. In E. Gellhorn, *Lehrbuch der allgemeinen Physiologie.* Leipzig.

Spemann, H., and H. Mangold. 1924. Über Induktion von Embryonalanlagen durch Implantation artfremder Organisatoren. *Arch. Mikr. Anat. Entw., 100:* 599–638.

Ter Horst, J. 1948. Differenzierungs- und Induktionsleistungen verschiedener Abschnitte der Medullarplatte und des Urdarmdaches von Triton im Kombinat. *Arch. Entw. mech., 143:* 275–303.

Townes, P. L. 1953. Effects of proteolytic enzymes on the fertilization membrane and jelly layers of the amphibian embryo. *Exp. Cell Res., 4:* 96–101.

Trinkaus, J. P. 1949. The surface gel layer of Fundulus eggs in relation to epiboly. *Proc. Nat. Acad. Sci., 35:* 218–225.

────── 1951. A study of the mechanism of epiboly in the egg of *Fundulus heteroclitus. J. Exp. Zool., 118:* 269–319.

Tyler, A. 1946. An auto-antibody concept of cell structure, growth and differentiation. *Growth, 10* (suppl.) : 7–19.

Vogt, W. 1913. Über Zellbewegungen und Zelldegeneration bei der Gastrulation von *Triton cristatus. Anat. H. I. Abt., 48:* 1–64.

────── 1929. Gestaltungsanalyse am Amphibienkeim mit örtlicher Vitalfärbung; II. *Arch. Entw. mech., 120:* 384–706.

Voigtlander, G. 1932. Neue Untersuchungen über den "Cytotropismus" der Furchungszellen. *Arch. Entw. mech., 127:* 151–215.

Weiss, P. 1941. Nerve patterns: The mechanics of growth. *Growth, 5* (suppl.) : 163–203.

────── 1945. Experiments on cell and axon orientation *in vitro:* the role of colloidal exudates in tissue organization. *J. Exp. Zool., 100:* 353–386.

────── 1947. The problem of specificity in growth and development. *Yale J. Biol. and Med., 19:* 235–278.

────── 1950. Perspectives in the field of morphogenesis. *Quart. Rev. Biol., 25:* 177–198.

Wilde, C. E., Jr. 1948. Technical procedures for the study of organogenesis *in vitro* in Amblystoma. *Proc. Soc. Exp. Biol. Med., 69:* 374–376.

Wilson, H. V. 1908. On some phenomena of coalescence and regeneration in sponges. *J. Exp. Zool., 5:* 245–258.

Yamada, T. 1950. Dorsalization of the ventral marginal zone of the Triturus gastrula; I. *Biol. Bull., 98:* 98–121.

Evidence for the Formation of Cell Aggregates by Chemotaxis in the Development of the Slime Mold *Dictyostelium Discoideum*[1]

JOHN TYLER BONNER

With an appendix by L. J. Savage.

INTRODUCTION

Dictyostelium discoideum is a member of that curious group of amoeboid slime molds, the Acrasiales, which forms one of numerous bridges between unicellular organisms and multicellular organisms. In its life cycle (see Raper, 1935, 1940a, 1940b, 1941, and Bonner,

[1] Reprinted by publisher's permission from *The Journal of Experimental Zoology*, Volume 106, pp. 1–26.

This work was carried out at Harvard University, under the auspices of the Society of Fellows, to which the author wishes to express his sincere gratitude.

1944 for descriptive details) there is both a unicellular stage which subsequently develops by the aggregation of cells to central collection points into a differentiated multicellular organism.

So far as is known the life cycle is completely asexual. Individual capsule-shaped spore cells germinate by splitting down the side and liberating a single, uninucleate myxamoeba. This myxamoeba feeds on bacteria by phagocytosis and divides by binary fission to form many of its own kind, but each daughter myxamoeba remains a separate, independent individual. At the end of this so-called *vegetative stage*, the myxamoebae cease to feed or multiply, thus having a natural separation in their own life histories between growth processes, and purely formative, morphogenetic processes. The myxamoebae subsequently enter the *aggregation stage* and stream in together to form a mass of cells known as a *pseudoplasmodium* (see Figs. 1, 2). The pseudoplasmodium then crawls as a body for variable distances during the *migration stage*. Finally the pseudoplasmodium rights itself and rises up into the air, forming a delicate tapering stalk set at its large basal end in a small *basal disk*, and holding at its apex the *sorus* which is a spherical mass of encapsulated spores. This rise in height and differentiation of the mature fruiting body or sorocarp comprises the *culmination stage*.

The problem that concerns us at the moment is the mechanism by which aggregation occurs; how can great numbers of independent myxamoebae be drawn together to form one unified organism.

In a number of papers Raper (1940a, 1940b, 1941) reviews the past work done on aggregation and his discussions of the subject will be briefly summarized. There are two aspects that he has considered: the external factors affecting aggregation, and the cause of aggregation.

Many authors believe that the primary external factor involved in the stimulation of the initiation of aggregation is food shortage (Potts, 1902; Oehler, 1922; von Schuckmann, 1924; Arndt, 1937; Raper, 1940b). Raper (1940b) found that the time of initiation of aggregation was shortened and the resulting patterns were made smaller by the following agents: decreased humidity, increased temperature, and light. Potts (1902) and Harper (1932) also noticed that smaller fruiting bodies were obtained in light.

With respect to the cause of aggregation, Olive (1902) and Potts (1902) independently suggested that there were chemotactic stimuli arising from the central mass of aggregating myxamoebae. Neither investigator offered any evidence for this hypothesis but believed that the general appearance indicated such a mechanism. Olive actually tried to influence

aggregating myxamoebae with malic acid and sugar solutions, placed in a sealed-off capillary tube, following the work of Pfeffer on the chemotaxis of spermatozoids of ferns, but with no encouraging results. The only other suggestion was that of von Schuckmann (1925) and Harper (1926), that aggregation is caused by a negative hygrotropic response; but Raper (1941) effectively proved that such a mechanism cannot be seriously considered.

There has been one more recent important contribution: that of Runyon (1942). He showed that, if a semi-permeable membrane of cellophane (regenerated cellulose) was placed over an aggregating pattern, and additional myxamoebae were placed on the upper side of the membrane, the upper myxamoebae would follow the myxamoebae below. The streams of incoming myxamoebae and the central collecting points would coincide above and below the cellophane sheet. Thus Runyon showed that the aggregation stimulus could pass through a semi-permeable membrane. From this he concluded that aggregation is caused by the chemotactic response of myxamoebae to a dialyzable substance.

It was thought, in the beginning of this work, that there was no real evidence that the theory of Olive, Potts, and Runyon was correct for they gave no supporting evidence at all, and Runyon's ingenious experiment is hardly conclusive. A variety of physical agents besides a diffusing substance could conceivably be responsible for the orientation of the myxamoebae and could also pass through a semi-permeable membrane. But it is clear from the experimental evidence that will be presented in the following pages that the only mechanism that was supported was that of diffusion of a substance to which the myxamoebae respond chemotactically.

METHODS

A large part of the experimental work described here was made possible by the development of new techniques for the study of Dictyostelium. The principal of such innovations is the discovery that, contrary to Runyon's (1942) statement, aggregation will

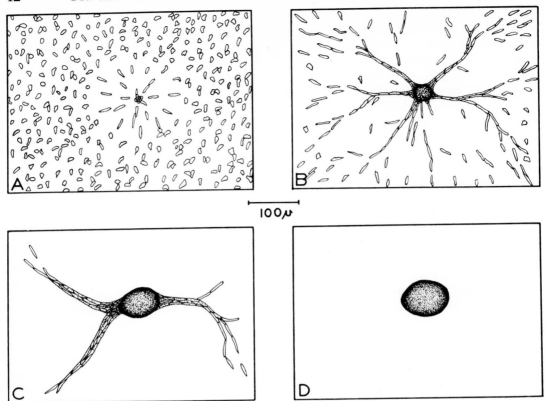

100μ

Fig. 1. A semi-diagrammatic representation of 4 stages of the aggregation of Dictyostelium taking place under water on the bottom of a glass dish. A, the beginning of aggregation showing the formation of a small center; B, C, successive stages of aggregation showing the thickening of the streams and the enlargement of the center; D, the final pseudoplasmodium.

occur under water. This can be achieved by *D. discoideum, D. giganteum, D. mucoroides, D. purpureum, Polysphondylium violaceum* or *Polysphondylium pallidum* on a water-glass interface in depths of water up to 10 cm. Depths greater than this have not been tested because there seem to be no practical or theoretical reasons for so doing. Figures 1 and 2 illustrate the appearance of this under-water aggregation. Development, however, does not proceed any further, leaving a rounded or irregular shaped mass of cells (see Fig. 1, D). Further development (migration and culmination) can only be attained by bringing the mass into contact with an air-water or mineral oil-water interface.

Before discussing the details of this under-water technique, the standard culture technique will be described, followed by a descrip-

tion of the method of preparing the myxamoebae for under-water aggregation.

Culture Technique

A large supply of myxamoebae are required for experiments on aggregation. As Dictyostelium feeds on bacteria, a large supply must be obtained and this is done by using a rich medium such as Raper (1940b) describes: (Raper's medium has been slightly modified by adding a buffer to insure a pH of about 6.0.) Peptone, 10 gm; dextrose, 10 gm; $Na_2HPO_4 \cdot 12 H_2O$, 0.96 gm; K_2HPO_4, 1.45 gm; agar, 20 gm; distilled H_2O, 1000 ml.

The inoculum of Dictyostelium spores and *Escherichia coli* (which is used as a source of food for the myxamoebae) is placed on the nutrient agar in a petri dish (90 mm diameter). The inoculum is spread over the entire

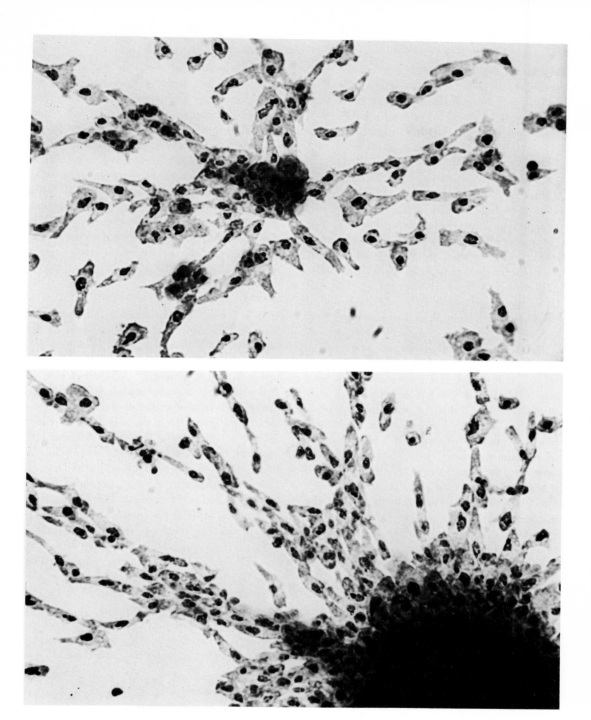

Fig. 2. Photographs of fixed and stained preparations showing 2 stages of the aggregation of Dictyostelium taking place under water on the surface of a coverslip. (Fixed in Shaudin's solution and stained by Bodian's silver impregnation method.) The upper photograph shows the beginning of aggregation with the formation of a small center; the lower photograph shows a middle stage of aggregation with a large center in the lower right-hand corner.

surface of the agar by adding a few drops of sterile water and smearing with a sterile glass rod. The culture is incubated at room temperature for 2 days, by which time there is a thick growth of vegetative myxamoebae.

Centrifuge Technique

In a culture which has been incubated for 2 days the myxamoebae are found spread out over the whole surface of the agar and surrounded by large numbers of bacteria. For the under-water technique the myxamoebae must be concentrated and freed from bacteria. A simple method is to wash them by centrifugation as was done by Runyon (1942), but since the details of his method have not to my knowledge, been published, the exact procedure used in this study will be described.

No sterile precautions are necessary in the centrifuge method since all nutrients are largely eliminated and there never has been any evidence of deleterious effects of contamination. The 2-day-old petri dish culture is now flooded with distilled water and thoroughly mixed with a glass rod. The suspension of myxamoebae and bacteria is placed in a centrifuge tube and centrifuged gently for 3 minutes. The force of centrifugation is regulated by a few trial experiments so that the myxamoebae will be separated from the bacteria, and thrown down to the bottom of the tube. The liquid containing bacteria is poured off, distilled water added, and the process repeated. A concentrated mass of myxamoebae relatively free of bacteria is finally left in the tube to which a small amount of distilled water is again added.

Under-Water Technique

The suspension of myxamoebae is placed with a pipette directly into a syracuse or other suitable flat dish containing water. The myxamoebae soon settle to the bottom of the vessel where they subsequently aggregate. At room temperature, with optimum myxamoeba concentrations, aggregation will start in 6 to 8 hours but may be delayed by placing the dish in a cooler environment. In distilled water the myxamoebae lack adhesiveness and the slightest agitation causes them to become detached

from the bottom of the dish, but if suitable electrolytes are added the myxamoebae adhere firmly to the glass substratum. This method is based on that of Mast (1929) who showed a similar effect of electrolytes on the adhesiveness of *Amoeba proteus*, and from his data the following standard salt solution (henceforth referred to as "standard solution") was devised and regularly used: NaCl, 0.60 gm; KCl, 0.75 gm; $CaCl_2$, 0.30 gm; distilled H_2O, 1000 ml. It is interesting to note that Mast showed that this is not a case of salt antagonism, for the effect of the various anions is slightly additive.

Thin Film of Water Technique

In a few of the experiments the myxamoebae were placed on a thin film of water on the underside of a coverslip. The procedure follows: a no. 1, 22×22 mm coverslip which has been carefully cleaned in 95% ethyl alcohol and wiped dry, is sealed with a mixture of approximately 2 parts vaseline and 1 part beeswax onto a van Tieghem cell (10 mm deep, 20 mm in diameter). This van Tieghem cell cup with the sealed-on coverslip serving as the bottom is filled about $\frac{1}{3}$ full with standard solution and the myxamoebae, prepared in the fashion already described, are added. A microscope slide is then sealed over the open end of the van Tieghem cell. In 20 minutes time all the myxamoebae will have settled to the bottom and adhered to the coverslip. The slide is then gently turned over so that the coverslip is on the upper surface. Since the myxamoebae are in a thin film of water in contact with moist air, the organism will go through its complete life cycle producing abundant sorocarps on the underside of the coverslip.

RESULTS

The Attraction of Myxamoebae at a Distance

That contact between myxamoebae is not a controlling factor in aggregation was first emphasized by Raper (1941). It can readily be seen in observing aggregation that isolated individual myxamoebae or groups of myxamoebae will move directly towards one of the radiating streams of incoming myxamoebae (henceforth referred to as "stream") or to the central mass of cells (henceforth referred to as "center").

With the under-water technique it was possible to get a clearer and more quantitative picture of this attraction at a distance. If one removes the center of an aggregation pattern at either of the 2 stages illustrated in Fig. 1, C and D, and places it beside the stream, in 3 to 5 minutes time each myxamoeba in the stream will independently turn and start to move toward the center at its new location. They will continue to move toward the center until they reach it and become incorporated into it in the normal fashion. An attempt was made to measure the maximum distance at which the center could influence the myxamoebae, care being taken to have no myxamoebae between the center and the myxamoebae under observation in order to eliminate the possibility that intermediate myxamoebae might affect the attractive power in some way. Some of the results of this type of experiment are given in Table 1.

It is clear that myxamoebae up to 200 μ distant will become, in 3 to 5 minutes, oriented toward the center. If the diameter of a rounded myxamoeba is considered to be about 15 μ, then the distance between the myxamoebae and the center can be represented as over 13 myxamoeba diameters. In a slightly modified type of experiment discussed later even larger gaps are bridged. In fact it was possible to obtain weak but definite orienting effect at a distance of 800 μ or 53 myxamoeba diameters.

The Inability of an Electric Field to Affect Aggregation

Both vegetative and aggregating myxamoebae were subjected to electrical currents of various densities. The type of chamber and the electrical circuit were essentially similar to those used by Hahnert (1932) on *Amoeba proteus*. Briefly the chamber is a small, rectangular cell (30 × 10 mm), in which the small ends are completely walled off with 2 platinum ribbon electrodes. To guard the cen-

TABLE 1. Table showing the ability of the centers to attract myxamoebae across various distances

Distance between Center and Myxamoebae	Attraction
770 μ	None
423 μ	None
358 μ	Weak
214 μ	Strong
180 μ	Strong
128 μ	Strong
98 μ	Strong

ter of the cell from harmful electrolytic products, a piece of porous material (porcelain or cellulose sponge) is placed directly in front of and parallel to each electrode. The experiments on Dictyostelium were done in tap water and distilled water with the same result in both cases. Parallel observations were made on *Amoeba proteus* (in tap water). The results are given in Table 2. As can be seen from the table *A. proteus* shows the characteristic migration toward the cathode, while the myxamoebae of Dictyostelium showed no response whatever to the electrical current.

The Inability of a Magnetic Field to Affect Aggregation

Some very cursory experiments, which are reported here for the sake of record, were done with an Alnico magnet (1 cm² pole face) at various angles to aggregation patterns of Dictyostelium. No effect was observed.

The Inability of a Conducting Metal (Tantalum) to Affect Aggregation

This experiment is basically similar to the previously described experiment of Runyon (1942), but instead of separating the center from the myxamoebae by a semi-permeable membrane, they were separated by a thin sheet of tantalum (about 12 μ thick). A 1 cm² sheet of the tantalum was placed in a syracuse dish containing standard solution. Myxamoebae free from bacteria were allowed to settle on one side of the tantalum, using the standard technique previously described. When the myxamoebae had just started to aggregate, which they did normally, the sheet was turned upside down and set on a small stand (a van

TABLE 2. Table showing the effect of 3 different current densities on *Amoeba proteus* and on the myxamoebae of *D. discoideum*

Current Density in μamp/mm²	Effect on *A. proteus*	Effect on Myxamoebae of *D. discoideum*
5	Possible slight orientation	Death
20	Streams towards cathode	No effect
70	Immediate death	No effect

Tieghem cell 5 mm deep, 20 mm in diameter) so that it was not touching the bottom of the dish and yet was completely submerged in the standard solution. A large active center from another dish was taken in a micro-pipette and placed on the upper surface of the tantalum.

In no case was the effect of the upper center transmitted through the sheet, and the myxamoebae below, while they aggregated normally, bore no relation in their pattern to the strong center above.

The Impermeability of Glass, Mica, and Quartz to the Aggregation Stimulus

By using the same technique as described immediately above, coverslip glass (120 μ thick), mica (100–150 μ thick), and quartz glass (50–100 μ thick) were tested. Again, in no case was there any visible orienting effect transmitted through these materials although aggregation appeared normal in each instance.

The Attraction of Myxamoebae Around Corners

This experiment was designed to see if a center could orient myxamoebae that were not in a direct line with the center, but were separated by an impermeable substance that could be circumvented. Some myxamoebae free of bacteria were spread on a no. 1 coverslip (22 × 22 mm, approximately 160 μ thick) which had been placed in the bottom of a syracuse dish full of standard solution. When the myxamoebae had just begun to aggregate the coverslip was turned upside down and held in such a position so that it formed a shelf, completely surrounded by standard solution. This is represented diagrammatically in Fig. 3, A. An active, strongly attractive center was placed approximately 60 μ from the edge of the coverslip, on the upper surface. Very shortly afterwards, the separate myxamoebae on the underneath surface became oriented towards the point on the edge nearest the center above and moved up around the edge to join the center (see Fig. 3, A). In other words the center exerted its influence around the corner, from the upper surface to the lower surface.

The Inability of the Orientation of the Substratum to Affect Aggregation

The following experiments involve using the techniques of Weiss (1945) who obtained oriented growth of fibroblasts of chick embryos by placing them on specific types of substrata. Myxamoebae were placed on a sheet of mica in which shallow grooves had been scratched with a fine steel needle (see Weiss, 1945 for the details of the preparation of the mica). Neither the aggregating myxamoebae, nor the wandering vegetative myxamoebae showed any preference for the grooves, but would pass across them as though completely unaffected by their existence. Glass fibers (from glass wool) lying in a heap under water in a syracuse dish were also covered with myxamoebae and again the myxamoebae showed no more tendency to adhere to the fibers than to the glass bottom of the dish.

Attempts to Observe Structural Connections Between Aggregating Myxamoebae

It is not possible in a living preparation, even using an oil immersion (1.8 mm) objective and preparing the material with the thin film of water technique, to see any connections between the aggregating myxamoebae except when the cells are half a cell diameter or less from one another. Then they often are attached by definite filopodia. To

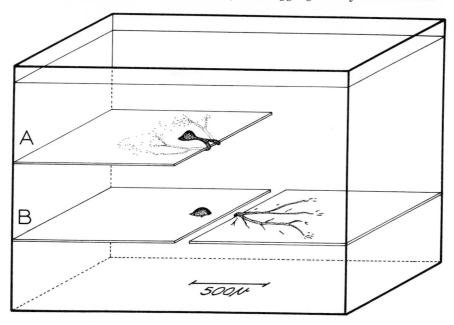

Fig. 3. A semi-diagrammatic representation of 2 experiments done on aggregation in Dictyostelium using coverslip shelves held under water. A, the myxamoebae previously at random under the coverslip are attracted around the edge to the center on the upper surface; B, the myxamoebae previously at random on the right-hand coverslip are attracted to the center on the left-hand coverslip, across the substratum gap.

examine this point further, aggregation stages were stained with silver using the technique of Bodian. Aggregation was allowed to occur on coverslips under water and at the desired stages they were removed, fixed in Shaudin's solution, and stained. The gold toning was not used. Photographs of such a preparation are shown in Fig. 2. As can be seen from the photographs, and also from careful oil immersion examination of the slides, there is no evidence of any filopodia extending any great distances. Nor is there any evidence of any material, exudate, or ground mat such as Weiss (1945) describes for oriented chick fibroblasts, which he stained in the same fashion.

An Attempt to Reveal a Deposit Made by Aggregating Myxamoebae That Might Orient Other Myxamoebae

It was possible to show by experiment that an aggregation pattern leaves behind no structure on the substratum that can orient myxamoebae. The standard solution was poured off a syracuse dish in which the aggregation was complete or nearly so for all the pseudoplasmodia. The dish was then placed in the ice compartment of an electric refrigerator and allowed to freeze. After removal from the refrigerator more standard solution and fresh myxamoebae were added. The old centers that had been killed by freezing could still be seen. Care was taken to observe if the live myxamoebae were affected in any way by any type of structure that the previous aggregation patterns might have created. No such effect was demonstrated; the new patterns bore no relation to the previous ones.

The Importance of an Interface Connecting the Center and the Myxamoebae

It was found that a center could attract myxamoebae to which it was not directly connected by an interface. This fact was first realized in an accidental observation. A hanging drop preparation had been made with myxamoebae free from bacteria in standard solution and a clear aggregation pattern formed at the base of the drop, at the air-water interface. I noticed that above this pattern, on the glass-water interface, a few myxamoebae were aggregating to a center directly above the center of the aggregation pattern below. Since the upper center formed at the nearest point to the lower center, one can reason that this was caused either by the fact that the positions of both the upper and lower centers were determined by similar tensions in the drop, or that the lower center, which was the farthest advanced of the two, directly influenced the upper myxamoebae without being directly connected to them by an interface.

In an effort to rule out the possible effect of the tensions in a hanging drop, an experiment was designed in which 2 no. 1 coverslips (22 × 22 mm) were prepared in standard solution, one with many myxamoebae just starting to aggregate, and the other with one large center. One was then turned over and placed on top of the other, taking care to prevent their surfaces from touching by placing 2 wedges between them, one on each side. The myxamoebae were then facing the center, separated by a thin layer of standard solution. Again an immediate response was obtained and the myxamoebae formed a pattern so that their center was directly opposite, that is the shortest distance from, the strong center on the opposite coverslip. Numerous attempts were made to determine how far apart the plates could be and still obtain an orienting influence of the center on the myxamoebae. If the plates were 500 μ apart the effect was obvious and strong. At 800 μ there was a weak and diffuse, but still discernible orienting effect. Thus without the disturbing surface tension effects of a hanging drop, a center again affected distant myxamoebae to which it was not directly connected by an interface.

This was done in another striking way illustrated in Fig. 3, B. Two coverslips were prepared as above and placed side by side in a dish to form 2 shelves, surrounded by standard solution, and separated by a small gap. The center was placed fairly near the edge, and it immediately affected the myxamoebae on the opposite shelf so they all streamed to the nearest point on the edge (see Fig. 3, B). Again the effect of a center was transmitted across a gap which possessed no interface but merely a layer of water.

A few observations on this experiment should be mentioned. The first myxamoebae that got to the edge appeared to be reaching out into the gap between the coverslips with a sort of hopeless pseudopodial waving. Later when they became more numerous, they formed their own center directly opposite the original center on the other coverslip. However, if the coverslips were closer together so that the gap was very small (about 20–30 μ) then the myxamoebae formed a stream, a bridge right across the gap and joined the center on the opposite side.

The Effect of Water Flowing over Aggregation Patterns

A flow of water was created over myxamoebae that were about to aggregate or that were in the process of aggregating and a distinct modification of the aggregation pattern was obtained. The flow of water was achieved 2 different ways. In one a glass rod (4 mm in diameter) bent into an "L" shape was attached to a shaft of a 6 rpm electric motor, and held over the center of a syracuse dish (containing bacteria-free myxamoebae) so that the lower bar of the "L" was just submerged in the water, forming a radius to the circular dish. In this way the water was slowly swirled in a circular fashion, creating a fairly linear flow at any spot in the dish other than near the center. The other method of creating a flow involved drawing water through a channel between 2 coverslips (approximately 100 μ apart). A controlled rate of flow was obtained by leading the water from a reservoir to the coverslips through a fine glass capillary tube.

If the myxamoebae were about to aggregate when placed in this current, they continued to do so, but the aggregation patterns, as shown in Fig. 4, A, were atypical. Each possessed only one unusually long stream which always approached the center from the downstream side. If the myxamoebae had already started normal aggregation before being subjected to the flow, they would quickly assume a similar

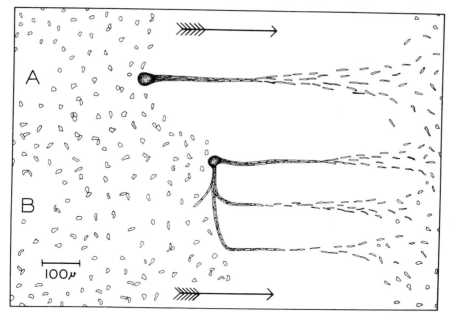

Fig. 4. A semi-diagrammatic drawing showing the effect of a moving stream of water (the arrows indicate the direction of movement) over an aggregation pattern in Dictyostelium. A, an aggregation pattern that formed while the water was in motion; B, an aggregation pattern that formed in still water and was subsequently subjected to a stream of moving water.

form as shown in Fig. 4, B. The streams that had existed on the upstream side would break up rapidly, and although the downstream and lateral streams remained, they would continue to form only in line with the direction of the flow of water. In both cases the most striking fact was that the myxamoebae, upstream of the center, even those almost touching it, showed no effect of any stimulus from the center and moved in a random fashion. Yet judging from the length of the streams, the stimulus from the center apparently had extended an abnormally long distance downstream. If vegetative myxamoebae were placed under such a current no effect was observed whatsoever, but they continued their random locomotion.

DISCUSSION

If the facts that have been obtained from the experiments described above, and those from the literature are summarized, the following statements can be made of the aggregation process in Dictyostelium: (1) the attraction can operate across a semi-permeable membrane (Runyon, 1942); (2) the center will attract myxamoebae at considerable distances; (3) it has been impossible to date to show any effect of an electric field or (4) of a magnetic field on the aggregation pattern; (5) aggregation occurs on the surface of a conducting metal (tantalum), but (6) a center will not attract myxamoebae when separated from the myxamoebae by a sheet of tantalum; (7) nor can a center attract myxamoebae through glass, (8) mica, or (9) quartz; (10) a center can attract myxamoebae around a corner of some impermeable substance; (11) the structure of the substratum does not appear to affect the aggregation pattern; (12) it has been impossible to demonstrate any sort of bridge or connection between a center and distant myxamoebae; (13) there is no evidence of any myxamoeba-orienting substance deposited on the substratum; (14) a center does not have to be directly connected to myxamoebae by an interface in order to attract them; (15) aggregation patterns forming under flowing water are deformed so that only the myxamoebae directly downstream of the center will show any orientation.

In our search for the immediate cause of aggregation in Dictyostelium, the first fundamental question that arises is, does the center pull in the myxamoebae by force or does it merely orient the myxamoebae by stimulation? There is every indication that the energy of locomotion is contributed by each individual myxamoeba, and that the center orients them by a differential stimulation.

The problem might be approached by examining various reasonable possible mechanisms suggested by investigations on other forms in the light of the facts known about aggregation in Dictyostelium. For instance one might consider the likelihood of aggregation to be: (1) an agglutination process; (2) in some way controlled by an electric or (3) magnetic field; (4) or by some form of radiation; (5) controlled by some type of orienting structure deposited on the substratum; (6) or by the oriented molecules in a molecular surface film; (7) or, finally, controlled by the gradient of a substance to which the myxamoebae respond chemotactically.

Agglutination Hypothesis

Some actual immunological work has been done on *D. mucoroides* by von Schuckmann (1925) who showed that when rabbit antiserum to vegetative myxamoebae is added to a culture of similar myxamoebae, they will agglutinate into clumps in an irreversible fashion. Unfortunately von Schuckmann does not describe the details either of the process or of further development, if any, of the clumps; but it is notable that he does not attempt to interpret normal aggregation in terms of agglutination. In some work that will be reported in detail at a future date, I have been able to obtain pseudoplasmodium formation by what is apparently agglutination, and these pseudoplasmodia develop into complete sorocarps. But in such an instance the normal aggregation process has been completely circumvented and the pseudoplasmodium has been achieved by an unnatural means.

There are a number of strong evidences against the "clumping" of myxamoebae found

in normal aggregation being an agglutination process. In the first place the fact that a center can attract myxamoebae across great distances is inconsistent with agglutination. A basic property of all agglutination processes is that the cells come together by chance collision; for example as a result of active random motion or brownian motion, followed by a firm adhesion of the collided cells.

Another evidence comes from the fact that the myxamoebae which are in contact can and do normally separate readily from one another. A striking example of this is the case mentioned where a center is removed and placed laterally to its stream. The compacted mass of myxamoebae forming the stream will break up, each myxamoeba becoming unattached and going independently to the new location of the center. Such a phenomenon is never seen in agglutination processes. The nearest they approach it is in the case of reverse agglutination, but then up to the point of reversal the cells are solidly stuck to one another. In Dictyostelium the myxamoebae can be separated at all times.

A final evidence that aggregation is not achieved by agglutination comes from the fact that attraction between the center and the myxamoebae is obtained through a semipermeable membrane as previously described in the experiment of Runyon (1942). Proteins or complex polysaccharides are the important molecules in immunological reactions, and even the smallest proteins will not (except possibly at an extremely slow rate) pass through the regenerated cellulose dialyzing membranes used. I have repeated Runyon's experiments many times with different types of membranes all presumably impermeable to proteins, and always obtained the same sort of rapid (3 to 5 minute) response of the myxamoebae to the center on the opposite side of the membrane. From these arguments it may be concluded that aggregation in Dictyostelium is not an agglutination process. This does not exclude the possibility that antigen-antibody reactions are factors in development at a later stage. But some other factor must be responsible for initiating the normal "clumping" of the Dictyostelium myxamoebae.

Electrical Hypothesis

The evidence weighs against the possibility that aggregation can be explained in terms of an electric field. Consider first the fact that an electric field surrounding aggregation patterns will not affect them. While it is true that such negative evidence is in no way conclusive, it is nevertheless indicative.

Perhaps better evidence comes from the tantalum experiment, where normal aggregation was found to occur on the surface of a conducting metal, but the attraction could not take place through a thin sheet of the metal. If the aggregation mechanism were electrical then the metal would most likely have created a short circuit preventing aggregation, which is not the case. Even granting that aggregation could occur on the surface of the metal, one would further expect the attraction to be conducted through the tantalum sheet.

Magnetic Hypothesis

Magnetism is also an unlikely possibility for reasons very similar to those mentioned for electricity. Not only was the aggregation pattern not affected by a magnetic field (which again is only indicative evidence) but also the attraction could not pass through a tantalum sheet, which could be readily achieved by a magnetic force.

Radiation Hypothesis

Rays emitted from the center of Dictyostelium could conceivably guide the myxamoebae, but the evidence does not support this view. First, if such a ray exists, it can penetrate water, and cellophane, but is stopped by glass, quartz and mica. This certainly does not eliminate the hypothesis but it narrows the possibilities.

Stronger evidence against a radiation phenomenon comes from the experiment in which a center on the upper surface of a coverslip attracted myxamoebae on the lower surface, around the edge (Fig. 3, A). It is difficult for me to see how a ray mechanism could operate here, for if the coverslip were permeable to the ray one would expect the underneath myxamoebae to aggregate to the point nearest the above center, which would be directly below the center on the underside of the glass. If the coverslip were impermeable to the hypothetical ray, then one would expect no effect whatsoever of the upper center on the myxamoebae underneath. But this is not the case; the myxamoebae go around the edge. Rays travel in straight lines and can hardly be expected to pass from one side of an impermeable barrier to the other.

Contact Guidance Hypothesis

"Contact guidance" designates the idea that the amoeboid processes of cells are oriented by being mechanically guided by either the ultra-structure of the substratum or the direction of flow of an exudate given off by the cell. The concept of contact guidance is that of Weiss (1929, 1934, 1945) who studied the causes of orientation in cell growth and movement of cells of higher animals in tissue culture.

There is no evidence to indicate that contact guidance plays a part in aggregation, for it has been impossible to demonstrate any guiding structure deposited on the substratum, or even that the orientation of the substratum itself has any orienting effect.

Molecular Surface Film Hypothesis

It was thought, since aggregation only occurs at an interface, that a molecular surface film might be involved in orienting the aggregating myxamoebae. But this hypothesis was invalidated by showing that it is quite possible for a center to attract myxamoebae when the center is not connected directly to the myxamoebae by an interface.

CONCLUSION

Diffusion Hypothesis

Good evidence that aggregation is achieved by the center producing a substance to which the myxamoebae respond chemotactically[2] comes from the experiment in which the

---

[2] A note should be made here concerning the use of the word chemotaxis in this paper. As Blum (1935) points out there are 2 separate factors to consider in oriented movements: (1) the orientation of the organism, in this case to the diffusion field of a chemical substance and (2) the movement of the

aggregation patterns are deformed by flowing water. In fact the following deductions can be made from this experiment: (1) No mechanical explanation, such as the direct effect of the current on the myxamoebae, could explain the patterns obtained under flowing water because vegetative cells in the current continued normal random movement. That is, the pattern was not imposed on the myxamoebae by the external moving water, but it arose in the normal fashion as a result of the activities of the myxamoebae themselves. (2) Under the flow of water the center remained the source of production of the stimulating agent for the myxamoebae were attracted to it. (3) The agent was washed downstream—the myxamoebae upstream were not attracted in any way by the center, whereas the myxamoebae downstream were attracted to it from great distances. (4) The only reasonable type of agent that could be carried along in such a fashion by a slow current is a free-diffusing chemical substance. (5) The fact mentioned previously that a substance can only be effective in orienting the myxamoebae when it is in a gradient helps interpret a number of phenomena. For instance: the myxamoebae upstream must have been surrounded by the substance which came from the other centers (and let us assume it is in a high enough concentration to be able to obtain a response), but they showed no orientation because the substance in that region became, by diffusion, more evenly distributed and not in a sufficient concentration gradient to cause orientation. (6) Also the only method in which a gradient could be maintained during aggregation would be by a constant production of the substance of the center. Since diffusion would tend always to obliterate the gradient, and the maintenance of a steady state is necessary, it must be assumed that the substance is produced either continuously or at frequent intervals by the center.

Therefore in summarizing we have deduced from this flowing water experiment that during

the aggregation of Dictyostelium there is some type of chemical substance (which is not necessarily homogeneous but might consist of a group of compounds) produced continuously or at frequent intervals by the center, which freely diffuses, and the myxamoebae move in the resulting gradient of this substance towards the point of its highest concentration. The final proof of the existence of the substance (and an important problem for future research) must be its isolation *in vitro*. But considering the present weight of evidence, it seems fitting to propose tentatively a name for the substance. The term *acrasin* is suggested, and it can be defined for the moment as a type of substance consisting either of one or numerous compounds which is responsible for stimulating and directing aggregation in certain members of the Acrasiales. It also may perform other duties in the development of these organisms but such considerations are not within the scope of this article. Also at a later date I plan to present an examination of the formation of streams during aggregation, a process which may appear puzzling in the light of the present discussion.

One of the most difficult factors to understand in any chemotaxis hypothesis is how it is possible for a single small amorphous amoeboid cell to be sensitive to gradients of diffusing substances. The concentrations of these substances in a great many of these cases must be small, and of course, the molecules in diffusion move at random in all directions. Thus the cell must detect very small concentration differences between one end of the cell and the other.

In an attempt to calculate just what this concentration difference would be between the ends of a myxamoeba in the gradient of a hypothetical substance, Dr. L. J. Savage has been kind enough to derive and evaluate the following approximation (see appendix):

$$-\frac{\Delta c}{c} \simeq \frac{\Delta r}{r}$$

where c is the concentration at any part of the myxamoeba, r is the distance from any part

---

organism which may quite possibly be in no way affected by the chemical substance (since there is movement in the absence of the substance).

of the myxamoeba to the midpoint of the bottom of the center, $\triangle c$ is the difference in concentration between the far and near ends of the myxamoeba, and $\triangle r$ is the length of the myxamoeba. If we choose some reasonable values, letting $\triangle r = 25 \mu$, $r = 500 \mu$ they can be substituted in the above expression:

$$- \frac{\triangle c}{c} \simeq \frac{25}{100}$$

$$- \triangle c \simeq .05c$$

Thus the concentration difference between the 2 ends of a myxamoeba at 500μ distance from the center would be 5% of the total concentration. Remember that a gap much over 800μ can no longer be bridged, which would mean that if the concentration difference of the hypothetical substance across a myxamoeba is less than 3%, it no longer would be effective in orienting the myxamoeba. These values appear sufficiently high so that from this point of view the chemotaxis hypothesis is not unreasonable.

SUMMARY

Dictyostelium discoideum is a member of that group of amoeboid slime molds (Acrasiales) characterized by forming the fruiting structure from a compacted mass of uninucleate myxamoebae known as a pseudoplasmodium. The pseudoplasmodium arises by the aggregation of many myxamoebae which were previously completely independent and separate from one another. In this so-called aggregation stage radial streams of elongate myxamoebae move towards a central point by means of pseudopodial locomotion. Attempts to discover the immediate cause of this centripetal streaming of myxamoebae revealed that it is not an agglutination process; that a spreading molecular surface film phenomenon is not responsible; that an electrical or magnetic force is improbable; that any form of directing ray is not involved; and that no type of predetermined structural matrix exists that could guide the myxamoebae to the center. However, evidence was obtained for a substance diffusing from a central mass of myxamoebae through the liquid medium and the incoming myxamoebae orienting them-

selves in the diffusion field, moving towards the point of highest concentration. This was shown by inducing a gentle stream of water to flow over an aggregation pattern, causing in the usually radial pattern of incoming myxamoebae an asymmetry that can only be interpreted as the warping of the diffusion field of a substance to which the myxamoebae are sensitive. This type of substance has been tentatively called *acrasin*.

APPENDIX

The derivation and evalution of the approximation used to calculate the difference in concentration of acrasin between the 2 ends of an aggregating myxamoeba.

L. J. Savage

If a hemispherical source resting on the bottom of a large tank produces Q gm/day of a stable compound with diffusion coefficient D cm²/day, then (after the source has been in position for some time) the concentration c of the compound at the distance r from the center of the base of the hemisphere is given by

$$C = \frac{Q}{2\pi D} \frac{1}{r} \qquad (1)$$

Equation 1 is derived in essentially the same way as equation 20 on page 17 of *Mathematical Biophysics* by Rashevsky (1938).

Let r_1 and r_2, $r_1 > r_2$, be any 2 different values of r, $\triangle r = r_1 - r_2$, and $\triangle c$ be the difference between the concentrations at r_1 and r_2. Then if r is between r_1 and r_2 and c is the concentration at some point r^1 also between r_1 and r_2 we have from equation 1

$$- \frac{\triangle c}{c} = r^1 \left(\frac{1}{r_2} - \frac{1}{r_1} \right) = \frac{\triangle r}{r} \frac{rr^1}{r_1 r_2} \qquad (2)$$

From equation 2 we conclude that if $\triangle r$ is small compared with r_2, then

$$- \frac{\triangle c}{c} \simeq \frac{\triangle r}{r} \qquad (3)$$

More precisely, we evaluate $- \triangle c/c$ thus:

$$- \frac{\triangle c}{c} \leq \frac{\triangle r}{r} \frac{r_1^2}{r_1 r_2} = \frac{\triangle r}{r} \frac{r_1}{r_2}$$

$$= \frac{\triangle r}{r} \left(1 + \frac{\triangle r}{r_2} \right), \qquad (4)$$

and

$$- \frac{\triangle c}{c} \gtreqqless \frac{\triangle r}{r} \frac{r_2^2}{r_1 r_2} = \frac{\triangle r}{r} \frac{r_2}{r_1}$$

$$= \frac{\triangle r}{r} \left(1 + \frac{\triangle r}{r_2} \right)^{-1} \quad (5)$$

Summarizing inequalities 4 and 5

$$\frac{\triangle r}{r} \left(1 + \frac{\triangle r}{r_2} \right)^{-1} \leqq - \frac{\triangle c}{c}$$

$$\leqq \frac{\triangle r}{r} \left(1 + \frac{\triangle r}{r_2} \right) \quad (6)$$

by way of a numerical example, suppose $r_2 = 585\,\mu$, $\triangle r = 30\,\mu$, and $r = r^1 = 600\,\mu$, then $\triangle r/r = .050$ and inequality 6 guarantees that $.0476 \leqq - \triangle c/c \leqq .0526$.

LITERATURE CITED

Arndt, A. 1937. Untersuchungen über *Dictyostelium mucoroides* Brefeld. *Roux' Arch. Entwmech.*, *136*: 681–747.

Bonner, J. T. 1944. A descriptive study of the development of the slime mold *Dictyostelium discoideum. Amer. Jour. Bot.*, *31*: 175–182.

Blum, H. F. 1935. An analysis of oriented movements of animals in light fields. *Cold Spring Harbor Symposia on Quantitative Biology, 3*: 210–223.

Hahnert, W. F. 1932. A quantitative study of reactions to electricity in *Amoeba proteus. Physiol. Zool.*, *5*: 491–526.

Harper, R. A. 1926. Morphogenesis in Dictyostelium. *Bull. Torrey Bot. Club.*, *53*: 229–268.

—— 1932. Organization and light relations in Polysphondylium. *Bull. Torrey Bot. Club.*, *59*: 49–84.

Mast, S. O. 1929. Mechanism of locomotion in *Amoeba proteus* with special reference to the factors involved in attachment to the substratum. *Protoplasma, 8*: 344–377.

Oehler, R. 1922. *Dictyostelium mucoroides* Brefeld. *Centbl. Bakt.* (etc.), *89*: 155–156.

Olive, E. W. 1902. Monograph of the Acrasieae. *Proc. Boston Soc. Nat. Hist.*, *30*: 451–513.

Potts, G. 1902. Zur Physiologie des *Dictyostelium mucoroides. Flora* (Jena), *21*: 281–347.

Raper, K. B. 1935. *Dictyostelium discoideum*, a new species of slime mold from decaying forest leaves. *Jour. Agric. Res.*, *50*: 135–147.

—— 1940a. The communal nature of the fruiting process in the Acrasieae. *Amer. Jour. Bot.*, *27*: 436–448.

—— 1940b. Pseudoplasmodium formation and organization in *Dictyostelium discoideum. Jour. Elisha Mitchell. Sci. Soc.*, *56*: 241–282.

—— 1941. Developmental patterns in simple slime molds. *Growth* (third Growth Symposium), *5*: 41–76.

Rashevsky, N. 1938. *Mathematical Biophysics*. Chicago.

Runyon, E. H. 1942. Aggregation of separate cells of Dictyostelium to form a multicellular body. *Collecting Net, 17*: 88.

Schuckmann, W. von, 1924. Zur Biologie von *Dictyostelium mucoroides* Brefeld. *Centbl. Bakt.* (etc.) (I), *91*: 302–309.

—— 1925. Zur Morphologie und Biologie von *Dictyostelium mucoroides* Brefeld. *Arch. Protistenk.*, *51*: 495–529.

Weiss, P. 1929. Erzwingung elementarer Strukturverschiedenheiten am in vitro wachsenden Gewebe. Die Wirkung mechanischer Spannung auf Richtung und Intensität des Gewebewachstums und ihre Analyse. *Roux' Arch. Entwmech.*, *116*: 438–554.

—— 1934. In vitro experiments on the factors determining the course of the outgrowing nerve fiber. *Jour. Exp. Zool.*, *68*: 393–448.

—— 1945. Experiments on cell and axon orientation in vitro; the role of colloidal exudates in tissue organization. *Jour. Exp. Zool.*, *100*: 353–386.

The Development *in Vitro* of Chimeric Aggregates of Dissociated Embryonic Chick and Mouse Cells*

A A R O N   M O S C O N A

Various embryonic tissues and organ rudiments can be dissociated into suspensions of discrete, viable cells following treatment with Ca- and Mg-free saline and trypsin.[1-3] When cultivated *in vitro* under appropriate conditions, such cells reaggregate into compact clusters (Figs. 1–6), which subsequently reestablish tissue-like relationships and differentiate histotypically.[2,3] These findings, originally established for chondrogenic, nephrogenic, and myogenic cells, have recently been extended to other embryonic tissues.[3-8]

If two different types of embryonic chick cells are intermingled in the same suspension, the resulting aggregates incorporate both types of cells; however, in the course of the further development of such heterotypic aggregates,† the diverse types of cells form distinct, histogenetically uniform groupings.[2] The problem of grouping of animal cells in its relation to morphogenesis was discussed in detail by Weiss[9] in reference to the concepts of "affinities"[10] and "coaptation";[11] its experimental implications were explored in the chick embryo[12] and in amphibian embryos[13,14] and larvae[15-17] and also under conditions of tissue culture.[3,18-20] Several of these studies strongly suggested that cells of diverse lineages manifested characteristic

preferences in establishing intercellular contacts and tissue contiguity. This view was further supported by the results of recent experiments on heterotypic aggregates of chick cells[2] which convincingly demonstrated a type-specific grouping of cells in the formation and development of such aggregates. These observations fell short of proof, however, due to the difficulty of identifying early embryonic chick cells when dissociated into discrete units in suspension; under these conditions, nearly all types of such cells look alike, and their identities in heterotypic mixtures are therefore not readily determined. The obvious solution to this impasse was to have cells marked in a way which would make them individually distinguishable in a mixed population. In searching for suitable "marker cells," an attempt was made to exploit the morphological differences between chick and mouse cells; mouse cell nuclei are larger than chick cell nuclei and stain differently with basic stains and hematoxylin. Previous studies have shown that mouse and chick tissues can be successfully cultured in heterologous media[21,22] and maintained simultaneously in culture without apparent incompatibility;[23-25] it has further been noticed that under such conditions the differences of size and staining properties of the cells and nuclei of the two species are retained.

Accordingly, the feasibility of obtaining composite aggregates, consisting of both chick and mouse cells, was explored. Preliminary experiments[26] demonstrated that aggregates formed in suspensions of intermingled chick and mouse cells incorporated, under appropriate conditions, cells of both species. Upon further cultivation, such heterologous aggregates developed histogenetically in accordance

Proceedings of the *National Academy of Sciences*, **43**, 184–194, 1957. Reprinted with permission.

* Research aided by grants (Paul Weiss, principal investigator) from the American Cancer Society (through the Committee on Growth, National Research Council) and the Public Health Service, National Institutes of Health.

† The following terms will be used: (1) *isotypic* and (2) *heterotypic* to designate suspensions consisting of (1) predominantly one type of cell and (2) two or more cell types; (3) *homologous* and (4) *heterologous* for cells from embryos of the same species (3) or (4) a mixture of cells from two species (i.e., chick and mouse cells).

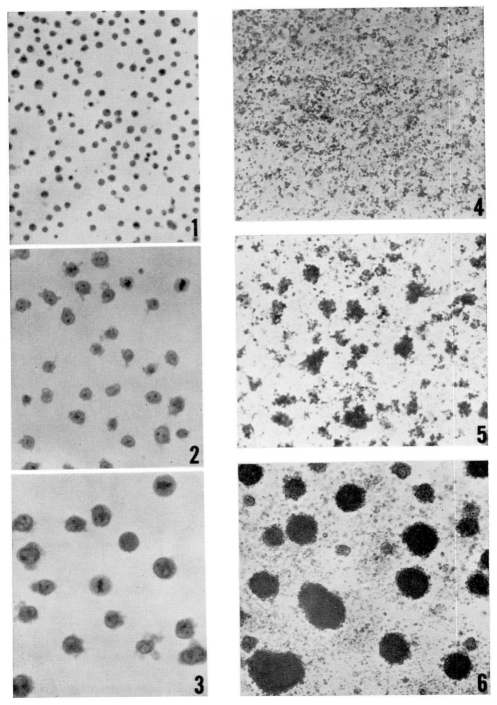

Fig. 1. Suspension of chondrogenic cells from limb-buds of chick (4-day) and mouse (12-day) embryos. Ehrlich's hematoxylin-Biebrich's. × 160.   Fig. 2. Suspension of chick chondrogenic cells. × 460.   Fig. 3. Suspension of mouse chondrogenic cells. × 460.   Fig. 4. Dissociated chondrogenic cells beginning to aggregate. 2-hour culture; living. × 50.   Fig. 5. A similar culture to that in Fig. 4, after 12 hours.   Fig. 6. A similar culture to that in Fig. 4, after 36 hours.

with the origin of their cellular components. Due to the differences in size and the staining properties of chick and mouse nuclei, the two types of cells could be easily distinguished and their precise distribution in the aggregates determined. As a further variation along this line, dissociated mouse tumor cells were introduced into suspensions of embryonic chick cells, and the structure and composition of the resulting aggregates were examined. With the aid of these differential cellular systems, various aspects of tissue reconstruction and development in cell aggregates were studied. Some of the observations bearing on the problem of cellular grouping are reported below.

MATERIALS AND METHODS

The preparation by treatment with trypsin of cell suspensions from embryonic organ rudiments and tumor tissue followed procedures described previously.[1-3] The experiments reported here were made with chondrogenic, mesonephric, and hepatic cells from chick and mouse embryos. Different age combinations of these tissues were tried, as it turned out that embryonic chick and mouse cells of diverse ages and types migrated and aggregated at different rates. This communication reports on tissues from 3- to 5-day chick embryos and from 11- to 13-day mouse embryos. The tumor tissue used was pigmented melanoma S91, maintained in a DBA/2JN strain of mice. Suspensions of cells were mixed in the desired proportions, and aliquots of the heterologous mixtures were distributed into hollow-ground (Maximow) slides with 1.0 cc. liquid culture medium in each. The medium consisted of 40 per cent chicken serum, 40 per cent embryo extract (freshly prepared from 10- to 12-day chick embryos), and 20 per cent Earl's balanced salt solution. Horse serum was sometimes added in proportions not exceeding 4 per cent of the total quantity of the medium. The culture medium was kept at room temperature for about an hour before being used. The slides with the cell suspensions were sealed and incubated at 38° C. for twenty-four hours.

The medium was then changed, and the cultures maintained for an additional day or two. The aggregates which had formed by that time were then transferred to a plasma clot for further cultivation in watch glasses. After fixation in Zenker's fixative, the cultures were sectioned at 6 or 8μ, and the sections were stained briefly with Ehrlich's hematoxylin and Biebrich's scarlet, which rendered cell nuclei of the chick a light purple tint, while mouse nuclei stained a deep blue.

ISOTYPIC COMBINATIONS OF CHICK AND MOUSE CELLS

Dissociated chondrogenic cells from the limb-buds of 4-day chick embryos were thoroughly intermingled in suspension with chondrogenic cells from the limb-buds of 12-day mouse embryos (Figs. 1–3). The amount of mouse cells was about double that of chick cells. At this stage of development, the presumptive chondroblasts of the limb-bud are still in the form of stellate mesenchyme cells. The aggregates that formed in such suspensions were cultured for 6 days. Histological sections showed that they consisted of typical cartilage formed by chick and mouse cells interspersed with each other (Fig. 7). Both types of cells were intimately associated and bound by the common cartilaginous matrix into a uniform tissue fabric: the matrix surrounding a mouse cell merged quite imperceptibly with that around the chick cell next to it (Figs. 8–10). Cultures of such aggregates were maintained for periods up to one month without evidence of deterioration or incompatibility between the chick and mouse cells. Evidently the common histogenetic fabric reconstructed by the cells under these conditions was acceptable to both chick and mouse cells and suitable for their histotypical development.

An additional instance of such formative integration of interspersed chick and mouse cells was observed in combinations of liver cells. Liver tissue was obtained from 5-day chick embryos and from 13-day mouse embryos. The dissociated cells from both sources aggregated to form hepatic cords that con-

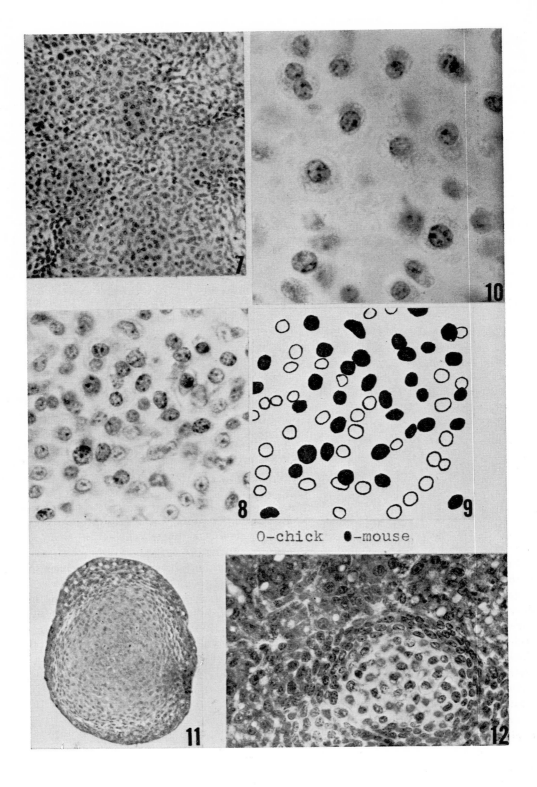

O-chick ●-mouse

sisted of interspersed chick and mouse cells producing glycogen or fat. In this case as well, the cells, regardless of their generic origin, reconstructed a common tissue fabric which developed in accordance with their pre-established properties.

HETEROTYPIC COMBINA-TIONS OF CHICK AND MOUSE CELLS

The cellular architecture of aggregates formed by cells of two diverse histogenetic types was quite different from that of isotypic cell aggregates. Mixtures of dissociated chick chondrogenic cells and mouse liver cells formed aggregates in which, after 4 days in culture, both cartilage and hepatic tissue were present. In this case, however, the two cell types had become regionally separated: the cartilage cells formed one or more central clusters, and the hepatic cells were situated around the periphery of the cartilage. In the present case, contrary to isotypic combinations, the two constituent tissues were not of mixed, chimeric composition, but each contained cells of the species that had furnished the respective cell type; that is, cartilage consisted solely of chick cells, hepatic tissue exclusively of mouse cells (Figs. 11, 12). This spatial arrangement was quite characteristic for the heterologous, as well as the homologous, combinations of these two types of cells (see also Wolff[24]).

Such type-specific grouping of cells was perhaps even more striking in combinations of mesonephric and chondrogenic cells, because of the structural characteristics of nephric tissue. In composite aggregates of 4-day chick mesonephric cells and 12-day mouse chondrogenic cells, cultured for 5 days, both kidney and cartilage cells reconstituted

their recognizable tissue patterns (Figs. 13–16). The cells became consistently grouped according to type: mouse chondroblasts formed areas of cartilage, chick nephroblasts built nephric tubules. Careful examination of this material revealed no chick cells that had become chondrocytes or mouse cells that had turned into nephrocytes. Single cells that were occasionally trapped in a nonmatching environment, if they took and multiplied, developed according to their original identities. In the reversed combination of cells, namely, in aggregates of mouse mesonephric with chick chondrogenic cells, similar type-specific, separate groupings of the corresponding tissues were formed. The reconstituted nephric and chondrified cells showed no regular distribution within the aggregates such as was typical of combinations of hepatic and chondrogenic cells.

COMBINATIONS OF EMBRYONIC CHICK CELLS AND MOUSE MELANOMA CELLS

In another aspect of this study of the grouping properties of embryonic cells, observations were made on their behavior in the presence of tumor cells. Dissociated hepatic or chondrogenic cells of the chick embryo were intermingled in suspension with dissociated cells of pigmented melanoma S91 of mice (Figs. 17, 18). Embryonic and tumor cells became incorporated in common clusters, which were then further cultured for 3–5 days. Aggregates of chondrogenic chick cells and S91 cells were found to consist of a central core of cartilage surrounded by S91 cells. In older cultures, scattered melanoma cells had infiltrated into the cartilage. Aggregates of hepatic chick cells and S91 cells consisted

Fig. 7. Cartilage masses composed of interspersed chick and mouse chondrogenic cells. × 120. (Figs. 7–19. Stained with Ehrlich's hematoxylin-Biebrich's scarlet.)   Fig. 8. Same at × 280. Compare with Fig. 9.   Fig. 9. Outlines of nuclei of Fig. 8 to show the distribution of mouse (*circles*) and chick (*dark*) nuclei.   Fig. 10. Full differentiated, composite cartilage, showing chick and mouse chondrocytes in a common matrix. × 980.   Fig. 11. Aggregate of mouse liver and chick chondrogenic cells, showing a "capsule" of hepatic tissue surrounding the globule of cartilage. 4-day culture. × 80.   Fig. 12. A 5-day culture of an aggregate of mouse hepatic and chondrogenic cells, showing the cells separated according to types. × 620.

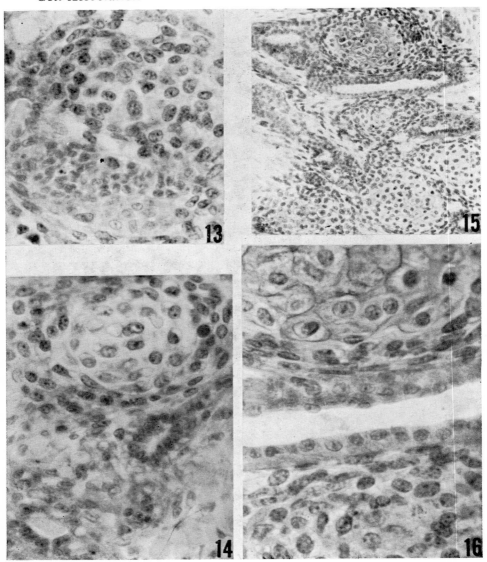

Fig. 13. Aggregate of mouse chondrogenic and chick mesonephric cells, showing groups of cells with beginning differentiation. 3-day culture. × 250. Fig. 14. 4-day culture of a chimeric aggregate as in Fig. 13, showing advanced histodifferentiation. × 250. Fig. 15. 6-day culture of a chimeric aggregate as in Fig. 13, showing mosaic distribution of the cellular groupings. × 100. Fig. 16. Enlarged part of Fig. 15 to show the topographical proximity of the reconstituted chick and mouse tissues. × 830.

of a central core of melanoma cells surrounded by a compact capsule of hepatic parenchyma (Fig. 19). It appears, then, that also when intermixed with tumor cells of this type, the embryonic cells clearly manifested their tendency for typewise association as well as for type-specific localization—cartilage centrally, liver peripherally.

COMMENT

The experiments reported in the foregoing demonstrated the following facts. (*a*) Chick and mouse cells, when cultured together *in vitro*, retained characteristics by which they could be identified as to their origins. (*b*)

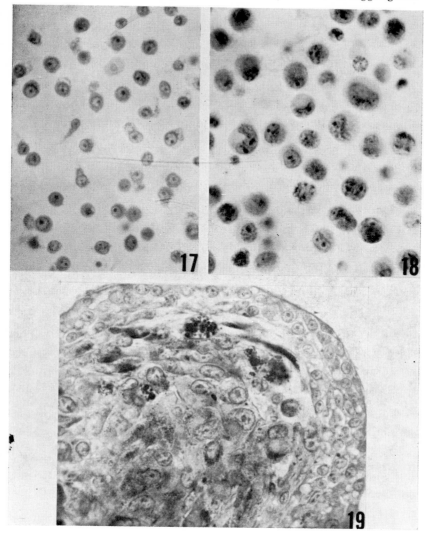

Fig. 17. Suspension of chick liver cells. × 530. Fig. 18. Suspension of S91 melanoma cells. × 530. Fig. 19. Section through a composite aggregate of hepatic chick and S91 cells, cultured for 4 days and showing a "capsule" of liver tissue surrounding the cluster of melanoma cells. × 530.

When cells from both species, belonging to the *same* histogenetic type, were cultured in random mixtures, they combined to form uniform chimeric tissues. (*c*) Chick and mouse cells belonging to *different* histogenetic types, however, did not readily combine but gave rise each to its discrete type-specific differentiation. Previous experiments with heterotypic cell combinations from a single species (chick embryo) had already suggested that dissociated cells tended to preserve their original type specificities and to sort out and differentiate accordingly:[2] these observations, together with the results obtained presently with cells marked clearly as to their species origin, lead to the conclusions that, under the experimental conditions explored, (1) type specificity prevailed over species specificity in guiding the association and grouping of embryonic cells of the given types of differentiation and (2) no transformation of cells of one type into another had taken place. It should be stressed at this point that these conclusions apply to cells which had evidently reached determination prior to their being dissociated, although they had not, at that time, become typically differentiated. It is thus conceivable that different results may be obtained with cells from earlier or later stages of development as well as with other types of cells, or different experimental conditions.

The problem of type-specific development in these experiments, as in the earlier ones, has two different aspects. One refers to the formation of the primary aggregates of cells, and the other to the sorting out of the cells according to kind, concurrently with or following aggregation and their subsequent differentiation. The former aspect, concerned mainly with the mechanisms of aggregation, has been only parenthetically mentioned here, and its discussion will therefore be postponed. In view of the pertinence of these problems to the observations reported, the following brief comment should be included. The formation of all types of aggregates and their histogenesis *in vitro* may be markedly affected by a variety of factors. Environmental changes, such as of the physical and chemical properties of the medium or the substrate, markedly influence cellular aggregation by their differential effects on the diverse types of cells. Changes in the proportionate concentrations of different cell types intermixed in the same culture become reflected in the histological development of the ensuing aggregates.[2] As mentioned before, the rates of migration of different types of cells, as well as of cells of different generic origin, vary considerably under identical conditions. For instance, mouse mesonephric cells migrate at a slower rate than chick mesonephric cells; in cultures containing both types of cells, this difference leads eventually to the formation of aggregates in which chick mesonephric cells predominate. Whether the different rates of migration are due to intrinsic cellular factors, to a differential response by the cells to culture conditions, or to specific activating stimuli is presently not clear.

Following formation of the primary cell aggregates, or perhaps concurrently with it, histologically identifiable tissues begin to develop, and eventually the cluster of cells becomes an organized tissue fabric. The available evidence suggests strongly that the processes of tissue formation are preceded or accompanied by a reshuffling of the aggregated cells; when more than one type of cell is incorporated in the cluster, they become sorted out to form type-specific cell groupings. The precise manner in which this occurs is still obscure, but time-lapse motion pictures, presently being undertaken in this laboratory, are expected to furnish pertinent information.

The structural differences between iso- and heterotypic cell combinations provide a striking indication of the specificities involved in cellular interactions which lead to grouping. In the tissues reconstituted from isotypic chick and mouse cells, the cells remained intermingled and interspersed in the form of cellular mosaics, without becoming segregated according to species origin. On the other hand, in aggregates of heterotypic cells the different types of cells became arranged in separate groups, so that the aggregates assumed the appearance of tissue mosaics. Thus, under the present experimental conditions, the type identities, rather than the generic identities, of the cells determined the manner of grouping. Typical grouping selectivity was also manifested by the dissociated embryonic cells when confronted with cells of the S91 tumor. However, following histogenesis of the embryonic tissue, S91 cells began, in some cases, secondarily to infiltrate between the normal cells. The nature of such manifestations, as well as the generality of such interactions, will become clearer when more is known of other combinations of dissociated normal and tumor cells and their patterns of aggregation.

The interpretation of cellular grouping in chimeric aggregates in terms of preferential, type-specific interactions between cells conforms well with observations on the tissue-specific localization of cells injected into the chick embryo[12] and into irradiated mice.[27-31] That the properties involved are effective across generic differences, not only under conditions of culture but in the organism as well, may be inferred from the successful implantations in the bone marrow of rat blood cells injected intravenously into irradiated mice.[28] In this connection, the question of the stability of chimeric cell aggregates is of interest. The successful persistence *in vitro* of cartilage chimeras beyond the embryonic age of their constituent cells suggested that, under such conditions, the cells, although generically alien, remained histocompatible. The response of heterologous combinations to suitable immune environments and to implantation into embryos and adults should provide additional information on the stability or the differential susceptibility of the cells under such conditions. Studies in this direction might also furnish information on the nature of histogenetic interactions between cells and the "recognition" (Weiss) effects involved, i.e., whether they function on the same basis as antibody-antigen systems[11, 32, 33] or whether they reflect specific properties, typical of this particular aspect of cellular behavior.

Summary

1. Dissociated cells from various organ rudiments of chick and mouse embryos, when intermixed in suspension cultures, readily aggregated and combined to form composite, chimeric tissues. Under suitable conditions of culture, such reconstituted tissues differentiated histotypically. This communication reports on combinations of chondrogenic, nephrogenic, and hepatogenic cells of chick and mouse embryos and S91 mouse melanoma cells.

2. In aggregates of intermixed chick and mouse cells of same type (i.e., chick and mouse chondrogenic cells) the cells reconstructed a uniform fabric which differentiated histotypically into a chimeric tissue consisting of interspersed chick and mouse cells.

3. In aggregates of intermixed chick and mouse cells of different types (i.e., chick nephrogenic and mouse chondrogenic cells) the cells became associated according to type and formed separate groupings which developed in accordance with the original histogenetic properties of the cells.

4. Due to the clear morphological differences between chick and mouse cells, it was possible precisely to identify and localize them in the chimeric aggregates. The evidence thus obtained suggested conclusively that (*a*) in the course of tissue reconstruction the dissociated embryonic cells became grouped preferentially, according to their original type identities, regardless of their generic origin, and (*b*) under the present experimental conditions no transformation of one cell type to another was observed.

The author wishes to thank Dr. Paul Weiss, head of the Laboratory of Developmental Biology, for his interest and indispensable advice throughout this study. The aid of Dr. Dorothea Bennett in some phases of this work is gratefully acknowledged.

[1] A. Moscona, *Exptl. Cell Research*, **3**, 535, 1952.

[2] A. Moscona, *Proc. Soc. Exptl. Biol. Med.*, **92**, 410, 1956.

[3] A. Moscona and H. Moscona, *J. Anat.*, **86**, 287, 1952.

[4] P. Weiss and R. James, *Exptl. Cell Research*, Suppl. 3, p. 381, 1955.

[5] M. W. Cavanaugh, *J. Exptl. Zool.*, **128**, 573, 1955.

[6] M. W. Cavanaugh, *Exptl. Cell Research*, **9**, 42, 1955.

[7] C. Grobstein, *J. Exptl. Zool.*, **130**, 319, 1955.

[8] J. P. Trinkaus and P. W. Groves, *Proc. N.A.S.*, **41**, 784, 1955.

[9] P. Weiss, *Yale J. Biol. Med.*, **19**, 235, 1947.

[10] J. Holtfreter, *Arch. f. exptl. Zellforsch.*, **23**, 620, 1939.

[11] P. Weiss, *Quart. Rev. Biol.*, **25**, 177, 1950.

[12] P. Weiss and G. Andres, *J. Exptl. Zool.*, **121**, 449, 1952.

[13] J. Holtfreter, *J. Morphol.*, **80**, 25, 1947.

[14] P. L. Townes and J. Holtfreter, *J. Exptl. Zool.*, **128**, 53, 1955.

[15] J. J. Chiakulas, *J. Exptl. Zool.*, **121**, 383, 1952.

[16] F. Baltzer, *Rev. suisse Zool.*, **48**, 413, 1941.

[17] G. Andres, *Genetica*, **24**, 1, 1949.

[18] M. A. Willmer, in *Essays on Growth and Form* (Oxford: Oxford Univ. Press, 1945).

[19] V. C. Twitty and M. C. Niu, *J. Exptl. Zool.*, **108**, 405, 1948.

[20] M. Abercrombie and J. E. M. Heaysman, *Exptl. Cell Research*, **5**, 111, 1953.

[21] H. B. Fell and H. Gruneberg, *Proc. Roy. Soc. London, B*, 127, 257, 1939.

[22] H. B. Fell, *Science Progr.*, No. 162, p. 212, 1953.

[23] C. Grobstein and J. S. Youngner, *Science*, **110**, 501, 1949.

[24] E. Wolff, *Bull. Soc. Zool. France*, **79**, 357, 1954.

25 E. Wolff and D. Bresch, *Compt. rend. Acad. sci.* (Paris), **240**, 1014, 1955.

26 Reported at the International Congress of Developmental Biology at Brown University, Providence, Rhode Island, July, 1956.

27 D. L. Lindsley, T. T. Odell, Jr., and F. G. Tausche, *Proc. Soc. Exptl. Biol. Med.*, **90**, 512, 1955.

28 C. E. Ford, J. Hamerton, D. W. H. Barnes, and J. F. Loutit, *Nature*, **177**, 452, 1956.

29 C. L. Miller, *Nature*, **178**, 142, 1956.

30 N. A. Mitchison, *Brit. J. Exptl. Pathol.*, **37**, 239, 1956.

31 E. S. Russel, L. J. Smith, and F. A. Lawson, *Science*, **124**, 1076, 1956.

32 R. E. Billingham, L. Brent, and P. B. Medawar, *Nature*, **172**, 603, 1953.

33 A. Tyler, in *Analysis of Development* (Philadelphia: W. B. Saunders Co., 1955).

Reconstruction of Tissues by Dissociated Cells

MALCOLM S. STEINBERG

Some morphogenetic tissue movements and the sorting out of embryonic cells may have a common explanation.

How is the structure of a multicellular animal generated? In the broadest terms, we can distinguish three kinds of developmental processes: growth, differentiation, and morphogenesis. The developing organism multiplies its cells and increases its mass. The emergent parts become different—different from what they were before and different from one another. And the differentiating parts bend inward or outward, expand, contract, disperse, condense, fuse, separate, elongate, even perish, and otherwise rearrange themselves in the process of constructing the animal. But what are the mechanisms which elicit and orient these tissue movements of morphogenesis?

BACKGROUND OF THE PROBLEM

Early workers envisioned the tissue movements as resulting from pressures or other inhomogeneities in the immediate environment, but a considerable body of evidence has meanwhile been accumulated to show that the

Reprinted from *Science*, **141**, No. 3579, 401–408 (August 2, 1963). Copyright © 1963 by the American Association for the Advancement of Science.

movements are due to intrinsic properties of the individual tissues themselves. Beyond this statement, however, we find ourselves in an area of uncertainty, for the character of these intrinsic properties has not been securely and rigorously established. A crack in the shell surrounding this problem appeared very early. H. V. Wilson discovered, in 1907, that the cells and cell clusters obtained by squeezing a sponge through the meshes of fine, silk, bolting cloth could reunite, and that aggregates obtained in this way could reconstitute themselves into functional sponges (*1*). The manner in which this reconstitution was effected remained problematical. Wilson continued to maintain (*2*) that a considerable amount of dedifferentiation and redifferentiation occurred, and that cells altered their cytological characteristics to conform with their newly established environments, while other workers (*3*) believed they had demonstrated the reconstitution to consist, in large measure, of a sorting out of the various types of cells, each coming again to occupy its accustomed haunts in the body of the sponge. The difficulty lay in the absence of permanent and recognizable characteristics by which one could accurately distinguish and follow the various types of cells during the process of reorganization.

In the meantime, Harrison (*4*) had laid the

foundation for modern neuroembryology, a foundation which included the concepts of the selection of paths by outgrowing nerves and of the specificity of nerve-end organ connection, and which was ably extended and built upon by the researches of P. Weiss, Hamburger, and others (see 5).

A second discovery of major importance appeared against this background in 1939. Holtfreter, working with carefully defined tissue fragments from young amphibian embryos, found that these fragments showed marked preferences in their adhesive properties. These preferences were correlated with their normal morphogenetic functions. For example, ectoderm and endoderm, isolated from a gastrula, would adhere to each other much as they do at the same stage *in vivo*. In time, however, these two tissues would separate from one another, an event which occurs in the embryo as well. This separation is accomplished, in normal development, by the penetration of the mesoderm between the ectoderm and endoderm. Mesoderm incorporated along with the isolated ectoderm and endoderm was indeed found to bind the latter two tissues together in a permanent union *in vitro* as it does *in vivo*. Furthermore, when the tissues were present in the right proportions, the ectoderm would take up an external position and the endoderm an internal position, with the mesoderm spread out in between, duplicating in the culture vessel not only the associations but also the anatomical relations which exist in the embryo. An impressive array of similar results with these and other tissues (6) led Holtfreter to frame the concept of "tissue affinities" to describe these associative preferences, which he had shown to be so closely related to normal morphogenetic events.

A third advance was made by Holtfreter in 1944. He found that by subjecting a fragment of an amphibian gastrula to an environmental *p*H of about 10, he could cause the individual cells to separate and fall away from one another, much as Herbst had earlier been able to cause the separation of sea urchin blastomeres in calcium-free sea water (7). Upon return to a more neutral *p*H, the amphib-

ian cells would re-establish mutual adhesions, attaching themselves to any neighbors with which they came into contact, and building, in this manner, masses of tissue into which cells of the various germ layers were incorporated at random. The situation resembled that in the sponges, but with one important distinction. Differences in the degree of pigmentation of the amphibian cells, together with their extraordinarily large size, allowed the investigator to follow the movements at least of the surface cells. Before his eyes the lightly pigmented mesoderm cells vanished into the depths of the tissue mass, while darkly pigmented ectoderm cells and the almost pigment-free endoderm cells emerged to replace them at the periphery (8). Sorting out was a reality. And the tissue affinities which Holtfreter had earlier described could with justice be renamed *cell* affinities, for it was now clear that they were inherent in the individual cells.

Other workers made significant contributions. Principal among these was Moscona, who opened the way for investigations with the cells of older avian embryos through his discovery that trypsin was effective in dissociating their tissues (9). Through the use of this technique, it was shown by Moscona (10) and by Trinkaus and Groves (11) that the reconstitution of body parts by aggregates of intermixed cells occurred even though the constituent cells were, in all likelihood, "determined" with respect to their fates, and even though they had already reached their appropriate positions within the embryo. The same fact was established for older amphibian embryos as well, by Townes and Holtfreter (12). The remarkable degree to which normal structure could be approximated by a "self-organizing" cell mixture was demonstrated by Weiss and Taylor (13), who, by culturing aggregates derived from highly differentiated organs in a site which provided vascularization, obtained organogenesis which strikingly approached the complexity of normal organization.

The foregoing historical account is only a sketch, which makes no pretense of complete coverage. It serves, however, to document the fact that formerly elusive problems concerning the mechanisms of morphogenetic movement have been brought more closely within the experimenter's grasp.

Sorting Out, Adhesion, and Motility

The most fundamental facts concerning tissue reconstruction are perhaps the following. (i) When the cells of different vertebrate embryonic tissues are dissociated and mixed, they are capable of establishing adhesions with one another and constructing common aggregates. (ii) Within such "mixed" aggregates, containing cells from different tissues, the differing kinds of cells regroup, each with the others allied to it, to reconstruct the various tissues of origin. (iii) These tissues are reconstructed in definite positions (see also *11*); for example, muscle is always built external to cartilage, never the other way around. (iv) When the tissues employed are parts of a complex within the embryo, the geometry of the entire normal complex is reflected in the re-established structures.

In normal development, tissue *X* may spread from some previous position to cover the surface of tissue *Y*. In a mixed aggregate *in vitro*, the same ultimate geometry would be achieved through the sorting out of the jumbled *X* and *Y* cells. The fact that the specific anatomical structure is established by pathways which differ so greatly in the two cases is to be regarded less as a curiosity than as a stroke of great fortune for the student of morphogenesis. It indicates that the features responsible for the ultimate anatomical organization are common to these two disparate systems. In the case at hand, two common features at once come to mind. They are the basic cellular properties of mutual adhesiveness and motility. It is not my purpose here to cover the extensive literature concerning cellular adhesion and cell movement, much of which is discussed in recent publications (*14, 15*). I wish rather to examine two particular assumptions which, either singly or in combination, are widely held to be necessary in order to account for sorting out and for tissue reconstruction. These assumptions are (i)

that the segregating cells exhibit actively directed movements, and (ii) that they display qualitatively selective mutual adhesion.

The segregation of cell species which takes place within mixed aggregates could, in principle, be brought about in either of two ways. Either the differing cells might seek out, by active and directed migration, different parts of the aggregate (or even one another), or they might possess type-specific differences in adhesiveness by virtue of which the old cellular alliances are again progressively built up through the agency of random collisions. Both possibilities, as well as a combination of the two, have been suggested by various authors. In view of the early experimental documentation by Holtfreter (*6, 16*) of differences in adhesiveness among such cells, and because of the apparent cellular selectivity involved in wound healing and in neurogenesis, most of the speculation has centered around possible mechanisms by which adhesion might be rendered selective. There is no body of evidence for mutual attraction (or repulsion) by embryonic cells.

It has been variously proposed that embryonic cells selectively adhere to one another by means of binding sites which possess singularities of conformation (*5, 17, 18*), of chemical composition (*19*), or of geometric arrangement (*5, 14, 17, 20*); that adhesion among differing cells is nonselective in character but varies in its intensity as a function of cell type and time (*21*) or as a result of selective influences which favor disjunction (*22*); and that in addition to (*12*), or possibly in lieu of (*23*), showing selectivity in their adhesion to one another, cells may migrate in a directed fashion either inward or outward within multicellular masses, the migration ultimately bringing about their mutual segregation.

In virtually all the hypotheses which have been advanced, attention has been focused upon the adhesive and motor properties of the segregating cells; for without adhesion there can be no coherent multicelluar aggregate, and without motility on the part of the component cells there can be no sorting out. Almost all authors who have dealt with this problem [with the exception of Stefanelli *et al.* (*23*)] have in addition assumed that the differences in adhesiveness between the different types of cells are type specific, at least throughout the period during which sorting out occurs. Ample justification for this assumption is to be found in the experimental literature, as I have pointed out. Beyond this point, each additional assumption increases the risk of error.

I wish now to develop the thesis that the behavior that is characteristic of cells in the process of sorting out and of tissue reconstruction follows directly from their possession of motility and of quantitative differentials in adhesiveness, unrestricted by any requirement for qualitative specificity. It will be helpful in this analysis to review first the behavior of inanimate physical systems which share with living cells precisely these attributes, and to examine the way in which this behavior is influenced by the particular quantitative adhesive relationships which apply. In this way we may see the consequences of the presence of these motor and adhesive properties, unobscured by any of the complex and often seemingly goal-directed activities of which cells are capable.

In the physical world, we recognize that the units which comprise a gas are mobile but not coherent—they fly apart to fill as much space as is provided. When the energy which drives them apart is sufficiently reduced, attractive forces begin to dominate and the units form a different type of system—a liquid, in which they retain mobility but gain coherence. Reduction of the thermal energy to a still lower point results in the domination of attractive forces to such an extent that mobility of the units is effectively inhibited, and we have a system in which coherence is retained but mobility is severely restricted—a solid. Thus, in the world of molecules, a liquid system is one which is composed of a population of coherent, mobile units.

Many of the properties of liquid systems depend exclusively upon this fact. It is of no substantive consequence that the units happen to be molecules and that their motility happens to be passive rather than active in nature.

These properties are independent of the composition of the units, independent of the causes of their motility, and independent of the nature of the adhesive forces. For example, a liquid drop assumes a spherical shape when subjected to uniform external conditions, because the mobile units of which it is composed attract or adhere to one another until the greatest possible number have the maximum possible contact. Adhesion being nothing more than close-range attraction, the same holds true for a population of actively motile, uniformly adhesive cells (Fig. 1).

The same principle can be expressed by saying that the *free energy* of the drop reduces to a minimum. Included in this quantity is the *surface free energy*, which provided the impetus in the simple illustration given. The surface free energy is merely the energy available for adhesion but "left over" in the surface, where adhesions could be formed but have not been. It is readily seen to be directly proportional to both (i) the area of exposed surface and (ii) the free energy per unit of surface area, the latter quantity being a direct reflection of the adhesiveness of the units which comprise the surface. The free energy is a potential energy and will tend spontaneously to decrease toward a minimum in

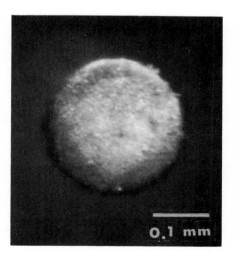

Fig. 1. An initially jagged fragment of liver that has assumed a spherical shape. Isolated from a 5-day chick embryo, it has been maintained in liquid medium at 37°C for 2 days under constant gyration. The same result is obtainable in a stationary culture.

any population of mobile, coherent units. At this minimum the system is in thermodynamic equilibrium.

Let us now consider the manner in which thermodynamic equilibrium is achieved in a coherent population consisting of two different kinds of mobile units which adhere to one another with different "strengths." The standard measure of the "strength" of such adhesions is called the work of adhesion. This is a measure of the work done by the system in the formation of an adhesion over a unit of area. [In common usage, the term *work of* ad*hesion* refers to adhesion between two different phases while the equivalent term *work of co*hesion refers to adhesion among the units of a single phase (*24*).] The units adhere to one another, rearranging themselves, as in our first example, until the free energy of the system is reduced to a minimum. This minimum is achieved when the total work done through adhesion in the system is raised to a maximum—in other words, when all of the individual units are mutually oriented in such a manner that they adhere to one another with the greatest average tenacity. At this point of thermodynamic equilibrium, the distribution of the two different types of units (phases) within the system is a function of the work of cohesion of each of the two phases and of the work of adhesion between them. There are three types of distribution, each corresponding with one of the following three sets of adhesive relationships, in which the two kinds of units are denoted, respectively, as *a* and *b:* (i) *a-b* adhesions equaling or exceeding in strength the average of *a-a* adhesions plus *b-b* adhesions; (ii) *a-b* adhesions weaker than this average but equaling or exceeding in strength the weaker of the other two kinds of adhesions; and (iii) *a-b* adhesions weaker than either the *a-a* or the *b-b* adhesions. Let us now explore the three situations with which these relationships correspond.

We will designate the work of cohesion among the units of type *a* as W_a, the work of cohesion among the units of type *b* as W_b, and the work of adhesion between *a* and *b* units as W_{ab}. If it happens that *a-b* adhesions equal or exceed in strength a value obtained by averaging the strengths of *a-a* adhesions and *b-b* adhesions, we can describe the situation by the relation

$$W_{ab} \geqq \frac{W_a + W_b}{2} \qquad (1)$$

In such a case the greatest average tenacity of adhesion is achieved when *a* and *b* units are alternately arranged in the coherent population, so as to have the maximum possible interconnection. Therefore, at thermodynamic equilibrium, the two populations are intermixed. This is our case 1 (see Fig. 2). If, on the other hand, the strength of the *a-b* adhesions falls below this average value, the situation is described by the opposite relation

$$W_{ab} < \frac{W_a + W_b}{2} \qquad (2)$$

In this case the greatest average tenacity of adhesion is achieved when *a* and *b* units are totally segregated in the population. However, even the mutual disposition of the segregating *a* and *b* phases is thermodynamically controlled, a fact which is shown as follows.

To begin with, let us establish the convention that when the cohesiveness of the units comprising the two phases differs, the more cohesive units will be designated *a* and the less cohesive units, *b*. Now, if *b* units adhere to *a* units with a tenacity that is equal to or greater than the tenacity with which they adhere to one another, we can express this by the relation

$$W_{ab} \geqq W_b \qquad (3)$$

Relations 2 and 3, taken together, determine the complete set of conditions

$$\frac{W_a + W_b}{2} > W_{ab} \geqq W_b \qquad (4)$$

These conditions can only be met when $W_a > W_{ab}$. What are the consequences for the mutual disposition of the segregating phases? Since *a-b* adhesions are intermediate in strength between *a-a* and *b-b* adhesions, the two kinds of units adhere relatively strongly, the whole coherent population tending to assume a spherical form, in which the exposed surface area is minimal. However the surface free energy of the system is the product of the exposed surface area and the free energy per unit of such area, and the free energy per unit area, as we saw earlier, is a measure of the cohesiveness of the units in the surface. Consequently, minimization of the surface free energy is achieved only when the surface is of minimal area and contains exclusively the less cohesive of the two kinds of units which comprise the population. Therefore, in the segregation of the *a* and *b* phases, phase *b* will come to occupy completely the surface of the system, which will, as a whole, tend to assume spherical form. Furthermore, the greatest possible segregation of the two phases will occur, a condition which requires that the interfacial area between the two be minimized. Phase *a* being totally subsurface, this condition is met when phase *a* itself assumes the form of a sphere totally enclosed by phase *b*. Thermodynamic equilibrium is thus established when the less cohesive units are arranged as a coherent sphere totally enclosing a second sphere composed of all of the more cohesive units. This is our case 2 (see Fig. 2).

Only one other set of possible adhesive relationships remains, at this point, to be explored. What will be the disposition of the phases at thermodynamic equilibrium if *a-b* adhesions, instead of being as strong as, or stronger than, the average of *a-a* and *b-b* adhesions (as in our case 1), or weaker than this average but yet as strong as, or stronger than, *b-b adhesions* (as in our case 2), are the weakest adhesions of all? This circumstance is described by the relationship

$$W_a \gtrsim W_b > W_{ab} \qquad (5)$$

Let us begin by considering the most extreme possible examples. At the one extreme, *a* and *b* units do not adhere to one another at all. Clearly, two separate, isolated populations will form. Each will consist at equilibrium of a sphere containing one of the two types of units. At the other extreme, *a* and *b* units adhere to one another with a strength ever so slightly less than that achieved by the ad-

hesion of a pair of *b* units to one another. Were the *a-b* adhesions any stronger, they would be equal in strength to the *b-b* adhesions and we would have at equilibrium the limiting example of case 2: a sphere within a sphere. Instead, the distribution of the phases at equilibrium is shifted slightly from this configuration in the direction toward isolation of the phases: phase *b* recedes at one spot, exposing a minute area of phase *a* at the periphery (*24*). The lower the strength of the *a-b* adhesions, the greater the recession, at equilibrium, of the margins of phase *b* around the spherical perimeter of phase *a*. This is our case 3 (see Fig. 2). This type of circumstance is classically described by the relationship known as "Young's equation" (*25*). Expressed in terms of work of adhesion, this equation becomes

$$2 \frac{W_{ab}}{W_b} = 1 + \cos \theta \qquad (6)$$

where θ represents the internal angle of contact, at equilibrium, of the margin of phase *b* with the surface of phase *a* (see *24*, however). It has recently been proved (*26*) that Young's equation is a "direct consequence of: (1) the existence of interfacial free energies and (2) the total free energy of a system at equilibrium being a minimum." The various possible relationships among W_a, W_b, and W_{ab}, and the topographic relationships which they engender, are shown diagrammatically in Fig. 2. They may be derived from equations presented in most standard texts on surface chemistry (see, for example, *25*).

PHASE REDISTRIBUTION IN COHERING POPULATIONS OF EMBRYONIC CELLS

The regroupings discussed in the foregoing section are those which tend spontaneously to occur, for thermodynamic reasons, within a population of mobile, mutually adhesive units of two kinds, when the latter are brought into contact. Vertebrate embryonic cells of different kinds are both mobile and mutually adhesive, and they tend, when mixed, to regroup themselves in a manner which often resembles

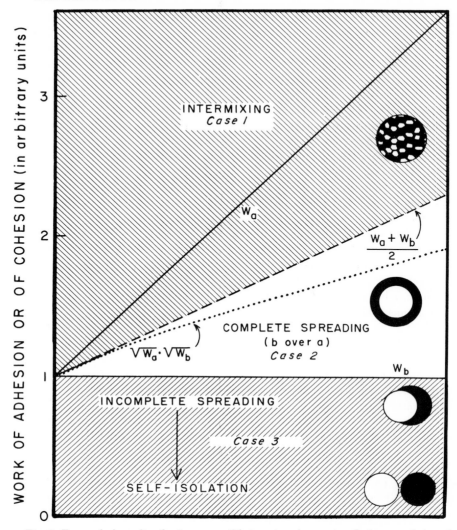

Fig. 2. Types of phase distribution, at equilibrium, in coherent populations consisting of mobile units of two kinds. The work of cohesion of the weakly cohesive *b* units, arbitrarily assigned a value of 1, is given by the line W_b. The work of cohesion of the more strongly cohesive *a* units is denoted by W_a. The diagram is used as follows. For any set of adhesive relationships, that vertical line is drawn which passes through the calculated value of W_a/W_b as read on the abscissa. The work of adhesion of *a* units to *b* units (W_{ab}), as read on the ordinate, is then entered upon this line. The background shading at this point indicates the distribution of the *a* and *b* phases for this system at thermodynamic equilibrium. *Example:* If $W_a = 3$, with W_b defined as 1, then $W_{ab} = 2.1$ would yield intermixing; $W_{ab} = 1.5$ would yield complete coverage of *a* by *b*; and $W_{ab} = 0.5$ would yield incomplete coverage of *a* by *b* (see *24*). The intersection of the vertical line with the dotted line $(W_a)^{1/2}\ (W_b)^{1/2}$ marks the value of W_{ab} which would be generated in the model system devoid of adhesive specificity, as described in the text. [Modified from Steinberg (*30*).]

the regroupings described in our cases 2 and 3. It is of considerable interest, therefore, to inquire in what measure such sorting out, with its anatomically precise consequences, may be explained by the thermodynamic con-

siderations which have been outlined. Precise measurement of the work of cohesion between living cells does not as yet appear to be feasible. It has proved possible, however, to examine in some detail the behavior of mixed

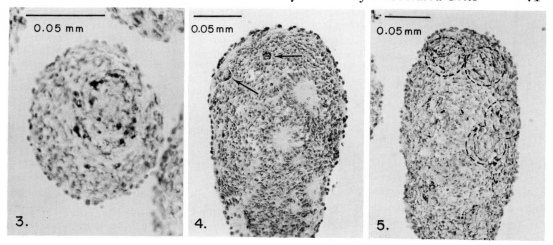

Fig. 3. Section through an aggregate formed by dissociated 5-day heart cells and 7-day retinal cells of chick embryo. Through sorting out, the reconstructed heart tissue has come to be enveloped by the reconstructed retinal tissue. Fig. 4. Section through an aggregate containing 99 percent retinal cells and 1 percent heart cells. The sparse heart cells, two of which are present in this section, leave the surface but otherwise remain generally distributed. Fig. 5. Section through a heart-retina aggregate early in the process of sorting out. Many small, discrete islets of heart cells (with black inclusions) have formed and are in the process of coalescing. Several islets are encircled on the figure.

populations of embryonic cells and to compare the observed behavior with that to be expected on thermodynamic grounds from a system conforming with one or another set of interunit adhesive relationships.

Chick-embryo heart and neural retinal cells, when mixed in appropriate proportions and allowed to coaggregate in a culture vessel, sort out to form islands of heart tissue totally encased by retinal tissue (*27, 28*) (Fig. 3). The system in this respect resembles that in our case 2, brought about by conformance with the adhesive relationships given in relation 4. The heart cells correspond with *a*, and the retinal cells with *b*. If these adhesive relationships actually operate to bring about the conformation depicted in Fig. 3, several predictions from thermodynamic theory ought to be fulfilled by the behavior of appropriate mixtures of such cells.

Prediction 1. The replacement of heart cells by retinal cells in the surfaces of heart-retina aggregates in which the heart cells are numerous should occur very early in the sorting out process, since reduction of surface free energy by this means requires far less rearrangement than a commensurate reduction of the total free energy of the system.

It was found that within 17 hours after the onset of aggregation, when sorting out was just beginning to be discernible, a marked depletion of heart cells was evident in the surfaces of the aggregates (*27*).

Prediction 2. When *a* units (heart cells) are very sparse in the population, so that their meeting one another is virtually precluded, minimization of surface free energy should cause them to be relegated to subsurface locations within the aggregates. They should be equally stable in all subsurface positions.

It was experimentally established (*28*) that sorting out of the two types of cells, to yield configurations such as that shown in Fig. 3, normally was accomplished within 2½ days. Reduction of the proportion of heart cells to 1 percent (by volume) of the population yielded aggregates whose surfaces at the end of this time were virtually devoid of heart cells, the latter being otherwise distributed apparently at random within the aggregates (Fig. 4). This result, in showing that heart cells do not "seek the center," would appear to exclude the possibility that directed migration plays a role in the sorting out of these cells.

Prediction 3. Sorting out should proceed by way of the progressive exchange of heteronomic adhesions for homonomic ones, in the course of which process the potentially internal tissue should appear as a discontinuous phase (that is, as coalescing islets), while the potentially external tissue should constitute a continuous phase.

Histological analysis of heart-retina aggregates fixed after graded intervals in culture bore out prediction 3 (27) (see Fig. 5). Similar observations have been reported for the sorting out of mixed amphibian neurula chordamesoderm and endoderm cells (11) and of mixed pigmented retinal and wing bud cells from chick embryos (29).

Prediction 4. If the distribution of the two phases after segregation is that at which the system is in thermodynamic equilibrium, this same terminal distribution should be approached regardless of the initial distribution of the phases. Thus, lateral fusion of an intact fragment of tissue *b* with an intact fragment of tissue *a* should be followed by the progressive spreading of the one over the surface of the other to yield the same configuration which is ultimately produced through the sorting out of intermixed *a* and *b* cells.

The accuracy of this prediction has been established, to date, for 11 different combinations of tissue fragments and of their dissociated cells (30, 31). In each case, fusion of undissociated fragments of two tissues leads to the progressive envelopment of one fragment by the other, the final disposition of the two tissues being the same as that which is arrived at when the starting material is a mixed suspension of the corresponding dissociated cells. Of these 11 combinations, nine behaved in the manner described for our case 2 (Figs. 6 and 7), while two behaved in the manner described for our case 3. The latter showed partial retraction of the earlier continuous, external tissue after segregation within mixed aggregates; correspondingly, they showed only partial enclosure of one fragment by the other after fusion of intact fragments which had never been dissociated.

Prediction 5. In a segregating community composed of two kinds of mutually adhesive, motile units, the less cohesive phase will tend to envelop, partially or completely, the more cohesive phase at thermodynamic equilibrium. The motile cells of a series of different embryonic tissues constitute a series of phases, each of which is adherent to, yet segregates from, any of the others. Therefore, when the cell populations comprising such a series are intermixed in all possible binary combinations, the mutual positions which they come to assume at equilibrium should establish a hierarchy definable by the specification that if *a* is covered by *b* and *b* is covered by *c*, *a* will be covered by *c*.

In testing this prediction all possible binary combinations among cell suspensions derived from six different chick-embryo tissues have been used. There are, in all, 15 different combinations. The segregation patterns obtained do indeed define a hierarchy such that one tissue is reconstituted internally in all combinations, another tissue is reconstituted externally in all combinations, and each of the remaining tissues falls into a specific intermediate ranking in complete accordance with prediction 5 (31). An example of this behavior is illustrated in Figs. 6, 8, and 9.

In all respects, then, the regroupings of cells in the populations which we have studied proceed along satisfyingly consistent and simple lines. They are precisely what is to be expected on thermodynamic grounds in any system composed of mobile units which are mutually adhesive, and between which certain quantitative adhesive relationships exist.

Those of us who have been seeking an explanation for sorting out and tissue reconstruction by dissociated cells have almost unanimously considered it necessary to assume that unlike cells adhere to one another less tenaciously than like cells do (expressed by relation 5)—a situation requiring selectivity in the mechanism of adhesion. The thermodynamic analysis of the situation shows, however, that under the circumstances of relation 5, while sorting out would be expected to occur, the reconstructed tissues would, in addition, be expected to continue their mutual self-isolation to a point at which each would come to occupy a portion of the surface of the aggregate (our case 3). Furthermore, the analysis shows that the most common outcome of segregation in a binary system—the production of a totally internal

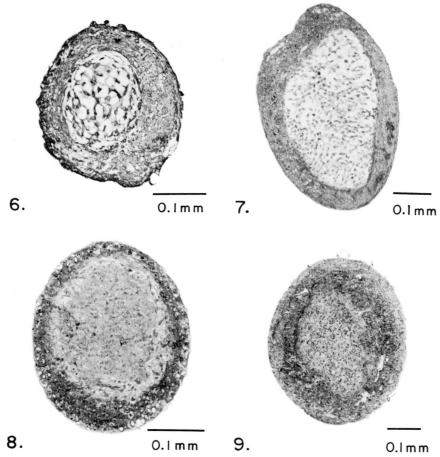

Fig. 6. Section through an aggregate formed by dissociated 4-day limb-bud chondrogenic cells and 5-day heart ventricle cells of chick embryo. The reconstructed heart tissue envelops the now-differentiated cartilage.   Fig. 7. Section through a structure formed by an intact fragment of the chondrogenic zone of a 4-day limb bud laterally fused with a fragment of 5-day heart ventricle. The heart tissue had spread over and enveloped the chondrogenic tissue prior to the deposition of matrix by the latter.   Fig. 8. Section through an aggregate formed by dissociated 5-day heart ventricle cells and 5-day liver cells. The reconstructed liver tissue envelops the reconstructed heart tissue.   Fig. 9. Section through an aggregate formed by dissociated 4-day limb-bud chondrogenic cells and 5-day liver cells. The reconstructed liver tissue envelops the chondrogenic tissue, in which the deposition of matrix has recently begun.

tissue entirely enveloped by another tissue— fulfills the expectation based upon a set of adhesive relationships quite different from that which we have previously assumed. In this set of relationships (relation 4), the unlike cells adhere to one another with a strength intermediate between the strengths of cohesion of the two kinds of like cells. Does logic lead us, then, to postulate the existence of selectivity in the adhesion mechanism itself?

The simplest possible assumption capable of accounting for type-specific differences in the strengths of adhesions between cells is the assumption that adhesive sites of a single kind are scattered more abundantly on the surface of one type of cell than on the surface of another. W, the work of adhesion between two cells, would then be directly proportional to the number of adhesive sites which are apposed, per unit of area, at the junction between the two cells. What would be the adhesive relationships which would derive from the operation of this simplest of systems?

If the frequency of adhesive sites per unit area on the surfaces of cells a and b is designated f_a and f_b, respectively, the probability of apposition of sites in the cell pairs a-a, b-b, and a-b is given by $(f_a)^2$, $(f_b)^2$, and $(f_a)(f_b)$ for the respective cases. Introducing the proportionality constant k, we may write the equations

$$W_a = k (f_a)^2 \qquad (7)$$

$$W_b = k (f_b)^2 \qquad (8)$$

$$W_{ab} = k (f_a)(f_b) \qquad (9)$$

Following the convention that $W_a \geqq W_b$, we obtain

$$f_a \geqq f_b \qquad (10)$$

Multiplying both sides of relation 10 by the value f_a-f_b and rearranging, we obtain

$$\frac{(f_a)^2 + (f_b)^2}{2} \geqq (f_a)(f_b) \qquad (11)$$

Multiplying both sides of relation 10 by the value f_b, we obtain

$$(f_a)(f_b) \geqq (f_b)^2 \qquad (12)$$

Combining relations 11 and 12, we get

$$\frac{(f_a)^2 + (f_b)^2}{2} \geqq (f_a)(f_b) \geqq (f_b)^2 \quad (13)$$

Substituting Eqs. 7–9 in relation 13, we obtain

$$\frac{W_a + W_b}{2} \geqq W_{ab} \geqq W_b \qquad (14)$$

Relation 14, representing the adhesive relationships which would be engendered in this simplest of systems, will be recognized as an expression of the limits represented by relation 4. And the conditions expressed by relation 4 are precisely those which yield, at thermodynamic equilibrium, our case 2—the result most commonly obtained experimentally, in which one phase is totally enveloped by the other. It is not necessary to assume the literal existence of discrete adhesive sites as distinguished from nonadhesive sites among which they are distributed. Relation 14 applies to any case in which the

force between two mutually adhesive (attractive) bodies is proportional to the product of the individual adhesive (attractive) forces. It may be seen from Eqs. 7–9 that the values of W_{ab} generated in this system are given by

$$W_{ab} = \sqrt{W_a} \cdot \sqrt{W_b} \qquad (15)$$

These values are represented by the dotted line in Fig. 2.

This analysis shows, then, that (i) the mutual sorting out of two kinds of cells to reconstitute tissues, one of which encloses the other, and (ii) the spreading of an intact fragment of the one tissue to envelop an intact fragment of the other are precisely the phenomena which are to be expected, in accordance with the principle of minimization of free energy, in the total absence of selectivity in the adhesion mechanism itself. Only quantitative differences in adhesiveness are necessary. The "information" required in the adhesion mechanism is, in such cases, restricted to "more" and "less."

This does not mean, of course, that molecules of different sorts, on the surfaces either of cells of a given kind or of cells of differing kinds, may not in such cases participate directly in the mediation of adhesions. It merely means that whatever the chemical nature of, or diversity among, the adhesives themselves, the quantitative adhesive relationships among the cells which bear them would be expected to approximate, within the limits shown in Fig. 2 (see also *24*), the relationships derived from the simple postulates which have been outlined. In cases in which, at equilibrium, one tissue covers the other incompletely or not at all, it becomes necessary to assume the additional operation of some other factor or factors, such as an ordered distribution of, or qualitative nonidentity among, adhesive sites.

Morphogenesis and Specificity

Thus we return, at the end, to the beginning: Where is the common denominator? What has sorting out to do with normal morphogenesis? Sorting out, after all, is not known to play a major role in morphogenesis. Such a role, however, *is* played by *spreading:* the spreading of one tissue over the surface of another, or—what is the equivalent—the penetration of one tissue into a mass of another. Differences in cellular adhesiveness which may be built into a system of tissues to bring about the spreading of one tissue over another, or the penetration of one tissue into another, would incidentally (and coincidentally) provide all the conditions required, in an artificial mixture of cells, for sorting out to occur, and for its morphological result to imitate the anatomy normally produced by mass tissue movements. The foundation for such a thermodynamic analysis, like much of the empirical groundwork upon which it rests, was laid by Holtfreter (*32*), whose treatment of the subject has been discussed separately (*33*).

Our recognition of the organization which is everywhere present in the living world has played a prominent role in the development of our biological concepts. It is not surprising that apparent meaningfulness or complexity in the design and functioning of organisms should have led us to assign corresponding attributes to the mechanisms governing the functioning and the design. Yet, as knowledge has grown, complex explanations have had a way of succumbing to relatively simpler ones. Thus, overt vitalism is gone from the scene. Organic molecules, it later developed, could be synthesized by the chemist after all. Proteins were not so simple as to preclude the possibility of their functioning as enzymes; nor was DNA, at a later stage, too simple to provide the vast stores of "information" for which the proteins, now recognized to be complex, might have seemed a more fitting receptacle.

While the *adaptedness* brought about through evolution appears complex, the *adaptiveness* which makes evolution possible is born of simplicity. The entire genetic code (and more) is expressible with an alphabet containing only four elements. It would appear that a not inconsiderable amount of the "information" required to produce,

through morphogenetic movement, the anatomy of a body part may be expressed in a code whose sole element is quantity: more versus less. There is, I think, reason to expect that as more realms of biological specificity yield to analysis, their most impressive feature may be the simplicity of the terms in which specificity—information, if you will—can be expressed (*34*).

REFERENCES AND NOTES

1. H. V. Wilson, *J. Exptl. Zool.* **5**, 245 (1907).
2. ——— and J. T. Penney, *ibid.* **56**, 73 (1930).
3. J. S. Huxley, *Phil. Trans. Roy. Soc. London* **B202**, 165 (1911); P. S. Galtsoff, *J. Exptl. Zool.* **42**, 223 (1925); H. V. Brønsted, *Acta Zool. Stockholm* **17**, 75 (1936).
4. R. G. Harrison, *J. Exptl. Zool.* **9**, 787 (1910).
5. P. Weiss, *Growth* **5**, suppl., 163 (1941).
6. J. Holtfreter, *Arch. Exptl. Zellforsch. Gewebezuecht* **23**, 169 (1939).
7. C. Herbst, *Arch. Entwicklungsmech. Organ.* **9**, 424 (1900).
8. J. Holtfreter, *Rev. Can. Biol.* **3**, 220 (1944).
9. A. Moscona, *Exptl. Cell Res.* **3**, 535 (1952).
10. ———and H. Moscona, *J. Anat.* **86**, 287 (1952); A. Moscona, *Proc. Soc. Exptl. Biol. Med.* **92**, 410 (1956); ——— *Proc. Natl. Acad. Sci. U.S.* **43**, 184 (1957).
11. J. P. Trinkaus and P. W. Groves, *ibid.* **41**, 787 (1955).
12. P. L. Townes and J. Holtfreter, *J. Exptl. Zool.* **128**, 53 (1955).
13. P. Weiss and A. C. Taylor, *Proc. Natl. Acad. Sci. U.S.* **46**, 1177 (1960).
14. M. S. Steinberg, *Am. Naturalist* **92**, 65 (1958).
15. P. Weiss, *Intern. Rev. Cytol.* **7**, 391 (1958); L. Weiss, *ibid.* **9**, 187 (1960); P. Weiss, *Exptl. Cell Res. Suppl.* **8**, 260 (1961); B. A. Pethica, *ibid.*, p. 123; R. D. Allen, *ibid.*, p. 17; R. J. Goldacre, *ibid.*, p. 1; M. Abercrombie, *ibid.*, p. 188; ——— and E. J. Ambrose, *Cancer Res.* **22**, 525 (1962).
16. J. Holtfreter, *Arch. Entwicklungsmech. Organ.* **139**, 110 (1939).
17. P. Weiss, *Yale J. Biol. Med.* **19**, 235 (1947).
18. A. Tyler, *Proc. Natl. Acad. Sci. U.S.* **32**, 195 (1946); P. Weiss, *Quart. Rev. Biol.* **25**, 177 (1950).
19. R. L. DeHaan, in *The Chemical Basis of Development*, W. D. McElroy and B. Glass, Eds. (Johns Hopkins Press, Baltimore, 1958), p. 339.
20. M. S. Steinberg, in *Biological Interactions in Normal and Neoplastic Growth*, M. J.

Brennan and W. L. Simpson, Eds. (Little, Brown, Boston, 1962), p. 127.

21. A. S. G. Curtis, *Am. Naturalist* **94**, 37 (1960); *Exptl. Cell Res. Suppl.* **8**, 107 (1961); *Biol. Rev. Cambridge Phil. Soc.* **37**, 82 (1962); *Nature* **196**, 245 (1962).
22. L. Weiss, *J. Theoret. Biol.* **2**, 236 (1962).
23. A. Stefanelli, A. M. Zacchei, V. Ceccherini, *Acta Embryol. Morphol. Exptl.* **4**, 47 (1961).
24. Mr. Herbert Phillips, a graduate student in our Thomas C. Jenkins Department of Biophysics, has performed calculations which show that when the surface of phase a is convex, the value of W_{ab} demarcating case 2 from case 3 varies from W_b to $2/3\ W_b$ as the volume ratio V_b/V_a varies from 0 to ∞. The general nature of the results remains unaffected when this refinement is made. The applicability of Young's equation, however, becomes subject to certain new boundary conditions.
25. J. T. Davies and E. K. Rideal, *Interfacial Phenomena* (Academic Press, New York, 1961), pp. 19–23, 34–36.
26. R. E. Collins and C. E. Cooke, Jr., *Trans. Faraday Soc.* **55**, 1602 (1959).
27. M. S. Steinberg, *Science* **137**, 762 (1962).
28. ———, *Proc. Natl. Acad. Sci. U.S.* **48**, 1577 (1962).
29. J. P. Trinkaus, *Colloq. Intern. Centre Natl. Rech. Sci. Paris* **101**, 209 (1961).
30. M. S. Steinberg, *Proc. Natl. Acad. Sci. U.S.* **48**, 1769 (1962).
31. ———, in preparation.
32. J. Holtfreter, *J. Exptl. Zool.* **94**, 261 (1943).
33. M. S. Steinberg, in *Cellular Membranes in Development*, M. Locke, Ed. (Academic Press, New York, in press).
34. I am indebted to Professor Michael Abercrombie for his penetrating discussions. The original work described here has been supported by grants from the National Science Foundation.

Mechanism of Tissue Reconstruction by Dissociated Cells, II: Time-Course of Events

MALCOLM S. STEINBERG

Abstract. The details of the process by which cells sort out and reconstruct tissues within aggregates containing two kinds of tissue cells have been correctly predicted from considerations of the kinetic and adhesive properties of such cells. The requisite properties are discreteness, motility, and differential mutual adhesiveness among the types of cells present.

Organs or regions of the body of vertebrate embryos may be dissociated into their component cells, which are then capable of re-aggregating and sorting out to reconstruct semblances of the original structure *(1, 2)*. In these autosynthetic structures the reconstituted tissues are deployed in their normal mutual histological relationships. Such organization usually involves the formation of discrete inner and outer tissues.

Reprinted from *Science*, **137**, No. 3532, 762–763 (September 7, 1962).

In a previous paper *(3)* it was shown that individual cells of the prospective internal tissue do not migrate in a directed fashion toward the center of an aggregate. There did appear to be selection against the residence of such cells at the very surface, however. It was concluded that sorting out must proceed in a manner analogous to that in which a dispersion of mutually immiscible liquids "breaks." In such a dispersion the liquid of lower surface tension (that is, lower molecular cohesiveness or mutual attraction) quickly occupies the surface of the liquid body, during and after which the droplets of the liquid of higher surface tension progressively coalesce to produce a decreasing number of increasingly large islands in the interior. Thus external (continuous) and internal (discontinuous) phases are established. The behavior of such a system is due to its possession of three properties: (i) the two phases are composed of units which are discrete; (ii) the units are mobile; (iii) the different kinds of units are differentially cohesive and adhesive. The first two of these properties are of course known to be characteristic of most cells; but differential mutual adhesiveness, while known for certain kinds of cells, is not established as of general applicability. If sorting-out indeed depends upon differential mutual adhesiveness among the cells in a mixed population, the time-course of events which characterize the process must conform with that given above with reference to dispersions.

Figure 1 shows the sequence of events in the sorting out of chick embryonic heart cells from chick embryonic retinal cells. By virtue of a staining reaction for glycogen (*4*), which they alone contain, the heart cells, derived from 5-day embryos, are distinguishable from the retinal cells, derived from 7-day embryos. Techniques are described elsewhere (*3*). The first event in sorting out is the withdrawal of heart cells from the surfaces of the aggregates. Accompanying this is an initial clustering of heart cells in innumerable foci throughout the interior of each aggregate. These heart foci continue to encounter and fuse with one another, progressively building up one or more coherent, internal masses of heart tissue, the number of which reflects the proportion of heart cells in the population. Townes and Holtfreter have previously described the same sequence of events with amphibian neurula chordamesoderm and endoderm (*2*).

An alternative explanation of the sorting-out phenomenon has been advanced by Curtis (*5*), who suggests that cells of different types undergo certain surface changes at different times after their dissociation. These changes would be such that cells which had experienced them would be trapped by contact either with the surface of an aggregate or with other cells already so trapped. Thus cells of the first type to experience the change would be trapped initially at the surface and then in sequential layers beneath it, leaving those of the type which experiences the change later to be trapped in the center of the aggregate. The operation of this mechanism would produce a herding of the cells of the potentially internal phase, in a centripetal wave, pro-

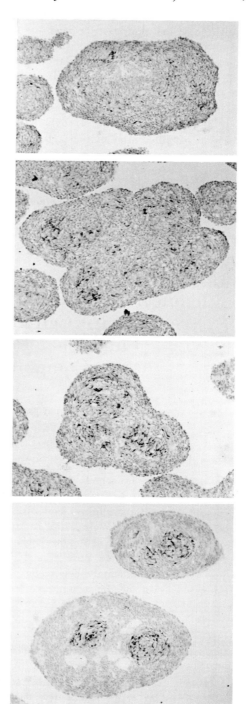

Fig. 1. Sections through aggregates containing chick embryonic heart (darkly stained) and retinal cells fixed at (top to bottom) 17, 24, 31, and 66 hours of incubation at 37°C, showing the process of sorting out (× 127).

gressively deeper into the aggregates until completion of the separation between the two phases. The actual process of sorting out, as observed, in fact bears no resemblance to that predicted by the "timing" hypothesis.

In the demonstrated absence of directed migration or of a "timing" mechanism, the events described here point strongly toward the action of differential mutual cellular adhesiveness which, acting in a system the units of which are both motile and discrete, is by itself capable of bringing about a separation of the phases in the precise manner and mutual orientation which have been observed. Heart cells must cohere more strongly than

retinal cells. The implications with respect to the mechanisms of normal histo- and organogenesis are clear (6).

REFERENCES AND NOTES

1. A. Moscona and H. Moscona, *J. Anat.* **86**, 287 (1952); P. Weiss and R. James, *Exptl. Cell Res. Suppl.* **3**, 381 (1955).
2. P. L. Townes and J. Holtfreter, *J. Exptl. Zool.* **128**, 53 (1955).
3. M. S. Steinberg, *Proc. Natl. Acad. Sci. U.S.* **48**, 1577 (1962).
4. D. Bulmer, *Stain Technol.* **34**, 95 (1959).
5. A. S. G. Curtis, *Am. Naturalist* **94**, 37 (1960); *Exptl. Cell Res. Suppl.* **8**, 107 (1961); *Biol. Rev. Cambridge Phil. Soc.* **37**, 82 (1962).
6. This work was supported by grant G-21466 from the National Science Foundation.

Chemical Dissolution and *in Vitro* Reconstruction of Sponge Cell Adhesions: Isolation and Functional Demonstration of the Components Involved[1]

TOM HUMPHREYS[2]

INTRODUCTION

The mechanisms by which the individual cells of multicellular organisms are held in their various specific groupings and ordered arrays are not known (Weiss, 1958). Many aspects of this selective cell adhesion have been strikingly revealed by numerous studies dealing with developmental phenomena. Cell adhesion is species specific in aggregation of

Reprinted from *Developmental Biology*, **8**, No. 1, 27–47 (August 1963). Copyright © 1963 by Academic Press Inc.

[1] This work was submitted in partial fulfillment of the requirements for the degree of Doctor of Philosophy in the Department of Zoology, The University of Chicago, Dr. A. A. Moscona, thesis advisor. It was supported by grants C-4272 from the National Cancer Institute, U. S. P. H. S., and from the Dr. Wallace C. and Clara A. Abbott Fund of the University of Chicago to Dr A. A. Moscona.

[2] During the course of this study the author held tenures of a National Science Foundation Predoctoral Fellowship and The Morris Miller Wells Fellowship of the General Biological Supply House.

dissociated sponge cells (Wilson, 1910; Galtsoff, 1923) and individual slime mold amebas (Raper and Thom, 1941; Bonner and Adams, 1958); and tissue specific in aggregation of dissociated cells from vertebrate embryos (Townes and Holtfreter, 1955; Moscona, 1957). Sorting of aggregating cells (Huxley, 1911; Galtsoff, 1925b; Moscona, 1952, 1956, 1957), morphogenetic movements during normal development (Swift, 1914; DuShane, 1943; Weiss and Andres, 1952), tissue architecture (Weiss and Moscona, 1959), and perhaps even tumor metastasis (Willis, 1952) may be directed by selective cell adhesion.

Although selective cell adhesion has been well documented and has evoked much interest (Moscona, 1960; DeHaan, 1958; Weiss, 1958; Rinaldini, 1958; L. Weiss, 1960; and others), the fundamental question of the general morphological and chemical nature of the cell adhesion is itself unclear. Present views suggest five basically different models: (1)

divalent cation stabilization of an intercellular cement (Ringer, 1890; Herbst, 1900; Gray, 1926; Chambers and Chambers, 1961); (2) bonding between sterically complementary surface groups (Tyler, 1947; Weiss, 1947); (3) calcium bridge bonding between cell surfaces (Coman, 1954; Steinberg, 1958); (4) long-range bonding between cell membranes (Curtis, 1960, 1962); and (5) function of specific cell products acting at the cell surface (Moscona, 1960, 1961b, 1962).

These proposed models have unique features which might be distinguished experimentally by appropriate tests. An aggregating system involving simple, defined and controllable techniques was sought. Dissociated sponge cells, the classical material for the study of cell aggregation (Wilson, 1907, 1910), seemed highly suitable, since they aggregate well in simple, defined salt solutions (Galtsoff, 1925a; deLaubenfels, 1932).

Previous studies on aggregation of dissociated sponge cells employed mechanical dissociation and self-aggregation techniques which are unsuitable for an analysis of the physical and chemical structure of a cell adhesion. The need to eliminate dependence on cell migration had already been recognized and met for embryonic vertebrate cells (Moscona, 1960, 1961a) and for slime mold amebas (Gerisch, 1959, 1960). The aggregating cells were maintained in suspension and brought randomly into contact by agitating the culture. Rotation-mediated aggregation (Moscona, 1961a) was easily adaptable for the study of sponge adhesion (Humphreys et al., 1960b). Also a chemical procedure for dissociation which would break the intermolecular bonds involved in the cell adhesion, but which would not destroy macromolecules that might be involved, was sought. Dissociation by removal of divalent cations was the most promising (Steinberg, 1958), although previous reports discounted the role of divalent cations in sponge cell adhesion (Agrell, 1951; Spiegel, 1954a). Exploratory experiments showed that sponge tissue could be dissociated in calcium- and magnesium-free sea water. Thus a method using cold calcium- and magnesium-free sea water was developed

which produced suspensions of single, viable cells capable of aggregation and development into sponges (Humphreys et al., 1960a). This method of dissociation, in fact, did preserve the functional integrity of the molecules involved and permitted the separation of the cell adhesion into three components: the cell surface (represented by whole cells), divalent cations, and an organic factor. When placed back together *in vitro* these three components would spontaneously reassemble to reform apparently normal cell adhesions (Humphreys, 1962).

MATERIALS AND METHODS

Sponges were collected near Woods Hole during the summer and fall and maintained in running sea water. Only specimens which had been in the laboratory less than 4 days were used, since cultures of older material contained much cellular debris which interfered with aggregation. Four species of monaxonic sponges, *Microciona prolifera* (referred to as *M*), *Haliclona occulata* (*H*), *Halichondria panicea* (*D*), and *Cliona celata* (*C*), were utilized. The work was conducted mainly on *Microciona*, and the descriptions refer only to this species unless stated otherwise.

The compositions of the artificial sea water used in these experiments are listed in Table 1.

For chemical dissociation of *M*, 1 gm of blotted tissue free of foreign material was immersed in 80 ml calcium- and magnesium-free artificial sea water at pH 7.2 (CWF-SW, see Table 1), at 0°C, cut into 3 mm³ fragments, and soaked for 30 minutes. These fragments were dissociated by pressing through no. 25 standard quality bolting cloth (Wilson, 1907) into a second 80 ml of cold CMF-SW. The concentration of the resulting suspension of cell clumps and single cells, estimated by hemocytometer counts, ranged between 10 and 40 × 10⁶ cells per milliliter depending on the time of year. The suspension was sedimented for 2 minutes at 2000 rpm, and the cells were resuspended in fresh, cold CMF-SW at a concentration of 20 × 10⁶ cells per milliliter. The suspension was agitated for 6–9 hours in order to complete dis-

TABLE 1.   Composition of artificial and modified sea waters

| | Salt (Grams per Liter Glass-Distilled Water) | | | | | | | |
Type of Sea Water	NaCl	Na_2SO_4	KCl	$CaCl_2$	$MgCl_2$ $6H_2O$	$SrCl_2$ $6H_2O$	$MgSO_4$ $7H_2O$	$NaHCO_3$
MBL-SW	24.7	—	0.7	1.0	4.7	—	6.3	0.18
CMF-SW	27.0	1.0	0.8	—	—	—	—	0.18
Ca- and Mg-free MBL-SW	24.7	—	0.7	—	—	—	—	0.18
Ca-substituted MBL-SW	24.7	—	0.7	6.8	—	—	—	0.18
Mg-substituted MBL-SW	24.7	—	0.7	—	12.4	—	—	0.18
Sr-substituted MBL-SW	24.7	—	0.7	—	—	16.3	—	0.18
Ca- and Mg-substituted MBL-SW	24.7	—	0.7	3.4	6.2	—	—	0.18
Ca- and Sr-substituted MBL-SW	24.7	—	0.7	3.4	—	8.2	—	0.18
Mg- and Sr-substituted MBL-SW	24.7	—	0.7	—	6.2	8.2	—	0.18

sociation and to maintain the cells in suspension. The loose cell clusters remaining after this treatment were easily disrupted by flushing the suspension through a Pasteur pipette with a 1-mm orifice. The single cells were gently sedimented and resuspended in about 1.5 ml cold Marine Biological Laboratory formula artificial sea water (MBL-SW, see Table 1) or in experimental medium by several more pipettings. The cell concentration was determined again, and the suspension diluted as required and immediately placed in the aggregation vessels.

Mechanically dissociated cells were obtained by pressing 1 gm sponge tissue through bolting cloth directly into 80 ml sea water (Wilson, 1907) at 0°C.

The following variations were required for dissociation of the other species; use of 2 gm *H*, *D*, and *C* tissue, concentration of *D* and *C* cells to 40×10^6 per milliliter for the 6- to 9-hour treatment in cold CMF-SW and doubling sedimentation time for *D* and *C* cells.

Standard conditions for rotation-mediated aggregation (Moscona, 1961a) were 30×10^6 *M* cells, 15×10^6 *H* cells, or 40×10^6 *D* or *C* cells suspended in 3 ml sea water in 25-ml Erlenmeyer flasks rotated at 80 rpm on a gyratory shaker with a three-quarter inch diameter of rotation. The experiments on effects of cell

concentration, frequency of rotation, and the other early tests of sponge aggregation were carried out at room temperature (usually 25° C); all other variables besides the one being tested were maintained at the standard values. In all other experiments the shakers were maintained at 22° ± 0.5° or 5° ± 1° as indicated. For interspecific mixtures, one-half the usual number of cells from each species was used.

For preparation of the organic factor, 5 gm of blotted *M* tissue or 20 gm of *H* tissue, were placed in 150 ml cold CMF-SW, cut into 1-cm pieces, and soaked for 10 minutes each in four changes of 150 ml CMF-SW at 0°. The tissue was collected and pressed through no. 14 standard quality bolting cloth into 50 ml cold CMF-SW. The resulting suspension was shaken gently for 4 hours at 0°C. It was then centrifuged at 0°C in a Servall SS-1 angle-head centrifuge for 10 minutes at 7500 rpm. The supernatant, which was light red (*M*) or blue (*H*) and slightly turbid, was decanted from the large cellular pellet and recentrifuged at 11,000 rpm for 90 minutes at 0°C. The clear, very slightly colored supernatant was decanted, and its activity was stabilized by adding one part 18.5 m*M* $CaCl_2$ solution to 9 parts of the factor solution.

Reconstruction of adhesions was accomplished by mixing the factor solution 1:1 with a suspension of chemically dissociated cells in MBL-SW and subjecting the mixture to rotation-mediated aggregation at 5°C.

EVALUATION OF METHODS AND GENERAL ASPECTS OF SPONGE AGGREGATION

Chemical Dissociation

Sponge tissue was chemically dissociated into single, viable cells (Fig. 1) by the described procedure for removal of divalent cations. The process of soaking the tissue in CMF-SW for only 30 minutes before mechanically disrupting the tissue loosened the cells considerably but did not yet free the numerous spicules, which upon longer treatment would also come out of the collagenous matrix. By dissociating at 5°, adjusting the cell concentration to 20×10^6 cells per milliliter, and shaking the suspension during dissociation, cell damage was minimized to the extent that no detectable loss of cells occurred between final and initial determinations and little cellular debris appeared in the cultures.

In order to establish that dissociation was due to the removal of calcium and magnesium, various permutations of the variables (temperature, pH, medium changes, ionic composition, mechanical dispersal, etc.) were tested. In all the cases the cells dissociated only when calcium and magnesium were removed. The removal of these ions is therefore clearly the effective parameter of the dissociation procedure.

The dissociation procedure was developed for *Microciona,* but it also proved effective and satisfactory for dissociation of *Haliclona, Halichondria,* and *Cliona* with the small changes indicated in the methods section. Chemically dissociated cells of all four of these species self-aggregated on glass at room temperature (Wilson, 1910) like mechanically dissociated cells of their species.

Rotation-Mediated Aggregation

Chemically dissociated cells placed in sea water in rotating flasks began to adhere im-

mediately at 22°. Within 15 minutes many cells were in small irregular clusters (Fig. 2a). Examination of living aggregates and of histological sections showed that they consisted of randomly mixed, closely apposed, round cells (Fig. 3a). By 30 minutes the aggregates had become larger through further accretion of free cells and fusion of the small clusters (Fig. 2b). Subsequently, the clusters rounded up and the cells moved into closer association. After about 1 hour all cells capable of aggregating had been incorporated into cell masses (Fig. 2c), and between 3 and 6 hours the aggregates attained final size. At 12 hours the aggregates resembled 3-hour aggregates (Fig. 3b) histologically except that a layer of flattened cells had appeared on the surfaces of the aggregates which were thus round and smooth. Thereafter the aggregates remained much the same for many hours. At this time there were about 2000 spherical, compact, smooth aggregates averaging about 0.14 mm in diameter in each flask (Fig. 2d). Occasionally, for unknown reasons, a ring of cells formed on the flask at the air-liquid interphase.

Aggregates were maintained in rotating flasks, the sea water being changed every 48 hours for over 2 months. After 10–14 days under these conditions translucent, canal-like areas could be seen in some aggregates. In histological sections some of the aggregates fixed on the 19th day showed canal-like structures, newly formed spicules, and spongin. These results indicated that the culture conditions were satisfactory for *M* tissue. Cells or aggregates of all other species of sponges tested do not survive more than a few days under any conditions tested.

Variables in Rotation-Mediated Aggregation

The standard conditions for aggregation were established by tests to determine the effects of frequency of rotation, cell concentration, and temperature.

Frequency of Rotation. Suspended, compact sponge aggregates formed over a range of 70–110 rpm; at the higher frequencies there

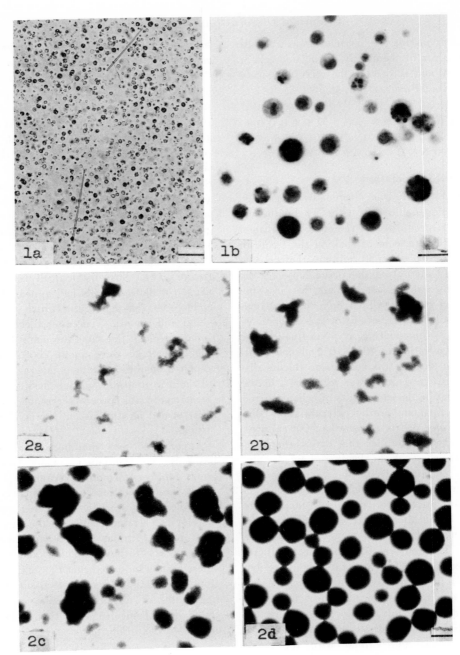

Fig. 1. Chemically dissociated cells. (a) Living preparation at low power. Line indicates 50μ. (b) Fixed and stained. Note wide range in cell size. Line indicates 10μ.
Fig. 2. Time sequence of rotation mediated aggregation of chemically dissociated sponge cells: (a) 15 minutes, (b) 30 minutes, (c) 1 hour, (d) 12 hours. Ragged aggregates quickly form, and these round up and become smooth. Line indicates 200μ.

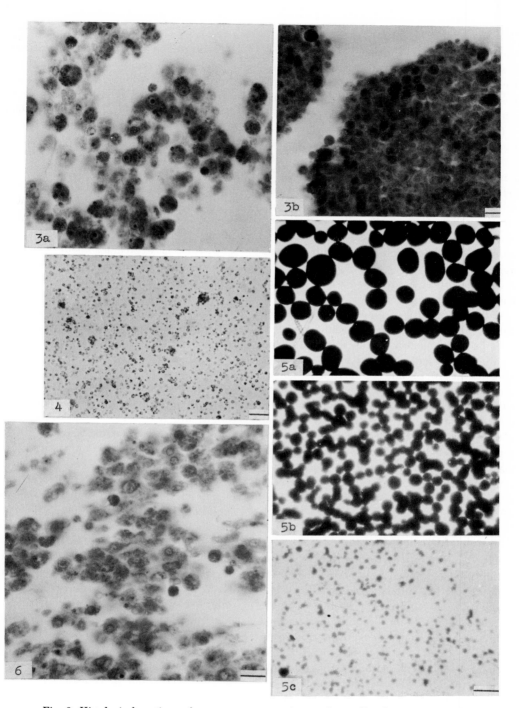

Fig. 3. Histological sections of sponge aggregates in rotation-mediated aggregation. At (a) 15 minutes, (b) 3 hours. The cells at first adhere over small areas and then move closely together. Line indicates 10μ. Fig. 4. Sample of single cells and small clumps from a culture at 5°C for 24 hours. Line indicates 50μ. Fig. 5. Aggregates formed when (a) calcium, (b) magnesium, or (c) strontium is substituted for the divalent cations of sea water. Line indicates 200μ. Fig. 6. Histological section of aggregate from reconstruction procedure at 5°C. The cells are in the association typical of early stages of aggregation at 22°C. Line indicates 10μ.

was much cellular damage. As with vertebrate cells, the size of aggregates varied with frequency (Moscona, 1961a). The most gentle frequency which maintained all cells in suspension (80 rpm) was chosen.

Cell Concentration. When cell concentration was varied, the final size of aggregates increased with concentration asymptotically to a maximum over the range of 0.17 to 17×10^6 cells per milliliter. The meaning of these cell concentration effects is unknown. The cell concentration of 10×10^6 cells per milliliter was chosen, since it was at a point where variation in cell concentration minimally affected aggregate size.

Temperature. Aggregation was studied at temperatures ranging from 5°C to 30°C. At 5°C the chemically dissociated cells did not adhere appreciably (Fig. 4) although they were brought together by the agitation of the medium. They adhered into many small aggregates at 10°C, and optimal aggregation occurred at 18–25°C. Cells which failed to adhere at 5°C would aggregate normally if the temperature was raised to the optimum within 6 hours. At 30°C the cells were adversely affected and loose and fuzzy cell masses resulted. Like vertebrate cells (Moscona 1961a), the aggregation of sponge cells is inhibited by suboptimal temperature (Galtsoff, 1925a).

The Role of Divalent Cations

The divalent cation requirement for aggregation was determined by studying the effects of a number of artificial, modified sea waters (Table 1) substituted for MBL-SW in the standard aggregation procedure. As described before, round, compact aggregates form in MBL-SW at 25°. If CMF-SW or MBL-SW without its divalent cationic salts was substituted for MBL-SW, the cells remained almost completely separate and did not adhere although brought together by agitation of the medium. These results, along with the results of dissociation, indicate that sponge cells are unable to adhere in the absence of calcium and magnesium, or possibly, divalent cations in general.

The specificity of this divalent cationic requirement was tested by using modifications of MBL-SW in which the divalent cationic salts were replaced by combinations of calcium, magnesium, or strontium chloride (Table 1). Normal aggregates formed when the divalent cations of MBL-SW were substituted with (1) $CaCl_2$ alone, (2) equimolar quantities of $CaCl_2$ and $MgCl_2$, or (3) equimolar quantities of $CaCl_2$ and $SrCl_2$. Figure 5a shows aggregates formed in MBL-SW with calcium only. When $MgCl_2$ or equimolar quantities of $MgCl_2$ and $SrCl_2$ were substituted, compact aggregates about one-half normal size were formed (Fig. 5b). Only very small, loose cell clusters formed with strontium alone (Fig. 5c). Other multivalent ions were not tested because normal aggregation can occur without them and because these results establish a preferential requirement for calcium.

General Aspects of Sponge Cell Adhesion

In the light of these findings that divalent cations are necessary for sponge cell adhesion the observations of Spiegel (1954a,b) should be reinterpreted. Confirming previous observations (Galtsoff, 1925a), Spiegel found that dissociated *M* sponge cells failed to aggregate in isotonic NaCl or KCl or in EDTA containing sea water. However, when cells maintained in these solutions for 24 hours were swirled, instantaneous clumping occurred. This clumping was considered to be the beginning of true aggregation and thus suggested that divalent cations were required only for sponge cell migration, not for cell adhesion. With the present evidence, however, this clumping can no longer be equated with normal aggregation, particularly since it is possible that many of these cells did not survive; according to Galtsoff (1925a) and in our experience, many do not participate in aggregation when returned to sea water.

The divalent cationic requirement for cell adhesion appeared to be totally satisfied by calcium since normal aggregates formed when it was the only divalent cation present. The role of magnesium in producing smaller aggregates is not clear; it may play a unique role in cell adhesion or it may only partially substitute for calcium. Sponge cells aggregating on a stationary surface require both calcium and magnesium (Galtsoff, 1925a; deLaubenfels, 1932). When each was tested alone, magnesium allowed far more aggregation than calcium. Galtsoff therefore concluded that magnesium was probably specifically necessary for cell migration and both calcium and magnesium were important for cell adhesion. These results indicate clearly that both these divalent cations have functions in cell aggregation which cannot be fulfilled by strontium or by each other. It is possible that magnesium is required for cell migration and calcium for cell adhesion; but in our experiments the small aggregates formed in the presence of magnesium alone appeared to be as firmly cohesive as normal aggregates. A more complete understanding of the specific roles of these two ions must await further analysis.

The chemically dissociated cells did not adhere at low temperatures even in the presence of divalent cations. Similar effects of low temperature on self-aggregation of mechanically dissociated cells was thought to be due to the failure of cells to meet because cell migration was inhibited (Galtsoff, 1925a). Since in rotation-mediated aggregation the cells are brought together, the failure of the chemically dissociated cells to aggregate must evidently be due to their lack of adhesiveness. Low temperatures prevent the aggregation of proteolytically dissociated embryonic vertebrate cells. This has been interpreted as being the inability of the cells to regenerate cell surface products because of inhibition of metabolic activities (Moscona, 1961b). The results with chemically dissociated sponge cells can also be so interpreted. Although the chemical dissociation of the sponge cells did not involve treatments that would be expected to destroy macromolecules, the assumption that the surface of these nonadhering cells was indeed functionally intact requires further proof before any conclusions concerning the nature of the cell adhesion can be supported.

In Vitro Reconstruction of Sponge Cell Adhesions

Adhesion of Mechanically Dissociated Cells at Low Temperatures

To find out whether cells would adhere at low temperatures if all components of the cell adhesion were present, the aggregation of mechanically dissociated cells at 5° was studied, since it seemed likely that the mechanical dissociation would not destroy or remove any macromolecule involved in adhesion. It was found, indeed, that mechanically dissociated cells adhered very rapidly in the rotating flask at 5°C and formed compact 0.1- to 0.2-mm aggregates. By their rough outlines and histological appearance they resembled early stages of aggregates produced at 22°C. At 5° they would not progress beyond this stage; but, if the temperature was raised, they quickly rounded up and continued to develop. This block to development was probably due to the low temperature inhibition of cell movement (Galtsoff, 1925a), which prevented the randomly adhering cells from proceeding with reorganization until the temperature was raised. It appeared that mechanically dissociated cells retained some factors which had been lost by the chemically dissociated cells.

Reconstruction of Cell Adhesions after Chemical Dissociation

The inability of chemically dissociated cells to adhere at 5° even though calcium had been added back was strikingly abolished if the cell-free supernatants from chemical dissociation were also added; the cells adhered into compact aggregates of randomly mixed cells resembling closely those of mechanically dissociated cells at 5°. At 5°C they remained at this stage for days. If the temperature was raised within 3 days they rounded up and proceeded to develop. It appeared that the supernatants from chemical dissociation contained the missing factor which had been dissolved from the cells by the removal of divalent cations.

Divalent Cation Requirement

In the presence of the factor and divalent cations, chemically dissociated cells adhered into one large aggregate at 5°C. With only the factor and no divalent cations, they did not adhere at all. The specificity of this cation requirement was examined, and calcium and magnesium were found equally effective, but strontium was completely ineffective. Just as divalent cations were necessary for aggregation, they were also required for the development of cell adhesions in the presence of the factor. It appears then that during dissociation the cell adhesion has been separated into three components; the cell surface, divalent cations, and an organic factor; which when placed back together *in vitro* spontaneously reassemble to form new cell adhesions.

Quantitative Assay of the Active Factor

In order to obtain supernatants with a higher concentration of the active factor, a modified dissociation procedure was adopted for extraction of the material (see Methods section). This yielded a very active solution. When it was tested in the reconstruction procedure at 5°, all the cells in the flask adhered into one large, rough, cylindrical aggregate about 1.5 mm in diameter and 5–6 mm long (Fig. 7a). This large aggregate consisted of smaller compact cell masses held loosely together by strands of cells. There were numerous unoccupied areas between (Fig. 6). Firm round clots and mucous strings of amorphous material with scattered cells also appeared at this high concentration. As the factor was diluted the aggregates became smaller (Fig. 7b) and the amorphous material did not develop. At the lowest effective concentration many rough, compact aggregates about 0.1 and 2.0 mm in diameter were formed (Fig. 7c). At greater dilutions the cells behaved as if they were in MBL-SW alone (Fig. 7d). This distinct end point provided a possibility of quantitating the activity of a preparation. The least effective concentration of factor was therefore defined as one unit activity per milliliter. The number of units per milliliter in a particular preparation was equal to the dilution required to reach the threshold minimal activity. Most preparations of crude factor had an activity of 128 units/ml. The activity of the solution was rapidly lost unless calcium was added to a concentration of 1.8 mM.

Source of the Active Factor

Three experiments were done to determine the source of the material: (1) a mock extraction of the factor was conducted using MBL-SW rather than CMF-SW; (2) sponge tissue was homogenized in MBL-SW; and (3) chemically dissociated cells were homogenized in CMF-SW. Examination of the homogenized cells showed that a majority were disrupted. None of the supernatants obtained from the extractions were active; none caused cell adhesion.

Species Specificity

Species specificity of aggregation in sponges has been repeatedly described (Wilson, 1910; Galtsoff, 1923; deLaubenfels, 1932). The existence of this specificity provided a very useful and important possibility of demonstrating the specificity of the reactions involved in reassembly of the cell adhesion.

Rotation-Mediated Aggregation of Haliclona. Rotation-mediated aggregation of a second species, *Haliclona occulata* (*H*), was studied. Chemically dissociated *H* cells aggregated rapidly at 22°C to form compact, round 0.1- to 0.2-mm aggregates (Fig. 8a). The aggregation process for *H* was very much like that for *M* cells at 22° except that the aggregates were short lived. At 5° much smaller, 0.05 mm, round aggregates formed from chemically dissociated *H* cells (Fig. 8b). Mechanically dissociated cells at 5° formed aggregates with sizes intermediate between 5° and 22° *H* aggregates.

Haliclona Factor. Supernatants from the extraction procedure applied to *H* tissue with the slight modifications specified in the Methods section caused chemically dissociated *H* cells to adhere into round aggregates about 0.3 mm in diameter at 5° (Fig. 9). This is about 200 times the cell mass of aggregates

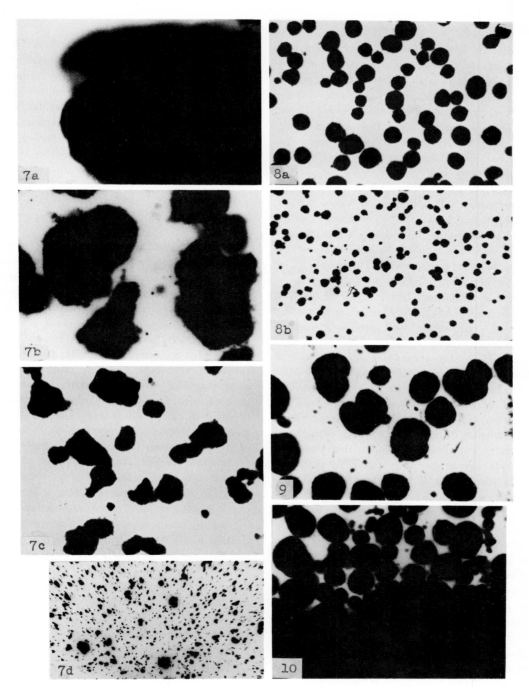

Fig. 7. Aggregates from reconstruction procedure at 5°C. (a) End of cylindrical aggregate formed at very high concentrations of factor. (b) Aggregates at intermediate concentration. (c) Aggregates at lowest effective concentration. (d) Cell adhesion which occurs below effective concentration. Fig. 8. *Haliclona* aggregates. (a) At 22°C, (b) at 5°C. Fig. 9. *Haliclona* aggregates formed at 5°C with *Haliclona* factor. Fig. 10. Separate aggregates formed when *Microciona* cells and factor and *Haliclona* cells and factor are intermixed in one aggregation flask. The large aggregate below is *Microciona*; the round ones above are *Haliclona*. Line indicates 200μ in Figs. 7–10.

formed in MBL-SW at 5°. There was a tenuous halo of clear amorphous material around each aggregate, and numerous firm, round clots with scattered small aggregates in the culture. Serial dilution of the *H* crude factor resulted in smaller aggregates until at about $\frac{1}{32}$ the concentration no effect could be detected. The *H* factor required divalent cations.

Interspecific Mixtures in Rotation-Mediated Aggregation.   *M* is bright red-orange, and *H* is bluish purple. This color difference can be used to determine the species of small aggregates and even single cells of the larger cell types in living preparations. The specificity of cell adhesion in mixtures of *M* and *H* cells was thus examined. Intermingled chemically dissociated *M* cells and *H* cells aggregated at 22° only with their own species. Within 15 minutes any aggregate observed was distinctly colored like one or the other species. Cells of the one species were rarely found associated with aggregates of the opposite species. Thus in these mixed suspensions, aggregated by rotation, cells of each species aggregated independently of the other; the final size of aggregates was generally smaller than for each species separately. Aggregation of mechanically dissociated *H* and *M* cells at 5° was equally specific.

Specificity of the Active Factor.   When *M* factor was added to chemically dissociated *H* cells at 5° or *H* factor was added to chemically dissociated *M* cells at 5°, they had no effect; the cells of both species behaved as if they were in plain MBL-SW. *M* factor added to a mixture of *M* cells and *H* cells caused the *M* cells to adhere into a large aggregate, while the *H* cells behaved as if they were in plain MBL-SW at 5°. *H* factor tested on a mixture of cells from the two species caused the *H* cells to form large 0.3-mm aggregates while the *M* cells behaved as if they were in MBL-SW. Finally, if *M* factor and *H* factor were added to a mixture of *M* cells and *H* cells, the cells from each species adhered into completely separate aggregates. After 15 minutes the cells in such a mixture were in large, rather loose but separate aggregates. The cells continued to adhere separately and finally formed aggregates exactly as they would if each species had been in a separate flask (Fig. 10). The failure of any of these preparations to develop interspecific adhesions demonstrated that the spontaneous reassembly of the cell adhesions involved specific bonds. This specificity evidently lies in the reactions between the cell surface and the factor of the other species would have resulted in interspecific adhesions in the bispecific cell mixtures.

DISCUSSION

The aggregation resulting upon recombination of cells, factors, and divalent cations could be due either to normal cell adhesions or to some nonfunctional agglutination of cells. Various evidence supports the conclusion that the separated components are involved normally in cell adhesion and that the reassembled adhesions are similar to normal, functional adhesions. The aggregates resemble early stages of normal aggregation and can proceed with development if the temperature is raised to 22°. Divalent cations are required as in normal sponge cell aggregation. Removal of divalent cations is required to release the factor from the cells, as it is required to dissociate cells. The factor cannot be extracted from the cells by homogenization, indicating that it is not a product of cell destruction during the dissociation procedure. Calcium stabilization of the factor demonstrates that divalent cations may be closely associated with its function. The species specificity of the factor parallels that of normal sponge aggregation and rules out the possibility that its activity is due to a nonfunctional agglutination of cells caused by some general physical or chemical characteristic of the substance such as charge (Schmitt, 1941). These various considerations indicate that the factor represents a dissolved intercellular matrix functioning in cell adhesion by binding the adjacent cell membranes together. This agrees with previously postulated role of cell surface materials in cell aggregation suggested by studies on embryonic cells (Moscona, 1960, 1962).

The factor demonstrated in the reconstruction of sponge cell adhesions fits historical expectations of an intercellular cement (Ringer,

1890; Herbst, 1900; Gray, 1926; and others) ; that is, it reacts with divalent cations to hold cells together. Thus, a model of sponge cell adhesion similar to these early ideas but including certain elaborations necessitated by the present data is supported. Sponge cells appear to be held together by an intercellular material bound to each cell surface *by specific bonds involving divalent cations.* The divalent cations are thought to be involved in the bonds between the material and the cell surface because the factor comes off the cell only when these ions are removed. In this binding the ions apparently do not simply counteract the effects of the negative charge on the cell surface (Schmitt, 1941; Curtis, 1962) but must interact with the intercellular material, since the ions are necessary for maintenance of the factor's functional activity. A possible explanation for their function is that divalent cationic bridges bind the material to the cell surface. The cationic and species specificities demonstrate that the bonds in which these divalent cations might be involved could not be simple electrostatic attractions between charged groups, but rather specific complementary reactions between chemical groups on the cell surface, groups in the material, and the cations. Another possibility is that the divalent cations hold the molecules of the intercellular material in the functional configuration necessary for their specific interaction with the cell surface. The nature of the chemical linkages within the intercellular material itself cannot be deduced from the present data; past ideas that they are cross links of a precipated calcium salt are interpretations which are not critically supported by evidence.

Various other morphological and experimental observations relating to cell adhesion agree with the above model. The importance of divalent cations in cell adhesion has been repeatedly confirmed (Steinberg, 1958). Many observations, such as morphological identification of intercellular materials (Gersh and Catchpole, 1949; Fawcett, 1958) or enzymatic dissociation of cells (Moscona, 1952), have indicated the presence of intercellular materials (Rinaldini, 1958; Moscona, 1960). Cell adhesion is specific in many instances (Wilson, 1910; Galtsoff, 1925a; Holtfreter,

1939; Raper and Thom, 1941; Townes and Holtfreter, 1955; Moscona, 1957). Also, antigenically specific cell surface substances, which may be equivalent to the specific intercellular material of the present studies, have been demonstrated to be important in cell adhesion (Spiegel, 1954a,b; Gregg, 1956; Gregg and Trystad, 1958).

The demonstration of a component other than the cell surface and divalent cations in cell adhesions does not lend support to the models of cell adhesion based on calcium bridges. (Coman, 1954; Steinberg, 1958) and long-range forces (Curtis, 1960). The 100–200 Å electron-lucid separation commonly observed between membranes of adjacent cells viewed with the electron microscope is the main evidence for these theories. However, the interpretation of this electron-lucid area as an empty space (Coman, 1954; Curtis, 1960, 1962) has been questioned (Robertson, 1960) and must be reconsidered with the present experimental demonstration of an intercellular material involved in cell adhesion.

SUMMARY

The purpose of this work was to study the mechanism of cell adhesion using aggregation of dissociated sponge cells as the experimental system.

A method of chemical dissociation was developed for marine sponges using cold calcium- and magnesium-free sea water. The viable, single cells resulting from this dissociation were able to aggregate and develop into functional sponges. Rotation-mediated aggregation was used to study various aspects of the aggregation of sponge cells.

By using these techniques, a specific requirement for the divalent cations calcium and magnesium was established for sponge cell adhesion. Low temperature was found to inhibit adhesion of chemically dissociated cells even when the divalent cations were added back to the cells. Mechanically dissociated cells aggregated rapidly at low temperatures.

This difference was shown to be due to a factor released into the supernatant during chemical dissociation of sponge tissue. When this factor was added back to the chemically dissociated cells along with divalent cations, they adhered rapidly at low temperatures. This factor was species specific, causing adhesion only of cells from the same species.

These results were interpreted to indicate that the sponge cell adhesion was composed of three basic components: the cell surface, divalent cations, and an intercellular material. These components had been separated during chemical dissociation and were capable of spontaneously and species specifically reassembling themselves to reform an apparently normal cell adhesion.

The implications of these results for models of cell adhesion are discussed.

REFERENCES

Agrell, I. (1951). Observations on cell differentiation in sponges. *Arkiv Zool.* **2**, 519–523.

Bonner, J. T., and M. S. Adams (1958). Cell mixtures of different species and strains of cellular slime moulds. *J. Embryol. Exptl. Morphol.* **6**, 346–356.

Chambers, R., and E. L. Chambers (1961). *Explorations into the Nature of the Living Cell.* Harvard Univ. Press, Cambridge, Massachusetts.

Coman, D. R. (1954). Electron microscopy of liver perfused with a chelating agent. *Cancer Res.* **14**, 519–521.

Curtis, A. S. G. (1960). Cell contacts: some physical considerations. *Am. Naturalist* **94**, 37–56.

Curtis, A. S. G. (1962). Cell contact and adhesion. *Biol. Rev. Cambridge Phil. Soc.* **37**, 82–129.

DeHaan, R. L. (1958). Cell migration and morphogenetic movements. *Symp. Chem. Basis Develop. Baltimore, 1958, Johns Hopkins Univ. McCollum-Pratt Inst. Contrib.* **234**, 339–377.

deLaubenfels, M. (1932). Physiology and morphology of Porifera exemplified by *Iotrochota biratulate* Higgin. *Papers Tortugas Lab.* **28**, 37–66.

DuShane, G. P. (1943). The embryology of vertebrate pigment cells. *Quart. Rev. Biol.* **18**, 109–127.

Fawcett, D. W. (1958). Specializations of the cell surface. In *Frontiers in Cytology* (S. L. Palay, ed.), pp. 19–41. Yale Univ. Press, New Haven, Connecticut.

Galtsoff, P. S. (1923). The amoeboid movement of dissociated sponge cells. *Biol. Bull.* **45**, 153–161.

Galtsoff, P. S. (1925a). Regeneration after dissociation (an experimental study on sponges). I. Behavior of dissociated cells of *Microciona prolifera* under normal and abnormal conditions. *J. Exptl. Zool.* **42**, 183–221.

Galtsoff, P. S. (1925b). Regeneration after dissociation (an experimental study on sponges). II. Histogenesis of *Microciona prolifera* Verr. *J. Exptl. Zool.* **42**, 223–251.

Gerisch, A. (1959). Ein Submerskulturverfahren fur entwicklungs-physiologische Untersuchungen an *Dictyostelium discoideum. Naturwissenschaften* **46**, 654.

Gerisch, G. (1960). Zellfunktionen und Zellfunktionswechsel in der Entwicklung von *Dictyostelium discoideum.* I. Zellagglutination und Induction der Fruchtkorperpolarität. *Arch. Entwicklungsmech. Organ.* **152**, 632–654.

Gersh, I., and H. R. Catchpole (1949). The organization of ground substance and basement membranes and its significance in tissue injury, disease, and growth. *Am. J. Anat.* **85**, 457–522.

Gray, J. (1926). The properties of an intercellular matrix and its relation to electrolytes. *Brit. J. Exptl. Biol.* **3**, 167–187.

Gregg, J. H. (1956). Serological investigations of cell adhesion in the slime molds *Dictyostelium discoideum, D. purpureum,* and *Polysphondylium violaceum. J. Gen. Physiol.* **39**, 813–820.

Gregg, J. H., and C. W. Trystad (1958). Surface antigen defects contributing to developmental failure in aggregateless variants of the slime mold, *Dictyostelium discoideum. Exptl. Cell Res.* **15**, 358–369.

Herbst, C. (1900). Ueber das Auseinandergehen von Furchungs und Bewebzellen in kalkfreien Medium. *Arch. Entwicklungsmech. Organ.* **9**, 424–463.

Holtfreter, J. (1939). Gewebaffinität, ein Mittel der embryonal Formbildung. *Arch. Exptl. Zellforsch. Gewebezucht.* **23**, 169–209.

Humphreys, T. (1962). The mechanism of sponge cell adhesions. Thesis, The University of Chicago.

Humphreys, T., S. Humphreys, and A. A. Moscona (1960a). A procedure for obtaining completely dissociated sponge cells. *Biol. Bull.* **119**, 294.

Humphreys, T., S. Humphreys, and A. A. Moscona. (1960b). Rotation-mediated aggregation of dissociated sponge cells. *Biol. Bull.* **119**, 295.

Huxley, J. (1911). Regeneration of Sycon. *Phil. Trans. Roy. Soc. London* **202**, 165–190.

Moscona, A. (1952). Cell suspensions from organ rudiments of chick embryos. *Exptl. Cell Res.* **3**, 535–539.

Moscona, A. (1956). Development of heterotypic combinations of dissociated embryonic chick cells. *Proc. Soc. Exptl. Biol. Med.* **92,** 410–416.

Moscona, A. (1957). The development *in vitro* of chimeric aggregates of dissociated embryonic chick and mouse cells. *Proc. Natl. Acad. Sci., U.S.* **43,** 184–194.

Moscona, A. (1960). Patterns and mechanisms of tissue reconstruction from dissociated cells. *Symp. Soc. Study Develop. Growth* **18,** 45–70.

Moscona, A. (1961a). Rotation-mediated histogenetic aggregation of dissociated cells. A quantifiable approach to cell interactions *in vitro. Exptl. Cell Res.* **22,** 455–475.

Moscona, A. (1961b). Effect of temperature on adhesion to glass and histogenetic cohesion of dissociated cells. *Nature* **190,** 408–409.

Moscona, A. (1962). Analysis of cell recombination in experimental synthesis of tissues *in vitro. J. Cellular Comp. Physiol.* **60,** Suppl. **1,** 65–80.

Raper, K. B., and C. Thom (1941). Interspecific mixtures in the Dictyosteliaceae. *Am. J. Botany* **28,** 69–78.

Rinaldini, L. M. J. (1958). The isolation of living cells from animal tissues. *Intern. Rev. Cytol.* **7,** 587–647.

Ringer, S. (1890). Concerning experiments to test the influence of lime, sodium, and potassium salts on the development of ova and growth of tadpoles. *J. Physiol. (London)* **11,** 79–84.

Robertson, J. D. (1960). The molecular structure and contact relationships of cell membranes. *Progr. Biophys. Biophys. Chem.* **10,** 343–418.

Schmitt, F. O. (1941). Some protein patterns in cells. *Symp. Soc. Study Develop. Growth* **3,** 1–20.

Spiegel, M. (1954a). The role of specific surface antigens in cell adhesion. I. The reaggregation of sponge cells. *Biol. Bull.* **107,** 130–148.

Spiegel, M. (1954b). The role of specific surface antigens in cell adhesion. II. Studies on embryonic amphibian cells. *Biol. Bull.* **107,** 149–155.

Steinberg, M. S. (1958). On the chemical bonds between animal cells—A mechanism for type-specific association. *Am. Naturalist* **92,** 65–81.

Swift, C. H. (1914). Origin and early history of the primordial germ cells in the chick. *Am. J. Anat.* **15,** 483–516.

Townes, P. L., and J. Holtfreter (1955). Directed movements and selective adhesion of embryonic amphibian cells. *J. Exptl. Zool.* **128,** 53–120.

Tyler, A. (1947). An auto-antibody concept of cell structure, growth and differentiation. *Symp. Soc. Study Develop. Growth* **6,** 7–19.

Weiss, L. (1960). The adhesion of cells. *Intern. Rev. Cytol.* **9,** 187–225.

Weiss, P. (1947). The problem of specificity in growth and development. *Yale J. Biol. Med.* **19,** 235–278.

Weiss, P. (1958). Cell contact. *Intern. Rev. Cytol.* **7,** 391–424.

Weiss, P., and G. Andres (1952). Experiments on the fate of embryonic chick cells disseminated by the vascular route. *J. Exptl. Zool.* **121,** 449–488.

Weiss, P., and A. Moscona (1958). Type-specific morphogenesis of cartilages developed from dissociated limb and scleral mesenchyme in vitro. *J. Embryol. Exptl. Morphol.* **6,** 238–246.

Willis, R. A. (1952). *The Spread of Tumors in the Human Body.* Butterworth, London.

Wilson, H. V. (1907). On some phenomena of coalescence and regeneration in sponges. *J. Exptl. Zool.* **5,** 245–258.

Wilson, H. V. (1910). Development of sponges from dissociated tissue cells. *Bull. Bur. Fisheries* **30,** 1–30.

2

Induction

Since Spemann's classic work on induction (1938), it has been considered almost axiomatic that differentiation progresses at least in part through tissue interactions. The primary induction in the amphibian has been the subject of many subsequent studies (see reviews by Holtfreter and Hamburger 1955; and Saxen and Toivonen 1962); but because of its complexity, it is still little understood. Other inductions concerned with the differentiation of the lens (McKeehan 1951), pancreas (Golosow and Grobstein 1962), kidney (Grobstein 1955), salivary glands (Grobstein 1953), thymus (Auerbach 1960), and skin (Sengel 1957, McLoughlin 1963, Bell 1964), for example, have lent themselves to more detailed analysis of the nature of tissue interactions.

Not all inductions are the same. Some might occur through transfer of an inducing substance, while others may be initiated by different stimuli. The mode of induction by the apical ectodermal ridge (Saunders 1948, Zwilling 1955) in limb development is still unexplained. It could be due to transfer of a substance from ectoderm to mesoderm; but, on the other hand, the geometry of the ectodermal jacket might itself be the inducer. Breakdown of basement lamellae at the future site of the amphibian limb (Balinsky 1956) may involve yet another inductive device.

Questions which have been asked about tissue interactions which involve diffusible inducers concern the nature of the inducer and the way in which it affects the target tissue which differentiates as a result of the interaction. Evidence that a diffusable substance from the inducing tissue is the causative agent responsible for initiating differentiation has been provided in the experiments of Niu and Twitty (1953), of *Grobstein (1956),** and of McKeehan (1951) and others. How the substance acts, whether directly on one or more genes, indirectly through the metabolic machinery of the target tissue, or by some other route, is unknown.

No one has yet chemically characterized an inducing agent although attempts have been made. Various RNA preparations, some called m-RNA (messenger-RNA), have been used in both embryonic and nonembryonic assay systems and have been shown to bring about changes in target tissues (Niu 1964; Amos, Askonas, and Soeiro 1964; and Friedman 1964).

None of the preparations play a proven role in development. A protein seems to be the active component of a particulate fraction from embryo extract which can induce differentiation in the epithelial rudiment of the pancreas (*Rutter, Wessells, and Grobstein 1964*, Chapter 9). The capacity of proteins and hormones to stimulate growth and differentiation will be considered in Chapter 13. Lash and his associates

* Italicized references indicate articles which appear in this book.

(*Lash, Hommes, and Zilliken 1962*; Hommes, van Leeuwen, and Zilliken 1962) have partially characterized a low molecular weight factor which can bring about cartilage differentiation in somites.

The response of the target tissue to the inducing substance has been assessed morphologically. For example, Weiss (1949) and later McKeehan (1951) found that in the earliest response of the presumptive lens cells to induction, nuclei migrate to the basal region of the cells and elongate. This occurs in advance of cell elongation. Recently Byers and Porter (1964) have pointed out that new subcellular structures, microtubules, can be seen in electronmicrographs of induced lens cells. It is not known though how an inducer can cause microtubules to appear in induced cells. The authors propose that the microtubules which are oriented parallel to the direction of cell elongation may play a part in establishing cell shape.

Grobstein (1955, 1953, 1964) and Kallman and Grobstein (1964) have described post-inductive morphological responses in mesonephros, salivary glands, and pancreas. Auerbach (1960) has studied structural changes in thymic tissue which are due to induction. Differentiation of epidermis can be directed along any one of numerous pathways by combining it with the appropriate dermis (McLoughlin 1963 and Rawles 1963).

The biochemical response of an induced tissue has been described by Lash (1963) who studied appearance of enzymes involved in the sulphation of chondroitin in the somite. These enzymes APS, PAPS, and the sulfate transferase enzyme can be detected in the induced somite some time before the tissue begins to undergo morphological differentiation (Lash, Glick, and Madden 1964). It is not clear whether gene activation or enzyme activation is responsible for their appearance in the induced somites.

Evidence that appearance of new proteins in epidermis is correlated with an inductive event has been presented by Ben-Or and Bell (1965) who showed that following induction of feathers in the skin by a humoral factor, three new antigens are detectible; two of these were shown to be stage specific, that is, present in other tissues as well as the skin, and one, skin specific. Their demonstration illustrates a correlation between induction and the appearance of new antigens but does not prove a causal connection. In a tissue such as the skin, in which the epidermis can differentiate into feathers, beak, scale, or muscosa depending upon the dermis with which it is associated, it is necessary to propose inducing substances of dermal origin which differ in some way from one another.

The duration of competence of a responding tissue has been examined by a number of investigators. For example (Yntema 1950, Holtzer 1961, and Rawles 1963) have shown that tissues can respond to an induction stimulus only over a well-defined limited period.

In summary, the principle unanswered question concerns the nature of inducers and their modes of action. Exploration of this question in well-defined tissue assay systems may be expected to provide a first step in approaching the general and central problem of how genes are activated during differentiation.

REFERENCES

1. Amos, H., B. Askonas, and R. Soeiro (1964). Evidence for messenger activity of alien ribonucleic acid in chick cells. In W. Rutter (ed.), *Metabolic Control Mechanisms in Animal Cells, Natl. Cancer Inst. Mon.* **13,** pp. 155–165, Government Printing Office, Washington, D.C.

2. Auerbach, R. (1960). Morphogenetic interactions in the development of the mouse

thymus gland. *Develop. Biol.* **2**:271–284.

3. Balinsky, B. I. (1956). A new theory of limb induction. *Proc. Natl. Acad. Sci. U.S.* **42**: 781–785.

4. Bell, E. (1964). The induction of differentiation and the response to the inducer. *Cancer Res.* **24**:28–34.

5. Ben-Or, S., and E. Bell (1965). Skin antigens in the chick embryo in relation to other developmental events. *Develop. Biol.*, Academic Press, New York.

6. Byers, Breck, and Keith Porter (1964). Oriented microtubules in elongating cells of the developing lens rudiment after induction. *Proc. Natl. Acad. Sci.* **52**:1091–1099.

7. Friedman, H. (1964). Acquisition of antibody plague forming activity by normal mouse spleen cells treated *in vitro* with RNA extracted from immune donor spleens. *Biochem. Biophys. Res. Comm.* **17**:272–281.

8. Golosow, N., and C. Grobstein (1962). Epitheliomesenchymal interaction in pancreatic morphogenesis. *Develop. Biol.* **4**: 242–255.

9. Grobstein, C. (1953). Epithelio-mesenchymal specificity in the morphogenesis of mouse sub-mandibular rudiments *in vitro*. *J. Exptl. Zool.* **124**: 383–404.

10. Grobstein, C. (1955). Tissue interaction in the morphogenesis of mouse embryonic rudiments *in vitro*. In D. Rudnick (ed.), *Aspects of Synthesis and Order in Growth*, Princeton Univ. Press, pp. 233–256.

11. Grobstein, C. (1964). Cytodifferentiation and its controls. *Science* **143**:643–650.

12. Holtfreter, J., and V. Hamburger (1954). Embryogenesis: progressive differentiation. In B. Willier, P. Weiss, and V. Hamburger (eds.), *Analysis of Development*, Saunders, Philadelphia, pp. 230–296.

13. Holtzer, H. (1961). Aspects of chondrogenesis and myogenesis. In D. Rudnick (ed.), *Synthesis of Molecular and Cellular Structure*, Ronald, New York, pp. 35–87.

14. Hommes, F. A., G. van Leeuwen, and F. Zilliken (1962). Induction of cell differentiation. The isolation of a chondrogenic factor from embryonic chick spinal cords and notochords. *Biochim. Biophys. Acta* **56**:320–325.

15. Kallman, F., and C. Grobstein (1964). Fine structure of differentiating mouse pancreatic exocrine cells in transfilter culture. *J. Cell Biol.* **20**:399–413.

16. Lash, J. W. (1963). Tissue interaction and specific metabolic responses: chondrogenic induction and differentiation. In M. Locke (ed.), *Cytodifferentiation and Macromolecular Synthesis*, Academic Press, New York, pp. 235–260.

17. Lash, J. W., M. C. Glock, and J. W. Madden (1964). Cartilage induction *in vitro* and sulfate-activating enzymes. In W. Rutter (ed.), *Metabolic Control Mechanisms in Animal Cells, Natl. Cancer Inst. Mon.* **13**, pp. 39–49, Government Printing Office, Washington, D.C.

18. McKeehan, M. S. (1951). Cytological aspects of embryonic lens induction in the chick. *J. Exptl. Zool.* **117**:31–64.

19. McLoughlin, C. B. (1963). Mesenchymal influences on epithelial differentiation. In G. E. Fogg (ed.), *Cell Differentiation*, No. XVII, pp. 359–388, Cambridge Univ. Press, Cambridge, England.

20. Niu, M. C., and V. C. Twitty (1953). The differentiation of gastrula ectoderm in medium conditioned by axial mesoderm. *Proc. Natl. Acad. Sci.* **39**:985–989.

21. Niu, M. C. (1964). Mode of action of the exogenous ribonucleic acid in cell function. In W. Rutter (ed.), *Metabolic Control Mechanisms in Animal Cells, Natl. Cancer Inst. Mon.* **13**, pp. 167–177, Government Printing Office, Washington, D.C.

22. Rawles, M. E. (1963). Tissue interactions in scale and feather development as studied in dermal-epidermal recombinations. *J. Embryol. Exptl. Morph.* **11**:765–789.

23. Saunders, J. W., Jr. (1948). The proximo-distal sequence of origin of the parts of the chick wing and the role of the ectoderm. *J. Exptl. Zool.* **108**:363–403.

24. Saunders, J. W., and M. Gasseling (1963). Trans-filter propagation of apical ectoderm maintenance factor in the chick embryo wing bud. *Develop. Biol.* **7**:64–78.

25. Saxen, L., and S. Toivonen (1962). *Primary Embryonic Induction*, Logos Press, London.

26. Sengel, P. (1957). Analyse experimentale du developpement *in vitro* des germes plumaires de l'embryon de poulet. *Experientia* **13**:177–216.

27. Spemann, Hans (1938). *Embryonic Development and Induction*, Yale Univ. Press, New Haven.

27. Weiss, P. (1949). Differential growth. In A. K. Parpart (ed.), *Chemistry and Physiology of Growth*, Princeton Univ. Press, Princeton, New Jersey, pp. 135–186.

28. Yntema, C. (1950). An analysis of induction of the ear from foreign ectoderm in the salamander embryo. *J. Exptl. Zool.* **113**: 211–244.

29. Zwilling, E. (1955). Ectoderm-mesoderm relationship in the development of the chick embryo limb bud. *J. Exptl. Zool.* **142**:521–532.

The *in Vitro* Induction of Vertebral Cartilage with a Low-Molecular-Weight Tissue Component

JAMES W. LASH

FRITS A. HOMMES

F. ZILLIKEN

Summary. *A nucleotide-containing fraction has been obtained from a cold perchloric acid extract of the chick embryonic spinal cord and notochord that simulates the chondrogenic action of the intact inducing tissues. This fraction induces the formation of cartilage in explanted somites. Upon partial purification of this fraction the ability to induce cartilage formation has been restricted to one nucleotide-containing component.*

INTRODUCTION

Of the many induction systems that have been described, one of the most rewarding in which to study the biochemistry of embryonic induction is that of cartilage formation. Since the major molecular components of cartilage are readily identifiable, and since some information is available regarding their biosynthesis,[1] it is feasible to analyze events attending their induction and subsequent synthesis.[2]

This paper is concerned with the processes involved during a comparatively late stage of embryonic development, *viz.* vertebral chondrogenesis. Past work has suggested that the ventral half of the embryonic spinal cord produces a transmissible substance that passes to the somite cells, there inducing the formation of vertebral cartilage, whereas the notochord induces cartilage formation in somite cells only when the cells are in direct apposition to the notochordal sheath.[3] Moreover, these specific chondrogenic influences occur within the first few hours of association between the tissues, even though cartilage cannot be detected histologically or biochemically until the fourth day of culture.[2]

Reproduced from *Biochimica et Biophysica Acta,* **56** (1962), 313–319. Reprinted with permission.

The work reported below has led to the isolation and tentative characterization of a chondrogenic factor of relatively small molecular weight that can be extracted from the embryonic spinal cord and notochord. This factor elicits the formation of cartilage in somites, thereby simulating the biological action of the intact inducing tissues.

MATERIALS AND METHODS

In order to perform biochemical analyses pertinent to the problem under investigation, it was necessary to use small pieces of tissues. Most of the cultures to be extracted varied in size between 0.5–1.0 mm.[3] Since the intent of the experiments was to isolate nucleotides, the phosphorus compounds were labeled by growing the tissues in the presence of radioactive inorganic phosphate, $Na_3{}^{32}PO_4$. The tissues readily incorporated the radioactive isotope into the phosphate-containing compounds, although the specific activity was not determined. Although radioactive phosphorus has a half-life of only 14.3 days, it was used satisfactorily to label, extract and partially characterize the chondrogenic factor in the inducing tissues.

When it was established that an active chondrogenic factor was present in the inducing tissues, chemical extractions were performed on large numbers of unlabeled spinal cords and notochords.[4]

Preparation of Tissues

Embryonic chick somites, spinal cords and notochords were isolated by methods previously published.[5] All tissues were taken from 2.5–3 day incubates (stages 16–18, Hamburger and Hamilton[6]), with the exception of the large numbers of 4.5 day unlabeled spinal cords used for chemical extractions. The latter tissues were obtained by cutting them free of surrounding tissues.

Labeling of Tissues

Inducing tissues (notochord and spinal cord), reacting tissues (somites) and chondrogenic cultures (inducing tissues plus somites), were grown in the presence of radioactive inorganic phosphate (20 µC $Na_3{}^{32}PO_4$/ 0.1 ml Simms'[7] balanced salt solution per dish of 5 explants). These tissues were placed upon lens paper floating on a liquid nutrient medium,[8] and incubated at 38° for 24 h before extraction. Chondrogenic cultures (inducing tissues plus somites) were incubated for longer intervals, until cartilage appeared.

Extraction of Tissues

Varying amounts of tissues, most frequently 20 cultures, were extracted with 1.0 ml of 0.25 *M* perchloric acid at 0° for 15 min. After this the solution was neutralized with potassium hydroxide. Following centrifugation the supernatant fluid was adsorbed onto a charcoal–celite (1 : 1) column (6 × 0.4 cm). The charcoal–celite column was prepared according to Threlfall.[9]

The charcoal–celite filtrate (i.e., substances not adsorbed onto the column) was found to contain sugar-phosphates and will hence be spoken of as the "sugar-phosphate" fraction. This fraction was analyzed separately by means of paper electrophoresis and paper chromatography.

The acid-soluble nucleotides which were adsorbed onto the charcoal–celite column were eluted with 10% aqueous pyridine.[9] This eluate will be called the "nucleotide fraction," since its electrophoretic and chromatographic patterns, its positive reaction with the Wade-Morgan colorimetric method,[10] and its ultraviolet spectrum all indicate the presence of nucleotides.

Electrophoresis and Chromatography

Both radioactive fractions (nucleotide and sugar-phosphate) were analyzed by means of paper (Whatman 3 MM) electrophoresis in pyridine–acetic acid–water (100 : 10:890, v/v)

at pH 6.5, 30 V/cm at 0° for 2.5 h. The air dried electropherograms were then scanned for radioactive components with a chromatogram scanner (Nuclear Chicago). One of the components of the sugar-phosphate fraction that appeared to be unique to the inducing tissues was eluted from the electropherogram and chromatographed in the solvent of Paladini-Leloir[11] (Whatman 1 paper, 95% ethanol–NH_4Ac (pH 3.8), (7.5 : 3, v/v)). The dried chromatogram was scanned for radioactive components, yielding R_F values corresponding to hexose phosphates, and giving a positive test with ammoniacal silver nitrate solution.[12] The other components have not yet been analyzed.

Preparation on Larger Scale

For further characterization of the nucleotide fraction, spinal cords and notochords from 1000 4.5-day chick embryos were prepared and analyzed as described in the Hommes, van Leeuwen and Zilliken paper.[4]

Testing Extracts for Chondrogenic Activity

All somites were grown on nutrient agar.[13] Each extract or fraction to be tested was dissolved in 1.0 ml of balanced salt solution, sterilized through a Swinny Hypodermic Adaptor (Millipore Filter Corp., Bedford, Mass.) and made up into a liquid nutrient medium (1.0 ml balanced salt solution–1.0 ml horse serum–0.5 ml embryo extract). Approximately 0.25 ml of this nutrient medium was placed in each dish containing 10–20 clusters of 6–8 somites. Control cultures received either plain nutrient medium or nutrient medium containing extracts of tissues other than spinal cord or notochord. The amount of extract or fraction added to the cultures was too small to quantitate, but according to the dilutions of the extract yielded by 1000 spinal cords and notochords, approximately 0.5–1.0 µg of the nucleotide fraction was added to each dish of somite cultures.

Assay for Induction of Cartilage

Cartilage in living cultures was determined visually through the dissecting microscope.

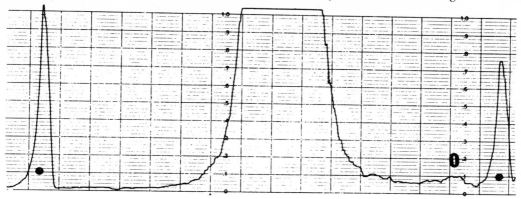

Fig. 1. Paper electrophoresis of partially purified cold perchloric acid extract (nucleotide components) from inducing tissues. Radioactive phosphate components move as a broad band. In Figs. 1–3 all conditions are the same. Electrophoresis at pH 6.5, 30 V/cm, at 0° for 2.5 h. The corresponding chart for the electropherogram was matched for radioactive components with the aid of radioactive markers (black dots on charts). Full scale on the chart represents 10,000 counts/min.

Tissues were also fixed in acetic acid–ethanol (1 : 3, v/v), sectioned and stained with aqueous thionin (1 : 1000 w/v for metachromic material.

RESULTS

Characterization of Extracts

Nucleotide fractions from radioactive cultures were analyzed by means of paper electrophoresis and scanning of the air dried electropherograms for radioactive components. The nucleotides moved as a broad band, without resolution of separate component nucleotides (Fig. 1). The peaks on the scanning charts indicate the amount of activity present (scale in Figs. 1–3 is 10,000 counts/min; Fig. 4, 3000 counts/min), but no attempt has been made yet to quantitate the data. Nucleotide fractions similar to the one in Fig. 1 were eluted from the electropherogram, made up into a nutrient medium solution, and added to somite clusters. The characterization of these fractions as "nucleotides" is based upon analytical tests performed on combined fractions of 80–100 3-day spinal cords. These fractions showed electrophoretic and chromatographic mobilities comparable to known nucleotide standards and gave positive tests typical of nucleotides. Further characterization of this fraction is given in the Hommes, van Leeuwen and Zilliken paper.[4]

The sugar-phosphate fractions upon electrophoretic separation contained five major peaks (Fig. 2), one of which was present only in extracts of the inducing tissues and somites which had been exposed to the inducing tissues. Somites which had not been induced possessed only four of the major peaks in the sugar-phosphate fraction (Fig. 3). The extra peak has not been completely identified yet, but upon elution and rechromatography it yielded two phosphorylated compounds with R_F values indicating the presence of a hexose phosphate and a hexosamine phosphate (Fig. 4). The hexosamine compound gave a positive Morgan-Elson reaction as modified by Reissig et al.,[14] indicating the presence of N-acetyl-hexosamine phosphate.

Effect of Extracts upon Somite Cultures

The extract thus yielded two fractions; a fraction containing sugar phosphates, and one containing nucleotides. Sugar-phosphate and "nucleotide fractions" from notochords and spinal cords were added separately to somite cultures to determine whether the extracts were capable of simulating the action of the intact inducing tissues. The extracts were taken from 3-day-old tissues approximately 1.0 mm³ in size, which had been grown in the presence of radioactive inorganic phosphate.

The sugar-phosphate fraction had no ob-

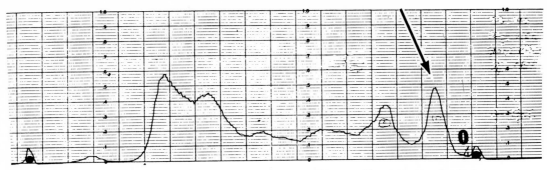

Fig. 2. Paper electrophoresis of components of perchloric acid extract not absorbed on charcoal-celite column (filtrate). The radioactive sugar-phosphate component found only in inducing tissue shown by arrow. Other components have not been analyzed. All other conditions similar as in Fig. 1.

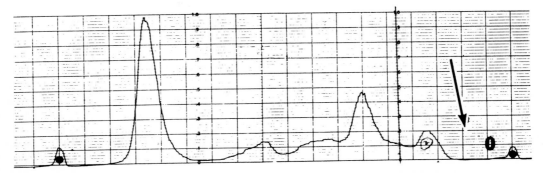

Fig. 3. Paper electrophoresis of charcoal-celite filtrate from non-induced somites. This shows the absence of the unique component (arrow). All other conditions same as in Fig. 1. Similar electropherograms are obtained from non-inducing tissues (e.g., muscle, limb buds).

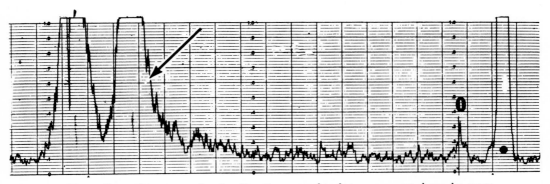

Fig. 4. Paper chromatography of radioactive sugar-phosphate component shown by arrow in Fig. 2. Descending chromatography 14 h, 95% ethanol–1.0 M NH$_4$Ac, pH 3.8 (7.5 : 3, v/v). The phosphate-compound indicated by the arrow gave a positive Morgan-Elson reaction. Full scale on the chart represents 3000 counts/min.

servable effect, but the "nucleotide fraction" and the non-fractionated perchloric acid extract from as few as eight 3-day spinal cords caused cartilage to appear regularly in embryonic somites. Subsequent experiments using non-radioactive extracts or "nucleotide fractions" from large numbers of 4.5-day spinal cords and notochords gave the same results.

Extracts of the notochord or the ventral half of the spinal cord induced cartilage formation, whereas extracts of the dorsal half of the spinal cord had no effect upon the somites. Moreover nucleotide extracts from other embryonic tissues (ectoderm, endoderm, muscle, limb buds) did not induce cartilage in somites.

Out of 228 cultures of explanted somites, 186 have been induced to form cartilage by adding the "nucleotide fractions" (Table I). After the addition of the "nucleotide fraction," the induced somites formed cartilage on the fourth day of culture. Control cultures of somites without the addition of an active "nucleotide fraction," or with the addition of a total yeast perchloric acid extract prepared in a similar fashion, yielded 38 small nodules of cartilage in 304 cultures.

Somites of varying ages were used to test the chondrogenic activity of "nucleotide fractions." When young somites were used (stages 16–17), fewer control cultures formed cartilage. Control cultures of stage 16 were completely negative with respect to cartilage formation whereas 9 out of 10 cultures receiving "nucleotide fraction" produced cartilage (Table I). Not only was the incidence of chondrogenesis less in the controls than that in the treated cultures, but the amount of cartilage per cluster of somites was also considerable less and formed later in the life of the culture. The low incidence and small quantity of cartilage formation in the control cultures of older somites is in agreement with the idea that there is a time at which the somites become induced *in vivo*, and if explantation occurs during this interval there will occur some cases of seemingly spontaneous cartilage formation.[5]

Resolution of the Nucleotide Fraction

To identify the components of the "nucleotide fraction," and to determine which component was the chondrogenic factor, combined "nucleotide fractions" from 4.5-day spinal cords and notochords were passed over the Dowex column. The resolution of the nucleotides eluted in the formic acid gradient is shown in Fig. 5. Each component was then lyophilized, redissolved in balanced salt solution, and tested for chondrogenic activity. The only component possessing such activity corresponded to the peak indicated by the arrow in Fig. 5. Out of 75 cultures, 55 formed cartilage after the addition of a nutrient medium containing this component. The other nucleotide components had no inducing effect, each fraction being tested on 20 cultures. Details on the methods of isolation and identification of this component on a larger scale is published in the Hommes, van Leeuwen and Zilliken paper.[4]

TABLE I.   Chondrogenic activity of nucleotide fractions

Age of Somites	Number of Cultures	Number of Cultures Forming Cartilage	Incidence of Cartilage (%)
Stage 16			
Controls	20	0	0
Plus extract	10	9	90
Stage 17			
Controls	80	9	11
Plus extract	53	44	83
Stage 18			
Controls	194	29	15
Plus extract	165	134	81

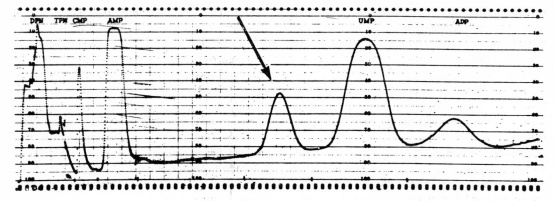

Fig. 5. Dowex 1 × 8 (200–400 mesh) chromatography of nucleotide fraction obtained from 4.5-day-old spinal cords and notochords. Column dimensions: 12 × 0.9 cm. Elution and characterization as specified in Fig. 2 of the Hommes, van Leeuwen and Zilliken paper. Nucleotide-containing component capable of chondrogenic induction indicated by arrow.

DISCUSSION

Previous work has shown that explanted somites form significant quantities of cartilage only when exposed to the embryonic spinal chord or notochord. This reaction is specific in the sense that no other tissues or agents have been found to induce the same chondrogenic response in somites.[3]

There is little doubt that in the induction of vertebral cartilage, a nucleotide containing component extracted from the spinal cord and notochord simulates the chondrogenic action of the intact inducing tissues. According to the methods of isolation, this component must be of relative small molecular size. The "nucleotide component" is fractionated from a perchloric acid extract, the other fraction (sugar-phosphate) possessing no chondrogenic activity.

At present we cannot say whether this component represents the only one capable of simulating chondrogenic induction, or whether the spinal cord and notochord are the only tissues containing such a component. An explanation of the biological action of this cartilage promoting factor and its significance to biosynthetic processes will have to wait until more work has been done.

ACKNOWLEDGEMENTS

This investigation was supported in part by grants from the U.S. Public Health Service (A-1980-C2), the National Science Foundation (G-11706), and a travel grant from the Wellcome Trust Fund (for J.W.L.). One of us (J.W.L.) is a Helen Hay Whitney Foundation Established Investigator.

F.A.H. is a Postdoctoral Fellow, Department of Biochemistry, R.K. University, Nijmegen (The Netherlands).

REFERENCES

[1] S. Roseman, *Ann. Rev. Biochem.*, 28 (1959) 545.
[2] J. Lash, H. Holtzer and M. W. Whitehouse, *Develop. Biol.*, 2 (1960) 76.
[3] H. Holtzer in D. Rudnick, *XIX Growth Symposium*, Ronald Press, New York, 1961.
[4] F. A. Hommes, G. van Leeuwen and F. Zilliken, *Biochim. Biophys. Acta*, 56 (1962) 320.
[5] G. Avery, M. Chow and H. Holtzer, *J. Exptl. Zool.*, 132 (1956) 409.
[6] V. Hamburger and H. L. Hamilton, *J. Morphol.*, 88 (1951) 49.
[7] H. S. Simms and M. Sanders, *A. M. A. Arch. Pathol.*, 33 (1942) 619.
[8] J. Lash, S. Holtzer and H. Holtzer, *Exptl. Cell Research*, 13 (1957) 292.
[9] C. J. Threlfall, *Biochem. J.*, 65 (1956) 694.
[10] H. E. Wade and D. M. Morgan, *Nature*, 171 (1953) 529.
[11] A. C. Paladini and L. F. Leloir, *Biochem. J.*, 51 (1952) 426.
[12] R. J. Block, E. L. Durrum and G. Zweig, *A Manual of Paper Chromatography and Paper Electrophoresis*, Academic Press, New York, 1958.
[13] J. Lash, *Methods in Medical Research*, in the press.
[14] J. L. Reissig, J. L. Strominger and L. F. Leloir, *J. Biol. Chem.*, 217 (1955) 959.

Trans-Filter Induction of Tubules in Mouse Metanephrogenic Mesenchyme

CLIFFORD GROBSTEIN [1]

A number of hypothetical mechanisms to explain phenomena of embryonic induction have been proposed, but none has yet been sufficiently strongly supported experimentally to command general acceptance. It is generally assumed that inductive effects reflect some transmission between the two interacting tissues, but the intimacy of association usually involved has complicated the problem of identifying the effective agent. Several investigators have interposed barriers to direct tissue contact and have found inductive effects to be obliterated [4, 18, 20]. Others have reported weak [5] or positive [10, 23] results in widely different inductive systems. It seems clear that barriers to cellular penetration which permit inductive effects consistently to cross them would provide an "interzone" within which the actual effective agent might be identified in transit.

Materials previously tested for such barrier action have usually been low porosity membranes such as cellophane which might be expected to exclude high molecular weight compounds. On the other hand, highly porous filters of interlacing fibers would not be expected to prevent cellular penetration. The behavior of filters of intermediate porosity, so-called membrane or molecular filters[2] which exclude passage of bacteria but not of high molecular weight materials such as proteins, is the subject of this report.

The inductive system selected for study involves embryonic spinal cord and metanephrogenic mesenchyme of the mouse. Origin of the epithelial precursors of secretory tubules in nephrogenic mesenchyme has been extensively studied in amphibia [6] and the chick [16] and there is a strong consensus that it normally depends upon an inductive stimulus from the Wolffian duct or, in the case of the metanephros, from the ureteric bud which branches from the duct. It has been shown that embryonic spinal cord can also provide the inductive stimulus [16]. These general conclusions have recently been substantiated for the mouse in studies *in vitro* [12] and the additional finding has been made that tubule-inducing activity in the cord is highest in the dorsal half prior to the 13th day of gestation. The strong inductive activity of embryonic dorsal spinal cord when directly combined with metanephrogenic mesenchyme, together with the relative abundance of available spinal cord in comparison with ureteric bud, suggested dorsal cord as a favorable inductive source for trans-filter studies.

MATERIAL AND METHODS

Filters

The general nature and properties of cellulose ester membrane filters, and their application to a number of microbiological problems, have been described [9]. The filters are commercially available in sheets of 150 micron thickness in two porosity grades, hydrosol (HA) and aerosol (AA). Data on the commercial filters, provided by the manufacturer,[2] indicate that the substance consists of a "network of cross-linked elements approaching molecular dimensions" and defining "uniform pores of a total volume equal to 80 to 85 per cent of the volume of the sheet." Performance data are said to suggest that the pore axes "may be considered for practical purposes as though perpendicular to the surface of the filter membrane." Calculated pore size is given as 0.45 micron for HA and 0.8 micron for AA filters. The

Experimental Cell Research, **10**, 424–440 (1956). Reprinted with permission.

[1] With the technical assistance of Gayle Bankard, Derrell Freese, George Parker and Edward J. Soban.

[2] Millipore Filter Corp., Watertown, Mass. Technical information provided in a brochure, "Millipore Filters," distributed by the manufacturer.

manufacturer's data are supported by a recent study of pore-size distribution in standard HA-type filters using a mercury-intrusion method [19]. The data on two samples suggest a peak in pore size distribution at effective pore radii of 0.5 and 0.6 micron respectively, with some gradation below these values but a sharp cut-off above.

It is to be emphasized, however, that the material used in the experiments to be described was *not* the standard 150 micron thickness filter but specially manufactured thinner sheets. These varied somewhat in thickness, measuring 20 ±4 microns for the HA-type, and 20 ±4 and 30 ±2 microns for the AA-type. For convenience, samples from these several sheets, despite thickness variation, will be referred to as 20H, 20A and 30A, respectively. The thinner sheets were chosen to bring the two tissues into closer association, and because their translucency when wet provided greater operative and observational convenience. Their use, however, is subject to the disadvantage that no physical data are available on their porosity, and there is reason to believe from the biological data that their porosity is not the same and probably is less than that of the thicker filters.

The filter sheets, received dry, were cut or punched into small pieces of suitable size and shape for the procedures to be described. Following preliminary tests which showed no difference in behavior when spinal cord was placed either on the more shiny or less shiny side of the filter no effort was made to control this orientation. An hour or two prior to use the dry filters were placed for not more than 30 minutes in 70 per cent alcohol, then transferred for a similar period to Tyrode's solution before being stored until use in horse serum—Tyrode's (1:1) solution. While wet, each filter was carefully examined with transmitted light at 18 × magnification and those with significant inhomogeneities were discarded.

Culture Methods

Several methods for incorporating the filter into the cultures were tested. The results to be reported are based on two, which will be designated as the "on-the-clot" and "supported-ring" procedures respectively (Fig. 1). The first is the earlier and more convenient for some purposes, but proved less reliable, particularly with the HA-type filter. The second requires more laborious preparation, but is more reliable and versatile in application. Both are modifications of standard plasma clot culture methods, employing fowl plasma and a nutrient medium of horse serum, Tyrode's solution and 9-day chick embryo juice in 2:2:1 ratio with added penicillin and streptomycin (5 mg of each per 100 ml). In both methods the culture vessel was a round flat "tissue dish,"[3] 4.5 cm in diameter and 1 cm high with a central depression or well 2 cm in diameter and of approximately 0.5 ml capacity. The dishes, provided with loosely fitting covers, were incubated on suitable racks in an incubator gassed to maintain approximately 5 per cent CO_2 in air at or close to 100 per cent humidity.

The "on-the-clot" procedure involved placing one tissue on a previously prepared clot in a minimum of fluid, laying a well-drained filter square over the tissue, and then orienting the second tissue over the first in a second clotting mixture. One ml of nutrient fluid subsequently was added as a supernatant which was changed daily. The procedure is simpler but gave less reliable inductions, particularly with the HA filter, than the more laborious but in many ways more convenient "supported-ring" method. The latter represents a modification of methods described by Algire, Weaver, and Prehn [1] for *in vivo* studies with membrane filter "sandwiches."

Discs of filter material (5.5 mm diameter) were cut out of the filter sheet by twisting a small punch against a moderately firm background such as is provided by a blotter on a table top. The discs were cemented to plexiglas (Acrylic plastic, without plasticizer) rings (I. D. = 3 mm; O. D. = 5.7 mm) cut out of ³⁄₃₂-inch thickness sheets with a drill press. The cement was made by dissolving

---

[3] Manufactured by F. Highhouse, glass technologist, whose cooperation is gratefully acknowledged.

enough filter material in acetone to yield a
fluid of syrupy consistency. A filter disc was
placed over a ring and cement carefully applied to the edges with an orally controlled
glass pipette of suitable diameter. When the
consistency of the cement, which could be
varied by adding either acetone or filter material, and the rate of application were proper
a smooth seal of the filter to the ring resulted.

Two fine glass rods (*ca.* 0.2 mm diam., 24
mm in length) were cemented to the plexiglas
ring, on the opposite side from the filter, in
such fashion as to allow suspension of the ring
over the tissue dish well (Fig. 1). The rods
were attached to the ring either before or
after cementing the filter, depending upon convenience. The resulting assembly was fairly
rugged and could be handled easily with
jeweler's forceps without damage to the filter.
It provided two culture surfaces, the first
within the "cup" formed by the walls of the
plexiglas ring and a second on the opposite
side. Cultures could be grown on either or
both surfaces, with medium above or below
the ring or both.

In preparing spinal cord-metanephrogenic
mesenchyme cultures the filter-ring assembly,
after passing through 70 per cent alcohol and
Tyrode's to horse serum-Tyrode's, was placed
across the well of an empty tissue dish with
the cup side up. To the drop of horse serum-
Tyrode's carried over in the well a piece of
dorsal spinal cord was added. Equal drops
of chilled plasma and medium were placed
side by side on the shelf of the tissue dish
ready to be mixed. The assembly was lifted
with jeweler's forceps, touched to the shelf
without disturbing the plasma and medium
drops, and all excess fluid was removed with
a fine pipette (I. D. at tip. *ca.* 0.2 mm). In
the process the nervous tissue was "stranded"
near the center of the filter surface, flattened
and pressed firmly against it by surface tension. The assembly was returned to its position over the well, the plasma and medium
drops combined in the pipette and the resulting clotting mixture added to nearly fill the
cup. The spinal cord adhered to the filter and
subsequently was supported in this position
after the clot had formed.

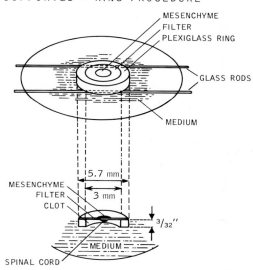

Fig. 1. Culture procedures. On-the-clot procedure
shown in cross-section through entire culture dish.
Supported-ring procedure shown in view of tissue
dish well above and cross-section of ring below.
Diagrammatic, not drawn to scale.

The assembly was then reversed to turn the
cup side down. Mesenchyme separated from
one metanephric rudiment was deposited over
the spinal cord in a minimum of fluid, and
excess fluid was again withdrawn. A second
clotting mixture, formed as before, was added
as a drop on top of the filter. After full clotting, medium was added first to the cup and
then in excess to fill the well. In early experiments enough medium (1 ml) was added to
cover the entire preparation; in later ones the
amount was reduced to 0.4 ml, enough to
nearly fill the well and to provide a "standing
drop" in continuous contact with the under
side of the assembly. Under the latter conditions the nutrient was "subjacent" rather than
"supernatant." In all cases the medium was
changed daily.

Tissue Source

Spinal cord and metanephrogenic mesenchyme were obtained from embryos (BALB/ C × C3H) on the 11th day after the mother was found with a vaginal plug. General procedures for isolation of the metanephric rudiment and separation of its epithelial and mesenchymal components in trypsin solution have been described [12]. The stage of the rudiments varied from simple ureteric bud to very early branching, with the great majority at the point of flattening and expansion of the bud without recognizable branching. Spinal cord was generally from the cervical and thoracic regions although some anterior lumbar cord may occasionally have been included. The more anterior cord regions were somewhat more convenient, supplying more tissue which was more easily separable from surrounding mesenchyme. For this purpose a short section of cord and adnexa was cut out and turned up on the cut cord surface. A slender iridectomy knife was worked in between spinal ganglia and cord for some distance and then manipulated so as to cut the peripheral tissue away from the dorsal half of the cord. After this was done on both sides, the cord was split in the dorsal mid-line, and the thinner dorsal wall cut in a strip from the thicker ventral wall. In the process any remaining surrounding mesenchyme usually separated without use of trypsin, giving clean dorsal cord. The short strips thus obtained were cut into pieces 0.2–0.4 mm on a side.

Histological

Cultures routinely were fixed in Zenker-acetic. In the supported-ring procedure the entire assembly was removed from the tissue dish and dropped directly into fixative. After washing, the filter was removed from the ring by gentle dissection around the periphery.

In many cases, particularly with the HA-type filter the spinal cord and its clot would separate from the filter either due to mechanical stresses during removal from the dish or ring, or due to curling of the filter as it went from alcohol to toluene. The latter tendency could be reduced by changing through a close series of increasing toluene concentration. Serial 5 or 10 micron sections, transverse to the plane of the filter, of over a hundred filter-cultures were prepared during the course of the studies. The sections were routinely stained with haematoxylin and eosin which gave the clearest visualization of the filter and contained material. Some cultures were stained with PAS (Hotchkiss) or toluidine blue. The histological observations which are described are representative for the entire series.

All experiments were designed so that comparisons were made between kidney rudiments from opposite sides of the same embryo. Where experiments involved more than two culture types, rudiment pairs were distributed so that each group allowed an equal number of paired comparisons with each other group.

RESULTS

Induction of Kidney Tubules across the 20A Filter

In one of a number of on-the-clot experiments involving the 20A filter 3 types of culture were prepared: (1) dorsal spinal cord below the filter; (2) dorsal spinal cord below and metanephrogenic mesenchyme above the filter; (3) metanephrogenic mesenchyme above the filter with no spinal cord below. Eight cultures of each type were made, two of each being fixed for sectioning at 20, 30, 40 and 52 hours respectively.

Spinal cord behavior was not significantly different in the presence or absence of mesenchyme. The tissue, up to 52 hours, remained healthy, showing little sign of necrosis or degenerative change. The fragment, invariably in close contact with the filter but not always exactly centered under the mesenchyme, frequently reorganized to establish a new lumen (Fig. 4).

Mesenchymal behavior was quite different in the presence or absence of spinal cord. Without cord the mesenchyme usually flattened rapidly and began spreading over the filter surface very much as on a glass substrate [12]. Although there was some variation, spreading generally had started by 20 hours and was well advanced in all cases by 30 hours

(Fig. 5). It continued in later stages, leading to a mesenchymal disc 4–8 cell layers thick which tapered to a peripheral outgrowth sheet a single cell-layer thick. The sheet remained cohesive during the 52-hour culture period with no indication of individual cell migration even at the periphery. At 52 hours mitotic activity was still present, though not conspicuous, and the tissue showed no sign of deterioration or degeneration.

The behavior of similar mesenchyme with spinal cord below the filter was distinctly different. Spreading was very much slower, never led to the degree of thinning exhibited by mesenchyme alone, and epithelial tubule rudiments gradually formed in the mesenchyme immediately above the spinal cord. At 20 hours the difference between the two types of behavior was suggested but not yet clear. Observation of the living cultures revealed more consistent spreading of the mesenchyme when there was no spinal cord below, but considerable individual variation was present, particularly in the group with spinal cord. By 30 hours the difference between the two groups was quite clear in the living cultures and was readily apparent in the sectioned material (Figs. 4 and 5). The mesenchymal mass over spinal cord remained considerably thicker than in the controls. In one of the two cases sectioned the cellular density was greater in the vicinity of the filter and somewhat less above and peripherally (Fig. 4). In the other case the general appearance was similar but the denser area showed local foci of somewhat greater condensation, basophilia and mitotic activity suggesting the beginning of tubule rudiments in close association with the filter. When the living cultures had been examined at this stage only one of the six had been recorded as having early tubule rudiments, and this was not one of the two fixed for sectioning.

At 40 hours tubule rudiments were recognizable in three of the four living cultures, and were clearly visible in sections of the two cultures fixed at this time. The rudiments (Fig. 6) were closely associated with the filter surface in the form of local condensations of basophilic cells set off in variable degree from

the surrounding looser mesenchyme. They were not as yet well organized, only showing the beginnings of orientation in layers and of change of shape to the columnar form characteristic of tubule epithelium. By 52 hours, however, better organization was present, the forming tubules standing out against the looser mesenchymal background (Fig. 7). The cells in the walls of the tubules were orienting in layers and cavitation of the epithelioid masses was beginning.

Fully organized tubules, and their relationships to the filter, are shown in Fig. 8. The culture illustrated is from another experiment than the one just described and was fixed after 65 hours of incubation. Epithelial character is clear and the tubules in this instance are closely associated with the filter. In other instances at this and later stages the epithelial tubules have been observed to be separated from the filter by mesenchyme. At these later stages, too, tubules were sometimes observed beyond the border of the spinal cord, almost certainly due to peripheral migration in association with the centrifugal mesenchymal spreading.

Comparison of Inductive Transmission through AA- and HA-Type Filters

Early trans-filter inductive effects between spinal cord and metanephrogenic mesenchyme were obtained with HA-type filters using the on-the-clot procedure [10]. These effects were of variable intensity and frequently quite weak or absent. Significantly more reliable results were obtained when the dorsal half of the spinal cord consistently was used as the inductive source, following the finding that this region of the cord is more active than more ventral regions [12]. Still greater reliability was achieved when AA filters were substituted for HA.

In two experiments, for example, a total of 31 cultures of metanephrogenic mesenchyme over dorsal spinal cord were prepared, 16 with 20H filters and 15 with 20A filters. On the 4th day of incubation the mesenchyme in 12 out of 15 20A cultures had formed 15 or more well-developed tubule rudiments, the other three had rudiments which were defi-

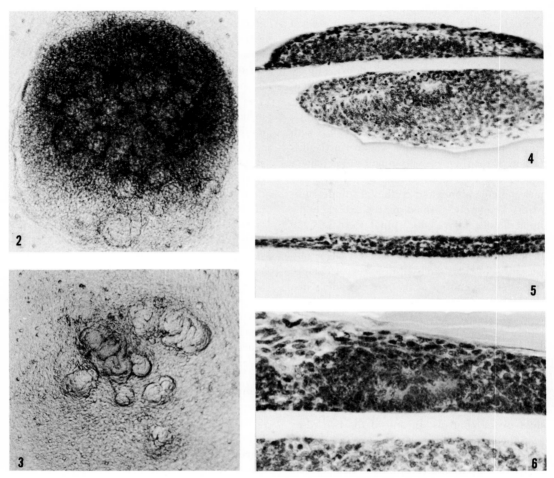

Fig. 2. Tubule rudiments massed over spinal cord with 20A filter between. Near the end of the 3rd day in culture, unfixed. × 60. Fig. 3. Tubule rudiments in metanephrogenic mesenchyme on 20H filter after removal of spinal cord from opposite side. Near the end of the 3rd day in culture, unfixed. × 60. Fig. 4. Metanephrogenic mesenchyme (above) separated from spinal cord (below) by 20A filter. Fixed at 30 hours of incubation. × 160. Fig. 5. Metanephrogenic mesenchyme on 20A filter with no spinal cord below. Fixed at 30 hours of incubation. × 160. Fig. 6. Early formation of tubule rudiment in close association with 20A filter with spinal cord below. Fixed at 40 hours of incubation. × 330.

nite but weakly developed and fewer in number. In the 20H group, however, six cultures were completely negative and none of the other ten had more than five tubule rudiments, all weakly developed. A series of experiments using the 20A filter and varying a number of procedural details led to the supported-ring technique as a method of greater convenience and reliability than the on-the-clot procedure. With this technique, which assured that the spinal cord was initially firmly adherent to the filter and remained in close contact with it subsequently, consistently positive inductions were obtained with both filter types.

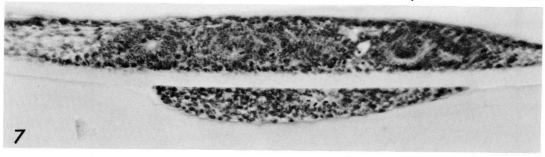

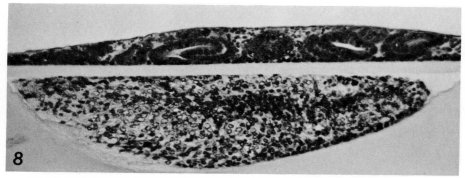

Fig. 7. Conspicuous cavitated tubule rudiments in metanephrogenic mesenchyme separated from spinal cord by 20A filter. Fixed at 52 hours of incubation. Stained with PAS (Hotchkiss). Section is close to edge of spinal cord, material apparently penetrating filter on mesenchymal side represents debris wiped across upper surface of the section during cutting and partly out of focus. × 220. Fig. 8. Well-formed epithelial tubules after 65 hours of incubation of metanephrogenic mesenchyme separated from spinal cord by 20A filter. Note that cord tissue now shows signs of deteriorative changes. × 220.

This is indicated in the following experiment in which the supported-ring procedure was used and all known factors were controlled to provide optimum conditions for inductive effects. Twelve cultures were prepared, six involving 20A and six 20H filters. At approximately 43 hours of incubation early tubule rudiments definitely were present on all six 20A filters, and on three of the 20H filters. The other three 20H filters were questionable. At approximately 65 hours all cultures showed definite tubule rudiments (Figs. 2 and 3). In the 20A group the number of tubules varied from 14 to 20 with an average of 18.2 tubules per culture. In the 20H group the number varied from 4–12 with an average of 7.0 tubules per culture. Inductive effects, therefore, can consistently take place through the 20H filter but apparently at quantitatively lower levels than through the 20A. Tests of the 30A filter in comparison with the 20A showed no reduction of effect.

Visual Penetrability of the Two Filter Types

The significance of the observations for distinguishing among the several proposed hypotheses for inductive mechanisms rests on determination of the nature of the materials which cross the interzone. Considerable interest therefore attaches to the question of what can be seen in the body of the filter. In no case has penetration by whole cells been observed. Stainable material penetrating into AA-type filters from both sides is, however, readily observable with the highest powers of the ordinary light microscope and stands out still more clearly when phase optics are used. The material includes some lightly staining, faintly granular, pseudopodium-like processes which almost certainly are cytoplasmic extension of cells. But more abundant than these recognizable cytoplasmic processes is heavily staining, flocculent or granular material, the

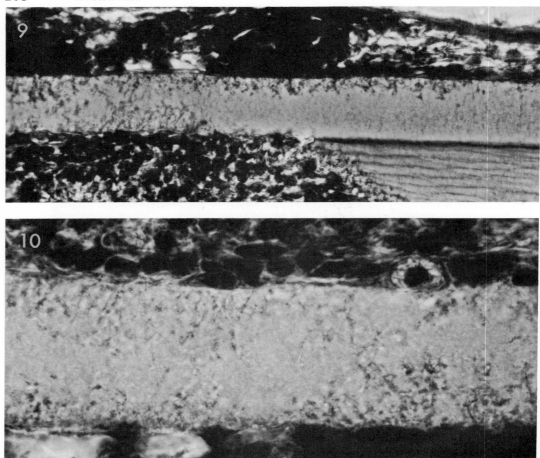

Fig. 9. Penetration of 30A filter as seen in fixed and stained preparation viewed with phase contrast. Fixed on 4th day of incubation. In photographing, tissues were underexposed in order to bring out detail in lighter filter area. Note that penetration occurs from both mesenchyme above and spinal cord below but is most abundant in "interzone," grading off peripherally. × 530. Fig. 10. "Interzone" of same preparation as Fig. 9, viewed with 90 × objective under the same conditions. × 1100.

appearance of which, in all of its variations, neither excludes nor demands its interpretation as cytoplasmic extensions of cells. The material is especially conspicuous in the 30A filter (Figs. 9, 10), where the beads or flocculi are quite large and deeply staining, but it is abundant also in the 20A filter (Fig. 11) where the beads are smaller and the impression is of tortuous fibers with local swellings. In both filters, despite much winding and irregular behavior, the overall orientation of the material is across the filter thickness and "fibers" frequently can be traced from one

edge well past the middle, or even all the way across. The general appearance is one of interpenetrating projections from both sides with ample opportunity for cross-connection.

The visible material is not limited to the interzone, i.e., the region with tissue on both sides (Fig. 9). Similar penetration is seen where only one tissue is present, whether in sections of cultures involving only one tissue, or in sections of cultures involving both tissues but in regions where mesenchyme has spread peripherally beyond the spinal cord. The material appears to be more abundant

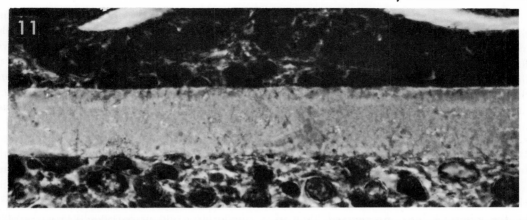

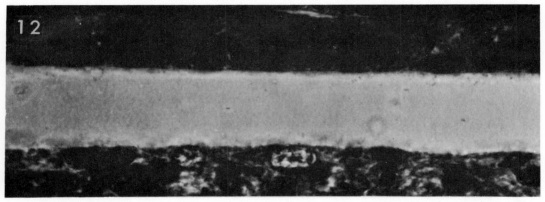

Fig. 11. "Interzone" of culture involving 20A filter viewed as Fig. 10. Fixed on 3rd day of incubation. × 1100. Fig. 12. "Interzone" of culture involving 20H filter viewed as Fig. 10. Fixed on 2nd day of incubation. Note fine shallow penetration along upper border. The photograph does not bring out all penetration visible by direct observation. × 1100.

and conspicuous, however, in the interzone (Fig. 9).

Penetration of the AA-type filter apparently begins quite early. In one experiment in which cultures were fixed after only 6 hours of incubation numerous fine "fibrous" penetrations were present on the mesenchymal side extending deeply into the filter. Material of more granular consistency was present on the spinal cord side, but not as abundantly or penetrating as deeply. Two cultures fixed at 16 hours showed considerably more penetration from both sides. These preliminary observations may imply that material, optically visible following fixation, is present in the filter as early as 6 hours of incubation but does not reach a maximum until some time later. No firm conclusion can be drawn, how-

ever, concerning the possible cytoplasmic nature of the observed material.

Penetrating material is very much less obvious in the HA-type filter (Fig. 12). The general impression with the ordinary light microscope is of almost complete blankness of the filter sections, with only occasional and quite shallow penetration of very fine, slightly beaded fibers. Such penetration has been observed as early as 12 hours of incubation, and on both sides of the filter. With phase optics penetration can be observed to be somewhat more abundant and deeper, but usually does not extend more than 6–8 microns into the filter, i.e., about one-third the filter thickness. However, in a few cultures, particularly among those fixed at 12 hours, fine penetration has been traced deeply enough so that cross-connections between the material from the two sides is conceivable. The fine "fibers" observed grade down in size toward an even finer background fibrillation, just at the limits of phase optics, which is present not only in the region in contact with tissue but in the more peripheral region as well. It appears to reflect the structure of the filter itself.

Deposition of Material in the Filter by Spinal Cord

Penetration of complex materials into both HA- and AA-type filters is further indicated by the following facts. An unfixed piece of spinal cord incubated for approximately 20 hours on the filter in the absence of mesenchyme can readily be lifted off. No visible trace is left in the filter, and no inductive activity is demonstrated if metanephric mesenchyme is cultured over the area of previous spinal cord contact. If, however, the filter with spinal cord in contact is fixed in absolute alcohol-formalin (9:1) for one hour, the spinal cord is found to be tightly cemented to the filter and can be scraped off only with great difficulty. On rehydration the tissue can be removed somewhat more easily, but in either case a "spot" is left in the filter, distinguished from its surroundings by greater translucency (Fig. 13*A*). The spot is sharply

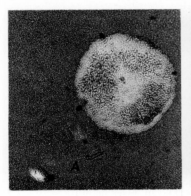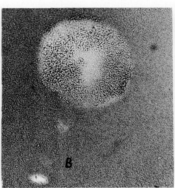

Fig. 13. *A*. "Spot" left in filter after removal of spinal cord incubated for 20 hours in contact with filter and fixed in alcohol-formalin. *B*. Same "spot" after 3 minutes in 3 per cent trypsin (crude) in Tyrode's without calcium and magnesium salts. *C*. As *B*, after 10 minutes.

bounded, conforming closely both to the area of adhesion of the spinal cord and to the area of tubule origin if metanephric mesenchyme were present on the upper surface of the filter. If such mesenchyme is placed on fixed and washed spotted filters, however, it spreads as in controls with no sign of tubule formation.

Exposure of spotted filters to trypsin (either crude or twice recrystallized) solution leads to gradual blurring of the outline (Fig. 13*B*), followed by virtually complete disappearance of the spot at 10 minutes of exposure (Fig. 13*C*). The material responsible for the spot appears to shrink during fixation in the alcohol-formalin, since the spot area is thinned and depressed somewhat with reference to the filter surface to form a small "crater." The spot is refractory to most stains tested. There is no metachromasia and little and variable

orthochromatic staining with toluidine blue, similar variability but occasional strong violet staining with the periodic-acid-Schiff (Hotchkiss) procedure and consistent but very light staining with eosin. On the basis of these incomplete data on fixing and staining reactions it seems probable that the spot represents an area where the filter pores have been filled by a protein-rich material of about the same refractive index as the filter. The data are consistent with, but do not require, the interpretation that some of the involved material is glycoprotein in nature.

DISCUSSION

The conclusion may be drawn that the tubule-inducing effect of spinal cord on metanephrogenic mesenchyme can cross an "interzone" up to 30 microns in thickness without passage of whole cells. The effect is strongest with the AA-type filters used, which are penetrated by probable cytoplasmic processes, and by conspicuous granular and flocculent materials of uncertain nature but clearly visible with the optical microscope following fixation. A weaker but regular effect is obtained with lower porosity HA-type filters, in which definite cytoplasmic processes have not been identified, visible penetration being limited to fine beaded "fibers" usually observed to extend only partly across the filter. From the strong localization of tubule initiation immediately over the spinal cord it seems clear that, whatever the nature of the mechanism involved, activity primarily moves perpendicular to the filter surfaces, with little or no tendency to spread peripherally either on the surfaces or within the body of the filter. This behavior is in harmony with the assertion[4] that the filter pore axes predominantly run in this same direction.

From the nature of the procedures required to obtain optimum effects, and consideration of other procedures which lead to technical failures, it seems probable that intimate contact of both tissues with the filter is essential. This recalls the conclusion from amphibian studies that contact of inductive and responding tissues is required in the normal inductive process, a conclusion which is not necessarily negated even if inductive activity can be concentrated in a supernatant solution under the special circumstances recently reported by Niu and Twitty [21]. In the interaction of spinal cord and metanephrogenic mesenchyme it appears, at least, that the required contact need not be between the tissues *en masse*, providing the interzone has certain not yet defined properties which are possessed by the filter.

Whether some degree of actual cytoplasmic contact is required cannot be regarded as settled by the reported observations. The presence of abundant optically visible material, some of it almost certainly cytoplasmic, in filters passing maximum activity, and the restricted activity across filters which show much less optically visible penetration, suggests some relationship between the visible material and inductive activity. The situation might be interpreted as favoring inductive dependence upon cytoplasmic contact. There is at the moment, however, no assurance that the bulk of the observed material, particularly the fine beaded fibers seen in the HA-type filter, is not precipitated extracellular substance rather than cytoplasm. It is of interest that the appearance recalls the description of processes emitted by amphibian organizer tissue toward overlying epiblast, and the occurrence of fine basophilic filaments in the large pore (3.4 micron) membrane across which Brachet and Hugon de Scœux [5] reported weak induction in the amphibian system. Further study, particularly with the electron microscope, is required before more conclusive statements may be made about the role of cytoplasmic contact in kidney tubule induction. Meanwhile it is worth noting that in relation to inductive mechanisms, too sharp a distinction between cytoplasm *per se* and complex material produced by and immediately contiguous with it may not be of much significance.

The apparent need for contact between tissues and filter, and the strong localization of effects immediately above the spinal cord, seem to militate against the hypothesis of primary involvement of diffusion in tubule induction. The impression is strengthened by the significant restriction of the passage of activity across the 20H filter which, since it does not completely exclude visible penetration as seen in sections, and is permeable to the unidentified proteins of the "spot," would not be expected to exclude most molecules subject to free diffusion. The complexities of transmission through porous membranes [22], however, discourage too rigid a conclusion even on this point.

The available facts, although they do not rule out uncomplicated hypotheses of simple diffusion on the one hand or direct cytoplasmic exchange or interaction on the other, invite consideration of the possible operation of mechanisms in some sense intermediate between the two. The early deposition in the filter by spinal cord of an alcohol-formalin-precipitable and trypsin-digestible material,

[4] See footnote p. 101.

in a pattern corresponding to the area of tubule initiation, points to such a possible intermediate mechanism.

Inductive mediation by a complex, primarily largemolecular material, organized at the macromolecular level so as to behave as a cohesive film closely associated with the cells which produce it, would not only rationalize available data on the spinal cord–metanephrogenic mesenchyme interaction, but would fit as well earlier data on epithelio-mesenchymal interaction in the sub-mandibular salivary rudiment [11]. If such an intercellular or matrix material ordinarily were present only in thin films and hence in relatively small quantities, and were soluble and dispersible to ineffective concentrations in physiological fluids, the requirement for intimate association without direct mass cellular contact would be explained. In this event the significant property of the filter would be to collect, and hold in its highly porous structure, surface exudate produced by the tissues and visualized as the "spot" following alcohol-formalin fixation of spinal cord incubated on the filter. It is conceivable that at least part of what is visible in the sectioned AA-type filter, and possibly all in the HA-type, is material of this sort precipitated in the filter channels. In such complex materials, involving simple and probably also conjugated proteins, adequate basis certainly would exist for the specificity of inductive interaction previously reported in *in vitro* inductive systems [11, 12, 14]. The interaction of such complex matrix materials, each produced by and characteristic of the two tissue masses involved, might well lead to alterations of macromolecular organization, possibly along lines suggested by recent studies of fibrogenesis [15, 17]. If the materials were not only produced by the tissues but, as the immediate micro-environment of the cellular components also influenced their character and behavior [7], the alterations resulting from interaction of two dissimilar films might provide the stimulus for the striking cellular reorganization involved in the transformation of massed mesenchyme into epithelial tubules. A speculation of this sort, while not demanded by the facts now available, is in harmony with earlier suggestions of the morphogenetic importance of embryonic ground substance [3, 8, 24] and would serve to link inductive phenomena with emerging understanding of the importance of ground substance and the more highly polymerized components of the matrix in the architecture and function of adult tissues [2, 7, 13].

SUMMARY

1. The tubule-inducing effect of embryonic mouse spinal cord on metanephrogenic mesenchyme can be transmitted across membrane filters of 20–30 microns thickness.

2. The filters completely prevent exchange of cells between the interacting tissues.

3. Across two types of membrane of differing porosity the effects are strongest in the more porous type where considerable penetration into the filter is visible in fixed material and weaker but definitely present in the less porous type where penetration is at a minimum.

4. The visible material penetrating the more porous filter includes probable cytoplasmic processes, in addition to other material of uncertain nature. The sparse material penetrating the less porous filter does not include any readily identifiable cytoplasmic processes, but the possibility of their existence is not excluded pending further studies.

5. An alcohol-formalin-fixable and trypsin-digestible material is deposited in the filter during incubation in contact with spinal cord. The pattern of its distribution appears to correspond with the area of tubule-initiation when mesenchyme is present.

6. The data are discussed in relation to the nature of inductive mechanisms, and the speculation is advanced that intercellular matrix or ground substance may play a significant role.

REFERENCES

1. Algire, G., J. Weaver, and R. Prehn, *J. Natl. Cancer Inst.* **15,** 493 (1954).
2. Asboe-Hansen, G., *Connective Tissue in Health and Disease.* Munksgaard, Copenhagen, 1954.

3. Baitsell, G. A., *Quart. J. Microscop. Sci.* **69**, 571 (1925).

4. Brachet, J., *Experientia* **6**, 56 (1950).

5. Brachet, J. and F. Hugon de Scœux, *Commun. 3mes Journées Cyto-embryol. belgoneerland*, **1949**, 56 (1949).

6. Burns, R. K., in B. H. Willier, P. Weiss, and V. Hamburger, *Analysis of Development*, p. 462. W. B. Saunders, 1955.

7. Duran-Reynals, F., *Ann. N.Y. Acad. Sci.* **52** (7), 946 (1950).

8. Gray, J., *Brit. J. Exptl. Biol.* **3**, 167 (1926).

9. Goetz, A. and N. Tsuneishi, *J. Amer. Water Works Assn.* **43**, 943 (1951).

10. Grobstein, C., *Nature* **172**, 869 (1953).

11. ——— *J. Exptl. Zool.* **124**, 383 (1953).

12. ——— *J. Exptl. Zool.* **130**, (2) (1955).

13. ——— in D. Rudnick, *Aspects of Synthesis and Order in Growth*, p. 233. Princeton University Press, 1955.

14. Grobstein, C. and H. Holtzer, *J. Exptl. Zool.* **128**, 333 (1955).

15. Gross, J., J. H. Highberger, and F. O. Schmitt, *Proc. Soc. Exptl. Biol. Med.* **80**, 462 (1952).

16. Gruenwald, P., *Ann. N.Y. Acad. Sci.* **55** (2), 142 (1952).

17. Highberger, J. H., J. Gross, and F. O. Schmitt, *Proc. Natl. Acad. Sci.* **37**, 286 (1951).

18. Holtfreter, J., *Roux' Arch. f. Entwicklungsmech.* **128**, 584 (1933).

19. Honold, E. and E. L. Skau, *Science* **120**, 805 (1954).

20. McKeehan, M. S., *J. Exptl. Zool.* **117**, 31 (1951).

21. Niu, M. C. and V. C. Twitty, *Proc. Natl. Acad. Sci.* **39**, 985 (1953).

22. Pappenheimer, J. R., *Physiol. Rev.* **33**, 387 (1953).

23. Tung, T., Y. Tung, and C. Chang, *Proc. Zool. Soc. London* **118**, 1134 (1949).

24. Weiss, P., *Am. Naturalist* **67**, 322 (1933).

3

Cytodifferentiation and Cell Division

EMBRYONIC CELLS in general undergo a number of cell divisions before they "begin" to differentiate. An erythrocyte or a muscle cell or any specialized cell does not arise from a blastomere or other early embryonic precursor without divisions. Whether cells are obliged to divide a *set* number of times in order to attain a specific differentiated state is not known. In fact it is not clear why they must divide at all in order to reach their final specialized conditions.

There are several possibilities. Heritable activation or repression of cistrons may take place primarily at the time of chromosome replication or they might occur at some other time; but in either event epigenetic* modifications might be triggered step by step by environmental changes which a succession of divisions create.

Berrill (1961) has presented data that the number of divisions which occurs at each stage of the developmental process is relatively constant and is a species characteristic. For example, to make an Amphioxus blastula, the zygote divides nine to ten times; to make a notochord, the presumptive material divides eight to nine times; and to make tail muscle, presumptive cells divide eight to nine times. Other sets of numbers were shown to be characteristic for Styela, Triturus, etc.

There is at least one example that a cell can transform from one state into another without the help of the division process. Immersion of ameboid Naegleria cells in distilled water will transform them into Englenoid-shaped cells having a stiff cuticle (Willmer 1963). This example may be one of a few exceptions to an otherwise general rule of development.

A corollary concern is the capacity of cells to differentiate after having divided more times than they ordinarily would have. It is considered in the four papers which make up this chapter.

A general review of older literature on the performance of differentiated cells *in vitro* has appeared recently Grobstein (1959). The overall impression is that cells lose phenotypic characteristics as a result of cell divisions *in vitro*. *Holtzer, Abbott, Lash, and Holtzer (1960)*† demonstrated clearly the loss of both biochemical and morphological characteristics associated with cartilage cells when these cells are grown *in vitro* as a dividing population.

This may be contrasted with *Konisberg's (1963)* results in which progeny arising from a single already differentiated cell form muscle cells and myotubes. Also Sato and Buonassisi (1964) found that alterations which cells undergo *in vitro* are reversible. Corticotropin secreting cell cultures can increase by a factor of 10^{50} and

---

* The word is used here to signify changes in expression of gene potential as distinguished from genetic changes which would modify the size, composition, base sequence of amount of DNA in a cell (Luria 1960).

† Italicized references indicate articles which appear in this book.

regain hormonal activity when transferred to an animal host. Bell, Schuler, and Merrill (1964) have shown that gradual loss of ability to differentiate occurs after growth *in vitro* without regard to division rate. Cultured skin cells lose their capacity to engage in feather morphogenesis or to synthesize skin-specific proteins at the same rate whether they are grown as a static or as a dividing population.

Recently Rappaport and Howze (1965) made the startling discovery that the loss of the differentiated state in culture can be traced directly to the means by which cells are dissociated and to the glass on which they are grown. For example, adult liver cells which are dissociated by tetraphenyl boron and then grown on specially prepared glass will retain their distinctive morphology for over a year even though they are fed a completely defined medium.

Retention of the capacity of cells growing in organisms to differentiate after dividing a great many times is illustrated by the work of *Stewart* (*1958*) and *Stephens* (*1960*). Also Hadorn (1963) has grown imaginal discs (wing, leg, germinal, etc.) in the body cavities of adult Drosophila and subcultured these partially differentiated but dividing cells for 50 or more times. If each cell divided only twice in each host (they probably divide many more times), the original line would have been diluted 100 fold. Despite the large number of cell divisions, when the progeny are challenged with hormone, a certain number differentiate in accordance with their original commitments, i.e., wing primordia become wing, and leg become leg, etc.

A further question to be asked about a dividing cell is whether it can synthesize a specialized product during periods of active division. In the germinal epithelium of the regenerating lens, Yamada detected alpha and beta crystallins immunologically. These epithelial cells continue to divide and by divisions are moved to the periphery of the lens where they ultimately differentiate into fiber cells. At that time they first begin to synthesize gamma crystallin. Hence during differentiation some of the structural proteins of the lens are made in cells which are in the process of dividing while others are made after cell divisions have ceased. A similar course of events occurs in the developing feather (Bell 1965; Malt and Bell 1965). In developing muscle on the other hand Holtzer (1961), and Stockdale and Holtzer (1961) have localized muscle proteins only in nondividing cells. But the problem is more complex than it seems. The number of structural proteins found in a tissue such as muscle may be greater than current methods can resolve. Hence it is too early to propose that dividing cells do not synthesize characteristic structural proteins. Such a conclusion must await identification of all proteins which uniquely characterize a particular differentiated cell.

There is evidence from both plant and animal cells that some divisions are asymmetrical. In the fern, for example, the filament cells which arise from the spore upon division give rise to one filament cell and one specialized rhizoid cell. When basal epidermal cells and basal cells of the glandular epithelium of the gut divide, one daughter cell remains a germinal cell, the other differentiates into a glandular cell or into a cell that will keratinize. Tchen *et al.* (1964) have proposed that unpigmented melanoblasts are stem cells. Daughter cells consist of one pigmented melanocyte and one unpigmented blast cell.

We can ask whether the decision of one of a pair of cells to specialize in each of the cases cited is made before or after chromosome duplication or before or after mitosis.

In review, the key questions raised concerned the number of cell divisions prerequisite for attaining a specific differentiated state, the retention, loss or apparent loss of both morphological and biochemical characteristics *in vitro*, retention of the capacity to differentiate by cells which divide a great many times in organisms, synthesis of specialized products by dividing cells, and asymmetrical divisions.

REFERENCES

1. Bell, E. (1965). Differentiation of skin. In R. Dehaan and H. Ursprung (eds.), *Organogenesis*, Holt, Rinehart and Winston, New York.
2. Bell, E., M. Schuler, and C. Merrill (1964). Feather formation and synthesis of keratin by primary skin cells and by skin cells grown *in vitro*. In W. Montagna (ed.), *The Epidermis*, Academic Press, New York, pp. 35–56.
3. Berrill, N. J. (1961). *Growth, Development and Pattern*, Freeman, San Francisco.
4. Grobstein, C. (1959). Differentiation of Vertebrate Cells. In J. Brachet and A. Mirsky (eds.), *The Cell*, Vol. 1, Academic Press, New York, pp. 437–496.
5. Hadorn, E. (1963). Differenzierungsleistungen wiederholt fragmentierter teilstucke mannlicher genitalscheiben von *Drosophila melanogaster* nach kultur *in vivo*. Develop. Biol. **7**:617–629.
6. Holtzer, H. (1961). Aspects of chondrogenesis and myogenesis. In D. Rudnick (ed.), *Synthesis of Molecular and Cellular Structure*, Ronald Press, New York, pp. 35–87.
7. Luria, S. E. (1960). Viruses, cancer cells, and the genetic concept of virus infection. *Cancer Res.* **20**:677–688.

8. Malt, R., and E. Bell (1965). Feather proteins during embryonic development. *Nature*. In press.
9. Rappaport, C., and G. B. Howze (1964). Dissociation of adult mouse liver into single cell suspensions with sodium tetraphenylboron (TPB). T. T. Puck (ed.), *Animal Cell News Letter.* **5**:4–9.
10. Sata, G. H., and V. Buonassisi (1964). Hormone-secreting cultures of endocrine tumor origin. In W. Rutter (ed.), *Metabolic Control Mechanisms in Animal Cells, Natl. Cancer Inst. Mon.* **13**, 1, pp. 81–91, Government Printing Office, Washington, D.C.
11. Stockdale, F., and H. Holtzer (1961). DNA synthesis and myogenesis. *Exptl. Cell Res.* **24**:508–520.
12. Tchen, T. T., R. Ammerall, K. Kim, C. Wilson, W. Chavin, and F. Hu (1964). Studies on the hormone-induced differentiation of melanoblasts into melanocytes in explants from xanthic goldfish tailfin. In W. Rutter (ed.), *Metabolic Control Mechanisms in Animal Cells, Natl. Cancer Inst. Mon.* **13**, pp. 67–80, Government Printing Office, Washington, D.C.
13. Willmer, E. N. (1963). Differentiation in Naegleria. In G. E. Fogg (ed.), *Cell Differentiation*, No. XVII, pp. 215–233, Cambridge Univ. Press, Cambridge, England.

Clonal Analysis of Myogenesis

IRWIN R. KONIGSBERG

Its relevance to the general problem of the stability of cell-type in cultured animal cells is discussed.

Ancient problems in biology, like the cities of antiquity, are frequently covered by many strata deposited during successive epochs. Knowing the scientific fashions of a given period, we can often classify the strata and date the artifacts therein, but unless we have a new way of examining the old ruins it is frequently better to leave them undisturbed than to deposit another layer of sediment.

One of the venerable controversies of developmental biology that has been repeatedly excavated is the problem of the stability of the differentiated state. The two experimental situations which have been employed to explore this question are regeneration, most popularly of the amphibian limb, and the behavior of cells in tissue culture.

From the facts emerging in recent studies

Reprinted from *Science*, **140**, No. 3573, 1273–1284 (June 21, 1963). Copyright © 1963 by the American Association for the Advancement of Science.

of regeneration where the newer ways of examining the phenomenon were utilized (*1*), we may draw three conclusions.

1. Differentiated cells need not be irreversibly fixed "postmitotics."

2. If differentiated cells are appropriately stimulated in some manner by the trauma of amputation, they may dedifferentiate, in the sense of losing some of their characteristic structures, regaining some of the cytological features typical of an earlier state of differentiation.

3. Such dedifferentiated cells may proliferate and finally redifferentiate. Whether they redifferentiate, invariably, into cells of the same type as the progenitor cell is a question difficult to resolve.

The tissue-culture approach, thus far, has been less fruitful. One observes events which superficially resemble the dedifferentiative and proliferative stages of regeneration (*2*). However, redifferentiation or even retention of some aspects of the differentiated state are rarer events (*3*). We might reasonably question the extent, then, to which the two situations are analogous. Are we indeed, in tissue culture, dealing with a set of conditions which favor dedifferentiation but are insufficient for initiating or supporting redifferentiation? Alternatively, the phenomenon observed in culture may be a completely atypical response unrelated to any process occurring *in vivo*. The failure of culture techniques to yield results conforming to what might be predicted may indicate either that the techniques are, as yet, imperfect or that they place demands on the cell which, because of its intrinsic limitations, it cannot fully meet. These are by no means novel postulates (see *4*). They are worthy of re-examination only because we do have new ways of examining the old problems.

The observed loss of overt indices of differentiation of cells in culture could arise by way of either of two general mechanisms. Culture conditions might select ubiquitous cell types whose identity in culture might be difficult to establish; or the progeny of differentiated cells might indeed become altered in response to some aspect of the artificial environment.

Two different approaches to the question have been reported recently. One approach exploits the two tissues, cartilage (*5*) and pigmented retina (*6*), which can reasonably be assumed to be homogeneous with respect to cell type. In both cases a rapid alteration in the biosynthetic capacity of the monolayered cells can be demonstrated, which cannot be ascribed to selection.

Another attack on the same question, in which both enzymological and immunochemical criteria are employed, demonstrates with equal clarity the operation of selection in the establishment of cell populations derived from the livers of newborn rats (*7*).

These two sets of results are not in conflict. They do illustrate, however, the need for circumspection and the danger of premature generalization. At the present time we can only evaluate data in relation to a given cell type or population, at a specific time in its ontogenetic history, and under a particular set of conditions.

Selection of cell types, then, cannot explain every case of morphological simplification (*8*). However, the criteria used in establishing culture conditions may select not only between different cell types but among the various metabolic capabilities of a single type of cell. In establishing conditions for the survival and growth of a particular cell we would be selecting for cellular activities common to all cells rather than for those peculiar to the type in question.

CELL AND ORGAN CULTURE CONTRASTED

Culture conditions have been devised, however, which do promote the maintenance of the differentiated state and, in fact, the reasonably normal continuance of developmental sequences. Developed largely by the group working at the Strangeways Research Laboratory in Cambridge, these techniques comprise the methodology of organ culture (*9*). They differ considerably from tissue and cell culture in several respects.

1. The normal tissue architecture is preserved.

2. The explant consists of a relatively compact mass of cells cultured under conditions which discourage cell migration and spreading of the explant.

3. Cell proliferation, it is generally thought, is minimal.

We have, then, two contrasting approaches; one favors cellular differentiation whereas the other promotes the morphological and biochemical simplification of the cell population. The obvious conclusion is that somewhere among the several points of difference between these techniques lie the clues to the problem of morphological simplification *in vitro*.

TISSUE AND CELL INTERACTIONS

Preservation of normal tissue relationships is undoubtedly significant in many instances. Many modes of differentiation depend upon the interaction of populations of *dissimilar* cells.

However, simplification frequently involves cytological features established after such interactions have occurred. Therefore, it seems improbable that cell-type instability is in all cases a result of disruption of precisely this type of "inductive" interaction.

Tissue and cell interactions are by no means limited to early embryogenesis, nor are they exclusively developmental phenomena. Endocrine regulation, trophic effects of nerve upon muscle, regulation of the internal milieu by the specialized functions of various organs are all forms of cell interactions.

One class of interactions whose significance is now being recognized is the interaction of embryonic cells of *similar* ontogenetic fate (10). This form of interaction is facilitated by the use, in organ culture, of compact masses of cells and the retardation of their dispersion through migration. A number of observations have shown a correlation between the degree of cell dispersion and the loss of developmental expression (11).

Conversely, either more diversified or more complete differentiation has been promoted by fusing and culturing progressively larger amounts of the same embryonic region (12)

or by crowding embryos (13) or embryonic primordia (14) into relatively small volumes of medium. Such observations have been classified as "tissue mass effects."

A body of comparable observations can be assembled which relate "mass effects" not specifically to cellular differentiation but to survival and multiplication in cell culture. The use of "conditioned medium" by Earle's group (15) to bring about cloning of single cells is one excellent example.

Another example is the ingenious use by Puck and Marcus (see 16) of irradiated "feeder layers" to support single-cell plating. From Puck's group, also, has come the demonstration that at least one of the roles of the feeder layer is the supplementation of an initially inadequate medium through the metabolic activities of the irradiated cells (see 17).

ROLE OF POPULATION DENSITY

The role of cell density in augmenting or "conditioning" the medium is nowhere more explicitly (and beautifully) demonstrated than in the work of Eagle and Piez (18). Thirteen amino acids and eight vitamins have been shown (19) to be "essential" for a broad spectrum of mammalian cells. In addition, three amino acids are required by specific cell lines or under specific culture conditions. At least six of these amino acids and one vitamin can, in fact, be synthesized by most of the cells which show the apparent requirement. The requirement for each, however, exists only at low cell density. As cell density is increased, a level is reached above which exogenous amino acid is no longer essential. Confirmation of the equilibration of the intercellular metabolic pool with the external culture medium is evident in the data presented on the gradual accumulation of amino acids as a function of both time and initial cell density. Within a given cell strain, the critical cell density differs for each amino acid. Thus, varying the size of the inoculum might result in the establishment of qualitatively different milieus invoking, perhaps, different expressions of the cell's biosynthetic capacities.

The two sets of phenomena, the one group dealing with activities (such as survival and growth) that are common to all cells and the other dealing with cell-specific properties, may have more than a superficial relationship (see *20*). Both maintenance and proliferation, on the one hand, and cytodifferentiation, on the other, depend on the maintenance of an adequate milieu, although the specific requirements for the two may be different.

Indeed, many disparate experimental situations have demonstrated that the component processes of development—growth, maintenance, differentiation, and morphogenesis—are separable (*21*). Thus, culture conditions may be adequate for maintenance and proliferation but may fail to support cytodifferentiation. With increasing cell mass relative to the volume of medium, a more nearly adequate environment for supporting differentiation might be established either by limiting leaching of cell components or by permitting cross-feeding within the population, either directly or by way of the medium. One might predict, on the basis of these considerations, that factors which limit diffusion or replace molecular species lost by diffusion might permit the attainment of a higher degree of differentiation.

The examples, cited earlier, of the effects of tissue mass on subsequent developmental expression are all amenable to such an interpretation. All involve a reduction either of the surface-volume ratio of the tissue mass or of the ratio of the volume of the medium to that of the cells. In a sense, they may represent the transitional states between organ and cell culture. Modifications of cell- and tissue-culture techniques which restrict losses by the cells to the extracellular compartment also seem to promote cytodifferentiation.

For example, recent experiments of Rose and his collaborators (*22*), in which cells were cultivated between sheets of dialysis membrane, do in fact demonstrate that cellular differentiation occurs in that portion of the culture which is confined. In like manner, an agar overlay has been employed in differentiating monolayer cultures, yielding comparable results (*23*).

Similarly, my associates and I have demonstrated that when conditioned medium is used in single-cell platings of skeletal muscle there is a higher incidence of differentiated colonies than there is when freshly prepared medium is used (*24*).

Since frequent change of medium could negate the role of the cell mass, it is of interest that an optimal frequency of replacement has been demonstrated with respect to myogenesis (see *25*).

THE SYNTHETIC ENVIRONMENT

Failure to obtain normal differentiation of a particular cell type in a synthetic environment might merely reflect inadequate reproduction of *in vivo* conditions. The criteria normally applied to appraise a particular set

TABLE 1. Plating efficiency and frequency of muscle differentiation in 20 experiments from June through December 1962, in which conditioned medium was used (see *60*); means, standard deviations $\{(s[x - \bar{x}]^2/[n-1])^{1/2}\}$, and ranges were derived from pooled sample of 69 petri plates

Total Colonies (*N*)	Total Muscle Colonies (*N*)	Plating Efficiency* Colonies/(Cells Plated) × 100		Frequency of Muscle Differentiation [(Muscle Colonies)/(Total Colonies) × 100]	
		Mean (± Standard Deviation, %)	Range (%)	Mean (± Standard Deviation, %)	Range (%)
3104		17.6 ± 5.9	$5.5 - 37.0$		
	1313			41.3 ± 12.1	$14.8 - 64.6$

* Inoculum sizes (number of cells per petri plate) were as follows: 100 in 1 experiment, 200 in 11 experiments; 400 in 8 experiments.

of culture conditions—survival, growth, and cytological appearance—are of limited value. Although one would not expect normal cell function in moribund cells, the healthy appearance of a cell is no guarantee that culture conditions are adequate for its differentiation. The uncertainty introduced by a limitless array of possible variables precludes the assumption that it is the inherent capacity of the cell that is being tested rather than the contrived milieu (see *26*).

A variety of culture media have been devised, representing an impressive application of skill and energy. Since they were developed primarily to maintain viable proliferating cells, their adequacy in supporting any specific differentiation would be fortuitous. There is, however, no *a priori* reason to believe that media which adequately support specific differentiation are unattainable.

One might expect to be confronted with the necessity not only of supplying and adjusting the amounts of known nutrients but also of providing more complex molecular entities whose concentration may normally be small and whose structures, properties, and mechanism of action are unknown (see *27*). Practical considerations, at present, may dictate the use of the less readily definable approaches cited earlier. This may seem a retrograde step in view of the important strides made in the elaboration of defined media; however, for the developmental biologist the choice between ill-defined cells cultivated in well-defined media and well-defined cells cultivated in ill-defined media is no choice at all (see also *28*).

DISAGGREGATION DAMAGE

An important distinction between organ and cell culture arises out of the procedures employed in the latter to render organized tissues into cell suspensions. It is often difficult to assess the cellular damage effected by mechanical factors, enzymatic digestion, and exposure to solutions which are frequently unphysiological (*29*). Even when no gross lesion is discernible (*30*), we cannot assume that cell function is unimpaired.

The damage may be sublethal, merely accelerating losses due to diffusion. Also, eventual expression of this damage may vary with the culture technique subsequently employed. For example, single-cell plating was feasible, at first, only in the presence of a feeder layer (*16*). The use of more rapid and gentle trypsinization procedures, as well as the development of a more complete medium, made it possible to eliminate the feeder layer (*31*). Similarly, dispersed cells which are subsequently reaggregated exhibit quite normal differentiation (*32*), despite prior exposure to conditions which, one would judge, would not facilitate single-cell plating. (It is doubtful whether such cells could develop as normally in monolayer culture as they do in a reaggregate.)

Perhaps an even more insidious form of damage, insofar as studies of morphological simplification are concerned, is that affecting the genetic apparatus itself. Threefold increases in mitotic and chromosomal abnormalities above control levels have been demonstrated in primary cultures prepared from embryonic mouse tissues subjected to prolonged (3 hours) trypsinization (*33*). Aneuploidy in 5 to 10 percent of the population of trypsinized embryonic cells has been reported after only 24 hours in culture (*34*).

That the judicious use of trypsin does not invariably produce such defects is attested to by the work of Hayflick and Moorhead (*35*), who maintained true diploid strains derived from human fetal tissues through as many as 50 passages. Although most strains were established from minced tissue, serial transfer was affected after brief trypsinization (0.25 percent Difco trypsin 1:250; digestion time, 15 minutes). Unfortunately, trypsin has generally been used rather indiscriminately. In preparing cell suspensions from tissue for primary explantation as monolayers, concentrations ranging from 0.05 to 1.00 percent trypsin (Difco 1:250 or the equivalent) have been used, with digestion times varying from 5 minutes to 3 hours. That cells subjected to the extremes of such treatment survive and multiply is surprising; that they may fail to retain all of their normal functions is not.

PROLIFERATION VERSUS DIFFERENTIATION

Organ culture, again as opposed to cell and tissue culture, is generally thought to be attended by little proliferative activity. Fell, however, has cited observations of her own which are diametrically opposed to this generalization. Further, she points out that those factors which promote proliferation also promote cell migration. It is the latter phenomenon, she suggests, which may prevent differentiation (*36*).

The assumption that cell division and the accumulation of specific cell products are mutually antagonistic processes is based primarily on the observation that the two processes are not concurrent *in vivo*. It is assumed that the same relationship holds for cultured cells. It may very well be that it does. However, there is reason to doubt that morphological simplification is invariably the result of this postulated antagonism alone, since the phenomenon in culture is not strictly parallel to the observations made *in vivo*. After proliferative activity has ceased *in vivo*, specific cell products can be detected, both during embryogenesis and in regeneration. Although cell cultures (unless they are subdivided) eventually reach a "stationary" phase (*37*), they do not then necessarily differentiate or redifferentiate. (See *26* and *38* for critical reviews of the reversibility of simplification in culture.) The best-documented case for reversibility concerns the loss and reaccumulation of pigment in cultures of iris and pigmented retina (*6, 38, 39*). The reappearance of pigment occurs under conditions in which the cells are crowded but in which proliferation is also reduced.

A recent re-examination of the pigment-cell problem indicates, however, that the primary event in depigmentation is not related to cell division (*6*). Dopa oxidase activity (but not cytochrome oxidase) drops sharply shortly after plating of pure suspensions of retinal pigment cells, reaching minimal levels before any cell division has occurred in some cultures, or after one division, at most, in others.

Tyrosinase-dependent incorporation of tyrosine-C^{14} declines in similar fashion, and secondarily, cell division causes dilution of the pre-existing pigment.

Apparently healthy, dispersed embryonic thyroid cells also lose hormone and hormone precursors within the first 3 to 5 days of culture, despite the absence of significant proliferative activity (*40*). Similarly, bovine mammary gland cells lose the ability to synthesize lactose within 24 hours after plating (*41*).

A few other rough approximations of the rate of alteration are as follows.

1. Loss of a specific kidney antigen, $3\frac{1}{2}$ days, 2.6 divisions (*42*).
2. Loss of the capacity to incorporate sulfur-35 into chondroitin sulfate, 4 days, maximum of 3 divisions (*5*).
3. Loss of the ability to reaggregate, 2 to 3 days (*43, 44*).

Other cell-specific properties have been reported to persist for longer periods (*3, 45, 46*), and in a few serially propagated cell strains the capacity to synthesize specific cell products is retained through many generations (*3, 38*). Even within the same cell type the various aspects of functional specificity are lost at different rates (*41*) or show varying degrees of stability (*40*). Moreover, alteration is not restricted to cell-specific proteins (*47*). Indeed, all cellular activities may be altered in culture, to greater or lesser extent.

It is clear that the primary event in cell alteration is not, in all cases, related to proliferation. There is, in fact, no conclusive demonstration that proliferation is directly responsible for cell alteration in any specific case.

UTILITY OF CLONAL ANALYSIS

The problem of simplification *in vitro* has currency not merely because, like Everest, "it is there," but because it represents a serious impediment to analysis.

Developmental phenomena in animal cells have, of necessity, been studied in cell populations of varying, and frequently great, heterogeneity. This limitation imposes two types of uncertainty. The first type is generated by the lack of precision inherent in dealing with mixed populations. In investigations of the molecular basis of cytodifferentiation we are all too frequently in the position of applying exact biochemical analysis to imprecisely defined biological material.

Secondly, we are unable to discriminate between cellular properties and properties which are consequences of supracellular organization. The growing body of evidence related to tissue mass effects in cytodifferentiation has prompted a re-examination of some of the classical concepts of the cellular basis of development (*11*). Indeed, the conventional approaches of developmental biology cannot specifically exclude the possibility that what we assume in many cases to be properties of the cells are in fact properties of the aggregate. The significant aspect of the dependence on mass may very well be simply an expression of the elementary physical laws governing diffusion, either between cells or into an extracellular compartment. However, the real impact of the observations relating to mass effects is that they delineate an important area of conceptual ambiguity.

We have, for these reasons, been engaged in analyzing myogenesis in colonial derivatives of freshly isolated individual cells from the leg musculature of 11- to 12-day chick embryos.

Our earlier studies of such cell populations grown as monolayers from mass inocula (*48–50*) indicated that dispersed cell culture was not, in itself, incompatible with the attainment of reasonably normal differentiation. The developmental sequence in such cultures can be summarized briefly as follows. Initially these cultures appear to be composed of fibroblast-like cells which multiply with a mean generation time of approximately 24 hours. As confluency is attained, long multinuclear cells form, probably by a process of successive cell fusion (see *48, 50–54*). The syncytia are further distinguished from the interspersed mononucleated cells by their intense cytoplasmic basophilia [presumably

ribonucleic acid (*51, 55*)] and by the appearance of large numbers of mitochondria (*56*) as well as histochemically demonstrable mitochondrial enzymes (*50, 57*). Shortly after their formation, vigorous spontaneous contractions can be observed in the elongated muscle cells. Concomitantly, the progressive accumulation of cross-striated myofibrils has been observed (*49*), along with a progressive increase in creatine-phosphokinase activity (*58*).

CLONAL ANALYSIS OF MYOGENESIS

Although monolayer culturing permitted a degree of control and sample replication far more favorable than that offered by conditions in the egg, it did not obviate the problem of cellular heterogeneity. To circumvent this limitation, the plating technique of Puck and his associates (*35*) was applied in a study of the myogenic differentiation of clones derived from single muscle cells (*24*). After culture for a sufficient length of time (10 to 13 days), the unmistakable indices of myogenic differentiation were observed in a small number (approximately 10 percent) of the colonies which had developed. We have since been able to increase the frequency of occurrence of differentiated colonies to more practical levels through the use of conditioned medium.

This approach was suggested by a parallel investigation directed toward exploring the relationship, observed earlier (*50*), between cell density and myotube formation. In the course of our study we found that medium recovered from confluent monolayer cultures induced myotube formation in newly initiated mass cultures some 24 hours earlier than in sister cultures in freshly prepared medium (*59*). By using an empirically determined technique (*60*), we are now able to obtain conditioned medium which consistently gives a higher frequency of differentiated colonies than was observed earlier.

Of all the factors tested thus far, the type of medium used seems to have the greatest influence on the frequency of formation of differentiated colonies. Figure 1, for example, shows a comparison of two plates established

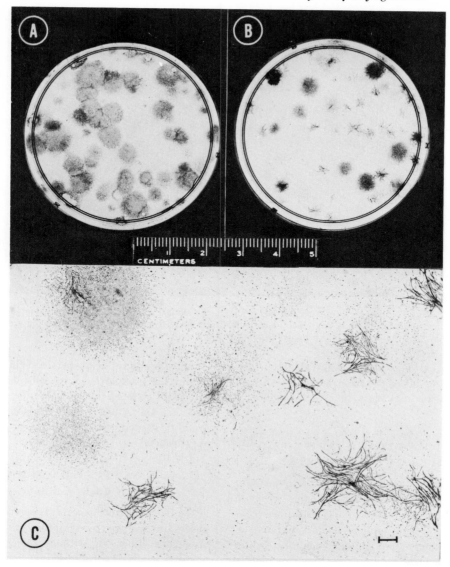

Fig. 1. Replicate cultures established with identical aliquots of the same cell suspension plated into equal volumes of conditioned medium prepared by two different methods. For *A*, fresh medium contained 5 percent embryo extract; the period of "conditioning" was limited to 3 days. For *B*, fresh medium contained 10 percent embryo extract; the period of conditioning was 6 days. The apparent colony density is deceptive, due to the large number of the smaller muscle colonies in *B*. (*C*) An area of *B* at higher magnification; the scale marker represents 1.0 mm.

with identical aliquots of the same cell suspension in conditioned medium prepared by two different methods. Although the plating efficiency is similar in the two cases, 49 percent of the colonies in group B are differentiated muscle colonies, in contrast to 1.8 percent in group A. Whether the effect operates by selection or by the promotion of differentiation is not known.

In obtaining the data presented below, the conditioning technique described (*60*) was used, and the data apply only to cultures grown in that medium. The variability in plating efficiency and the frequency of differ-

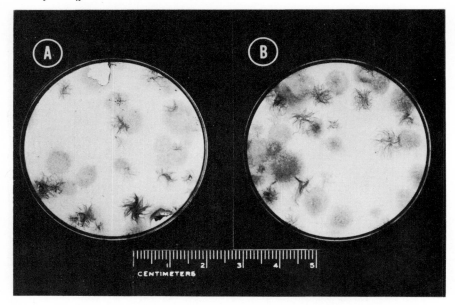

Fig. 2. Plating cultures established with inocula of 200 cells, freshly isolated from the leg musculature of 12-day chick embryos. Cultures were fixed on day 13 (*A*) and on day 16 (*B*). Staining was in Ehrlich's hematoxylin (no counterstain).

entiation can be judged from Table 1, which summarizes all of the experiments performed with this medium from June to December of 1962.

IDENTIFICATION OF MUSCLE COLONIES

In addition to their higher frequency of differentiation, individual colonies of both muscle and nonmuscle cells grown in conditioned medium tend to be larger (at comparable times) than similar colonies grown in unconditioned medium, and they are readily identified by macroscopic features alone.

In the cultures shown in Fig. 2, two distinctly different colonial morphologies can be observed: (i) colonies with a more or less regular circular outline, with little internal structural detail discernible with the unaided eye, and (ii) colonies which have an irregular, frequently elongated shape and which appear to be composed of darkly stained fibers which are often aligned, forming large swirls.

These "fibers," at higher magnification, are revealed to be elongated multinuclear cells (see Fig. 3), comparable to the myotubes observed in monolayer culture. They can be

demonstrated, by appropriate techniques, to obtain the cross-striated myofibrillar pattern typical of striated muscle. The disk-like colonies, on the other hand, are composed of greatly flattened cells, generally fibroblastic in appearance.

DIAGNOSTIC FEATURES OF SINGLE CELLS

We have, up to this point, been considering observations made by sampling our material at regular intervals without attempting sequential analysis of individual clones. The higher incidence of differentiated colonies obtained with conditioned medium made the latter approach practical.

Petri plates seeded with 200 cells each were examined 18 to 24 hours after plating; phase-contrast optics were used at a magnification of 100 diameters. Cells were selected which had neither divided nor started to divide and which were separated by at least 4 millimeters from the nearest neighbor. The position of the cell was marked on the bottom of the petri plate by means of an inking slide marker (Leitz). Photographic records were made at regular intervals.

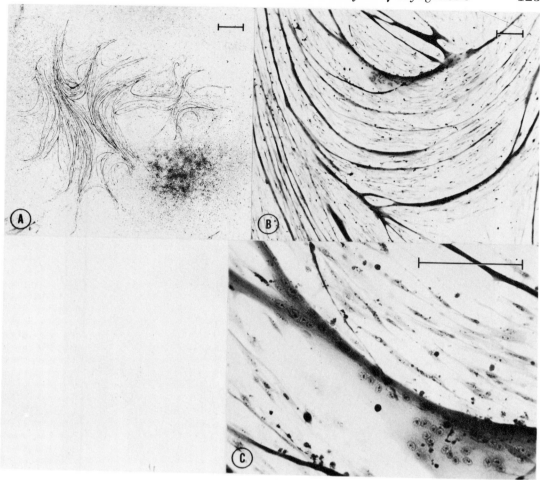

Fig. 3. (*A*) Higher magnification of an area of culture *B* of Fig. 2. Note the alignment of the dark-staining fibers into swirls. The scale marker represents 1.0 mm. (*B*) Segment of the muscle colony in *A*. Fibers are clearly syncytial ribbon-like myotubes. Scale marker represents 0.1 mm. (*C*) Branched portion of a myotube from the field represented in *B*. The multinuclear character of the myotube is evident. The scale marker represents 0.1 mm.

The two main objectives of these studies were to determine whether the muscle colonies have a unicellular origin and to establish the temporal sequence of proliferation and myotube formation. During the preliminary trials it became apparent that we could recognize those single cells which, if viable, would yield muscle colonies. In Fig. 4 myogenic and nonmyogenic cell types are compared. An attempt has been made to indicate the degree of variability. The consistent features of the myoblast class are the marked bipolar shape and the small ruffled membrane, usually restricted to one tip of the cell. In contrast, the cells which give rise to fibroblast-like colonies are extremely flattened (see *44*) and consequently are less refractile. A much more extensive ruffled membrane is generally present, with no apparent localization.

The reliability of these criteria has been evaluated. The data are summarized in Table 2. Single cells were located, and their positions were marked in accordance with a color code as a means of recording our prediction of colony type directly on the petri plate. The results were scored after fixation and staining on the 13th day of culture.

The data in Table 2 indicate good correla-

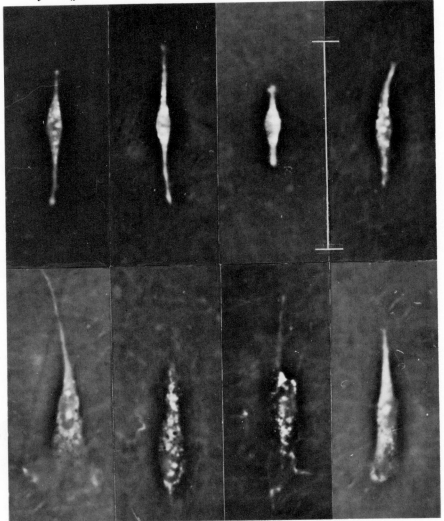

Fig. 4. Photomicrographs of living cells photographed 18 to 24 hours after plating. (The photomicrographs were taken at an initial magnification of 200; bright-medium phase-contrast optics were used.) The cells in the top row produced muscle colonies; those in the bottom row produced colonies of fibroblast-like cells. The scale marker represents 0.1 mm.

tion between the morphology of single cells and the type of differentiation observed in the clones derived from them. The error involved may be indicative of the observer's error in resolving differences between individual cells. The area of morphological overlap is indicated by the cells at the extreme right, top and bottom rows, in Fig. 4.

Cell shape, *in vitro*, can be modified both through change in the texture of the substratum (*61*) and through change in the com-

position of the medium (*31, 62*). In plating experiments these factors are, at least initially, uniform throughout the culture. The differences observed can only be ascribed to intrinsic differences between cells.

Table 2 also indicates approximately equal viability of the two types. If we assume that one group represents cells which have undergone some process of simplification we must also assume that (i) simplification has not affected viability, and (ii) the process of simplification has occurred during the 18 to 24 hours that have elapsed between dissection of the muscle and observation of the single, isolated cell.

Although we can assume, with the degree of confidence warranted by the data in Table 2, that the bipolar cell is a myoblast, we can make no appraisal of its previous developmental history. Cytodifferentiation is markedly asynchronous in the leg musculature of the chick embryo (55). Despite this developmental heterogeneity, our cell suspensions consist largely of mononucleated cells (50), from which finding we conclude that the cell suspension is not representative of the tissue of origin. We cannot as yet exclude the possibility, however, that the single, mononucleated cells which we observed and followed were secondarily liberated from syncytia by the trauma involved in disaggregating the tissue.

The identity of the nonmyogenic cells is uncertain. They may be (i) prospective myoblasts whose instability reflects different intermediate stages of differentiation, or biosynthetic variation from cell to cell, or alteration through trauma, or (ii) discrete cell types other than myoblasts (for example, fibroblasts).

TABLE 2. Distribution of colony type (muscle or "fibroblastic") from single cells scored on the basis of morphological criteria (see text)

Class of Cell	Total Number of Cells	Total Number of Colonies	Distribution of Colony Types	
			"Fibroblastic"	Muscle
"Fibroblastic"	99	61	52	9
Bipolar	72	53	2	51

Moreover, we cannot be certain that we are dealing with a single class of nonmyogenic cells. Consistent, distinguishable differences can be discerned between the cells of different colonies of fibroblast-like cells. These differences would probably not be obvious in mixed populations of these same cells.

In the tempo of modern research, the brilliant work of earlier eras is often overlooked. It seems appropriate here to recall the pioneering studies of the Lewises (63), who observed, in the outgrowth area of muscle explants, cells similar to the bipolar cells described here. They noted the striking resemblance of these cells to the myoblast *in vivo*, and they correctly interpreted their significance. To their remarks we can add only that the spindle shape is an intrinsic property of the cell itself and is not dependent upon intercellular associations.

The distinctive bipolar shape of the myoblast is maintained through many generations. Compare, for example, the single cells scattered among the muscle syncytia in Fig. 5G with the cells of the invading colony of fibroblast-like cells at the bottom of the photomicrograph.

PATTERN OF MUSCLE COLONY FORMATION

Of the two recognizable cell types, the myoblast thus far has understandably occupied our attention. Applying the criteria discussed earlier, we have been able to select with a high degree of accuracy for those cells which, if viable, will yield colonies of differentiated muscle cells. Figure 5 is a sequence of photomicrographs taken of the living cells, showing the development of such a macroscopic colony (Fig. 5G) from the single cell seen in Fig. 5A. The colony in Fig. 5G, photographed on the 13th day of culture, measures 3.9 by 4.8 millimeters. It arose from a cell roughly 0.05 millimeter long.

Examination of the first four photomicrographs in this sequence indicates that, during this initial period at least, the cells are dividing with a generation time of the order of 12 to 18 hours. This is by no means unusual in these cloning experiments in conditioned medium, although the doubling time for DNA in the tissue of origin is approximately 48 hours (64) and the generation time previously determined for monolayer cultures (50) is 24 hours.

The first striking evidence of further differentiation can be observed in Fig. 5E, which is

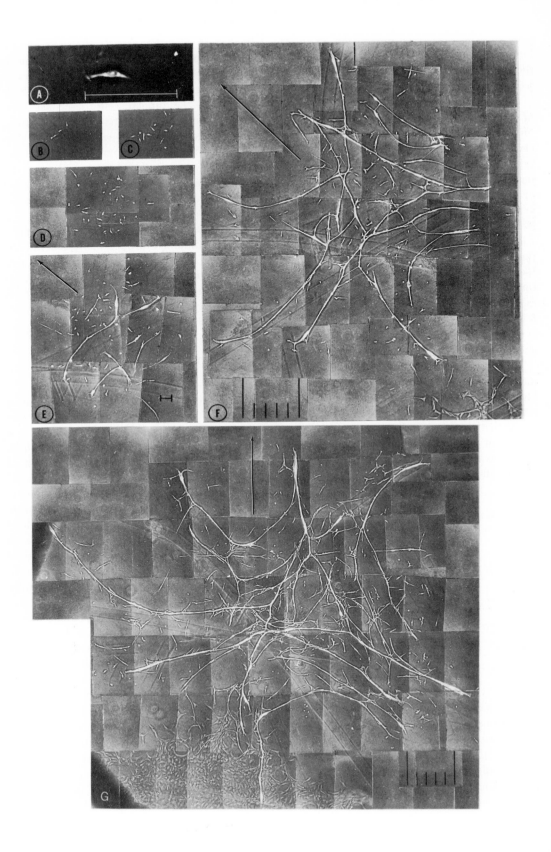

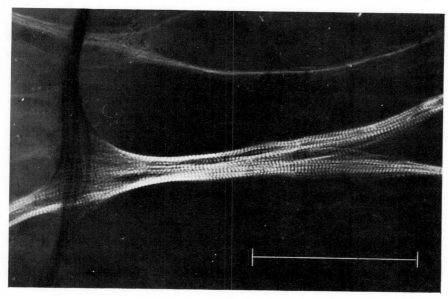

Fig. 6. An area of the colony shown in Fig. 5G (roughly, the area at the lower edge of the sixth frame from the right in the fourth row from the bottom). The use of polarizing optics demonstrates the presence of cross-striated myofibrils typical of striated muscle. Fixation: osmium vapor after storage at −20°C in 50 percent glycerol. Scale marker represents 0.1 mm.

a photomicrograph of the colony on the 6th day of culture [when unconditioned medium was used, differentiation was first observed considerably later than day 6 (*24*)]. The greatly elongated structures are multinucleated myotubes, which presumably formed through a process of successive cell fusion.

Various experimental approaches (*48, 50–54*) indicate that cell fusion is the predominant, if not the sole, mechanism of the origin of multinuclearity in skeletal muscle. In this colony, mononucleated myoblasts can be found scattered throughout the enlarging colony (Fig. 5F, day 9; Fig. 5G, day 13). It is our view

Fig. 5. Photomicrographic record of the development of a muscle colony from a single bipolar cell. The living cells were photographed at an initial magnification of 200 (*A*) or 100 (*B* through *G*); bright-medium phase-contrast optics were used. (*D–G*) Composites of several successive overlapping frames covering the progressively greater expanse of the colony on succeeding days. (*A*) The single cell photographed some time between 18 and 24 hours (day 1) after plating. The nucleus contains one prominent nucleolus. A cluster of highly refractile granules is present in each zone next to the nucleus. Note the ruffled membrane at the tip of the process at left. The scale marker represents 0.1 mm. (*B*) A colony produced by the cell in *A* during the first 24 hours of recording (day 2). The scale marker in *E* pertains to photomicrographs *B* through *E* and represents 0.1 mm. (*C*) The colony on day 3. Three of the cells in the field are rounded and are presumably in an early stage of division. (*D*) The colony on day 4. (*E*) The colony on day 5. Long multinuclear myotubes have formed (these were first observed 24 hours earlier). The arrows in photomicrographs *E*, *F*, and *G* indicate orientation of the colony with respect to the orientation in *G* (the orientation was changed to facilitate photographing). The orientation is confirmed by the matching pattern of strain marks in the plastic petri plate. (*F*) The colony on day 9. The network of myotubes has expanded considerably, but not the presence of single cells among the myotubes. Cells of the leading edge of an invading colony of fibroblast-like cells can be seen at lower right. Each division of the scale represents 0.1 mm. (*G*) The colony on day 13. The myotubes are longer and more numerous than they are in *F*. Single cells are still present. Continued proliferation of these single cells is suggested by the rounded appearance of some of them and by associations typical of late anaphase. The invading fibroblast-like cells observed in *F* are now quite obviously the periphery of a contiguous colony. Compare the cells of the impinging colony with the single cells of the muscle colony. (Scale, same as in *F*.)

that these mononucleated cells constitute a proliferating "stem cell" line which contributes to the subsequent enlargement of the network of muscle cells. A comparison of Figs. 5E, 5F, and 5G indicates the pattern of enlargement of this muscle-cell network. Not only do pre-existing muscle fibers grow longer but new ones are formed.

The individual cells of the colony, in the early stages of its development, do not remain in intimate contact after cell division. This is true of the early stages of nonmyogenic colonies as well. This type of colony, which is composed of single mononucleated cells, does not form a coherent, tightly packed colony until 4 to 6 days have elapsed, and even at late stages some free cells can generally be observed at the advancing edge of the colony (see Fig. 5, F and G). If we assume that, under the conditions of our experiments, the cells adhere preferentially to the substratum rather than to each other, these observations are in harmony with current concepts of cell locomotion and adhesion (65).

The pattern of growth of this colony is consistent with its origin from a single cell. Although all of the colonies which we have followed (irrespective of their developmental type) are, in their early stages, composed of dispersed cells, the degree of dispersion is limited, and the colonial foci remain discrete.

As the population of the colony increases, a more cohesive pattern is established; the network of muscle fibers of myogenic colonies and the circular colonies of contiguous nonmyogenic cells (see Fig. 5). These two types of colonies, as they enlarge, frequently impinge upon each other, as do the muscle colony and the invading edge of the fibroblast-like colony in Fig. 5.

Physical Isolation of Single Myoblasts

The conclusive proof, however, that a single cell can give rise to a macroscopic colony of differentiated muscle cells rests on a modification of the described procedures that excludes any possible contribution of cells other than the progeny of the single cell originally isolated. After cells had been located and their positions had been marked, a small pyrex cylinder (inside diameter, 6 mm; height, 5 mm), bearing a continuous bead of silicone grease on its lower rim, was pressed down in the petri plate to encompass the selected cell. [This is essentially an adaptation of the technique used by Puck's group (31) to transfer single colonies.] The cylinder was filled with medium, and a cover slip was laid across the top to create two parallel surfaces which would permit examination, by means of phase optics, of the floor of the chamber thus created. Provision was made for the relief of pressure and for gas exchange by grinding two wide, shallow grooves into the upper surface of the cylinder. After positioning of the cylinder and cover slip, the floor of the chamber was scanned carefully to make sure that only one cell was included. The medium was then drained from the petri dish; this resulted in the destruction of all cells not protected by cylinders. The medium in the cylinder was replaced every 3rd day, and the cultures were terminated on day 13 or 16. Figure 7 depicts such a colony after fixation but prior to the removal of the cylinder. Figure 8 shows two colonies which developed from such single, isolated cells. The cylinder was placed directly over the cell from which the colony in Fig. 8A was derived. The cylinder was eccentrically positioned over the cell which gave rise to the colony in Fig. 8B, to avoid inclusion of a neighboring cell; hence its crescent shape.

From these studies, in which single cells were either followed sequentially or physically isolated, it is clear that single myogenic cells drawn from the population that we sampled did indeed give rise to a clone that formed a colony, of macroscopic dimensions, which clearly contained large numbers of differentiated muscle cells. It is our impression that the vast majority of colonies which we see are, in fact, clones.

Number of Cell Generations

To establish the degree of stability of myogenic properties with reference to the number of antecedent cell generations is of considerable importance. The data presently available permit only a rough approximation of the lower limits, since the modes of growth and differentiation of skeletal muscle cells make accurate estimation impossible. There is good evidence that most, if not all, of the nuclei in muscle syncytia are nonproliferative (*48, 51, 52*). Thus, the nuclei of cells which had been incorporated into syncytia at some early time would have passed through fewer divisions than nuclei added later. If our interpretation of the mode of growth of muscle networks is correct, then nuclei added between day 9 (Fig. 5*F*) and day 13 (Fig. 5*G*) could have passed through 9 to 12, 15 to 19, or 20 to 26 divisions, depending upon whether one assumes a generation time of 24, 18, or 12 hours for the complement of mononucleated cells. In contradistinction, the nuclei of the *earliest* myotube (in this colony it was observed on day 5) would have passed through only 4, 6, or 8 divisions. We cannot, under these circumstances, derive the number of divisions

Fig. 7. A colony derived from a single cell isolated by a glass cylinder (see text). The colony was photographed *in situ* in darkfield illumination after fixation with Bouin's fixative. The bright semicircle is not the glass cylinder itself but a continuous bead of silicone grease extruded by pressing the cylinder into position.

by a simple tally of the number of nuclei in syncytial association. We also must know the rate at which potentially proliferating nuclei are removed from the population of mononucleated cells relative to their rate of division. One can envision three different patterns of colony development.

1) Myotube formation occurs late, after considerable proliferative activity has occurred.

2) Myotube formation occurs early and involves all of the single cells of which the colony is composed.

3) Myotube formation occurs early and involves a variable fraction of the single cells.

Actually, all three modes have been observed, under one or another set of conditions.

The majority of the cases studied, however, fall into class 3, with considerable variability of the fraction of single cells initially involved.

If there *is* an intrinsic limitation to the number of times a cell may divide in culture and retain its capacity to differentiate, we have found no supporting evidence for it thus far.

Cellular differentiation in culture has previously been achieved only through the use of an explant, considerably larger than a single cell. In the studies reported here, single, isolated cells were observed to proliferate and to form macroscopic colonies of differentiated muscle.

The use of conditioned medium (that is, medium harvested from mass cultures of mus-

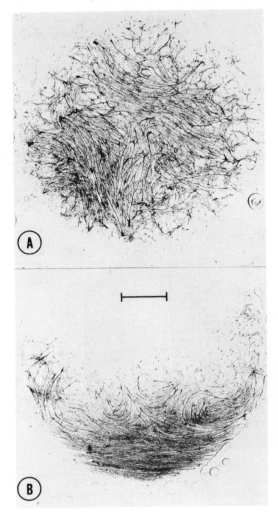

Fig. 8. Two examples of colonies which arose from single cells isolated by glass cylinders. The darkly stained "fibers" are multinucleated myotubes (see Fig. 2). See text for an explanation of the shape of the colony. Fixation, in Bouin's fixative, was followed by staining in Ehrlich's hematoxylin (no counterstain). Scale marker represents 1.0 mm.

cle cells) was found to be the most effective means of achieving differentiation in a high proportion of the colonies. Conditioned-medium and feeder-layer techniques, both of which simulate the effects of a large mass of cells, have been used effectively in supporting the proliferation of single cells. Our studies suggest that such techniques may, in addition, be useful in reproducing an environment which will permit differentiation as well.

It has been argued that high rates of proliferation are implicated in the loss of cell-type specificity in culture. The argument needs clarification. The premise itself is largely untested and remains unproved. In our experiments certain aspects of differentiation (for example, myofibril formation) are detected only after proliferation has ceased. However, the characteristic shape of the progenitor cell of the muscle clone is itself a differentiated feature, and it is retained by the proliferating cells of the muscle colony. Neither the observed rates of cell division nor the total number of divisions seem to affect the capacity of these cells to differentiate (see also *46*) (*66*).

REFERENCES AND NOTES

1. E. D. Hay, in *Regeneration*, D. Rudnick, Ed. (Ronald Press, New York, 1962), p. 177.
2. W. Bloom, *Physiol. Revs.* **17**, 589 (1937).
3. L. Levintow and H. Eagle, *Ann. Rev. Biochem.* **30**, 605 (1961).
4. R. G. Harrison, *Anat. Record*, **6**, 181 (1912); *Am. Naturalist* **67**, 306 (1933).
5. H. Holtzer, J. Abbot, J. Lash, S. Holtzer, *Proc. Natl. Acad. Sci. U.S.* **46**, 1533 (1960).
6. J. R. Whittaker, thesis, Yale University (1962).
7. G. Sato, L. Zaroff, S. E. Mills, *Proc. Natl. Acad. Sci. U.S.* **46**, 963 (1960); L. Zaroff, G. Sato, S. E. Mills, *Exptl. Cell Res.* **23**, 565 (1961).
8. I have restricted use of the term *dedifferentiation* to discussion of those phases of regeneration to which it is, by common usage, appropriate. My purpose is merely to avoid the implication that superficially similar events in cultured cell populations are necessarily similar mechanistically.
9. H. B. Fell, in *Cytology and Cell Physiology*, G. Bourne, Ed. (Oxford Univ. Press, London, 1951), p. 419; in *Synthesis of Molecular and Cellular Structure*, D. Rudnick, Ed. (Ronald Press, New York, 1961), p. 139.
10. C. Grobstein, *J. Cellular Comp. Physiol.* **60**, suppl. 1, 35 (1962).
11. —— and E. Zwilling, *J. Exptl. Zool.* **122**, 259 (1953); C. Grobstein, *Ann. N.Y. Acad. Sci.* **60**, 1095 (1955); E. Zwilling, in "Symposium on Normal and Abnormal Development," *Natl. Cancer Inst. Monograph No. 2* (1960), p. 19.
12. G. Lopaschov, *Biol. Zentr.* **55**, 606 (1935); W. B. Muchmore, *J. Exptl. Zool.* **134**, 293 (1957).

13. J. P. Trinkaus and J. W. Drake, *Develop. Biol.* 1, 377 (1959).
14. J. R. Harrison, *J. Exptl. Zool.* 118, 209 (1951).
15. K. K. Sanford, W. R. Earle, G. D. Likely, *J. Natl. Cancer Inst.* 9, 229 (1948).
16. T. T. Puck and P. I. Marcus, *Proc. Natl. Acad. Sci. U.S.* 41, 432 (1955).
17. H. W. Fisher and T. T. Puck, *ibid.* 42, 900 (1956).
18. H. Eagle and K. Piez, *J. Exptl. Med.* 116, 29 (1962).
19. H. Eagle, *Science* 122, 501 (1955).
20. ———, *J. Cellular Comp. Physiol.* 60, suppl. 1, 45 (1962).
21. J. Needham, *Biochemistry and Morphogenesis* (Cambridge Univ. Press, London, 1950), p. 505.
22. G. G. Rose, C. M. Pomerat, T. O. Shindler, J. B. Trunnell, *J. Biophys. Biochem. Cytol.* 4, 761 (1958); G. G. Rose, *J. Cell Biol.* 13, 153 (1962).
23. S. Howarth and R. Dourmashkin, *Exptl. Cell Res.* 15, 613 (1958).
24. I. R. Konigsberg, *Proc. Natl. Acad. Sci. U.S.* 47, 1868 (1961).
25. L. Resseguie, *J. Exptl. Zool.* 148, 41 (1961).
26. J. P. Trinkaus, *Am. Naturalist* 90, 273 (1956).
27. J. W. Lash, F. A. Hommes, F. Zilliken, *Biochim. Biophys. Acta* 56, 313 (1962); F. A. Hommes, G. Van Leeuwen, F. Zilliken, *ibid.*, p. 320; J. W. Lash, in *Cytodifferentiation and Macromolecular Synthesis*, M. Locke, Ed., in preparation.
28. J. P. Trinkaus, in *Conference on the Biology of Connective Tissue Cells*, C. W. Castor, D. J. Merchant, L. E. Shulman, Eds. (Arthritis and Rheumatism Foundation, New York, and National Institute of Arthritis and Metabolic Diseases, Bethesda, Md., 1962), p. 99.
29. L. M. J. Rinaldini, *Intern. Rev. Cytol.* 7, 587 (1958); H. J. Phillips and J. E. Terryberry, *Exptl. Cell Res.* 13, 341 (1957); W. Magee, M. Sheek, B. Sagik, *Proc. Soc. Exptl. Biol. Med.* 99, 390 (1958); H. J. Phillips and R. V. Andrews, *Exptl. Cell Res.* 16, 678 (1959); G. Kellner, E. Broada, O. Suschny, W. Rücker, *ibid.* 18, 168 (1959); S. Levine, *ibid.* 19, 220 (1960); C. Raut Hebb and Ming-Yu Wang Chu, *ibid.* 20, 453 (1960).
30. R. J. Lesseps, *Am. Zoologist* 1, 458 (1961); thesis, Johns Hopkins University (1962).
31. T. T. Puck, P. I. Marcus, S. J. Cieciura, *J. Exptl. Med.* 103, 273 (1956).
32. A. A. Moscona and H. Moscona, *J. Anat. London* 86, 287 (1952); J. P. Trinkaus and P. W. Groves, *Proc. Natl. Acad. Sci. U.S.* 41, 787 (1955); P. Weiss and A. C. Taylor, *ibid.* 46, 1177 (1960); A. A. Moscona, in *Developing Cell Systems and Their Control*, D. Rudnick, Ed. (Ronald Press, New York, 1960), p. 45.
33. A. Levan and J. J. Biesele, *Ann. N.Y. Acad. Sci.* 71, 1022 (1958).
34. E. H. Y. Chu, *J. Cellular Comp. Physiol.* 60, suppl. 1, 77 (1962).
35. L. Hayflick and P. S. Moorhead, *Exptl. Cell Res.* 25, 585 (1961).
36. H. B. Fell, *J. Natl. Cancer Inst.* 19, 601 (1957).
37. J. Paul, *Cell and Tissue Culture* (Williams and Wilkins, Baltimore, 1961), chap. 4.
38. C. Grobstein, in *The Cell*, J. Brachet and A. E. Mirsky, Eds. (Academic Press, New York, 1959), vol. 1.
39. B. Ephrussi and H. M. Temin, *Virology* 11, 547 (1960).
40. S. R. Hilfer, *Develop. Biol.* 4, 1 (1962).
41. K. E. Ebner, E. C. Hageman, B. L. Larson, *Exptl. Cell Res.* 25, 555 (1961).
42. E. Weiler, *Exptl. Cell Res. Suppl.* 7, 244 (1959).
43. A. A. Moscona, *J. Cellular Comp. Physiol.* 60, suppl. 1, 65 (1962).
44. P. Weiss, *ibid.*, p. 45.
45. V. Buonassisi, G. Sato, A. I. Cohen, *Proc. Natl. Acad. Sci. U.S.* 48, 1184 (1962).
46. E. Bell and M. Schuler, "Abstracts of Papers, 13th Annual Meeting, Tissue Culture Association, Washington, D.C." (1962), p. 39.
47. I. Lieberman and P. Ove, *J. Biol. Chem.* 233, 634 (1958); H. Burlington, *Am. J. Physiol.* 197, 68 (1959).
48. I. R. Konigsberg, N. McElvain, M. Tootle, H. Herrmann, *J. Biophys. Biochem. Cytol.* 8, 333 (1960).
49. I. R. Konigsberg, *Exptl. Cell. Res.* 21, 414 (1960).
50. ———, *Circulation* 24, 447 (1961).
51. J. W. Lash, H. Holtzer, H. Swift, *Anat. Record* 128, 679 (1957).
52. H. Holtzer, in *Regeneration in Vertebrates*, C. Thornton, Ed. (Univ. of Chicago Press, Chicago, 1958); in *Cytodifferentiation*, D. Rudnick, Ed. (Univ. of Chicago Press, Chicago, 1958); H. Firket, *Arch. Biol. Liége* 69, 1 (1958); S. Bintliff and B. E. Walker, *Am. J. Anat.* 106, 233 (1960); F. E. Stockdale and H. Holtzer, *Exptl. Cell Res.* 24, 508 (1961); H. Holtzer, in *Synthesis of Molecular and Cellular Structure*, D. Rudnick, Ed. (Ronald Press, New York, 1961), p. 35.
53. C. E. Wilde, in *Cell, Organism and Milieu*, D. Rudnick, Ed. (Ronald Press, New York, 1959); C. R. Capers, *J. Biophys. Biochem. Cytol.* 7, 559 (1960).
54. W. G. Cooper and I. R. Konigsberg, *Anat. Record* 140, 195 (1961).

55. A. Kitiyakara, *ibid.* **133**, 35 (1959).
56. M. R. Murray, in *The Structure and Function of Muscle*, G. H. Bourne, Ed. (Academic Press, New York, 1960), p. 111.
57. W. G. Cooper and I. R. Konigsberg, *Exptl. Cell Res.* **23**, 576 (1961).
58. M. C. Reporter, I. R. Konigsberg, B. L. Strehler, *ibid.* **30**, 410 (1963).
59. I. R. Konigsberg, *Carnegie Inst. Wash. Yearbook No. 61* (1962).
60. The technique finally adopted for preparing conditioned medium is as follows. Growth medium (10 cm³) in petri plates 150 mm in diameter is inoculated with 6×10^6 cells [prepared as described in I. R. Konigsberg *et al.* (*48*)]. The medium is replaced with 15 cm³ of fresh medium on the 2nd and 5th day of culture, and the old medium is discarded. On day 11 the medium is removed, under conditions of sterility, and passed through a Millipore filter (type HA) to insure removal of any possible cellular or microbial contamination. This medium is our standard conditioned medium. It is prepared each week; unused portions are stored at 5°C and discarded after 2 weeks.

    The growth medium used is that described in I. R. Konigsberg *et al.* (*48*), modified as described in I. R. Konigsberg (*24*), except for the following changes. (i) The inorganic salt and glucose concentrations of both the Hanks solution and the amino acid-vitamin supplement have been altered and are now the same for the two solutions (the concentrations, in millimoles per liter, are as follows: NaCl, 128.6; KCl, 4.1; CaCl₂, 1.12; MgCl₂, 0.49; Na₂HPO₄, 0.93; KH₂PO₄, 0.45; NaHCO₃, 15.3; MgSO₄, 0.21; and glucose, 6.10). (ii) The growth medium now contains 50-percent embryo extract to a concentration of 10 percent. The only other innovation in our recent techniques is the use of polystyrene petri plates (obtained from Falcon Plastics).
61. P. Weiss and B. Garber, *Proc. Natl. Acad. Sci. U.S.* **38**, 264 (1952); P. Weiss, *Intern. Rev. Cytol.* **7**, 39 (1958).
62. I. Lieberman and P. Ove, *Biochim. Biophys. Acta* **25**, 449 (1957); H. W. Fischer, T. T. Puck, G. Sato, *Proc. Natl. Acad. Sci. U.S.* **44**, 4 (1958); A. C. Taylor, *Exptl. Cell Res. Suppl.* **8**, 154 (1961).
63. W. H. Lewis and M. R. Lewis, *Am. J. Anat.* **22**, 169 (1917).
64. I. R. Konigsberg and H. Herrmann, *Arch. Biochem. Biophys.* **55**, 534 (1955).
65. M. Abercrombie, *Exptl. Cell Res. Suppl.* **8**, 188 (1961); P. Weiss, *ibid.*, p. 260.
66. I acknowledge my indebtedness to Mrs. Wilma Gabbay and Mr. Francis J. Kupres for their invaluable and unstinting assistance during the progress of the original work reported. I wish to thank Drs. D. W. Bishop, D. D. Brown, J. D. Ebert, M. S. Steinberg, and J. P. Trinkaus for their valuable criticisms during the preparation of the manuscript.

The Loss of Phenotypic Traits by Differentiated Cells *in Vitro*, I: Dedifferentiation of Cartilage Cells*

HOWARD HOLTZER[†]

J. ABBOTT

JAMES W. LASH[‡]

SIBYL HOLTZER

    The experiments to be described were designed to approach the following type of question: Will the differentiated state of a tissue cell survive multiple divisions *in vitro*? Do the cultured progeny of differentiated cells inherit the cellular mechanisms determining the unique somatic traits of their parental cells in a manner analogous to the way in

Proceedings of the National Academy of Sciences, **46**, No. 12, 1533–1542 (December 15, 1960). Communicated by David R. Goddard and read before the Academy, November 16, 1960. Reprinted with permission.

* This investigation was supported, in part, by Research Grants B-493 and B-1629 from the National Institute of Neurological Diseases and Blindness of the National Institutes of Health, U.S. Public Health Service.

† Scholar in Cancer Research of the American Cancer Society, Inc.

‡ Helen Hay Whitney Foundation Research Fellow.

which (1) Paramecia transmit Kappa particles to their daughter cells (Sonneborn,[33, 34] Beale,[2] Preer[31]), (2) bacteria inherit genes for constitutive or inducible enzymes in the absence of substrate (Novick and Weiner,[28] Spiegelman[35]), or (3) temperate phage particles give rise to lysogenic progeny (Jacob and Wollman[20])? Information of this kind is essential if the roles of the nucleus (i.e., genes) and the cytoplasm in cell differentiation are to be defined.

An unambiguous approach to these problems requires that the following five conditions be fulfilled: (1) The initial population of differentiated cells must be *homogeneous*. (2) The cells must divide many times during the experiment. (3) The cells must not back-differentiate to the parental type immediately after each division. (4) The initial population must consist of differentiated cells and not dividing precursor cells whose progeny differentiate and thereafter cease dividing (e.g., presumptive muscle cells, presumptive blood cells, presumptive pigment cells, etc.). (5) The somatic traits used as markers must be specific to the parent cell and readily characterized.

Given this list of conditions, it is clear that many kinds of somatic cells are excluded as test material. For example, both nerve cells and keratinizing skin cells do not divide. Liver and kidney cells offer difficulties of another kind; since it is difficult to secure a homogeneous population of either type of epithelial cell, it is possible that in long-term cultures the epithelial cells are selected against and the surviving population is derived from one of the "contaminating" cell types.

Cartilage cells from vertebrae of 10-day chick embryos, on the other hand, satisfy the five conditions outlined. Pieces of cartilage may be obtained which consist only of chondrocytes and a few chondroblasts.[15, 18] Chondrocytes retain their capacity to divide when liberated from their surrounding matrix, and they may be cultured under conditions which preclude their differentiation back to cartilage between cell divisions. Lastly, the metachromatic reaction of the mucopolysaccharide matrix with thionin and the incorporation of

radioactive S^{35} into chondroitin sulfate allow identification of terminally differentiated cartilage cells.

MATERIALS AND METHODS

Cartilaginous vertebrae from 10-day chick embryos were stripped of muscle, connective tissue, and perichondrium. Microscopic examination of cartilage so prepared reveals few cells (considerably less than 1%) not embedded in a metachromatic matrix or surrounded by metachromatic capsules. The cartilage was cut into small pieces (~1 mm³) and incubated in a 1% trypsin (Difco 250) solution (Ca- and Mg-free Simms') for 2.5–3 hours.[26] The small pieces of cartilage were then transferred to a centrifuge tube and drained of excess trypsin. Two to three ml of nutrient medium A (3 Simms' solution, 2 bovine serum ultrafiltrate, 1 embryo extract) were added and the cartilage cells liberated from the softened mucopolysaccharide matrix by flushing through small bore pipettes. Insoluble fibrous material was removed by filtering through a Swinney filter in which a double thickness of lens paper replaced the millipore filter (Millipore Co.). The cells passing through the lens paper were spun down and the medium removed. The resultant pellet was resuspended in medium to a concentration of $7–10 \times 10^4$ cells/ml. One half ml aliquots of this suspension were pipetted into 8 to 10 Carrel flasks each of which had been coated with a plasma clot. The volume of the suspension *not* used to seed Carrel flasks was so adjusted that after centrifugation a pellet was obtained containing 5×10^6 cells. This pellet, consisting of freshly liberated chondrocytes, was organ cultured on nutrient agar (1.2% agar in nutrient medium B). Nutrient medium B consisted of 2 parts Simms' solution, 2 parts horse serum, 1 part embryo extract.

The cells in the Carrel flasks were fed every 3rd day and subcultured anytime between the 2nd and 7th days. At this time, the cells, even though they had increased 2 to 7 times in number, presented a stellate, fibroblast-like appearance. The progeny of the liberated chondrocytes, grown in Carrel flasks, were resuspended, counted, and handled as the freshly liberated chondrocytes except that a 0.5% trypsin solution was used for only 5 minutes and the suspension was not filtered through lens paper.

The organ-cultured pellets on nutrient agar, whether prepared from freshly liberated chondrocytes or from the resuspended progeny of the chondrocytes grown in Carrel flasks, were fed daily with nutrient medium B. After 10 days the organ-cultured pellets were fixed, stained, and examined for the presence of cartilage. Pellets from cells grown in Carrel flasks were also (1) grafted to the chorioallantoic membrane of 9-day chick embryos or into the coeloem of 4-day chick embryos and (2) cultured by the ascending culture technique of Gaillard.[12]

To summarize: Freshly liberated chondrocytes were either immediately organ cultured for 10 days or reared in Carrel flasks for varying periods. From time to time some of the progeny of the liberated chondrocytes were removed from the Carrel flasks, suspended, packed, and organ cultured as pellets to see whether they still would form cartilage.

Thus far, 8 strains of chondrocytes have been established, and some strains maintained for as long as 60 days.

Embryonic cells are injured when dissociated by trypsin.[14] To understand better the growth curves of cells in the Carrel flasks, it proved desirable to determine the condition of the cells after trypsinization. For this purpose, entry into injured cells of fluorescein labeled rabbit globulin was used. The procedures for preparing and using labeled proteins for detecting damaged cells has been described by Holtzer and Holtzer.[17]

To follow histologically the chondrogenic activity of freshly liberated chondrocytes and their cultured progeny, three staining techniques were used: hematoxylin and eosin, Alcian blue, and thionin.[24] The term chondrocyte will be reserved for cells which exhibit a metachromatic extra cellular matrix with thionin.

Mature[4, 7] and embryonic[23, 29] chondrocytes actively incorporate inorganic sulfate, and the amount of ester bound sulfate is an index of the amount of chondroitin sulfate synthesized by chondrocytes. After 6 days of organ culture on nutrient agar, the pellets were transferred to a piece of lens paper floating on 1.0 ml of nutrient medium B in a watch glass. One-tenth of a ml of balanced salt containing 5.0 μc of $Na_2S^{35}O_4$ was added to each watch glass and the pellets incubated for an additional 3 days. The procedures used to extract and to identify the chondroitin sulfate synthesized in the tissues have been described in detail.[22] To facilitate comparisons between experiments, the radioactivity of the chondroitin sulfate was expressed as counts/ 5×10^6 cells, the number of cells in each organ cultured pellet. Each pellet assayed for ester bound sulfate was matched with a control pellet stained with thionin.

RESULTS

Chondrogenic Activity of Freshly Liberated Chondrocytes

Freshly liberated chondrocytes from all 8 "strains" spun down into pellets and immediately organ cultured invariably form a typical hyalin matrix. The matrix and capsules are metachromatic after staining with thionin. Microscopically, the cells are typical chondrocytes. Estimates of the percentage of chondrocytes to the total population of cells in each pellet is of the order of 98% (Table 1). The fact that almost all of the cells in the organ-cultured pellets are chondrocytes indicates that the initial population of cells is reasonably homogeneous.

The size of the pellets organ cultured is not critical to chondrogenesis. Often pellets of freshly liberated chondrocytes fragment into smaller groups when placed on agar. Aggregates of 20–30 cells behave as do collections of many thousands of cells.

Growth of the Progeny of Chondrocytes

Figure 5 illustrates the growth curves of 3 "strains" of cells derived from embryonic chondrocytes and grown in Carrel flasks. The variability in the over-all growth rates in the different "strains" is probably due to the trauma incident to trypsinizing the cells. That

TABLE 1. The chondrogenic activity of freshly liberated chondrocytes organ cultured for 10 days contrasted with the chondrogenic activity of the progeny of chondrocytes grown for varying periods in Carrel flasks and then organ cultured for 10 days

Days in Carrel Flasks	Number of Pellets Examined	Chondrocytes in Organ-Cultured Pellets, %	Chondrocytes in Chorion or Coeloemic Grafts, %
0	20	98	—
1.5	8	98	—
2	8	98	—
3	12	98	—
4	10	40–60	—
5	9	40–60	—
8	2	20–40	—
9	2	0	—
11	4	0	—
13	5	—	0
14	4	0	—
21	8	—	0
26	2	0	—
28	12	—	0
33	8	0	—
46	3	0	—
49	5	—	0

The figures of percentage of chondrocytes in the individual pellets are visual approximations based on thionin-stained sections inspected under the microscope. The data in this table are derived from 8 different "strains" of chondrocytes isolated over a period of 8 months.

many freshly liberated cartilage cells and suspended cells from the Carrel flasks are injured by the cell dissociation procedures is demonstrated by their uptake of fluorescein labeled rabbit globulin. Incubating the suspended cells for one hour in labeled globulin results in a diffuse fluorescence in the nucleus and cytoplasm of many of the cells. This reaction is characteristic for injured cells.[17] After trypsinization, the number of fluorescing cells varies from run to run: in some approximately 5%, in others as high as 20% of the total population take up the labeled protein. Chondrocytes in normal cartilage and cultured cells in Carrel flasks before trypsinizing do not take up the labeled protein.

The calculated generation time for the 8 "strains" used in these experiments is 34 hours. Owing, however, to the variable number of cells killed each time the cells are suspended the actual generation time must be considerably less. The growth curves make it improbable that the multiplying cells in the Carrel flasks are restricted to a small, actively dividing stem population.

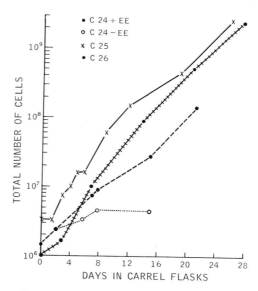

Fig. 5. Growth curves of 3 "strains" of cells reared in Carrel flasks. See text for further details.

Chondrogenic Activity of the Progeny of Chondrocytes

Cells derived from chondrocytes grown in Carrel flasks lose their capacity to differentiate into cartilage when subsequently organ cultured (see Table 1, p. 137). Microscopic inspection of pellets consisting of cells that are reared 10 or more days in Carrel flasks and then organ cultured fails to reveal the close packing of the rounded cells typical of chondroblasts or chondrocytes. The cells are healthy and occasional mitotic figures are found. The texture of the pellets varies from specimen to specimen and within a single specimen. In some regions the cells are tightly packed, whereas in other regions the ratio of cellular to extracellular material is low. When stained with thionin, scattered cells exhibit prominent metachromatic granules *within* individual cells. There is no extracellular metachromatic material. Many cells contain large vacuoles and give the impression of being fat cells with nucleus and cytoplasm peripherally displaced. The vacuoles are fixed and blackened by osmic acid.

There are changes in the aggregative behavior of cells reared in Carrel flasks which accompany their loss of chondrogenic activity. When placed on top of a *plasma clot*, a concentrated suspension of freshly liberated chondrocytes spontaneously aggregates into a nodular sheet within 24 hours. This nodular sheet does not spread radially. Most of these cells differentiate into chondrocytes. After several passages through Carrel flasks, the cells form a thin, rapidly spreading sheet when placed on top of a clot: they neither spontaneously aggregate nor differentiate into chondrocytes.

Effect of Depressing Growth Rate in Carrel Flasks

Cell division and cell differentiation are thought to be antagonistic processes and there are reports[6, 9] that when the division rate of dedifferentiated cells in culture is depressed, the cells redifferentiate. To test this, cells, after 15 days of rapid growth in normal medium, were reared for 6 days in Carrel flasks in the absence of embryo extract. Under these conditions, the cells did not increase in number, in contrast to control cells grown in the presence of embryo extract, which multiplied 6 times. The cells whose division rate was suppressed were organ cultured. Chondrocytes

did not differentiate in any of the nine pellets formed from these cells.

Behavior of Cells in Ascending Cultures

Gaillard[12] reported that cultured embryonic chondroblasts reared in press juices from successively older embryos differentiate into mature chondrocytes and even form osteocytes. Cells after 4 passages through Carrel flasks were cultured as pellets in the press juices of 15-day, 18-day, and 20-day chick embryos. Eight pellets so treated did not differentiate into chondrocytes.

Behavior of Cells in Confronted Cultures

Embryonic cartilage cells differentiate in association with striated muscle. Often, in mature animals, ectopic cartilage forms in muscle tissue.[21, 25] It was thought that muscle cells might provide an environment which would permit dedifferentiated cartilage cells to express latent chondrogenic capacities. Therefore pieces of 18-day chick muscle (1 mm^3 to 2 mm^3 in size) were excised and cultured with pellets from cells which had passed through five subcultures in Carrel flasks. Chondrocytes did not appear in 11 pellets grown under these conditions.

Behavior of Cells in *In Vivo* Grafts

Culture conditions are not optimal for cell differentiation. For example, embryonic somites which fail to differentiate into cartilage *in vitro* differentiate into typical chondrocytes when grafted to the chorioallantoic membrane.[1] Accordingly, the pellets formed from cells, passed through Carrel flasks 4 to 8 times, were grafted either to the chorioallantoic membrane of 9-day embryos or to the coeloem of 4-day embryos. Neither the 18 grafts to the chorion nor the 12 grafts to the coeloem yielded chondrocytes.

Incorporation of Radioactive Sulfate

The quantitative experiments on the uptake of $S^{35}O_4$ parallel the results obtained on sectioned material stained with thionin. Table 2 and Fig. 6, part A, show that the incorporation of S^{35} into bound sulfate by cells in pellets in organ culture varies inversely with

TABLE 2. The amount of S^{35} bound by pellets of equal cell number grown on nutrient agar after varying lengths of time in Carrel flasks

Days in Carrel Flasks	Total Counts per Minute per 5×10^6 Cells Grown in Organ Culture	Chondrocytes in Organ Cultures, %
0	505,233	98
5	265,851	40–60
11	.2,144	0
21	1,806	0
26	2,205	0

All the cells in this table were derived from the same "strain," were exposed to the same amount of $S^{35}O_4$, and were extracted in the same way. The estimate of percentage of chondrocytes in the pellets is only approximate. Each measurement is based on the mean value of 5 cultures.

the time grown in Carrel flasks. Table 2 correlates the histological condition of the organ-cultured pellets with the amount of ester bound isotope.

Part B of Fig. 6 suggests that the loss of chondrogenic activity of cells grown in Carrel flasks is a function of at least two variables—the number of divisions the cells have experienced and the length of time cultured. Freshly liberated chondrocytes were cultured for 3 days in Carrel flasks and then divided into two populations. One population was grown in flasks in the presence of embryo extract (+EE), the other in flasks in which the embryo extract was omitted (−EE). The growth curves of these two populations is indicated in Fig. 5 (C24 + EE and C24 − EE). The loss of chondrogenic activity of cells grown in the absence of embryo extract for the first 8 days is considerably less than cells grown in the presence of embryo extract. During this period, the −EE cells have doubled in number, whereas the +EE cells have increased over fourfold. Between the 8th and 15th day in the flasks, the −EE cells have not increased in total number, while the +EE cells have multiplied 3 times. Nevertheless, during the period from the 8th to the 15th day, both groups of cells lose their capacity to differentiate into chondrocytes.

DISCUSSION

"Dedifferentiation" is used in this paper as a convenient word to describe cells derived from mature chondrocytes which have lost

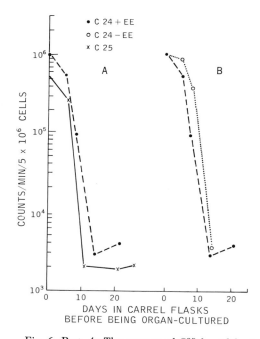

Fig. 6. Part *A:* The amount of S^{35} bound by two "strains" of chondrocytes and their progeny grown as pellets in organ culture. Pellets with counts below 10,000 did not form microscopically recognizable cartilage, and they failed to yield detectable quantities of glucuronic acid or galactosamine. Part *B:* Cells of "strain" C24 were divided into two groups and grown in Carrel flasks: C24 + EE were grown in the presence of embryo extract; C24 − EE were grown in the absence of embryo extract. The reduced growth rate of the cells grown in the absence of embryo extract is shown in Fig. 5. Note that the pellets formed from cells which underwent fewer divisions for the first eight days in Carrel flasks, when organ cultured, bound greater amounts of S^{35} than the more rapidly dividing cells. After approximately 10 days in Carrel flasks, both strains lose the capacity to synthesize insoluble polysaccharide when organ cultured.

the ability to form recognizable chondrocytes and to synthesize chondroitin sulfate. It is not meant to imply a reversion to an "embryonic state." Failure of these cells to form chondrocytes is unlikely to be due to failure to achieve a critical mass or to general environmental deficiencies. Presumptive embryonic and regenerating cartilage cells differentiate under a variety of *in vivo* and *in vitro* conditions too restrictive for other types of cells (see examples in refs. 13, 15, 16). Rather, it is assumed that rapidly dividing chondrocytes lose one or more factors indispensable for the formation of chondroitin sulfate. Whether this loss is cytoplasmic or nuclear, whether it is due to dilution of an enzyme or a critical part of the cell surface, or whether it is reversible or irreversible is unknown. From the work of Hsu,[19] it is unlikely that ploidy is implicated, for chromosomal aberrations in cultured cells appear only in cells grown for longer periods of time.

Perske, Parks, and Walker[30] report a comparable case of dedifferentiation where liver cells in culture lose several enzymes. Likewise, Eagle's report[8] on the similar metabolic requirements of a variety of cells in culture can be interpreted as the dedifferentiation of the progeny of specialized cells. After embryonic muscle or notochord is grown in Carrel flasks for several generations, cells are recovered which do not synthesize myosin or form vacuolated cells.[15] On the other hand, Schindler, Day and Fisher[32] report that mast tumor cells in culture continue to produce 5-hydroxytryptamine, thus demonstrating the preservation of specialized metabolic pathways in at least one type of malignant cell (see also Waltz *et al.*[37] on the formation of progesterone by hydatiform mole in culture).

Clearly, the old problem of "dedifferentiation vs. modulation" of cells in tissue culture is by no means settled (see reviews by Bloom,[3] Weiss,[38] Ephrussi,[10, 11] and Trinkaus[36]). That chondrocytes and probably other somatic cells do dedifferentiate is, in our opinion, no longer debatable. But the interesting problems remain: (1) Does a given chondrocyte dedifferentiate gradually or abruptly? (2) How dependent upon mitotic divisions is the process of dedifferentiation? (3) Do dedifferentiated chondrocytes continue to synthesize collagen or the protein associated with chondroitin? (4) Can dedifferentiated chondrocytes differentiate into other types of cells or can they only differentiate back into chondrocytes?

In spite of many theoretical discussions, virtually nothing is known of the respective roles of the nucleus and cytoplasm in differentiating cells.[5, 27] Nevertheless, the results of these experiments on dedifferentiation invite one speculative comment: If the mitotic divisions of the cultured cells transmit the functioning genes of the original chondrocytes, then it must be a cytoplasmic difference which distinguishes the dedifferentiated cells from their parental chondrocytes. Whatever the role of genes in controlling enzymes responsible for the synthesis of chondroitin sulfate, such activity may be inhibited by an altered cytoplasm. Whether such inhibition is mediated by the activation of "regulatory" genes or is confined to cytoplasmic mechanisms is unknown.

SUMMARY

Chondrocytes liberated from embryonic cartilage by means of trypsin and immediately organ cultured continue to synthesize chondroitin sulfate and incorporate inorganic S^{35} into ester bound sulfate. After being cultured under conditions that suppress differentiation but encourage cell multiplication, these cells, when organ cultured, (1) fail to differentiate into recognizable chondrocytes, (2) fail to synthesize chondroitin sulfate, and (3) fail to incorporate S^{35} into ester bound sulfate. Dedifferentiated cartilage cells may differentiate into fat cells.

[1] Avery, G., M. Chow, and H. Holtzer, *J. Exp. Zool.*, **132**, 409 (1958).

[2] Beale, G., *The Genetics of Paramecium aurelia* (Cambridge University Press, 1954).

[3] Bloom, W., *Physiol. Rev.*, **17**, 589 (1937).

[4] Bostrom, H., *J. Biol. Chem.*, **196**, 477 (1952).

[5] Briggs, R., and T. King, in *The Cell*, ed. J. Brachet and A. Mirsky (New York: Academic Press, 1959), pp. 537–611.

[6] Doljansky, L., *C. V. Soc. Biol., Paris,* **105,** 343 (1930).

[7] Dziewiatsowski, D., *Int. Rev. Cytology,* **7,** 59 (1958).

[8] Eagle, H., *Harvey Lectures,* **54,** 156 (1960).

[9] Ebling, A. H., and A. Fischer, *J. Exp. Med.,* **36,** 285 (1922).

[10] Ephrussi, B., in *Enzymes: Units of Biological Structure and Function,* ed. O. H. Gaebler (New York: Academic Press, 1956), pp. 29–40.

[11] Ephrussi, B., *J. Cell and Comp. Physio.,* Suppl. I, **52,** 35–55.

[12] Gaillard, P., *Actualitiés Scientifiques et Industrielles* (Paris: Hermann et Cie, 1942), p. 923.

[13] Holtzer, H., in *Regeneration in Vertebrates,* ed. C. Thornton (University of Chicago Press, 1958).

[14] Holtzer, H., *Exp. Cell Res.,* Suppl. 7, 234 (1959).

[15] Holtzer, H., in *19th Growth Symposium* (in press), ed. D. Rudnick (New York: Ronald Press, 1960).

[16] Holtzer, H., and S. Detwiler, *J. Exp. Zool.,* **123,** 335 (1953).

[17] Holtzer, H., and S. Holtzer, *Compt. Ren. Trav. (Carlsberg), ser. chim.,* **31,** 373 (1960).

[18] Holtzer, H., J. Abbott, and J. Lash, *Anat. Rec.,* **131,** 567 (1958).

[19] Hsu, T., in *18th Growth Symposium,* ed. D. Rudnick (New York: Ronald Press, 1959).

[20] Jacob, F., and E. L. Wollman, in *The Chemical Basis of Heredity,* ed. W. D. McElroy and B. Glass (Baltimore: The Johns Hopkins Press, 1958).

[21] La Croix, P., *The Organization of Bones* (Philadelphia: Blakiston Press, 1950).

[22] Lash, J., H. Holtzer, and M. Whitehouse, *Dev. Biol.,* **2,** 76 (1960).

[23] Layton, L., *Proc. Soc. Exp. Biol. and Med.,* **76,** 596 (1951).

[24] Lillie, R. D., *Histopathologic Technic and Practical Histochemistry* (New York: McGraw-Hill Book Company, 1954).

[25] McLean, F. C., and M. R. Urist, *Bone: An Introduction to the Physiology of Skeletal Tissue* (University of Chicago Press, 1955).

[26] Moscona, A., *Exp. Cell Res.,* **3,** 535 (1952).

[27] Nanney, D. L., in *The Chemical Basis of Heredity,* ed. W. D. McElroy and B. Glass (Baltimore: The Johns Hopkins Press, 1958).

[28] Novick, A., and M. Weiner, *Proc. N.A.S.,* **43,** 553 (1957).

[29] Pelc, S., and A. Glücksmann, *Exp. Cell Res.,* **8,** 336 (1955).

[30] Perske, W. F., R. E. Parks, Jr., and D. Walker, *Science,* **125,** 1290 (1957).

[31] Preer, J., in *Developmental Cytology,* ed. D. Rudnick (New York: Ronald Press, 1959).

[32] Schindler, R., M. Day, and G. Fisher, *Cancer Res.,* **19,** 47 (1959).

[33] Sonneborn, T., *Harvey Lectures,* **44,** 145 (1950).

[34] Sonneborn, T., *Proc. N.A.S.,* **46,** 149 (1960).

[35] Spiegelman, S., in *The Chemical Basis of Heredity,* ed. W. D. McElroy and B. Glass (Baltimore: The Johns Hopkins Press, 1958).

[36] Trinkaus, J. P., *Am. Naturalist,* **90,** 273 (1956).

[37] Waltz, H. K., W. W. Tullner, V. J. Evane, R. Hertz, and W. R. Earle, *J. Natl. Cancer Inst.* **14,** 1173 (1954).

[38] Weiss, P., *Quart. Rev. Biol.,* **25,** 177 (1950).

Growth and Organized Development of Cultured Cells, I: Growth and Division of Freely Suspended Cells[1,2]

F. C. STEWARD

MARION O. MAPES

JOAN SMITH

Since the time of Haberlandt (1902), the culture and continued growth of isolated plant tissues and organs in defined media and under standard conditions have been major objectives, important alike to physiologists and to morphologists. A considerable measure of success was first achieved with explanted tissues and organs of selected dicotyledonous plants, mainly through the pioneer efforts of Robbins (1922), Gauthert (1935), White (1942, 1954), and others. Later, Wetmore and Morel (1949), using tissues explanted from various cryptogams and also those derived from certain monocotyledonous plants (Morel and Wetmore, 1951), showed that the tissue culture technique is much more generally applicable, although apical regions of angiosperms proved to be more refractory unless they were able to root (for references see Wetmore and Wardlaw, 1951). Now, even leaves (Steeves, 1956; Steeves et al., 1957), ovules (Maheshwari, 1958), and immature fruits (Nitsch, 1951) all have responded to culture treatments.

Haberlandt saw, as an ultimate goal, the culture of single cells and the control of their

American Journal of Botany, 45, 693–703. Reprinted with permission. Unless otherwise stated all photographs were taken with the phase contrast microscope from living cells grown in liquid medium.

[1] Received for publication June 1, 1958.

[2] This work is part of a program of research which has been supported by grants from the National Cancer Institute, National Institutes of Health, United States Department of Health, Education, and Welfare. A grant from the Damon Runyon Foundation for Cancer Research made it possible to carry out much of the microscopical work. This aid, without which the work could not have been done, is gratefully recognized.

During the developmental phases of the technique for culturing cells the senior author was assisted by Miss K. Mears, whose help is here acknowledged.

growth and subsequent development by nutritional and environmental means, but this has proved to be a more difficult accomplishment than was suggested by the apparent totipotency of so many cells of the vascular plant body. The growth of single cells of bacteria and fungi in nutrient media is so familiar that the difficulty inherent in culturing single cells of angiosperms seems surprising, the more so, since the free culture of single cells from the animal body is now extensively practiced (Marcus et al., 1956, and references there cited; Earle et al., 1956, also have described a special form of liquid, shaken, culture for animal cell suspensions).

The present group of papers is, therefore, a contribution to this general field of work. It describes methods which enable cells from certain dicotyledonous plants to be kept indefinitely available in the freely suspended state and which induce them to grow, to form discrete culture masses, and, subsequently, to develop roots and even shoots. It will be shown in the second paper of the series that all the essential tissues of the plant body can form in cell masses that have been derived from single cells, although this has not yet been accomplished in a medium which contained only *one* such cell. No doubt, by extending the methods here described, this should follow. While this paper describes the potentialities of the tissue culture technique for the growth of the floating cells, it does not deal with the causative agents and limiting factors which regulate the stages of growth and development that are here portrayed. This will require further work. The methods described have been in use in this laboratory for several years, and the plant materials mentioned have been successfully and continuously cultured, using cells derived from different varieties grown in different seasons. Thus it is now possible to describe the behavior of the growing cells in greater detail than hitherto. No attempt will be made to furnish complete citations to previous papers which touch upon the growth of isolated cells of angiosperms. Earlier steps in this direction by Muir *et al.* (1954), De Ropp (1955), Reinert (1956), Torrey (1957), Tulecke (1957), and others, are here appreciatively recognized.

METHODS OF CULTIVATION OF FREELY SUSPENDED ANGIOSPERM CELLS

The present technique by which populations of freely suspended cells are obtained and kept continuously available for use is an outgrowth of a technique previously designed, and extensively used, for the growth of freshly explanted tissue from the carrot root (Steward *et al.*, 1952). This technique embodies the following cardinal features: (1) a specially designed culture tube, rotated "end over end" around a horizontal axis; and (2) a relatively small volume (10 ml.) of a modified White's medium, supplemented with whole coconut milk, i.e., the liquid endosperm from the coconut. As the tubes slowly revolve (1 r.p.m.), the explanted piece of tissue is alternately exposed to air and submerged in the medium; as the liquid medium flows along the tube, it is maintained in equilibrium with air and, as it gently mixes, it distributes to the tissue the contents of the ambient fluid. Thus single explants, or even 2–5 small (2 mg.) explants, of carrot root phloem tissue can be grown uniformly in a single tube under controlled conditions of light and temperature. However, this technique set definite limitations upon the amount of material that could be kept growing conveniently. Therefore, to provide a much larger bulk of growing material for purposes of biochemical analysis, a larger vessel was designed; this is a flask with a volume of approximately one liter which accommodates up to 250 ml. of nutrient medium. The flask, like the culture tubes, is

mounted with its neck horizontal so that it revolves slowly (1 r.p.m.) around a shaft. Around its circumference, however, a number of glass nipples are blown. Each of these nipples has a diameter of approximately 3 cm. and corresponds to the rounded end of the original culture tube and projects at right angles to the axis of the neck of the flask. Like the end of the culture tube, each nipple contains nutrient medium in which the cultures are submerged, when it is in one position, and the explants adhere to the glass and are exposed to air, when it is in another. It was found possible to place about 10 of these nipples around a single flask, and when the flask is mounted on a wheel so that it revolves around the horizontal shaft, each nipple traverses the same path in space that would normally be traced by a single tube (for illustration see Steward and Shantz, 1955, Fig. 1a). It was possible, by exercising special care, to isolate aseptically as many as 100 initial carrot phloem explants, each about 2 mg. in weight, and to insert them, without contamination, into flasks of this type. The subsequent growth of these 100 explants was extremely uniform (Steward and Shantz, 1955), and the total crop of tissue cultured in this manner in a single flask could be as much as 10 g. in about 28 days. Under these conditions it was noted, unexpectedly, that many cells floated free from the tissues being cultured, and that they also grew sufficiently in the ambient fluid to make the liquid appear opalescent. Microscopical examination revealed that these free-floating cells were alive, that they exhibited active protoplasmic streaming, and it was apparent that in some cases cell division had occurred. (By plating out the medium in agar it was also established that sterility had been maintained.) Transfers of these cells to new flasks of the same kind led to the continuous sub-culture of such free-floating suspensions.

The general appearance of the cells at the time of sub-culturing can be seen in Figs. 1–6, which show representative cell suspensions of carrot root (*Daucus carota* L.), potato tuber (*Solanum tuberosum* L.) tissue, and cells from the cotyledons of the peanut (*Arachis*

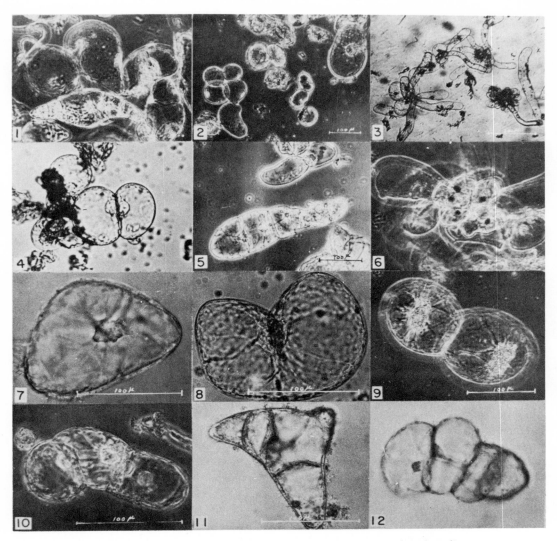

Fig. 1. Typical group of freely suspended carrot cells growing in liquid medium containing coconut milk showing internal divisions in two isodiametric cells and one giant cell. Fig. 2. Representative group of freely suspended potato tuber cells growing in liquid medium containing coconut milk and 2, 4–D, showing one giant cell and groups of isodiametric cells. Fig. 3. Typical groups of cells from peanut (*Arachis hypogea*) cotyledons as grown in liquid medium containing coconut milk, showing clusters of small growing cells and radiating elongate cells. Fig. 4. Potato tuber cells after division in the freely suspended state. Fig. 5. Potato tuber cells, internal divisions in a large cell. Fig. 6. Clusters of growing cells. Fig. 7. Isodiametric, free cell of carrot, taken with the interference microscope. Fig. 8. Free cell of potato about to divide, shown under bright field. Fig. 9. Free cells of potato tuber after recent division, showing cytoplasmic and granular contents. Fig. 10. Potato cells: three-celled staged with "mother" cell and two "wing" cells. Fig. 11. Carrot cells originated from a "mother" cell, showing divisions in the "wing" cells (photographed with interference microscope). Fig. 12. Carrot cells originated from a mother cell showing divisions in the "wing" cells and beginning of growth at right angles (photographed with interference microscope).

hypogea L.). When transferred to another flask, cells first multiply and grow freely in the nutrient solution and, as cell aggregates increase in size, a very large number of independently growing tissue cultures may be obtained. Individual strains, or clones, of cells originally obtained in this way have been kept in continuous cultivation in this laboratory over a period of approximately 3.5 years, and particular strains have been transferred in small liquid inocula from flask to flask as many as 41 times to date. The minute amount of material at each inoculation increases in each flask to a total crop of approximately 12 g. before dense growth and staling products make it desirable to start another culture. Therefore, the total increment by growth of the original cellular material from which these freely suspended cultures were obtained now has reached astronomical proportions. Not only is there no sign of decreasing vigor in their growth, but, on the contrary, it has been noted that after a few passages, even somewhat slow-growing strains or tissues seem to gather momentum.

According to the technique employing carrot root phloem, tissues are excised at a distance of 1–2 mm. from the cambium; the phloem cells they contain would not ordinarily divide in the intact root. The behavior of the cells in such explants, growing in the form of standard tissue cultures, has been described previously (Steward *et al.*, 1955). In large part, this article will be concerned with the appearance, behavior and subsequent growth of the free cells originally obtained from such carrot explants, although, by repeated transfer and growth, all traces of material actually present in the original explant have long since disappeared.

The methods have also been applied to tissue derived from the potato tuber and from the cotyledons of peanut. To culture the explanted tissue of the potato tuber requires, in addition to the basal medium supplemented with coconut milk, an auxin-like substance for which 2,4–D (2, 4-dichlorophenoxyacetic acid) at the rate of 5 p.p.m. is particularly suitable (Steward and Caplin, 1951). Therefore, to culture freely suspended cells of the potato tuber, the nutrient medium is kept *continuously* (Steward and Shantz, 1955, cf. Fig. 2) supplemented with 5 p.p.m. of 2,4–D, but otherwise the methods are those devised for carrot cells. Although the cell cultures of potato tuber so obtained tend to be slower at the outset, they are able to grow well both as isolated cells and as discrete cellular masses.

TYPES OF GROWTH AND OF CELL DIVISION ENCOUNTERED IN FREELY SUSPENDED CELLS

Ideas on the mode of cell division in the angiosperm plant body tend to be dominated by some familiar concepts. These are that (1) equational division forms two approximately equal masses; (2) divisions tend to produce walls, or septa, of minimal area; (3) new walls, or septa, are laid down along directions which tend to intersect the old walls at right angles. Therefore, despite such conspicuous but still regular exceptions as the vascular cambium, one normally tends to think of cell divisions in the angiosperm plant body occurring more or less in accordance with what have become known as Sachs' and Errera's laws, respectively. This being so, the writers were hardly prepared for the many anomalous features observed in these freely suspended cells, especially when it became clear that they also give rise eventually to apparently normal tissues and organs of the plant body.

The method of observing the cells which were cultured in flasks has been to examine them, or their aggregates, both under the microscope using bright field illumination, and also using a Zeiss-Winkel Plankton microscope fitted with attachments for observations under phase contrast and also for photographic work. Proceeding in this way, a large number of photographic records has been obtained. These show the status of cultured cells, individually or as aggregates or colonies. Various types of behavior are repeatedly recognized. The figures show obvious sequences in the behavior of these cultures even though all the stages here described have not been successively obtained from any one growing cell. Several sequences have been chosen to illustrate types of behavior which have occurred over and over again as these cultures have been kept under observation and repeatedly sub-cultured.

Proliferation of Isodiametric Cells

The phenomena here described stem from single, small, rather densely protoplasmic, isolated cells (in contrast to events which begin with the giant-cells to be described later). Free cells commonly grow in this way in cellular suspensions of both carrot and potato tissue. One may regard each single potentially dividing cell as the "mother cell" of the ultimate tissue aggregate to which it gives rise. The photographs (Figs. 7–12) and diagrams (Fig. 13a-d) which were made from photographs show a typical sequence of events leading from free cells to a multicellular mass.

Stimulated by nutrients and cell division factors, which are present in the medium, the freely suspended cells divide in a typically equational fashion, cutting off a "daughter" cell to one side and then, apparently, by a repetition of these events, a second "daughter" cell is formed opposite to the first (Fig. 10). This produces a characteristically wing-like appearance in which the "mother" cell is flanked by two "daughter" cells (Figs. 10, 11). By repeated division in the "daughter" cells growth progresses, as it were, along this "horizontal" axis, but meanwhile growth develops also along a "vertical" axis by divisions in the initiating cell approximately at right angles to the first (Fig. 12); this establishes a new tier of cells capable of dividing laterally in the manner of the first. Thus, from an original cell, a mass of cells develops, and these divide in such a way as to establish major and minor axes of development (Fig. 13a-d); this type of growth seems to occur especially well in a stationary, submerged culture when the dramatic extension of the marginal cells, in a manner still to be described, seems not to occur readily. When cultures are grown in this way, they frequently produce a dense, moruloid mass of actively dividing cells, each one of which is capable of further growth (Fig. 13d). Tulecke (1957) derived

a somewhat similar colony of growing cells (*loc. cit.*, cf. Fig. 11) from the pollen tube of *Ginkgo*, also by the effect of coconut milk.

Behavior of Giant Cells

Unusually large uninucleate cells with very conspicuous cytoplasmic strands, along which active protoplasmic streaming occurs, were among the first to be observed in this freely suspended state. Such cells may have dimensions of the order of 300 μ long and 100–150 μ in diameter, and thus are much larger than typical carrot phloem parenchyma cells as they occur in the original carrot root. Indeed, they are very much larger than the average size of the cells in rapidly growing cultures derived from carrot tissue explants (Steward and Shantz, 1955, cf. Fig. 3). It is clear, however, that these especially large vacuolated cells can divide, more often than not forming very unequal daughter cells. This process may continue until a densely packed mass of small cells has been formed which fills the original lumen of the large cell. The photographs (Figs. 14–16) show typical cells at various stages along this course and the drawings (Fig. 13e–j) show a typical sequence from a single large cell to a multicellular mass. This mass resembles in organization the outcome of the events depicted in Figs. 7–12, but it will be noted that the means by which it is achieved are different. The starting point in the first sequence is a single, small, isodiametric cell that proliferates externally as repeated divisions occur, whereas, in the later sequence, the starting point is a single, large, highly vacuolated cell which divides internally to form a compact mass of cells. From the resultant compact, moruloid mass further growth may occur as cells at the margin become rounded, enlarge, and divide (Fig. 13i, j).

In an interesting paper by Tulecke (1957), a condition very similar to that of certain of the drawings in Fig. 13 (especially 13c, g) is described in the development of a tissue culture from the pollen tube cell of *Ginkgo* under the stimulus of coconut milk. The tube cell elongates, becomes polynucleate and divides by internal septation (cf. Tulecke, Fig. 7g).

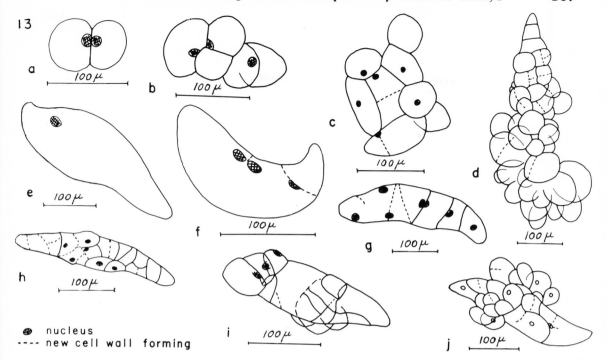

Fig. 13a–d. Diagrammatic drawings, from photographs, showing the transition from freely suspended isodiametric cells to moruloid mass of growing cells. Fig. 13e–j. Diagrammatic drawings, from photographs, showing the transition from freely suspended giant cells to a cluster of growing cells.

In the light of the effects of coconut milk on both carrot phloem and/or *Ginkgo* pollen, it is interesting to note that a growth-promoting effect of an extract of *Ginkgo* female gametophytes on carrot tissues had also been observed (Steward and Caplin, 1952)!

The sequence of events depicted (Figs. 13e–j, 14–16) is self-explanatory. While this phenomenon is common in fusiform initials of the cambium and in certain other places, it is noteworthy that cells as large and as highly vacuolate as those illustrated can divide, and it is also noteworthy that, until the entire cellular mass is occupied by small compact cells, *external growth* does not occur. By this time, the average cell size will have been reduced to something which approximates that in the most rapidly growing carrot explants in coconut milk media (Steward and Shantz, 1955, cf. Fig. 3). It is apparent, however, that the internal divisions which occur in these large cells (Fig. 13g, h) are certainly not along planes of division that would easily

have been anticipated from Sach's and Errera's laws, respectively. Later illustrations (Figs. 33, 34) indicate the way in which this occurs. The impression is inescapable that the large cells become polynucleate as, or before, these divisions take place. New walls form along planes that seem to follow the direction of conspicuous cytoplasmic strands and fibrils (cf. Figs. 16, 13g). The subsequent behavior of such a tissue mass may be much modified by the state of aeration in which it is placed. Be that as it may, however, Figs. 13e–16 clearly show how a dense, compact mass of potentially growing cells may originate from a single, large, highly vacuolate, freely suspended cell.

Sachs (1887) visualized that the shape of a cell aggregate was much affected by the shape and directions of growth in the "mother" cell, and he showed the variety in form that could occur even at the eight-cell stage from pollen "mother" cells. He states (*loc. cit.*, p. 433) ". . . the mode in which the cell divisions follow one another depends by no means on the physiological or morphological nature of the cells, but upon their mode of growth and external form—especially upon the latter." The cell masses here described, which are formed by internal divisions in cells that have deviated during growth from the isodiametric condition, do not, therefore, obey in any simple way the rules of cell division—nor should this be expected—for these divisions occur in an already asymmetric system. The relevance of this quotation to the case just described is apparent.

Tubular and Filamentous Growth

In any freely suspended population of cells under the conditions here described, unusually long, nonseptate filamentous cells may be encountered, and in fact such may be seen in sections to wind among the marginal cells of tissue cultures as these are commonly grown from carrot root explants. Figure 3 shows long filamentous cells occurring typically in a free cellular population from the peanut. These filaments present an appearance quite different from the isodiametric parenchyma cells of the tissue from which they were derived.

It may now be shown, however, that septate filaments can grow out from the large cells. The origin of a filamentous outgrowth in these cells occurs quite unexpectedly by the extrusion of a tube-like protuberance, or extension of the wall, from a cell which is already vacuolated, and relatively large, and furnished with a well established wall. The sequence of events is illustrated in Figs. 17–25, in which one can visualize the emergence of a distinctive growth pattern from single cells in the liquid cultures, and by a different route from those already described.

Even large vacuolated cells may put out one or more protuberances (Figs. 17, 18). Such tube-like extensions often occur in cells which are attached to the margins of cultures grown from tissue explants (Fig. 19). These protuberances enlarge and may, under appropriate conditions, grow in filamentous fashion. In fact, there seems to be something particularly conducive to the filamentous type of growth when it originates in close association with an already existing large cell or cluster of cells. Figure 25 shows a situation in which a multicellular filament has clearly originated from a basal cell attached to a very large vacuolated cell. Apparently, however, any large, free, or marginal cell of the cluster may elongate and form a filament which divides transversely and grows at its tip (Figs. 20–22). It is apparent that this method of cell growth is not only quite different from those portrayed in the series which deals with isodiametric cells (Figs. 7–13d) and the series which deals with giant cells (Figs. 13e–16), but it is also unexpected for normal angiosperm cells. However, some parallels might be seen, even in the intact plant body, if one considers the way in which fibers and idioblasts grow at their tips and insert their way between the surrounding tissues of the plant body. Also, the tubular filamentous type of growth, emerging from a rounded cell, is reminiscent of the growth of root hairs in the piliferous region of the root. Indeed, Tulecke (1957), studying the stimulus upon the growth of *Ginkgo* pollen tube cells, also describes the formation of a filament with transverse septa (*loc. cit.*, Fig. 9). Perhaps the closest parallel in normal growth to this growth habit may be seen in the growth of the basal cell of certain embryos to form a large multicellular suspensor with a row of cells attached in a manner that superficially resembles Fig. 21 very closely. In fact, the embryo of *Daucus* itself is known to pass through a markedly filamentous stage (Borthwick, 1931; also see Wardlaw, 1955, p. 243). Be this as it may, however, one can now recognize that a frequently occurring method of cell growth in free cell suspensions in coconut milk is by the extrusion of a filament and its subsequent extension and growth by transverse divisions. Again one cannot yet be specific concerning the stimuli that induce cells to grow in this particular manner in contrast to the others that have been described in Figs. 7–16. However, it is possible for all these types of behavior to occur in the same nutrient medium, i.e., the basal medium supplemented with coconut milk. Although this is

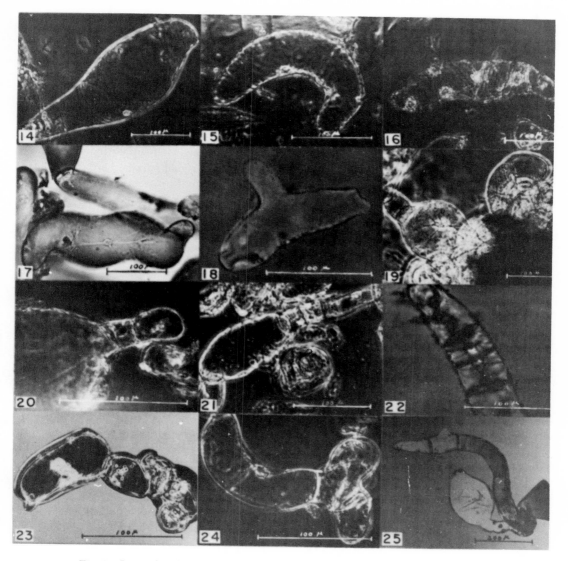

Fig. 14. Large, free-floating, cultured cell of carrot root phloem, showing nucleus, radiating cytoplasmic strands and spiral bands of protoplasm within the wall. Fig. 15. Large, free cell of carrot showing cytoplasmic strands suggestively arranged in the light of the method of internal division by septa (see Fig. 16). Fig. 16. Large, free cell of carrot showing internal divisions, multiple nuclei evident even before new walls appear (cf. Fig. 13g). Fig. 17. Large, free cell of carrot showing tubular extrusions, nucleus, and prominent cytoplasmic strands. Fig. 18. Peanut cell with tubular extrusion. Fig. 19. Cellular detail at edge of a tissue cultured colony showing large, rounded cell with contents and short, tubular extrusion. Fig. 20. Giant free cell, with tubular process or filament showing transverse divisions. Fig. 21. Giant free cell with a multicellular filament. Fig. 22. Detail of cell division in a filament of carrot showing recently divided nuclei and a new wall; incomplete wall at the tip. (Photograph taken with interference microscope.) Fig. 23. Basal cluster of peanut cells showing a filamentous outgrowth and the formation of a small papilla at the tip. Fig. 24. Basal cluster, or foot, of carrot cells showing a filamentous outgrowth with a transverse division. Fig. 25. Giant cell of carrot with a long multicellular filament attached (photographed with interference microscope).

largely hypothetical at this point, one idea is that aeration is a potent factor in determining which of these different types of behavior prevail.

Budding: Formation of Papillae

Three distinct ways in which development may proceed from a single free cell in liquid cultures have now been described. Figures 26–30 illustrate yet another type of behavior which is conspicuous in the case of cell cultures from the peanut plant, but it also occurs, not infrequently, in cultures obtained from the carrot root. The emphasis here is upon the emergence of small papillae on the surface of cells which already possess a well-formed wall. In a manner reminiscent of the budding of yeast, the papillae enlarge while they remain constricted at the base, and an open channel occurs between the "mother cell" and the "bud." As cytoplasmic material and nucleus enter the papillae, they become independently growing cells, in some cases remaining attached to the "mother" cell, but in others they seem to constrict and are "pinched off" at the base.

Figure 27 shows three cells, two of which have clearly developed from the central cell and, in the case of the smaller of these, the connection with the "mother" cell remains open (Fig. 28), whereas the larger bud was already permanently sealed off at its base by a wall (Fig. 27). These curious bud-like papillae occur very frequently on the cells isolated from peanut, often more than one occurring on each cell (Figs. 29, 30); and again (Fig. 30), some of these have enlarged to form lateral winglike cells as appendages to those from which they originated, whereas others still remain small and unexpanded. Figure 26 shows a minute papilla on a spherical cell, which exhibits clear cytoplasmic detail and the definite, first-formed wall, and Fig. 30 shows papillae which have expanded into bladder-like structures to become "daughter" cells.

Presumably the wall of these cells already contains the now familiar laminated fibrillar structure of cellulose in which the fibrillar direction may change from layer to layer. If this is so, a curious problem is here presented, for one would hardly expect such a wall to give way locally at the point where the papillae originate, unless this occurs at the sites of primary pit fields. Nevertheless, this clearly does occur and, when it has happened, the papillae so formed can obviously enlarge, grow and become self-supporting. There may also be a superficial parallel here with tyloses as they occur in the intact plant body. At some point of weakness in the wall, believed to be at the place where a pit membrane separates a parenchyma cell and a vessel cavity, the membrane of the parenchyma cell is "blown out" into a vesicle in the vessel cavity, and the nucleus of the parenchyma cell may enter the extruded portion (Esau, 1953). However, one cannot at this stage locate precisely the point on the cell surface where these papillae form and grow with a point of weakness or the sites of simple pit fields, probable as this idea may seem to be.

Brief reference to a recent study of budding in yeast (Falcone and Nickerson, 1958) may be made. This study shows that the yeast bud originates at an open pore (cf. Fig. 28) through which the bud emerges with explosive force and the new wall forms around the daughter protoplast, the old wall acting as a "primer." Electron microscope studies of yeast have shown that the randomly oriented fibrils of the yeast wall acquire a circular, rope-like form at the base of the bud; this is regarded as a response, tangentially, to the outwardly directed force that forms the bud. These ideas are suggestive in relation to the extrusion of buds and filaments in carrot cells. Circular structures have been seen at the base of tube-like protuberances from carrot cells (cf. Fig. 14); a protuberance in process of formation is visible in Fig. 25.

THE CONTENTS AND WALL FORMATION IN FREE VACUOLATED DIVIDING CELLS

Several of the figures taken with the phase contrast microscope illustrate the conspicuous cytoplasmic strands along which very active

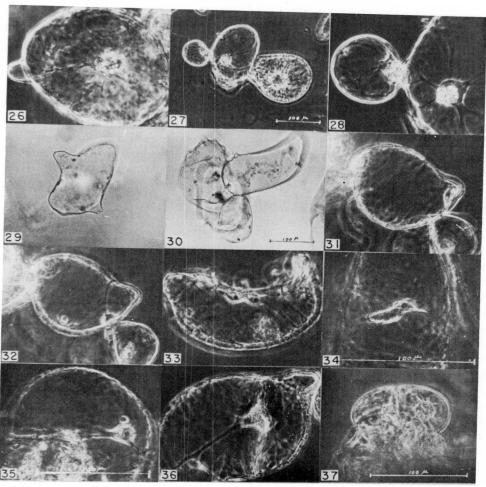

Fig. 26. Free cell of peanut, showing radiating strands from cytoplasm surrounding the nucleus, and the origin of a minute papilla. Fig. 27. Peanut cells multiplying by "budding" in the freely suspended state, showing nuclei and cytoplasmic strands in each cell. Fig. 28. Detail of cells shown at Fig. 27, emphasizing the still open pore between the small "bud" and the "mother" cell. Granular cytoplasmic material flowed through this open channel whereas the larger "bud" was sealed off by a wall. Fig. 29. Free cell of peanut showing papillate extrusions. Fig. 30. Cells of peanut with many papillae, one of which has extended to form a new cell. Fig. 31. Carrot cells showing one which has recently divided and the nucleus and dense cytoplasm which was observed to move into the tip of another cell. Fig. 32. View 15 minutes later than Fig. 31, showing the withdrawal of the nucleus from the cell tip and a prominent "strand" in the position where a new wall was about to form in a direction continuous with the division in the adjacent cell. Figs. 31 and 32 were taken from cells at the edge of a colony. Fig. 33. Free cell of carrot, showing two recently divided nuclei (each with a conspicuous nucleolus) in the center of the field; the new wall has not yet formed. Prominent cytoplasmic strands are visible and, at a different plane of focus, a third nucleus, situated along a cytoplasmic strand, could be seen to the right. Fig. 34. Recently divided nuclei (the nucleolus distinctly visible) in a large vacuolate cell with new septum forming along the cleavage plane between them. This condition is that described by Bailey (1920) as the phragmoplast and by Sinnott and Bloch (1941) as the phragmosome. Fig. 35. Free cell of carrot, with nucleus and prominent nucleolus adjacent to a prominent strand indicating the position of the new wall. Fig. 36. Free cell of carrot showing new wall between recently divided nuclei, and a heavy cytoplasmic strand which probably indicates the position of the next wall. Note the papillate extrusion similar to those described above in Fig. 26. Fig. 37. Cells at the edge of a cultured carrot colony after recent division showing prominent nuclei.

streaming was observed to occur. The nucleus in these cells is often surrounded by small granules but may be clearly seen with the interference microscope and may also be recognized by the often conspicuous nucleolus. Usually the nucleus is suspended by cytoplasmic strands, and the surrounding granules (about 1 μ in size) may well be mitochondria (Fig. 9); other larger cell inclusions (Figs. 26, 28) may be the spherosomes or proplastids of Sorokin (1956).

Properly to convey a sense of the dynamic activity in these cells, motion pictures would be necessary. However, a series of photographs was taken at short intervals to show movements which occurred in a carrot cell which had divided, the presumed "daughter" cell being still attached. Figures 31, 32 are from this series. The nucleus and some cytoplasm was observed to migrate into the papilla-like tip of the cell, and it then withdrew. Meanwhile, a well-defined sheet of cytoplasm formed a conspicuous layer across the base of the papilla-like tip, and the proximity of the nucleus to that cytoplasmic sheet indicated that wall formation would seal it off from the rest of the cell.

Cytological detail of these nuclei when they are dividing has not yet been investigated. The impression is, however, that the nucleus occupies a central position, suspended by cytoplasmic strands, in the most actively growing cells (Figs. 9, 14, 26, 27). The first clear indication of division in these vacuolated cells is the presence of a stout cytoplasmic strand which progressively thickens.

The direction of this strong strand establishes the place of the new wall (Fig. 32) and it may be recognized early under the phase microscope by its thickness, and because the nucleus, embedded in cytoplasm, lies conspicuously adjacent (Figs. 34–36). On numerous occasions, this appearance (Fig. 34) has been observed. In Fig. 33 two nuclei are in close proximity after recent division, and in Fig. 34 a new septum is forming along a plane of cleavage between them. This (Fig. 34) is the appearance, quite exactly, which was described first by Bailey (1920) for the cam-

bium, and later by Sinnott and Bloch (1941) as the mode of division in relatively large vacuolate cells; in fact, Sinnott and Bloch's Fig. 3, H (*loc. cit.*, p. 227) could serve as an interpretative drawing to Fig. 34 of this paper! Sinnott and Bloch thus recognized that the first indication of the future plane of division is to be seen in the cytoplasm *before* the nuclei divide. The strong, transverse, cytoplasmic strands which radiate from the nucleus across the cell in the plane of the future division, and within which the wall will form, were described by Bailey as the phragmoplast, and later by Sinnott and Bloch as the phragmosome. Sinnott and Bloch described cell division occurring in this way in a variety of situations in response to the stimulus of wounding, but they also showed that they occur normally below meristems wherever vacuolated cells (the vacuolating-dividing cells of Priestley, 1929; also see Priestley and Scott, 1939) divide. Much physiological work has used parenchymatous tissue with large vacuolated cells. "Internal" division and cell multiplication may, therefore, have often passed unnoticed because the nuclei and the new septa are relatively inconspicuous.

The foregoing descriptions of cellular behavior relate to freely suspended cells but it is also evident that cells at the margin of tissue culture masses show similar effects: this can be seen in cells at the edge of the tissue culture colony (Figs. 19, 37).

RECENT ATTEMPTS TO DEMONSTRATE GROWTH IN ISOLATED CELLS

Reference should be made to recent attempts to demonstrate the growth of isolated, or even single, cells. These are the work of Muir *et al.* (1954), of De Ropp (1955), and of Torrey (1957), though loose colonies of cells of *Rubus* and of *Pinus* were illustrated by Gautheret (1956). Although these papers indicate that cells had been observed in some of the conditions here described, it is also true that it was not shown in detail the way in which such cells as those of carrot can grow when freely suspended. In part, this may be due to the preoccupation of the authors in question with attempts to demonstrate growth of *one* cell in a medium which contains no others. Muir, *et al.* (1954), however, placed the single cells they observed on a tissue culture mass of "nurse" tissue, from which it was separated by a thin sheet of paper tissue, and Torrey (1957) introduced single cells (from the root cambium of *Pisum*) into a drop of medium which surrounded a piece of callus tissue. De Ropp (1955) kept cells which were removed from friable carrot cultures under observation in small volumes (0.2 ml.) of media which contained coconut milk solids.

Torrey's work showed that cell division did occur, but he stressed that it did so in only a small percentage of the isolated cells which were transferred for observation in the manner he describes, although the bulk of the cells survived and enlarged. De Ropp, on the other hand, categorically denied the ability of any large vacuolated carrot cells to divide and lead to the establishment of active cultures. Although he clearly saw large cells of the kind here shown (Fig. 14 and even Fig. 27) and saw the cyclosis and gross movements of cytoplasm frequently observed in this work, he rigorously excluded much of the behavior which is here described (Figs. 13e–16). De Ropp admits only that certain small cambial cells will grow, and these he obtained by teasing tissue cultures which were already somewhat organized and which contained the nodule-like growing centers described by Gautheret (1935). When these small cells grew, they gave rise to clumps or clusters of rather large cells, not unlike those here described in Figs. 12, 13, but four distinct methods by which both large and small cells of carrot grow and divide when these exist in the freely suspended state, as here described, were not observed by De Ropp. In fact, on re-examination of De Ropp's figures in the light of this work, there are suggestions that division, and even budding, in large cells may have occurred (cf. Figs. 1–3, 10 of De Ropp).

The ability of freely suspended cells, completely disassociated from the plant body, to grow into a multicellular mass posed the problem whether this mass could organize, develop organs, and even form a complete plant. This is the topic of the second of this group of papers.

SUMMARY

A technique which permits disassociated cells from carrot root phloem tissue to be obtained and kept constantly for use is described. The freely suspended cells, grown in a basal medium supplemented with coconut milk, exhibit a wide range of size and form. Under the phase microscope, they show active protoplasmic streaming, prominent nuclei, and nucleoli, cell inclusions and cytoplasmic strands. The different ways in which these cells divide and grow, giving rise to a multicellular mass, are described with particular reference to carrot phloem cells, potato tuber cells, and cells from the cotyledon of peanut. These methods consist of: (1) proliferation of an isodiametric "mother" cell and colony formation by successive divisions, (2) internal divisions and formation of a moruloid mass within the confines of the original cell wall, (3) extrusion of tube-like or filamentous processes and formation of multicellular filaments, and (4) extrusion of small papillae or buds which enlarge into full-grown cells. The behavior of freely suspended cells is not readily interpreted according to classical concepts of cell behavior in plant tissues because each cell behaves independently, unrestricted by its neighbors or by lack of nutrients, and the culture mass at first lacks the mechanism of integration that is present in the plant body. It is, therefore, surprising that cells, which are freely suspended in a uniform liquid environment under uniform light and gravity neutralized by rotation around a horizontal shaft, do grow in such various, unsymmetrical, and distinctive ways.

LITERATURE CITED

Bailey, I. W. 1920. The cambium and its derivative tissues. III. A reconnaissance of cytological phenomena in the cambium. *Amer. Jour. Bot.* 7: 417–434.

Borthwick, H. A. 1931. Development of the macrogametophyte and embryo of *Daucus carota*. *Bot. Gaz.* 92: 23–44.

De Ropp, R. S. 1955. The growth and behavior *in vitro* of isolated plant cells. *Proc. Royal Soc. of London, Series B—Biological Science* 144: 86–93.

Earle, W. R., J. C. Bryant, E. L. Schilling, and Virginia J. Evans. 1956. Growth of cell suspensions in tissue culture. *Ann. New York Acad. Sci.* 63: 666–682.

Esau, Katherine. 1953. *Plant Anatomy*. John Wiley. New York.

Falcone, G., and W. J. Nickerson. 1958. Enzymatic reactions involved in cellular division of micro-organisms (First draft of manuscript seen).

Gautheret, R. J. 1935. *Recherches sur la Culture des Tissus Vegetaux*. Librairie E. le François, Paris.

———. 1956. Histogenesis in plant tissue cultures. *Jour. Nat. Cancer Inst.* 19: 555–573.

Haberlandt, G. 1902. Kulturversuche mit isolierten Pflanzenzellen. Sitzungsber. *Akad. Wiss. Wien, math.-nat.* Kl. 111: 69–92.

Maheshwari, Nirmala. 1958. *In vitro* culture of excised ovules of *Papaver somniferum*. *Science* 127: 342.

Marcus, P. I., S. J. Cieciura, and T. Puck. 1956. Clonal growth *in vitro* of epithelial cells from normal human tissues. *Jour. of Exp. Med.* 104: 615–628.

Morel, G., and R. H. Wetmore. 1951. Tissue culture of monocotyledons. *Amer. Jour. Bot.* 38: 138–140.

Muir, W. H., A. C. Hildebrandt, and A. J. Riker. 1954. Plant tissue cultures produced from single isolated cells. *Science* 119: 877–878.

Nitsch, J. P. 1951. Growth and development in vitro of excised ovaries. *Amer. Jour. Bot.* 38: 566–577.

Priestley, J. H. 1929. Cell growth and cell division in the shoot of the flowering plant. *New Phytol.* 28: 54–81.

———, and L. I. Scott. 1939. The formation of a new cell wall at cell division. *Proc. Leeds Phil. Lit. Soc.* 3: 532–545.

Reinert, J. 1956. Dissociation of cultures from *Picea glauca* into small tissue fragments and single cells. *Science* 123: 457–458.

Robbins, W. J. 1922. Cultivation of excised root tips and stem tips under sterile conditions. *Bot. Gaz.* 73: 376–390.

Sachs, J. 1887. *Lectures on the Physiology of Plants*. Clarendon Press. Oxford.

Sinnott, E. W., and R. Bloch. 1941. Division in vacuolate plant cells. *Amer. Jour. Bot.* 28: 225–232.

Sorokin, Helen P. 1956. Studies on living cells of pea seedlings. I. Survey of vacuolar precipitates, mitochondria, plastids, and spherosomes. *Amer. Jour. Bot.* 43: 787–794.

Steeves, T. A. 1956. *Proceedings of the Decennial Review Conference on Tissue Culture*, pp. 583, 584. P. R. White, Editor. Woodstock, Vermont.

———, H. P. Gabriel, and M. W. Steeves. 1957. Growth in sterile culture of excised leaves of flowering plants. *Science* 126: 350–351.

Steward, F. C., and S. M. Caplin. 1951. Tissue culture from potato tuber: the synergistic action of 2,4-D and coconut milk. *Science* 113: 518–520.

———, and ———. 1952. Growth and metabolism of plant cells. IV. Evidence on the role of coconut milk factor in development. *Ann. Bot.* 16: 491–504.

———, ———, and F. K. Millar. 1952. Investigations on growth and metabolism of plant cells. I. New techniques for the investigation of metabolism, nutrition, and growth in undifferentiated cells. *Ann. Bot.* 16: 57–77.

———, ———, and E. M. Shantz. 1955. Investigations on the growth and metabolism of plant cells. V. Tumorous growth in relation to growth factors of the type found in coconut. *Ann. Bot.* 19: 29–47.

———, and E. M. Shantz. 1955. The chemical induction of growth in plant tissue cultures. I. Methods of tissue culture and the analysis of growth. In *The Chemistry and Mode of Action of Plant Growth Substances*. Ed. by R. L. Wain and F. Wightman. Butterworths. London.

Torrey, J. G. 1957. Cell division in isolated single plant cells *in vitro*. *Proc. National Acad. Sci. (U. S.)* 43: 887–891.

Tulecke, W. 1957. The pollen of *Ginkgo biloba: In vitro* culture and tissue formation. *Amer. Jour. Bot.* 44: 602–608.

Wardlaw, C. W. 1955. *Embryogenesis in Plants*. Methuen Co. London.

Wetmore, R. H., and G. Morel. 1949. Growth and development of *Adiantum pedatum* L. on nutrient agar. *Amer. Jour. Bot.* 36: 805–806.

———, and C. W. Wardlaw. 1951. Experimental morphogenesis in vascular plants. *Ann. Rev. Plant Physiol.* 2: 269–292.

White, P. R. 1942. Plant tissue culture. *Ann. Rev. Biochem.* 11: 615–628.

———. 1954. *The Cultivation of Animal and Plant Cells*. The Ronald Press Co. New York.

Growth and Organized Development of Cultured Cells, II: Organization in Cultures Grown from Freely Suspended Cells[1]

F. C. STEWARD
MARION O. MAPES
KATHRYN MEARS

The first of this group of papers (Steward *et al.*, 1958) described the various ways in which freely suspended cells from certain dicotyledonous plants grow and multiply to form a relatively unorganized multicellular mass. The growth in question occurs under prescribed and controlled nutritional and environmental conditions. The purpose of this paper is to show how the growth may be carried forward into the formation of roots and shoots and, in fact, the development of whole plants.

DIFFERENTIATION TO FORM ROOTS

Tissue cultures grown directly from cambium-free explants of differentiated carrot root phloem in the basal medium supplemented with coconut milk do not normally form roots. On the very rare occasions when this has occurred, it may have been due to the presence of a preformed root initial in the explant. At any rate, root formation occurs extremely infrequently when the culture is started from freshly explanted phloem tissue. On the other hand, the minute tissue cultures formed by the development of cell aggregates from these freely suspended and frequently sub-cultured cells will develop roots with great ease. This may be due to the disappearance of some factor antagonistic to the formation of an organized root apical meri-

American Journal of Botany, 45, 705–708, No. 10, December 1958. Reprinted with permission.

[1] Received for publication June 1, 1958. This work forms part of a program of research which has been supported by grants to one of us (F.C.S.) from the National Cancer Institute, National Institutes of Health, United States Department of Health, Education, and Welfare.

stem that is present in the central core of tissue in the explant removed from the carrot root. Or, it may be said that the differentiated phloem tissue must first "dedifferentiate"— whatever that may mean. Whatever explains the ease of root formation in these small aggregates, which are grown from cultured cells, the events that lead to root initials can be illustrated in Figs. 1–5.

A root initial does not form until the cell aggregate or colony reaches such a size that the inner cells of the mass behave differently from the outer cells. A sign of this is the presence of a new type cell in the central region of the culture (Fig. 1); this cell loses its contents, becoming somewhat lignified and forming a tracheid-like element of the kind so often observed in plant tissue cultures (Gautheret, 1956). A single xylem element is frequently followed by similar ones in close association. It is interesting that they form in a tissue which was wholly derived originally from the secondary phloem. Surrounding these nests of lignified elements, which lose their contents (Figs. 2–4), there develops a ring, or hollow spherical sheath, of cambium-like elements (cf. Gautheret, 1956, Fig. 8) which encloses a mass of cells; these cells now *have only limited access to the external medium.* This can be seen in Figs. 3, 4.

It appears that so long as all the cells of the culture have free access to the external medium, they grow in a random and independent fashion by one or other of the methods already described (Steward *et al.*, 1958). The ring of cambium-like tissue develops, however, as if in response to an injury or a wound, under the stimuli derived from the formation of these lignified elements. The

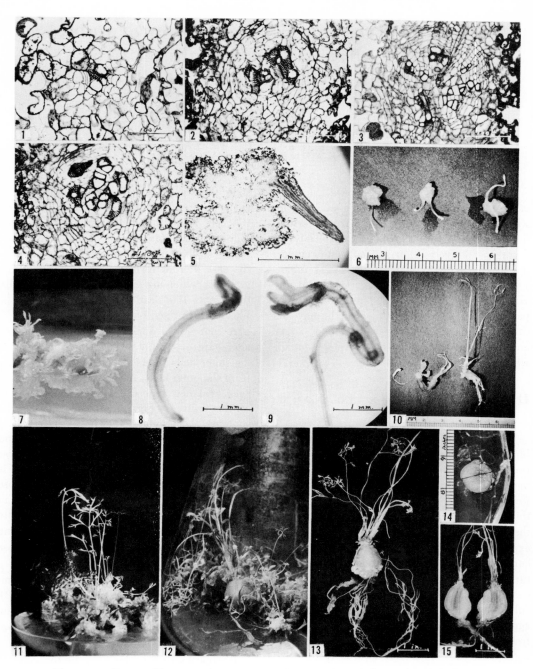

Figs. 1–15. Carrot. Figs. 1–4. Stages in the formation of "nodules" or growth centers which enclose "nests" of lignified elements. Fig. 1 shows the first lignified element and adjacent cell division; Fig. 3 shows complete ring of dividing tissue enclosing "nests" of lignified elements; Fig. 4 shows the beginning of organization in a nodule leading to root formation. Figs. 5, 6. Emergence of roots from tissue cultures. Figs. 7, 11, 12. Stages in the growth of carrot plants on agar. Figs. 8, 9, 10. Stages in the development of young plantlets, which originate from individual nodules (Fig. 8 shows very young stage in this development). Fig. 13. Carrot plant with storage organ. Fig. 14. Transverse section of cultured storage root shows callus-like growth in contact with the medium plus coconut milk and normal secondary phloem on side away from the medium. Fig. 15. Longitudinal section of cultured storage root.

cells in this cambium-like region are separated from the external medium, and they develop in a nutrient condition which is controlled by the closely packed zone of cells and the tissue which they enclose. In fact, the dividing cells lie along a gradient from the dead cells within, to the nutrient without, which contains the cell division stimuli. In this cambium- or pericycle-like region, a root apex forms and it subsequently grows out through the tissue mass into the surrounding medium (Fig. 5). These events are not demonstrably different from the normal origin of lateral roots. When such root initials form, they grow apace and the more callus-like growth of the original colony of cells tends to be suppressed. When grown in this way, on cultures revolved around a horizontal axis, the roots emerge in all directions (Fig. 6). Longitudinal sections of roots so formed show that they are normal and develop apparently normal protoxylem tissue.

FORMATION OF SHOOTS

When culture flasks or tubes are inoculated by liquid suspensions which contain freely suspended cells or small cell aggregates, they form very large numbers of freely growing colonies, and many root initials may originate in the manner described. The conditions most conducive to root formation have not been investigated fully, though some early evidence seemed to indicate that in a culture which is prone to form roots this occurred more readily in the dark and more readily if the calcium content of the medium was reduced. Furthermore, it has been noted that certain active growth-promoting fractions, isolated from extracts of immature corn (Shantz and Steward, 1957) also tended to foster copious root formation. However, once a root initial has formed, it continues to grow, and thereafter the growth of the tissue culture is retarded, or suppressed. If, however, cultured cell aggregates with roots already developed are transplanted to nutrient agar in flasks, complete with basal medium and coconut milk, the cultures can be indefinitely continued. Under

these circumstances a copious growth of roots occurs. Indeed, if cultures remain in the normal rotating culture tubes in which explants are commonly grown, the roots may grow until they virtually fill the tube (Steward and Shantz, 1955. Fig. 1d). If, however, tissue aggregates which have been reared from free cells are transplanted to agar media they may, as they grow, also form buds and shoots spontaneously.

The shoots which first emerge have leafy appendages which, like primitive leaves, tend to be entire (Fig. 7), though later more typical, much dissected, carrot leaves develop (Figs. 11, 12). Again, the stimuli which promote the development of buds and shoots have not yet been fully investigated. From the frequency with which this development occurs, it would appear that the irregular, randomly proliferated cultures that develop from the freely suspended cells do this spontaneously and with comparative ease when they are furnished with the basal medium plus coconut milk on a stationary, semisolid medium. No doubt the shoot is more dependent on regular orientation to gravity than is the root. The loosely proliferated culture, which originated from aggregates grown from free cells and later transferred to agar, presents the general appearance shown in Fig. 7. From such a mass many minute plantlets can be dissected, such as those illustrated in Figs. 8–10.

REGENERATED PLANTLETS: SIMILARITIES TO YOUNG EMBRYOS

In the regenerated plantlets, the axis, with shoot and root apices, is completely established (Fig. 8). The impression is inescapable that each of the many nodule-like growing centers (Fig. 5) which develop in the cultured mass can first form roots; then, if transferred to a stationary agar medium, they will form shoots. Thus, the spherical masses of cultured cells, enclosed by their sheath of cambium-like initials (Figs. 3, 4), really behave like a proembryo; they form both roots and shoots and, significantly enough, do this in a fluid (of another species) that normally nourishes immature embryos. Figures 7–12 show various stages in the organization of the shoot in cultures of this sort. Even more surprisingly, it may be observed that a secondarily thickened storage carrot root may grow in the tissue mass which had originated, in the manner described, from material that had been frequently sub-cultured and reduced to the free cell state (Figs. 12, 13).

Thus the cycle of development is now complete, because cells withdrawn from the phloem of the storage carrot root and which have passed through many transfers in which they were reduced to the single cellular state, have developed into cell aggregates, which have, in turn, differentiated to form roots and, when transplanted, have given rise also to shoots and to a secondarily thickened storage carrot root.

A curious, but suggestive, observation was made on the way the secondarily thickened carrot root grew in culture (Figs. 13–15). The surface of the enlarging organ which was in contact with the agar medium containing coconut milk grew irregularly at its base, with green callus-like swellings (Fig. 13). The side of the storage root which was away from the medium, and, therefore, not in direct contact with coconut milk, grew normally, forming a broad band of secondary phloem, rich in carotene, as seen in transverse section (Fig. 14). This tissue appeared normal in every way, in contrast to the liquid-cultured, unorganized tissue which never achieves this rich, orange-red color or content of carotene. The only other abnormality was some green color in the xylem, which was seen in the longitudinal section (Fig. 15); this is a not uncommon feature near the crown of normal carrot plants, especially when they have been grown in the light. The obvious suggestion is that direct contact with the stimuli to growth, which are in the coconut milk, leads to cell proliferation (Fig. 13) but, when these stimuli are modified by the intervening tissue of the growing root, apparently normal secondary growth may occur (Figs. 14, 15).

THE STIMULI TO DEVELOPMENT

Much remains to be done to define the variables and the stimuli which regulate each of the definitive steps in the organization of cellular aggregates to form roots and shoots. It is suggestive that the effective nutrient conditions for this development also furnish all the nutrients and growth factors that normally nourish immature embryos. Thus, it is now clear that parenchyma cells, which are already far advanced toward maturity in the plant body, may return in culture, under appropriate nutrient conditions, to the dividing state and, as they do this, they can eventually recover the totipotency that was originally inherent in the egg. However, no single parenchyma cell can *directly* recapitulate the familiar facts of embryology, but, through the formation first of an unorganized tissue culture, which is in fact a colony of dividing cells, the necessary degree of organization is recaptured, first to form roots and then to form shoots.

One may well ask why the cells of tissue explants, withdrawn from the phloem of a carrot root, will not as readily organize to form roots and shoots, even though they can be brought by coconut milk into a rapid state of cell division and may form very large callus-like masses if they are grown on an appropriate medium. The full explanation of the contrasted behavior of the cells which have passed through the freely suspended condition and the cells of the explants from which they were originally derived requires further investigation. Though the process may be described as "dedifferentiation," this term is hardly illuminating. It is, however, interesting to recall that in the early work of Van Overbeek *et al.* (1941), some young embryos were induced to grow in an unorganized proliferative fashion by the use of coconut milk. In the present investigation, already differentiated cells have been induced to grow again and eventually to produce structures that normally originate from the embryo. This surely means that the coconut milk contains the inherent stimuli and nutrients that make for active growth by cell division, but that the progress toward organized growth requires the growing system to acquire a measure of independence from the coconut milk stimuli which, if unregulated, lead to unorganized growth. This independence first occurs through the formation of an unbroken surface of dividing cambium-like cells, surrounding a region in which some cells of a tissue culture mature and die. Within this "walled-off" zone, some cells are confined and a root initial forms (Fig. 7) and, thereafter, having formed roots, the culture may grow in response to the coconut milk and also form buds. It is difficult, therefore, to avoid the concept that the root initial must originate, under restraint, in a controlled environment, within a ring of cells which permit only *controlled access* to the coconut milk stimuli; buds, in turn, form only after this special nodule of cultured cells has responded to the culture medium in a polarized manner brought about by the presence of roots.

It will be a major landmark when the fertilized egg is removed from the environment of the embryo sac and the facts of early embryogeny can be recapitulated with the production of leaf, stem, and root under culture conditions in a synthetic medium. The present series of papers show that free-living, disassociated cells may be caused to grow in media containing coconut milk so that they achieve similar ends to those which result from the growth of the zygote, for they produce roots and shoots and even secondarily thickened storage organs. However, the freely suspended cells do not do this, as it were, directly, but only more deviously through the summation of the events which have here been described.

Summary

This paper describes the way in which organization may develop in a cultured mass of cells which originates by the growth of freely suspended cells that have been obtained in the manner previously described (Steward *et al.*, 1958). For carrot tissue, it is demonstrated that normal roots may arise in the liquid medium and, once these have originated, the cultures will develop shoots when they are placed on a semisolid agar medium and are enabled to grow in a polarized way in stationary cultures exposed to air. The stages by which plantlets develop are illustrated, and eventually secondary thickening occurs around a newly formed nest of xylem cells, after which there may occur production of a carrot storage root. Thus the cycle from carrot root-phloem to free cell, to carrot root, to carrot plant has been completed. The essential stages in this reorganization involve: (1) The formation, within the cultured mass, of a spherical sheath of cambium-like cells which completely encloses a nest of lignified elements so typically observed in tissue cultures; (2) this spherical nodule, or growing center, plays a part equivalent to the proembryo in normal development, for it can give rise eventually to roots and subsequently to shoots; and (3) the formation of a shoot initial occurs at a point diametrically opposite to the emergence of the root apex, producing a simple, embryo-like structure reminiscent of that which occurs in normal development. The stages in the development of a plantlet into a completely organized plant with storage root are illustrated. It is emphasized that this orderly development becomes possible when cells are enclosed within, and limited by the restraints of— probably more physiological than physical— this wall of cambium-like cells which effectively cuts off the internal cells from direct access to the coconut milk stimuli that cause random proliferation. Wherever the coconut milk has direct access, more random callus-like growth occurs.

LITERATURE CITED

Gautheret, R. J. 1956. Histogenesis in plant tissue cultures. *Jour. Nat. Cancer Inst.* 19: 555–573.

Shantz, E. M., and F. C. Steward. 1957. The growth-stimulating substances in extracts of immature corn grain: a progress report. *Proc. Amer. Soc. Plant Physiol.*, p. 8. A. I. B. S. meeting, Stanford, California.

Steward, F. C., Marion O. Mapes, and Joan Smith. 1958. Growth and organized development of cultured cells. I. Growth and division of freely suspended cells. *Amer. Jour. Bot.* 45: 693–703.

——, and E. M. Shantz. 1955. The chemical induction of growth in plant tissue cultures. I. Methods of tissue culture and the analysis

of growth. In *The Chemistry and Mode of Action of Plant Growth Substances.* R. L. Wain, and F. Wightman (eds.). Butterworths. London.

Van Overbeek, J., M. E. Conklin, and S. F. Blakeslee. 1941. Factors in coconut milk essential for growth and development of very young *Datura* embryos. *Science* 94: 350, 351.

Embryonic Potency of Embryoid Bodies Derived from a Transplantable Testicular Teratoma of the Mouse[1]

LEROY C. STEVENS

Structures morphologically similar to early embryos were observed in human testicular teratomas by Peyron in 1939. Since then, many other workers have recognized embryoid bodies in teratomas of the human testis and ovary (Friedman and Moore, 1946; Dixon and Moore, 1953; Melicow, 1955; Masson, 1956; Simard, 1957; Gaillard, 1955–1958; Cabanne, 1957; and Evans, 1957). These structures, like human blastocysts of about 13–18 days, are composed of ectodermal and endodermal vesicles with mesodermal cells between them. Many are incompletely and irregularly developed; some, however, are remarkably similar to normal embryos. Peyron offered one of his tumors as an atlas of presomite human embryology that was more complete than any other source at that time. Teratomatous embryoid bodies are considered by some to be homologous to early embryos; however, prominent students of germinal tumors have rejected this assumption (Nicholson, 1929; Willis, 1953).

Testicular teratomas occur relatively frequently in inbred strain 129 mice (Stevens and Little, 1954; Stevens and Hummel, 1957). A

Developmental Biology, **2,** 285–297 (1960). Reprinted with permission.

[1] This investigation was supported by research grant C-2662 from the National Cancer Institute, National Institutes of Health, Public Health Service, and by a grant, E-121, from the American Cancer Society, Inc.

developmental study (Stevens, 1959) of these primary testicular teratomas of the mouse has shown that the earliest tumors observed (in newborns) are composed of a nest of undifferentiated embryonal cells with ectopic germ cells interspersed. In other tumors of newborns, epithelial vesicles enclose pools of blood and products of cellular degeneration. The epithelium rapidly becomes transformed into two different types. One resembles ectoderm, and the other endoderm. Mesenchymal cells located between the epithelial vesicles resemble embryonic mesoderm. Examination of primary tumors in progressively older mice revealed that the ectoderm-appearing epithelium gives rise to neural tissue; the endoderm-appearing epithelium to respiratory, alimentary, and glandular epithelium; and the mesenchyme to muscle, cartilage, bone, marrow, and adipose tissue. This is interpreted as a demonstration of the formation of germ layers in testicular teratomas.

Teratomatous embryoid bodies of the mouse were first observed in a retroperitoneal metastatic growth of testicular origin (Stevens, 1959). They exhibited the inversion of the primary germ layers typical of early mouse embryos and were composed of two layers of epithelia: the outer resembling endoderm; the inner, ectoderm. When a highly pleomorphic transplantable testicular teratoma of the mouse (402A VI) is maintained as an ascites tumor, thousands of free-floating embryoid bodies similar to mouse embryos 5 and 6 days of age (Figs. 1–3) are contained in the peritoneal fluid (Stevens, 1959). They are composed of a layer of endoderm which invests morphologically undifferentiated embryonal cells. The morphologically undifferentiated cells may assume an epithelial arrangement resembling ectoderm (Fig. 4), or they may exist as a compact mass within the enveloping endoderm.

The aim of this investigation was to test the developmental capacity of these embryoid bodies. It will be shown that like normal embryos they give rise to a wide variety of tissues. It is concluded that embryoid bodies derived from a transplantable testicular teratoma of the mouse are similar in histogenetic potency as well as in morphology to normal mouse embryos.

MATERIALS AND METHODS

Two sublines (402A III and 402A VI) of a transplantable teratoma derived from the testis of a strain 129 mouse were employed. These tumors have been maintained by serial transplantation for nearly six years; their morphological characteristics have been previously described (Stevens, 1958). The behavior of 402A VI as an ascitic tumor has been investigated by Pierce and Dixon (1959a, b).

Solid tumors were homogenized in saline and injected intraperitoneally. The ascitic fluid resulting from these injections was serially transplanted. The tumor 402A VI was used at the twenty-seventh to thirty-first transplant generations as ascites tumors, and 402A III at the ninth. Thousands of free-floating embryoid bodies, homogeneous in size (Fig. 5), were observed in the ascitic fluid. They were washed in tissue culture medium, and, with the aid of a stereoscopic microscope and a micropipette, single embryoid bodies were grafted into the anterior chambers of the eyes of mature strain 129 mice. The anterior chamber of the eye was used as the transplant site since it permitted direct observation of the grafts during and after operations. Since the embryoid bodies are composed of

neoplastic cells, the resulting growths were large enough to be minced and grafted subcutaneously via trocar. Transplantable tumor sublines were established from the intraocular grafts.

Sixteen mice received grafts of single embryoid bodies from the same donor. The intraocular grafts were observed daily, except Sunday, with the aid of a stereoscopic microscope.

Of 68 intraocular grafts, 49 were recovered. Twenty-five of these were fixed in Vandegrift's solution and prepared for histological examination at various intervals after grafting, and 24 were transplanted subcutaneously to strain 129 weaning-age animals.

OBSERVATIONS

A. Intraocular Grafts of Single Embryoid Bodies

During the first week, the grafts enlarged, became vascularized, and were composed of both cystic and solid portions (Fig. 6). The solid portions of the growths were composed mainly of undifferentiated embryonal cells.

In many cases as the embryoid bodies enlarged, constrictions appeared that resulted in the formation of several embryoid bodies connected by thin stalks. Occasionally separated embryoid bodies were observed, indicating that the stalks had broken and new embryoid bodies similar in size and shape to the original grafts had formed. Histologically the buds or branches of the embryoid bodies were composed of endodermal epithelium enclosing undifferentiated embryonal cells (Figs. 7, 8). Frequently, intraperitoneal embryoid bodies showed constrictions indicating fission (Fig. 9). It appears that the embryoid bodies can reproduce by budding.

Grafts fixed during the second to fourth weeks were more highly differentiated than younger grafts. They contained undifferentiated embryonal cells, primary ectoderm and endoderm, cuboidal, columnar, and pseudostratified ciliated epithelia, neuroepithelium, muscle, cartilage (Figs. 10–15), and trophoblastic giant cells.

The structure of one intraocular graft was

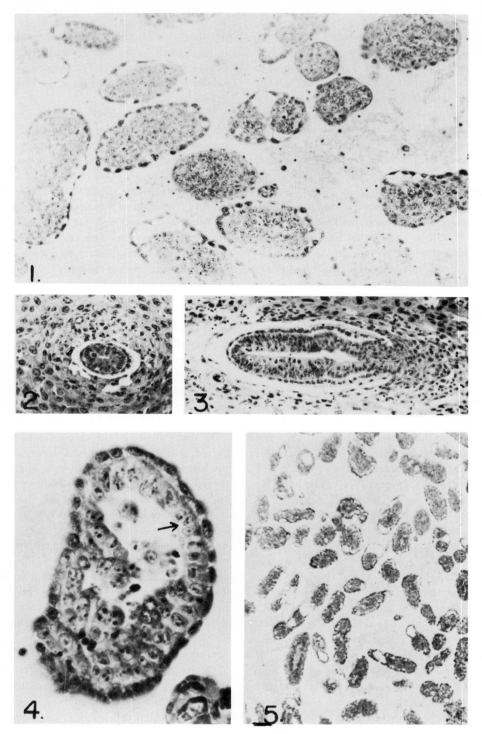

Fig. 1. Free-floating embryoid bodies in ascitic fluid. Magnification: × 150. Fig. 2. Normal 5-day-old mouse embryo (× 150). Fig. 3. Normal 6-day-old mouse embryo (× 150). Fig. 4. Embryoid body showing ectodermal epithelium formation (arrow) (× 350). Fig. 5. Free-floating embryoid bodies in ascitic fluid (× 35).

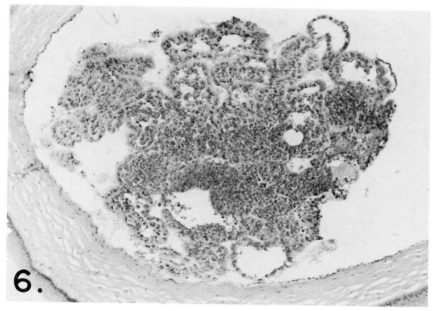

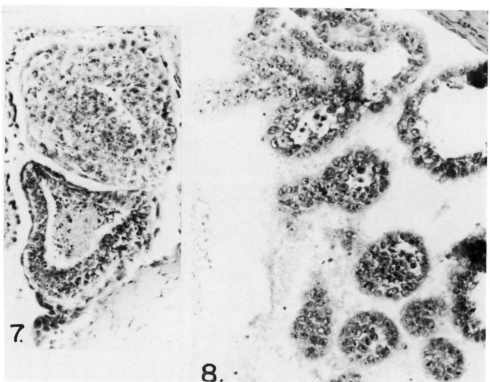

Fig. 6. Four-day-old intraocular growth resulting from a single embryoid body. Magnification: × 120. Figs. 7 and 8. Branches or buds of growths derived from grafts of single embryoid bodies (× 160).

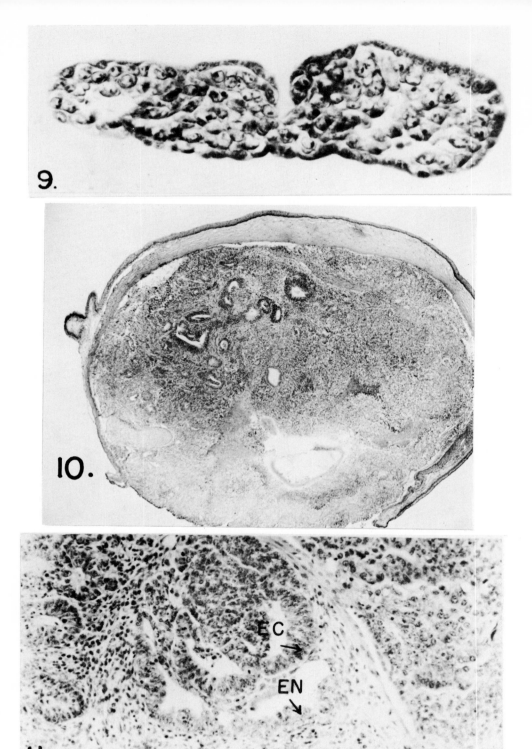

Fig. 9. Intraperitoneal embryoid body with constriction suggesting fission. Magnification: × 350. Fig. 10. Twenty-three-day growth in anterior chamber of eye derived from single embryoid body (× 35). Fig. 11. Early ectodermal (*EC*) and endodermal (*EN*) vesicles in graft derived from single embryoid body (× 160).

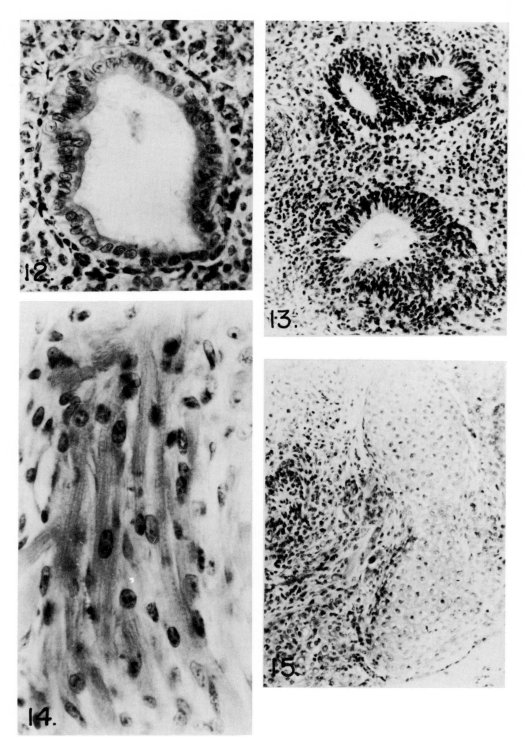

Figs. 12–15. Ciliated epithelium, neuroepithelium, cardiac muscle, and cartilage derived from intraocular graft of single embryoid body, respectively.

of particular interest (Fig. 16). It contained several formations that were unmistakably similar in structure to portions of normal embryos of approximately 9 days. These formations contained folded neuroepithelium continuous laterally with flattened to cuboidal epithelium resembling amnion, and were enclosed by yolk sac epithelium. Mesodermal cells occupied the area between the folded neuroepithelium and yolk sac epithelium, giving the appearance of condensations of mesenchymal cells. An epithelium reminiscent of coelomic epithelium was also represented, but positive identification is not claimed. Figures 16 and 17 illustrate the similarity of these em-

bryoid formations to the posterior region of a normal 9-day mouse embryo.

Intraocular grafts of embryoid bodies derived from subline 402A III were not as highly differentiated as those from subline 402A VI, reflecting a corresponding difference in morphology of these tumors maintained in solid form (Stevens, 1958).

B. Subcutaneous Transplants of Intraocular Grafts

Twenty-four embryoid bodies from one donor (3008) were grafted singly into the anterior chamber of the eye, and 16 of these were allowed to grow until they were large

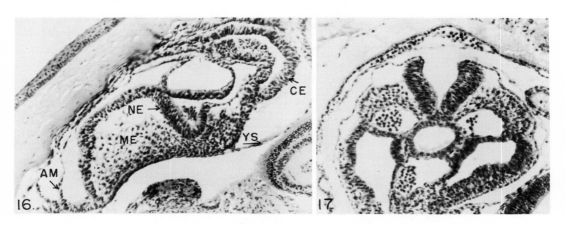

Fig. 16. Intraocular embryoid body containing structures resembling folded neuroepithelium *(NE)*, amnion *(AM)*, embryonic mesenchyme *(ME)*, coelomic epithelium ? *(CE)*, and yolk sac *(YS)*. To the left is the host's cornea, to the right, retina. Magnification: × 160. Fig. 17. Cross section through posterior level of normal 9-day-old mouse embryo (× 160). Compare with Fig. 16.

enough to be minced and regrafted subcutaneously via trocar. Portions of the subcutaneous grafts were fixed and prepared for histological examination after approximately 3 weeks' growth, and other portions were retransplanted and maintained as sublines of the original tumor. The subcutaneous grafts were similar to each other in histologic composition, containing both immature and adult tissues including neural tissue, epithelia, muscle, and cartilage.

Eight additional subcutaneous grafts derived from intraocular grafts of single embryoid bodies from sublines 402A III and VI behaved similarly to the grafts described above.

DISCUSSION

Pierce and Dixon (1959a, b) described the behavior of the transplantable testicular teratoma (402A VI) of strain 129 origin during many transplant generations as an ascitic tumor. During the first five transplant generations, numerous free-floating large cysts ranging up to 7 mm in diameter were observed in the ascitic fluid. They were composed of visceral yolk sac cells, mesenchymal cells, hematopoietic and immature nucleated red blood cells, embryonic epithelial cells often resembling neural tubes, early neuroglia and squamous cells. We have also observed these cysts and have found muscle in addition. Pierce and Dixon (1959a) transplanted the cysts subcutaneously and observed their histogenetic capacities. They suggested the possibility that the cysts are "fetiform derivatives of teratocarcinoma."

In addition to these large cysts, Pierce and Dixon described minute "granules" containing a central core of embryonal carcinoma invested with a layer of visceral yolk sac. We have designated these "granules" as embryoid bodies (Stevens, 1959), the subject of this article.

Pierce and Dixon (1959a) traced logical transitions from embryoid bodies (granules) to the large cysts, indicating a common origin. We have confirmed Pierce and Dixon's finding that large cysts, formed during the first few transplant generations fail to appear in later generations, even though enormous numbers of embryoid bodies are present. The embryoid bodies referred to in this article were derived from late transplant generations, when the cysts no longer develop.

The embryoid bodies used in the experiments described here bear an unmistakable morphological resemblance to normal mouse embryos 5–6 days of gestation. They are uniform in size (0.1–0.2 mm in diameter) and structure, being composed of endodermal cells and other primitive embryonal cells having ectodermal and mesodermal potencies. When grafted singly into the anterior chamber of the eyes of mature mice, they develop into large growths composed of a variety of tissues. These results are in accord with recent studies on early primary teratomas of strain 129 mice which demonstrated the formation and subsequent differentiation of the three germ layers in these tumors (Stevens, 1959). Furthermore, they demonstrate that the embryoid bodies derived from the transplantable teratomas in ascitic form are similar in embryonic potency as well as morphology to normal mouse embryos. It is stressed that these embryoid bodies are composed of truly neoplastic cells, since they give rise to tumors that grow progressively when serially transplanted.

Pierce and Dixon (1959a) have suggested that the embryoid bodies (granules) may be derived from aggregates of cells overlying necrotic portions of solid intraperitoneal implants which break off and seed the peritoneal space. Our observations show that they may also arise as buds from pre-existing embryoid bodies. Peyron has suggested that embryoid bodies in human testicular teratomas may divide symmetrically to form daughter structures like themselves. He compared this process with the division of the armadillo blastocyst into four identical embryos.

The term *parthenogenesis* (a modification of sexual reproduction, usually defined as involving an unfertilized ovum), used by many pathologists to explain the origin of teratomatous embryoid bodies, is inappropriate. Our observations and those of Pierce and Dixon based on teratomatous embryoid bodies of the mouse demonstrate that a form of asexual multiplication is involved.

We have no evidence that embryoid bodies may be precursors of primary teratomas. They have not been observed in early primary testicular tumors of strain 129 mice, and only rarely in the progressively growing teratomas that have been serially transplanted as solid tumors for many years. The undifferentiated embryonal cells of the transplantable tumors give rise to embryoid bodies, and apparently the ascitic fluid favors this development.

Embryoid bodies in one intraocular graft were in a more advanced stage than we have observed previously, containing, in their proper relationships: folded neuroepithelium, amnion, condensations of mesodermal cells resembling somites, and yolk sac. Pierce and Dixon (1960) observed teratomatous embryoid bodies almost identical to these in subcutaneous grafts of large cysts of subline 402A VI origin. They believe these advanced embryoid bodies to be homologous with normal mouse embryos, and we agree with this interpretation.

The findings reported here lend further support to the interpretation that the embryoid bodies resembling 6-day mouse embryos are actually homologous with them. Furthermore, our observations are in accord with Peyron's descriptions of trophoblast, amnio-ectodermal vesicles, endoderm, and mesoderm in human teratomatous embryoid bodies.

SUMMARY

Testicular teratomas occur relatively frequently in inbred strain 129 mice. Occasionally they grow progressively and survive serial transplantation indefinitely. One such tumor has been maintained for approximately six years, and it still retains its highly pleomorphic nature. When established as an ascitic tumor, this teratoma is capable of producing thousands of free-floating formations that resemble 5- and 6-day mouse embryos. The aim of this investigation was to test the histogenetic capacities of these embryoid bodies. Single embryoid bodies were transplanted into the anterior chamber of the eyes of mature strain 129 mice. Growths resulting from these intraocular grafts were examined histologically and some were retransplanted subcutaneously to form solid tumor sublines. Both the intraocular and subcutaneous grafts contained many types of tissues, including a variety of epithelia; neural tissue; cartilage with peripheral ossification; smooth, cardiac, and voluntary muscle; trophoblastic giant cells; layers of ectoderm and endoderm; and undifferentiated embryonal cells. It is concluded that the embryoid bodies derived from the testicular teratomas of strain 129 mice have similarities in embryonic potency as well as in morphology to normal mouse embryos.

REFERENCES

Cabanne, F. (1957). Les dysembryomes du testicle. *Arch. anat. pathol. Semaine hôp.* **5**, A 165-A 182.

Dixon, F. J., and R. A. Moore. (1953). Testicular tumors. A clinicopathological study. *Cancer* **6**, 427–454.

Evans, R. W. (1957). Developmental stages of embryo-like bodies in teratoma testis. *J. Clin. Pathol.* **10**, 31–39.

Friedman, N. B., and R. A. Moore. (1946). Tumors of the testis, a report on 922 cases. *Military Surgeon* **99**, 573–593.

Gaillard, J. A. (1955). Histogenèse des dysembryomes et des tumeurs du testicle. *Bull. assoc. franç. étude cancer* **42**, 486–495.

Gaillard, J. A. (1956). Histogenèse des dysembryomes testiculaires. Les images initiales et les aspects évolutifs. *Bull. assoc. franç. ètude cancer* **43**, 53–68.

Gaillard, J. A. (1957). Évolution unilatérale d'un dysembryome testiculaire. Histogenèse et systématique du carcinome embryonnaire. *Bull. assoc. franç. étude cancer* **44**, 124–134.

Gaillard, J. A. (1958). Les dysembryomes polyembryoniques. Origine et destinée des boutons embryonnaires. *Bull. assoc. franç. étude cancer* **45**, 104–120.

Masson, P. (1956). *Tumeurs Humaines.* Librairie Maloine, Paris.

Melicow, M. M. (1955). Classification of tumors of testis: A clinical and pathological study based on 105 primary and 13 secondary cases in adults, and 3 primary and 4 secondary cases in children. *J. Urol.* **73**, 547–574.

Nicholson, G. W. (1929). The histogeny of teratomata. *J. Pathol. Bacteriol.* **32**, 365–386.

Peyron, A. (1939). Faits nouveaux relatifs à l'origine et à l'histogenèse des embryomes. *Bull. assoc. franç. étude cancer* **28**, 658–681.

Pierce, G. B., and F. J. Dixon, Jr. (1959a). Testicular teratomas. I. Demonstration of teratogenesis by metamorphosis of multipotential cells. *Cancer* **12**, 573–583.

Pierce, G. B., and F. J. Dixon, Jr. (1959b). Testicular teratomas. II. Teratocarcinoma as an asctic tumor. *Cancer* **12**, 584–589.

Pierce, G. B., F. J. Dixon, Jr., and E. L. Verney (1960). Teratocarcinogenic and tissue-forming potentials of the cell types comprising neoplastic embryoid bodies. *Lab. Invest.* **9**, 583–602.

Simard, L. C. (1957). Polyembryonic embryoma of the ovary of parthenogenetic origin. *Cancer* **10**, 215–223.

Stevens, L. C. (1958). Studies on transplantable testicular teratomas of strain 129 mice. *J. Natl. Cancer Inst.* **20**, 1257–1275.

Stevens, L. C. (1959). Embryology of testicular teratomas in strain 129 mice. *J. Natl. Cancer Inst.* **23**, 1249–1295.

Stevens, L. C., and K. P. Hummel. (1957). A description of spontaneous congenital testicular teratomas in strain 129 mice. *J. Natl. Cancer Inst.* **18**, 719–747.

Stevens, L. C., and C. C. Little. (1954). Spontaneous testicular teratomas in an inbred strain of mice. *Proc. Natl. Acad. Sci. U. S.* **40**, 1080–1087.

Willis, R. A. (1953). *Pathology of Tumours*, 2nd ed. Butterworth, London.

4

Role of the Nucleus

IN A CLASSICAL experiment performed five decades ago, Spemann (1914) found that a nucleus from a cell of the amphibian morula could support the development of an enucleate portion of the egg which was separated from the nucleated portion before first cleavage by means of a loose hair loop. When, as a result of successive divisions, cells near the loop became sufficiently small, the nucleus from one slipped into the half of the germ which had remained undeveloped. A second embryo whose development lagged behind that of the twin on the other side of the loop was observed to form. This led to the conclusion that even though a nucleus cleaved many times and was exposed, presumably, to increasingly specialized environments, it was still able to direct the complete development of an organism in collaboration with original egg cytoplasm.

Since Spemann's (1914) early experiment, Briggs and King (1952), *King and Briggs (1956)*,* Fishberg, Gurdon, and Elsdale (1958), Moore (1960) and others have studied the problem of nuclear differentiation by transplanting nuclei from cells in various late stages of development to enucleate eggs.

The results thus far can be summarized as follows: (1) In a small number of cases nuclei from developmentally advanced cells can collaborate with enucleated cytoplasm to make a complete animal. This almost certainly rules out an irreversible change in the DNA of the nucleus. (2) An inverse relationship exists between the stage of the donor nucleus and the degree of development of the enucleate host egg which has received the transplant. That is a nucleus from a late stage is less able to promote the advanced development of an egg than a nucleus from a cell in an earlier developmental stage. (3) Eggs which develop incompletely can be divided into two classes: those in which abortive development can be correlated with chromosomal abnormalities and those in which it cannot. Why do eggs in the latter class develop abnormally then? Possibly, even where no chromosomal abnormalities are observed, molecular genetic damage yet undefined may be responsible for the developmental arrest. (4) When nuclei from arrested embryos are used as donors, the recipient egg will not develop beyond the final stage of the original arrested embryo. Whatever change has occurred in nuclei of developmentally arrested embryos seems irreversible. (5) Malignant cells may have characteristics in common with early embryonic cells since enucleate eggs which receive nuclei from cells of the Leuké tumor (a renal adeno-carcinoma) (King and McKinnell 1960) can develop to advanced embryos. (6) When primordial germ cells serve as a source of donor nuclei, a high proportion of animals which develop normally are observed. If developmental arrest was due to the injury

* Italicized references indicate articles which appear in this book.

imposed during transplantation of the nucleus, one might expect to get the same low proportion of normally developing organisms regardless of the source of nuclei. Hence, this experiment supports the proposition that nuclei may differentiate irreversibly. It is assumed that germ cell nuclei are less differentiated than neighboring endodermal cell nuclei.

One well-documented example of nuclear control of morphogenesis is that which concerns cap formation in the marine alga acetabularia. *Hammerling (1963)* has shown in a number of experiments that cap morphology (smooth or crenellated cap) is determined specifically by the cell nucleus. The determining factor from the nucelus is some species of RNA which persists for a long period in the cytoplasm Brachet (1957). It can be suggested that it is an m-RNA on which a protein for the specific macromolecules responsible for cap morphology is made.

It is now well established that templates for protein synthesis in the cytoplasm are made in the nucleus. It is not known though to what extent they are used in the nucleus, or whether the nucleus participates in the synthesis of specialized cell products. There is evidence that proteins made in the cytoplasm make their way back to the nucleus (Prescott 1963, Byers *et al.*, 1963). Whether these proteins play a part in establishing or maintaining the differentiated state of chromosomes and nucleus is an unanswered question.

REFERENCES

1. Brachet, J. (1957). *Biochemical Cytology*, Academic Press, New York.
2. Briggs, R., and T. King (1952). Transplantation of living nuclei from blastula cells into enucleated frogs eggs. *Proc. Natl. Acad. Sci.* **38**:455–463.
3. Byers, T., D. Platt, and L. Goldstein (1963). The cytonucleoproteins of amebae. II Some aspects of cytonucleoprotein behavior and synthesis. *J. Cell Biol.* **19**:467–475.
4. Fischberg, M., J. B. Gurdon, and T. R. Elsdale (1958). Nuclear transfer in Amphibia and the problem of the potentialities of the nuclei of differentiating tissues. *Exptl. Cell Res. Suppl.* **6**:161–178.
5. King, T. J., and R. G. McKinnell (1960). An attempt to determine the developmental potentialities of the cancer cell nucleus by means of transplantation. In *Cell Physiology of Neoplasia*, Univ. of Texas Press, Austin, pp. 591–617.
6. Moore, J. (1960). Serial back-transfers of nuclei in experiments involving two species of frogs. *Develop. Biol.* **2**:535–550.
7. Prescott, D. M. (1963). RNA and protein replacement in the nucleus during growth and division and the conservation of components in the chromosome. In R. J. C. Harris (ed.), *Cell Growth and Cell Division*, Vol. 2, Academic Press, New York, pp. 111–149.
8. Spemann, H. (1914). Über verzögerte kernversorgung von keimteilen. *Verh. d. D. Zool. Ges. Freiburg*, pp. 216–221.

January 1997	February 1997	March 1997	April 1997	May 1997	June 1997
S M T W T F S	S M T W T F S	S M T W T F S	S M T W T F S	S M T W T F S	S M T W T F S
1 2 3 4	1	1	1 2 3 4 5	1 2 3	1 2 3 4 5 6 7
5 6 7 8 9 10 11	2 3 4 5 6 7 8	2 3 4 5 6 7 8	6 7 8 9 10 11 12	4 5 6 7 8 9 10	8 9 10 11 12 13 14
12 13 14 15 16 17 18	9 10 11 12 13 14 15	9 10 11 12 13 14 15	13 14 15 16 17 18 19	11 12 13 14 15 16 17	15 16 17 18 19 20 21
19 20 21 22 23 24 25	16 17 18 19 20 21 22	16 17 18 19 20 21 22	20 21 22 23 24 25 26	18 19 20 21 22 23 24	22 23 24 25 26 27 28
26 27 28 29 30 31	23 24 25 26 27 28	23 24 25 26 27 28 29	27 28 29 30	25 26 27 28 29 30 31	29 30
		30 31			

July 1997	August 1997	September 1997	October 1997	November 1997	December 1997
S M T W T F S	S M T W T F S	S M T W T F S	S M T W T F S	S M T W T F S	S M T W T F S
1 2 3 4 5	1 2	1 2 3 4 5 6	1 2 3 4	1	1 2 3 4 5 6
6 7 8 9 10 11 12	3 4 5 6 7 8 9	7 8 9 10 11 12 13	5 6 7 8 9 10 11	2 3 4 5 6 7 8	7 8 9 10 11 12 13
13 14 15 16 17 18 19	10 11 12 13 14 15 16	14 15 16 17 18 19 20	12 13 14 15 16 17 18	9 10 11 12 13 14 15	14 15 16 17 18 19 20
20 21 22 23 24 25 26	17 18 19 20 21 22 23	21 22 23 24 25 26 27	19 20 21 22 23 24 25	16 17 18 19 20 21 22	21 22 23 24 25 26 27
27 28 29 30 31	24 25 26 27 28 29 30	28 29 30	26 27 28 29 30 31	23 24 25 26 27 28 29	28 29 30 31
	31			30	

4

Tuesday
February
1997

7:00	
7:30	
8:00	
8:30	
9:00	
9:30	
10:00	
10:30	
11:00	
11:30	
12:00	
12:30	
1:00	
1:30	
2:00	
2:30	
3:00	
3:30	
4:00	
4:30	

January 1997	February 1997	March 1997
S M T W T F S	S M T W T F S	S M T W T F S
1 2 3 4	1	1
5 6 7 8 9 10 11	2 3 4 5 6 7 8	2 3 4 5 6 7 8
12 13 14 15 16 17 18	9 10 11 12 13 14 15	9 10 11 12 13 14 15
19 20 21 22 23 24 25	16 17 18 19 20 21 22	16 17 18 19 20 21 22
26 27 28 29 30 31	23 24 25 26 27 28	23 24 25 26 27 28 29
		30 31

Serial Transplantation of Embryonic Nuclei[1]

THOMAS J. KING
ROBERT BRIGGS

Over the past many years genetical research has revealed large number of gene effects on cell differentiation. These are usually effects on the final phases of differentiation, but may also be manifested at early developmental stages (Gluecksohn-Waelsch, 1954; Hadorn, 1948, 1956; Poulson, 1945; and others). In principle, the analysis of these effects depends upon the permanent alteration or deletion of a chromosome segment, and the subsequent detection of a change in differentiation— usually a deficiency. The evidence so obtained permits the conclusion that a particular gene or gene set is required for a particular type of differentiation to proceed normally. However, in general it leaves unanswered the questions which are of greatest concern to students of development. First, the genetic evidence as yet provides no explanation of the orderly segregation of cell types during development—of the fact that a given gene comes to have one effect in one part of the organism while in another part it has no effect or a different one. This must, of course, involve interactions of the geneticist's nucleus with the embryologist's cytoplasmic localizations, but the nature of this interaction is unknown. Second, the available evidence fails to account for the stability or irreversibility of differentiation. In other words, while genes have particular functions in differentiation, in general, it is not known how they acquire them, nor whether they are themselves altered in the performance of these functions in such a way as to confer stability on the differentiated cells.

It has been apparent for some time that in order to obtain answers to the questions posed above it would be necessary to devise new methods for detecting changes in gene function in somatic cells. Essentially, such methods should yield recombinations of nucleus and cytoplasm and of different types of nuclei of somatic cells, comparable with the natural recombinations of germ cells from which most genetic information is obtained.

Experiments of the type mentioned above, involving artificial transfer of cytoplasm or nucleus, were accomplished with unicellular organisms some years ago. Hämmerling (1934, 1953), using the unicellular uninucleate alga, *Acetabularia*, grafted stalk pieces from one species to the nucleated rhizoidal ends of another and demonstrated that the form of the cap that regenerated from the grafted stalk was controlled by the nucleus. Later Hämmerling (1953) produced heterokaryons and showed that the form of the regenerated cap was intermediate between the forms characteristic of the species contributing the nuclei. This and other evidence led to the conclusion that the nucleus produces specific morphogenetic substances which pass into the cytoplasm and there control the differentiation of the cap.

Another instance in which new combinations of nucleus and cytoplasm have been produced artificially is provided by the studies by Danielli and co-workers on amoebae. By using a method devised by Comandon and de-Fonbrune (1939), these investigators transferred nuclei from one species of amoeba to another (Lorch and Danielli, 1950). In the best analyzed case, a combination of *A. proteus* nucleus with *A. discoides* cytoplasm, a clone was obtained which has survived more than six years. Some properties of the individuals in this clone (division rate, nuclear diameter) are determined by the cytoplasm, others (shape when migrating) are intermedi-

Cold Spring Harbor Symposia on Quantitative Biology, **21**, 271–290, 1956. Reprinted with permission.

[1] The experimental work reported in this paper was aided by a research grant from the National Cancer Institute of the National Institutes of Health, United States Public Health Service, and in part by an institutional grant from the American Cancer Society.

ate, while the type of antigen(s) produced is under nuclear control (Danielli, Lorch, Ord and Wilson, 1955). Similar experiments, involving transfers of nuclei between different species of *Stentor*, have been done by Tartar (1953). The ciliates, with their highly organized cytoplasmic structures, possess obvious advantages over amoebae for this type of study. Tartar was able to make successful intraspecific transfers, but unfortunately the interspecific combinations did not survive long enough to permit an analysis of the relative contributions of cytoplasm and nucleus in the control of cytoplasmic differentiation.

So far, we have restricted ourselves to those instances in which nucleo-cytoplasmic recombinations have been produced artificially in unicellular organisms. There is, of course, a much larger body of information, not to be reviewed here, which is based on regeneration studies in ciliates and on various naturally occurring genetic recombinations in a variety of microorganisms. In the majority of cases, it appears that cell type is determined by nuclear genes, but cytoplasmic particulates or conditions have also been shown to be a part of the genetic system(Sonneborn, 1954; Ephrussi, 1953; Weisz, 1951). This work with unicellular organisms is extremely valuable in revealing a larger range of recombination mechanisms, both natural and artificial, than had been suspected 25 years ago. It has also provided us with a set of beautifully analyzed types of nucleo-cytoplasmic interactions, which have led to several theories of metazoan differentiation. However, as Lederberg (1956) has pointed out, the problems of embryology cannot be solved with microbes, and we should now pass to a consideration of some of the attempts that have been made toward an analysis of nuclear function in metazoan differentiation.

This subject was of intense interest in the early years of experimental embryology, largely as a result of the stimulus provided by the somatic segregation theory of differentiation proposed by Weismann and by Roux. The large literature of the period has been summarized by Wilson (1925). Of this, we should like to mention only two experi-

ments. The first, by Jacques Loeb (1894), involved placing fertilized sea urchin eggs in diluted sea water, in which they swell and sometimes burst the egg membrane. When this happens a portion of the cytoplasm protrudes as a hernia. This may not at first contain a nucleus, but after a few divisions of the main part of the egg one of the cleavage nuclei may migrate into the herniated portion and initiate its development, which then proceeds to the formation of either a complete embryo or half a double monster. A similar result was obtained later in the famous constriction experiment of Spemann (1914), who observed a delayed nucleation of one half of the newt egg resulting from the migration into it of a nucleus from the other half after it attained the 16 to 32 cell stage. Again the part experiencing the delayed nucleation developed into a complete embryo.

In both Loeb's and Spemann's experiments, as well as in numerous other investigations, the results showed that the cleavage nuclei are equivalent and "totipotent." However, the actual evidence was restricted to the first few cleavages and, as Spemann (1938) later pointed out, it remained undecided whether the nuclei might come to have different properties in different tissues later in development. Spemann further suggested that decisive information on the question might perhaps be afforded if it were possible to transfer nuclei from cells of older embryos to non-nucleated eggs, the development of which should then reveal the character of the transplanted nucleus. This type of experiment was also suggested independently by Schultz (personal communication, 1943; 1952), Ephrussi (1951), Rostand (1943) and perhaps others.

To the best of our knowledge, the transfer of nuclei (by pricking frog's eggs coated with embryonic brei) was first attempted by Rostand in 1943, with uncertain success. A few years later, we began to work on the problem, and after a considerable number of failures devised a different procedure for the transplantation of living nuclei from embryonic cells into enucleated eggs of the frog, *Rana pipiens* (Briggs and King, 1952). More recently transfers of embryonic nuclei have also been made by Waddington and Pantelouris (1953), Lehman (1955, 1956), Markert (referred to in Lehman, 1956) and Subtelny (1956). The method used is not without its difficulties and complications, but it appears to represent the most direct experimental approach for obtaining evidence of the genetic condition of nuclei in differentiating embryonic cells.

NOTE ON METHODS

A brief description of the nuclear transplantation procedure was given in previous papers (Briggs and King, 1952, 1953; King and Briggs, 1955). Since then, certain refinements, particularly in the construction and use of micropipettes, have been added, which will be described elsewhere. Here we wish to mention only the main features of the method —those which are essential to an appraisal of the significance of the results obtained with it.

The transplantation operation is carried out in two main steps. First, the recipient eggs (*Rana pipiens*) are activated with a glass needle and subsequently enucleated, following Porter's (1939) technique. With practice and care, the enucleation operation is 100 per cent successful. The second part of the procedure involves the isolation of the donor cells and the nuclear transfer itself. Free donor cells may be obtained by the appropriate use of Versene (Ethylene diamine tetra acetic acid, Na salt) alone or in combination with trypsin, as previously described (King and Briggs, 1955). A given cell, in Niu-Twitty (1953) solution, is then drawn into the tip of a micropipette, the inner diameter of which is somewhat smaller than that of the cell. When this is properly done the cell surface is broken, but the contents are not dispersed. In this way the nucleus is protected by its own cytoplasm until the pipette is inserted into the recipient egg and the broken cell ejected, liberating the nucleus into the egg cytoplasm. The technique sounds deceptively simple, but it takes practice to perform these operations consistently well.

Two features of the method that bear on the interpretation of results are first the in-clusion of donor cell cytoplasm along with the injected nucleus, and second, the possibility of inadvertently damaging the nucleus in the course of the operation. Nuclear damage can be appraised by a study of control eggs injected with undifferentiated blastula nuclei, and by observations on cleavage patterns and chromosomes of test eggs. With reference to the donor cell cytoplasm, it should be mentioned that it represents in volume only $1/40,000$ to $1/500,000$ the volume of cytoplasm of the recipient egg. Still, the possibility that it might contain self-replicating units controlling differentiation must be considered, and where necessary, control transfers of cytoplasm from differentiating cells must be carried out—as will be mentioned in a subsequent section of this paper.

TRANSPLANTATION TESTS OF BLASTULA NUCLEI

The first successful transplantations were carried out with nuclei of mid- to late blastulae. The donor blastulae were 18 to 24 hours old (at 18°C) and consisted of approximately 8,000 to 16,000 cells (estimates of cell number based on Sze's (1953) determinations). Only nuclei of undetermined animal hemisphere cells were used. In the first set of experiments, about one-third of the transfers led to normal cleavage and blastula formation on the part of the recipient eggs, and the majority of these blastulae, some 75%, developed into complete embryos. Half of the embryos appeared to be perfectly normal while the remainder displayed minor abnormalities (Briggs and King, 1952). In more recent experiments, the number of transfers of this type leading to normal cleavage has been larger (40% to 80%) and the majority (*ca.* 80%) of the resulting embryos develop normally to larval or later stages (King and Briggs, 1955 and unpublished).

The proof that the nuclear transfers are successful, and that the test eggs contain only the transplanted nuclei, consists of the following:

1. Control operations for removal of the egg nucleus, performed on normally fertilized

eggs, show that all eggs develop as androgenetic haploids. Failures would lead to the development of diploids, of which there were none in control series of more than 500 embryos during the past two years.

2. Sections of eggs which cleave following enucleation and nuclear transplantation reveal the egg nucleus outside the egg, in the enucleation exovate, while the blastomeres contain nuclei derived from the transferred nucleus (Briggs and King, 1952).

3. Enucleated eggs which were injected with diploid nuclei and which begin cleavage at the normal time after activation, develop into diploid embryos, ploidy being determined by cell size, nucleolar number, and chromosome counts (see Table 2 of this paper for chromosome counts). If the first cleavage is initiated one cleavage interval late, the resulting embryos are tetraploids.

4. Enucleated eggs injected with haploid nuclei develop into haploid embryos unless there is a delayed initiation of cleavage—in which case the embryos become diploids (Subtelny, unpublished).

5. When enucleated *Rana pipiens* eggs are injected with *R. catesbeiana* nuclei the resulting development duplicates exactly that of the normally produced lethal hybrid between these two species (King and Briggs, 1953).

The results summarized above proved that late blastula nuclei could be transplanted in undamaged condition, and since the test eggs developed normally it was further demonstrated that the nuclei were unchanged, that is, equivalent to the nucleus at the beginning of development.

This result has been independently confirmed in this Institute by Subtelny, who also worked with *Rana pipiens*. So far as we are aware, the only other work on this species which has been mentioned in the literature (by Lehman, 1956) is that of Markert and Freedman. From 256 transfers these workers obtained 32 blastulae of which 20 gastrulated and 9 neurulated. While this represents a positive result, the yield from the transfers is relatively low and it would be difficult on this basis to draw conclusions concerning the properties of the nuclei tested.

Some attempts have been made to transfer embryonic nuclei into newt's eggs. The newt embryo would seem to offer important advantages for this work, with its large cells, relatively small chromosome number, and ease of handling in the usual tissue grafting and explanation techniques. However, the results so far have been disappointing. Waddington and Pantelouris (1953) transferred nuclei from blastula and later stages of *Triturus* (*Triton*) *palmatus* into non-nucleated egg fragments, which had been previously produced by constricting normally fertilized eggs. About 12% of the fragments developed into blastulae which failed to gastrulate. No chromosome studies of these blastulae were reported and for this and other reasons the interpretation of the results was uncertain.

More recently, H. E. Lehman (1955) has reported on the transplantation of *Triton* blastula nuclei into enucleated eggs. Apparently the *Triton* egg cannot be activated with a glass needle and then enucleated in the manner which works so well with the frog's eggs. Furthermore, attempts to inject nuclei and then enucleate eggs also failed; eggs so treated did not cleave. Either the egg cytoplasm is damaged by these manipulations, or the injected nucleus for one reason or another fails to provide an effective cleavage center. In any event, Lehman was forced to resort to a more complicated procedure in which the eggs were first fertilized with heavily irradiated sperm (50,000 r), then pricked and enucleated, and finally injected with a blastula nucleus. About 65% of the recipient eggs cleaved, and one-third of these formed blastulae which failed to gastrulate. Since the enucleations were only 50% successful, and there was in addition some question of the survival of chromosome fragments from the irradiated sperm, the interpretation of this experiment depended on an accurate chromosome analysis. This Lehman did, finding haploid, diploid and hyperdiploid numbers. The occurrence of diploid, and particularly of hyperdiploid chromosome numbers, indicated that the injected nuclei or chromosomes therefrom were participating in the cleavage. As Lehman pointed out, the reasons for the failure of the embryos to gastrulate could have been (a) irregular distribution of chromosomes during cleavage, leading to lethal chromosome imbalance (Fankhauser, 1934b), (b) operative damage to the egg or the transferred nucleus or both, and (c) nuclear determination at the blastula stage. In view of the fact that the blastula donor cells are not themselves determined, and in view of the results obtained with the frog, it seems likely that the failure of the recipient newt eggs to develop normally is due principally to their greater susceptibility to damage in the course of transfer.

NUCLEI OF EARLY GASTRULAE

As has been appreciated for a long time, the beginning of gastrulation is a crucial phase of development. At this time the regional localizations of materials present from the beginning in the egg cytoplasm have their first morphogenetic expression. For example, in the amphibian egg the gray crescent material, localized on the dorsal side of the egg shortly after fertilization, is known to determine the position of the dorsal lip of the blastopore, and consequently the point of origin of the chorda mesoderm and the whole axial organization of the embryo. While the position of the dorsal lip is thus determined by the gray crescent cytoplasm, it is also known that in order for it to invaginate and form chorda mesoderm, it must be provided with a "normal" set of chromosomes. Prior to gastrulation, cleavage and blastula formation may proceed with nuclei containing variable numbers of chromosomes (Fankhauser, 1934b), no chromosomes (Fankhauser, 1934a; Stauffer, 1945; Briggs, Green and King, 1951); or with various foreign genomes (see review by Moore, 1955). However, in all these cases development stops at or before the beginning of gastrulation, from which it is concluded that gastrulation and later phases of development require the participation of a balanced chromosome set. Furthermore, nucleus and cytoplasm must be of the same or closely related species. This and other information indicates

that the nuclei come to have specific essential functions at the beginning of gastrulation. Whether they undergo irreversible or quasi-irreversible changes, and whether these are the same or different in different parts of the early gastrula, are questions we have approached by means of nuclear transplantation. The work is not quite finished yet, and will be described in full elsewhere. Here we may give only a brief account to provide a background for the following portions of this paper.

Nuclei from the following portions of the early gastrula were tested: (1) animal hemisphere, near the pole, (2) dorsal lip region, (3) endoderm including the floor of the blastocoel, and a region between the vegetal pole and the dorsal lip. The nuclei were transplanted to enucleated eggs in the usual way, giving the following results:

1. Animal hemisphere nuclei—39% of 33 test eggs formed complete blastulae, 69% of the blastulae developed into tadpoles.

2. Dorsal lip nuclei—25% of 77 test eggs formed complete blastulae, of which 74 % developed into tadpoles.

3. Endoderm nuclei—54% of 107 recipient eggs cleaved normally, 66% of the blastulae so produced developed into tadpoles.

These preliminary experiments provide no definite evidence of differences among the nuclei from the various regions of the gastrula. The proportion of recipient eggs forming complete blastulae was smaller in the case of animal hemisphere and dorsal lip nuclear transfers than it was in the case of the endoderm transfers, but this is probably due to differences in donor cell size and ease of isolation. With respect to the development of the complete blastulae, there was some indication (in one experiment) that blastulae containing endoderm nuclei were more frequently arrested in gastrula or post-neurula stages. However, in the majority of experiments endoderm, dorsal lip, and animal hemisphere nuclei appeared equally capable of promoting normal development to the early larval stage, at least.

This result, indicating equivalence of early gastrula nuclei, is to some extent to be expected. One of the donor regions, the animal pole, is definitely undetermined and would not be expected to contain differentiated nuclei. The dorsal lip area is, of course, determined to form chorda mesoderm. However, the determination is on a regional and not a cell basis, for if parts of the region are explanted they are found to be capable of differentiating into neural and endodermal as well as mesodermal structures (Holtfreter, 1938). The endoderm, on the other hand, gives evidence of being already determined in the early gastrula (Holtfreter, 1938). Whether the individual cells are irreversibly set in their path of differentiation appears uncertain, but the endoderm cell mass and portions of it are apparently determined to form gut and gut derivatives. Yet the endoderm nuclei, along with nuclei of other regions, give no definite evidence of differentiation in the transplantation experiments. This could mean either that the individual endoderm cells are not irreversibly determined, or that if they are, the determination does not involve irreversible nuclear changes. Since our experiments involve the transfer of donor cell cytoplasm along with the nuclei, the results also indicate that there are no genetic units in the cytoplasm which are capable of directing the differentiation of the recipient eggs.

The nuclear transplantation work summarized above emphasizes a point which has been familiar to embryologists for some time; namely, that the morphogenetic events in the early gastrula depend on the regional localization of cytoplasmic materials present in the egg at the beginning of development. Normal nuclei are essential for morphogenesis to proceed, but neither the nuclei nor the individual cells (except possibly endoderm cells) are irreversibly specialized at this stage. In other words, the intrinsic properties of the individual cells provide no explanation of the morphogenetic events, which are directed by the aforementioned cytoplasmic localizations. Thus, the role of the nucleus in this early phase of development will eventually have to be studied prior to fertilization, when these materials are being laid down in the oocyte.

NUCLEI OF LATE GASTRULAE

During gastrulation the germ layers are established, and by the late gastrula stage are determined in the sense that they cannot be transformed, one into the other, by grafting to inductive sites. In order to see if the determination of the layers involves detectable changes in the nuclei, we have made transplantation tests of nuclei from chorda mesoderm, presumptive medullary plate and endoderm. The first tests were done on nuclei of the presumptive plate and the chorda mesoderm. These nuclei elicited normal cleavage in a considerably smaller proportion of the test eggs than had been the case with the blastula nuclei. Furthermore, about half the normally cleaved eggs were arrested in blastula and gastrula stages, and of the ones completing gastrulation the majority displayed abnormalities later in development (King and Briggs, 1954). However, a few embryos did develop normally, indicating that at least some of the chorda mesoderm and medullary plate nuclei were undifferentiated. The significance of the cases in which development was arrested or abnormal remained in doubt because of the technical problems in handling the small donor cells. At the time, these cells were being isolated with glass needles with some risk of injury; and being small they were difficult to handle in the micropipette without some dilution of the cytoplasm with the Niu-Twitty medium and consequent damage to the nucleus. In order to circumvent these problems, we began to use trypsin as an aid in separating embryonic layers, and Versene to dissociate the cells (King and Briggs, 1955). In addition, it was decided to concentrate on the endoderm since this tissue appears to be definitely determined in the late gastrula, and still consists of large cells which are as readily managed in the transfer procedure as are those of mid- to late blastulae.

Late Gastrula Endoderm Nuclei

In view of the considerations mentioned above, an extensive series of transfers of late gastrula endoderm nuclei has been made, the donor cells being taken usually from the presumptive anterior midgut region (King and Briggs, 1955 and unpublished). These nuclei elicited normal cleavage and blastula formation in about 40% of the test eggs, and were therefore equivalent to undifferentiated blastula nuclei in this respect. However, the later development of the "endoderm blastulae" differed from that of the controls. Approximately 80% of the control blastulae, containing transplanted blastula nuclei, developed into normal larvae. By contrast, the majority of the endoderm blastulae displayed pronounced abnormalities in their development. About one-third were arrested in late blastula or gastrula stages, one-half gastrulated normally but later displayed deficiencies, while the remaining minority developed normally into tadpoles.

The nature of the abnormalities in the endoderm embryos has been studied, and will be described in more detail elsewhere. In brief, the embryos had the following characteristics.

Arrested late blastulae or early gastrulae were uniformly cleaved, contained nuclei of uniform size, and possessed a normal blastocoel. Before the onset of arrest the cleavages occurred at about the normal rate, and the cells contained the normal number of chromosomes ($2N = 26$) although in some cases the form of the chomosomes was changed (see below). After the embryos were arrested the nuclei tended to become vacuolated, and some loose cells appeared in the blastocoel.

Abnormal Post-Neurula Embryos

These embryos completed gastrulation in apparently normal fashion, but later showed in varying degrees the following conditions. First, there was a reduction, sometimes extreme, in size and degree of differentiation of the central nervous system, sense organs, and neural crest derivatives, accompanied by nuclear pycnosis in the affected organs. The inductor system (notochord and somites) was well developed and displayed no significant pycnosis. However, somites were usually abnormal in form. Other mesodermal organs (cardiovascular system, pronephros) were generally less well developed. Endoderm, in the stages studied, is not normally highly differentiated. In the endoderm embryos, its differentiation was retarded, in keeping with the general retardation in development, but it did not display significant numbers of pycnotic nuclei.

Endoderm Nuclei from Later Stages

Nuclei from the anterior midgut region of mid-neurulae elicited normal cleavage and blastula formation in only 16% of the test eggs, compared with 40% or more in the case of the late gastrula nuclei. Of the blastulae obtained, a larger proportion (70%) were arrested early, in blastula or gastrula stages. The remaining embryos gastrulated, but the large majority later displayed the abnormalities mentioned above. Endoderm nuclei from the same region of tail bud embryos displayed a still further reduced capacity to promote cleavage of recipient eggs. Only 7% of the test eggs developed into complete blastulae 9 in number. Seven of these blastulae were arrested in late blastula or early gastrula stages, and two were abnormal "endoderm embryos."

These results on endoderm nuclear transfers indicate that the nuclei are going through definite changes. Nuclei from the late gastrula show an undiminished ability to promote cleavage and blastula formation. However, in their subsequent development the endoderm blastulae fall into three general classes—(a) embryos which are arrested before or during the formation of chorda mesoderm, (b) embryos which complete gastrulation but later show deficiencies, especially in ectodermal derivatives, and (c) normal embryos. This suggests that in the late gastrula some endoderm nuclei are unchanged; others are limited in their capacity to promote ectodermal differentiation; and still others are incapable of participating in chorda mesoderm formation. Results of transfers of mid-neurula and tail bud endoderm nuclei indicate that as differentiation proceeds the number of unchanged nuclei decreases, and that some nuclei may lose their capacity even to promote cleavage of recipient eggs.

That the changes described above occur in the nucleus or some nucleus-associated structure is indicated by the fact that endoderm cytoplasm, injected into normally nucleated eggs, has no influence on their development. This does not exclude cytoplasmic participation in the effects observed, but does indicate that cytoplasmic factors would be nucleus-dependent in their activity. In what follows, we shall refer to the changes detected by the transplantation procedure as nuclear changes, with the understanding that these changes may actually involve either the nucleus itself or some perinuclear organelle, or both.

SERIAL TRANSPLANTATION OF ENDODERM NUCLEI

From the experiments described above, it looks very much as if there is, during development, a progressive restriction of the capacity of endoderm nuclei to promote the coordinated differentiation of the various cell types required for the formation of a normal embryo. The two most pressing questions concerning these nuclear changes are (1) are they specific? and (2) are they stable or irreversible? For various reasons it seemed that the question of specificity could be solved more readily if that of irreversibility were first settled. A method of doing this is illustrated in Fig. 1.

The experiment consists of first making transfers of a series of endoderm nuclei to enucleated eggs. Each egg receives one nucleus as usual, and a sizable proportion of the eggs then cleave and form complete blastulae. Each blastula will be, so to speak, populated by descendants of a single endoderm nucleus. Different blastulae contain nuclei derived from different endoderm cells, and develop in the different ways shown in the figure. Now, in order to test the descendants of any given endoderm nucleus we may sacrifice one of the original recipient eggs at the blastula stage, and make from it a new series of nuclear transfers. All of the new group of recipient eggs will contain descendants of one original endoderm nucleus. If the expression of the

nucleus with respect to differentiation is uniform and not much affected by vagaries of experimentation all of this new generation of test eggs (called the 1st blastula generation) should develop in the same fashion. It will, in effect, represent the first generation of a clone of embryos all containing descendants of a single nucleus, and is referred to as a nuclear clone. The characteristics of the clone may be studied further by sacrificing an individual of the first blastula generation to provide nuclei for another group of test eggs, referred to as the second blastula generation. The development of this group of eggs will tell us not only how uniform is the differentiation-promoting activity of the nucleus but also, by comparison with the preceding generation, how stable.

The actual experiments were carried out in the following way. In any given experiment we first transferred approximately 15 endoderm nuclei to the same number of enucleated eggs. Anywhere from 6 to 12 of these eggs cleaved and formed complete blastulae. The first two or three cleavages were observed and recorded, and the eggs were then placed in a water bath at 14°C. On the following day (*ca.* 24 hours later) the blastulae were removed from the 14° tank to the 18° room, three donors were selected, and the remaining embryos were set aside for observation. The donors were always blastulae of perfectly normal appearance which had records of having initiated cleavage at the normal time. It was important to select the donors on this basis to avoid the complication of polyploidy (see p. 173). Nuclei from each of the three donors were transferred to ten enucleated eggs to give the first blastula generation of three nuclear clones. Again cleavages were observed and on the following day one of the resulting blastulae in each clone was selected as the donor for the second blastula generation, while the remaining blastulae were allowed to develop. Usually the experiments were not carried beyond the second blastula generation, and as outlined above, each such experiment, producing three nuclear clones, required at least 75 nuclear transfers. The

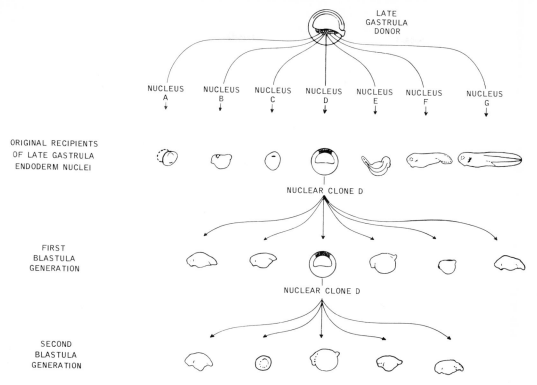

Fig. 1. Diagram illustrating serial transplantation of endoderm nuclei. Donor nuclei are actually taken from the presumptive anterior midgut region of the late gastrula. Transferred to enucleated eggs, they promote the various types of development shown for the "original recipients" in the diagram. One of the original recipients, sacrificed at the blastula stage, provides nuclei for a single clone which shows the more uniform development illustrated for the first and second blastula generations. In this and subsequent figures the illustrations of embryos are in the form of either camera lucida drawings or photographs.

work reported below on 27 nuclear clones (9 control nuclei, 18 endoderm nuclei) is based on a total of about 850 nuclear transfers.

RESULTS

Results of serial transplantation of nuclei are given in the form of actual records of representative experiments and in a summary table and chart (Figs. 1–8 and Table 1). The experimental records reproduced here include only the test eggs that cleaved completely forming normal blastulae. Not included are eggs that failed to cleave, or cleaved abnormally or partially, since for one reason or another these provide no test of the capacity of the transferred nuclei to promote differentiation.

Figure 1, illustrating the principle of the experimental procedure, is also an accurate record of the development of one nuclear clone. In this experiment, the original transfers of endoderm nuclei as usual led to quite different types of development, ranging from arrested gastrulae to normal embryos, as illustrated by the camera lucida drawings. One blastula was sacrificed to provide nuclei for transfer to a new group of enucleated eggs, giving rise to a nuclear clone which, in the first blastula generation, displayed a quite uniform type of development—in contrast to the wide variety of developmental types seen among the original recipients of the different endoderm nuclei. The embryos of this generation gastrulated normally, but later showed

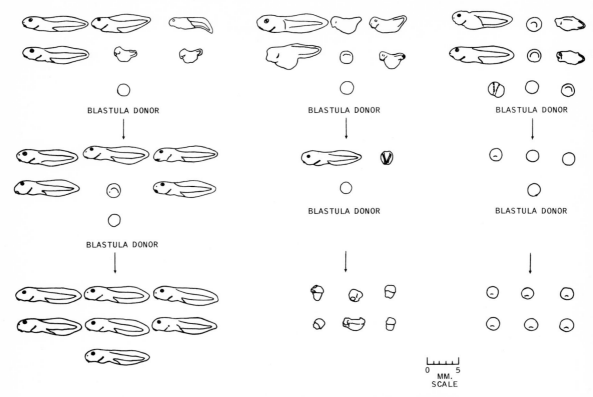

Fig. 2. Camera lucida record of serial transplantation experiment. Three late gastrula donors were used (not diagrammed in above record). Nuclei from these donors were transferred to 3 groups of enucleated eggs, which developed in the various ways illustrated in the upper part of the figure. The derived clones developed much more uniformly.

marked deficiencies, particularly in the ectodermal derivatives. One of the blastulae of this generation was sacrificed to provide nuclei for the second blastula generation, which also developed fairly uniformly and in a manner nearly identical with that of the first generation.

Figure 2 is a camera lucida record of another experiment in which three different original donors were used. Endoderm nuclei from each of these donors were transferred to ten enucleated eggs, which then showed the usual range of developmental types, as illustrated in the three groups of drawings in the upper part of Fig. 2. One blastula from each group of embryos was sacrificed to provide nuclei for the first blastula generation. Endoderm nuclei from blastula "A" promoted completely normal development in practically all of the recipient eggs that showed complete

cleavage, in both the first and second blastula generations. Nuclei from blastula "C" also promoted uniform development, stopping in late blastula or early gastrula stage. Nuclei from blastula "B," on the other hand, elicited normal blastula formation in only three of the test eggs, of which one developed normally, one arrested in neurulation, while one was sacrificed at blastula stage to provide nuclei for the second blastula generation. The second generation developed abnormally and displayed somewhat greater variability than usual. The variable development of this clone poses a problem of interpretation. Possibly some nuclei, chosen by chance at the time when they are beginning to undergo a change, will continue to change following transfer to egg cytoplasm. An alternative explanation would be that the variations in development within clone "B" are accidentally induced.

SERIAL TRANSPLANTATION OF ENDODERM NUCLEI

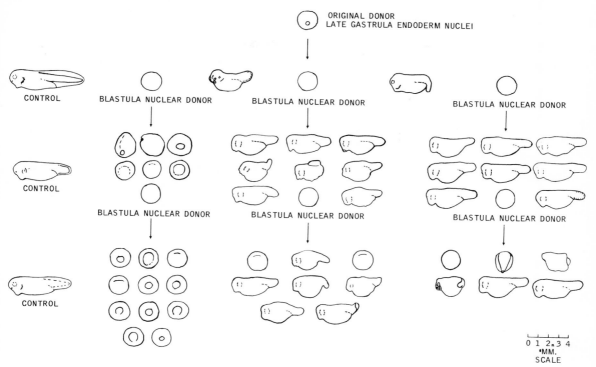

Fig. 3. Camera lucida record of a serial nuclear transplantation experiment. See text for description.

Another serial transplantation experiment is summarized in Fig. 3. In this experiment all three nuclear clones were derived from a single donor. Descendants of nucleus "A" promoted development only to gastrula stages, in both the first and second blastula generations. Descendants of nucleus "B" promoted development of abnormal post-neurula embryos. The abnormalities were similar to those described in the previous section of this paper, being most pronounced in the ectodermal derivatives, and were quite uniformly expressed in the first blastula generation. The majority of embryos of the second generation were similar to those of the first, but two out of the eight embryos were arrested earlier, at gastrula stage. Embryos of nuclear clone "C" also developed to an abnormal post-neurula stage. In the first blastula generation they were uniformly somewhat better developed than individuals in clone "B," but none the less displayed typical characteristics of endo-

derm embryos. In the second generation two of the five individuals were apparently identical with the embryos of the first generation while the remainder showed more marked deficiencies, as shown in Fig. 3.

The actual appearance of the embryos is shown in the photographic record of another experiment. Figure 4 consists of photographs of living embryos and illustrates clearly how uniform are the individuals within a given clone, and how distinct the clones are from each other. Some of the internal morphology of these embryos is illustrated in Fig. 5. Figure 5 shows sections through the eye region. In clone "A" the brain is poorly developed, the eye is in the form of a small vesicle, there is no lens, head mesenchyme is poorly formed, and the development of the foregut is retarded. Although it is not visible in the low power photographs, there is pycnosis in the nuclei of the brain, eye, and dorsal mesenchyme, but not significantly in the ventral

RETRANSPLANTATION OF ENDODERM NUCLEI

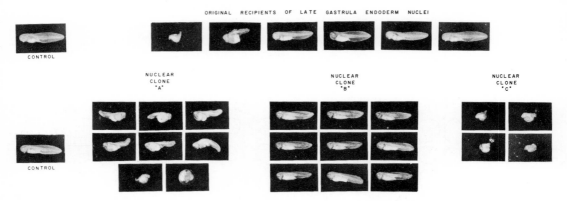

Fig. 4. Photographs of living embryos. Two generation serial transplantation experiment.

mesenchyme and foregut. Sections through the trunk show the notochord well formed and of about the same diameter as the notochord in the controls. Somites are also present, although abnormal in form. On the other hand, both the spinal cord and the dorsal mesenchyme are very poorly developed and con-

tain pycnotic nuclei. The midgut is still in the form of a large endoderm mass in controls and experimental embryos at this stage. In clone "A" it is distorted by swelling of the coelomic space, but does not contain pycnotic nuclei.

Clone "B" displays more advanced differ-

RETRANSPLANTATION OF ENDODERM NUCLEI

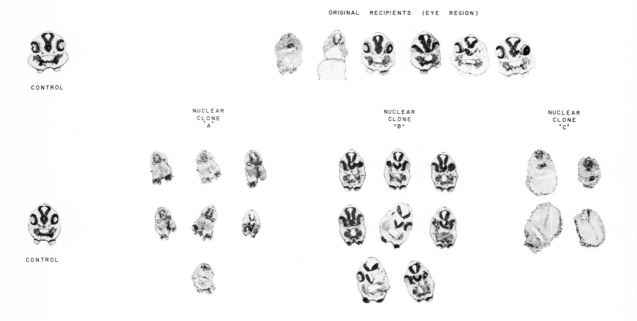

Fig. 5. Sections through eye region of embryos shown in Fig. 4. Description given in text.

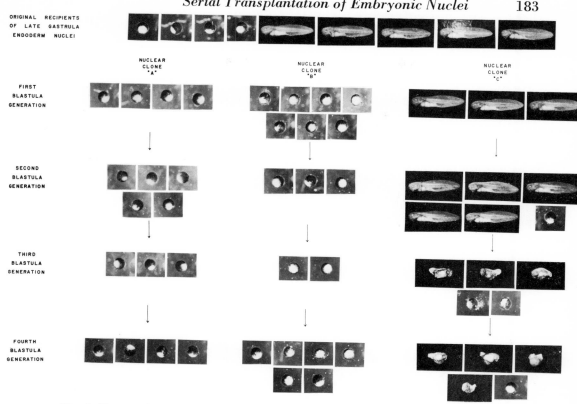

ORIGINAL RECIPIENTS OF LATE GASTRULA ENDODERM NUCLEI

NUCLEAR CLONE "A"   NUCLEAR CLONE "B"   NUCLEAR CLONE "C"

FIRST BLASTULA GENERATION

SECOND BLASTULA GENERATION

THIRD BLASTULA GENERATION

FOURTH BLASTULA GENERATION

Fig. 6. Photographic record of 5 generation serial transplantation experiment. See text.

entiation than clone "A" but is still deficient compared with the controls. The deficiencies, although less pronounced, are of the same general character as those in clone "A." Brain and dorsal head mesenchyme contain numerous pycnotic nuclei. The eye cup has induced a lens which is still in the form of a simple vesicle whereas in the controls it has differentiated into the main body of the lens and the lens epithelium. Foregut and ventral mesenchyme are somewhat retarded but contain no significant number of pycnotic nuclei. Sections through the trunk show a modest but definite reduction in the size and degree of differentiation of the spinal cord.

Clone "C" shows extreme deficiencies, the brain and head mesenchyme being absent or very poorly formed and containing numerous degenerating nuclei. In the trunk the notochord and somite material is present. A rudimentary spinal cord is present in three of four cases examined. The gut is poorly developed, but contains no pycnotic nuclei.

Figure 6 gives the results of one experiment in which the serial nuclear transfers were carried on for a total of four blastula generations. The experiment was unique in that the original transfers of late gastrula endoderm nuclei led to only two types of development. The recipient eggs were either arrested in the very early gastrula stage, or they developed into perfectly normal post-neurula embryos, as shown in the top line of photographs of Fig. 6. There were no embryos of intermediate type. Correspondingly, clones derived from this group of embryos also expressed at first only the two types of development. Clones "A" and "B" showed uniformly an arrest of development in early gastrula stage, and even though the transfers were carried on for four blastula generations there was no evidence of reversal to a more normal type of development. Clone "C" embryos, on the other hand, developed normally for the first two blastula generations, but in the third and fourth generations the development changed,

SUMMARY SERIAL TRANSPLANTATION OF ENDODERM NUCLEI

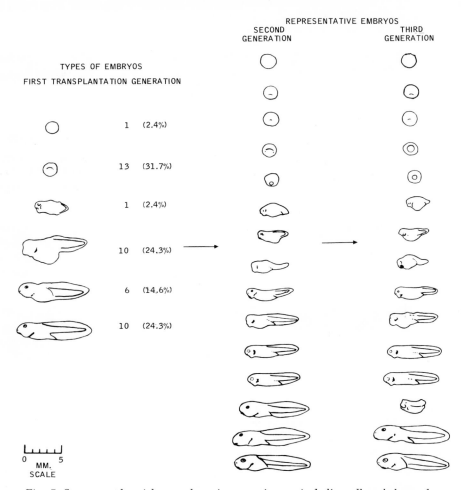

Fig. 7. Summary of serial transplantation experiments including all endoderm clones except the ones shown in Fig. 4 (not included because the experiment was carried on for only 2 generations). The row of drawings on the left illustrates the types of embryos developing from the original recipient eggs injected with endoderm nuclei. The middle row shows typical embryos from the clones in the second generation (referred to in text as the first blastula generation). Each embryo represents a single clone. The same clones in the third generation are represented in the right-hand row of drawings. Note that in general the development in the third generation is similar to that in the second, with no evidence of change to a more normal type of differentiation.

giving rise to abnormal post-neurula embryos of the type commonly seen in the other endoderm experiments.

A summary of the serial transplantation tests of endoderm embryos is given in Table 1 and Fig. 7. The main point to be emphasized concerning the data in Table 1 is that the same types of embryos occur in about the same proportions in both the original population of

endoderm embryos and in the derived clones. Each clone displays a fairly uniform type of development and as a clone corresponds to one or another of the individual embryos in the original population. In other words, in the process of deriving the clones we obtain a faithful representation of the original types.

We have included also in Table 1 the data on serial transfers of undifferentiated blastula

SERIAL TRANSPLANTATION OF BLASTULA NUCLEI

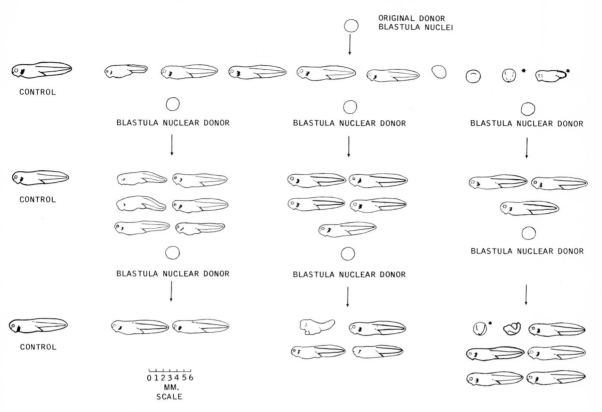

Fig. 8. Camera lucida record of serial transplantation experiment with nuclei of un-differentiated blastula cells. Embryos marked * died from some infectious or toxic process after developing normally to the stages shown.

nuclei, for the purpose of showing that in the majority of experiments these give rise to clones of normal embryos. A detailed record of one of these experiments is given in Fig. 8.

Figure 7 gives a comparison of the development of the endoderm clones in the successive blastula generations. Each generation of each clone is represented in the figure by a single typical embryo. The important fact emerging from this summary is that in no case so far studied is there a reversal to a more normal type of development in the second (or later) blastula generation compared with the first. In other words, the nuclear condition responsible for given deficiencies in differentiation is irreversible under the conditions of these experiments. However, it is possible that nuclear changes leading to more restricted development may sometimes progress in the course of

repeated transfers. Two instances of a more restricted development in the later generations have been noted (Figs. 2 and 6) and it is possible, though far from certain, that endoderm nuclei may continue "differentiating" in egg cytoplasm.

CHROMOSOME STUDIES

Since it is known that embryos with unbalanced chromosome sets develop abnormally and are frequently arrested at early developmental stages (Fankhauser, 1934b), it was important to determine the condition of the chromosomes in the endoderm embryos described above. This was done as follows:

In each experiment portions of the original donor gastrula and of the blastula donor for each transplant generation were handed over

TABLE 1. Development of original recipients of endoderm nuclei compared with development of endoderm clones

Source of Nuclei	Total No. Complete Blastulae	Development		
		Blastulae and Gastrulae	Abnormal Post-neurulae	Normal Larvae
Endoderm (late gastrula) Original recipients (individual eggs)	44	14 (32%)	20 (45%)	10 (23%)
Clones	18	5 (28%)	8 (44%)	5 (28%)
Control (blastulae) Original recipients (individual eggs)	22	2 (9%)	2 (9%)	18 (82%)
Clones	9	0	2 (22%)	7 (78%)

to Miss Marie DiBerardino, who immediately prepared acetic-orcein squashes of the material. All the subsequent work on the chromosomes was done by Miss DiBerardino.

The preparation of satisfactory squashes of blastula chromosomes posed some problems. If the cells are squashed directly from the Niu-Twitty medium it is very difficult to obtain adequate separation of the chromosomes. A photograph of a typical metaphase plate is reproduced in Fig. 9A, showing the long blastula chromosomes intertwined and impossible to count accurately. Adequate separation of chromosomes can be produced by pre-treating the cells with hypotonic medium and colchicine (Hungerford, 1955), but still better results can be obtained by pre-treatment for 30 minutes with a Niu-Twitty medium lacking Ca^{++} and Mg^{++}, and buffered to pH 7.5 with phosphate. A photograph of a plate from such a preparation is given in Fig. 9B. The effect of pre-treatment with the modified Niu-Twitty medium is immediately reversed if the cells are returned to the normal medium before squashing. The effect is also different for tissues from more advanced stages of development. These and other phenomena are being studied by Hungerford and DiBerardino and will be described elsewhere.

The results of the chromosome studies are presented in Table 2 and Figs. 10 and 11. With respect to chromosome number the results are clear. In the majority of cases, the normal diploid number (26) was found, regardless of the type of development promoted by the nuclei. In one clone there was a shift from diploidy to a triploid or near triploid number between the first and second blastula generations. Otherwise the numbers remained at the diploid value throughout.

With respect to chromosome morphology there was also no detectable change in the majority of donors. However, in three clones the donor nuclei contained a few small ring chromosomes (see Fig. 10) similar to those noted by Fankhauser (1934a) in one merogonic fragment of a salamander egg. These clones developed only to the late blastula or very early gastrula stage. In a fourth clone, displaying development to a mid-gastrula stage, ring chromosomes were present in the first blastula generation but not in the second. In the remaining eleven clones studied chromosome morphology appeared to be normal even though the different clones developed in quite different ways.

Even though there were, for the majority of clones, no variations in chromosome number or morphology that could be correlated with type of development, it was still possible that deletions or translocations might have occurred that would have escaped detection. A rough attempt to detect such alterations was made in the following way. The lengths of the camera lucida drawings of chromosomes were measured with a Keuffel and Esser map reader. In order to put chromosome lengths in different figures and squashes on a comparable basis we calculated the relative length as the ratio: individual chromosome length/total length of all 26 chromosomes (L/Total L). The relative lengths of the chromosomes in any given figure were then plotted in the manner shown in Fig. 11. From a comparison of such plots one can determine whether the distribution of chromosome lengths is the same or different in the different clones. The results of this analysis are illustrated in Fig. 11. In general, the distribution of chromosome lengths did not appear to differ in the different types of clones. One of the clones containing ring chromosomes did differ from the others in displaying a wider range of chromosome lengths (Fig. 11). Otherwise, there were no differences that could be definitely related to type of development. This does not eliminate the possibility that deletions, etc. may have occurred, but does suggest that they would have to be on a relatively small scale. It also does not mean that more subtle types of chromosomal (or other) changes may not be occurring as a regular concomitant of differentiation (for example, see Beermann, 1956).

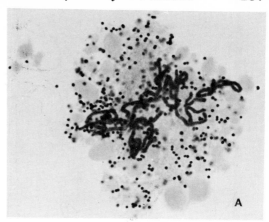

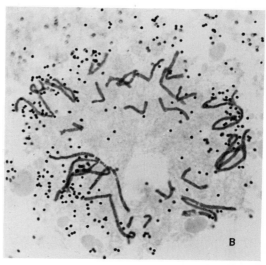

Fig. 9. A. Blastula metaphase plate. Prepared from cells transferred directly from Niu-Twitty solution to acetic-orcein stain-fixative. B. Blastula metaphase plate showing increased spreading of chromosomes resulting from pretreatment of cells with modified Niu-Twitty solution (lacking Ca^{++} and Mg^{++}). Black spots are pigment granules. Magnification: $\times$ 1370. Photographs by David A. Hungerford.

DISCUSSION

The serial transplantation experiments described above show that the changes occurring in endoderm nuclei during differentiation are highly stabilized, in the sense that they are not reversed in egg cytoplasm. Each transfer is followed by cleavage of the recipient egg to produce a donor blastula consisting of approximately 8000 cells, requiring about 13 divisions (or generations) of the original nucleus. In the majority of experiments, three such transfers were done serially and therefore involved about 39 nuclear generations. In the most extensive experiments (5 serial transfers) there would have been 65 reproductions of the original endoderm nucleus, with still no evidence of reversal. Thus, regardless of its exact character and mode of origin, we are dealing with a heritable change in the capacity of the nucleus to promote differentiation. At the least, it could be a change induced in the original endoderm nuclei accidentally during the transfer operation. At the most, it would represent a specific genetic change elicited somehow by particular cytoplasmic localizations, and responsible in turn

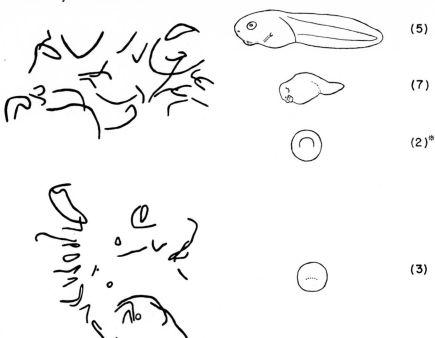

Fig. 10. Chromosome complements of endoderm embryos. Types and numbers of endoderm nuclear clones are illustrated by the drawings of representative embryos. The corresponding chromosome complements are shown in the form of camera lucida drawings of typical metaphase plates. Rings were present in clones displaying arrest of development in late blastula or early gastrula stage. Of two clones arresting at about mid-gastrula stage (*) one displayed rings in the first blastula generation but not in the second. Otherwise the chromosome complements appeared normal regardless of type of development.

for the stabilization of differentiation of individual cells.

The idea that nuclear changes such as we see in endoderm cells might be accidentally induced cannot be ignored. The hazard of nuclear damage is always present in this kind of experimentation. The arguments against it are as follows:

1. The technical problems of making nuclear transfers from endoderm cells are no greater than they are for blastula cells. Yet, the blastula nuclei promote normal differentiation of recipient eggs while the endoderm nuclei generally do not.

2. Although the original transfers of endoderm nuclei give a variety of types of development, subsequent transfers of descendants of a particular nucleus lead to fairly uniform development of the recipient eggs. If the variation were accidentally induced one would expect to find it in the clones as well as in the recipients of the original nuclei. (Unless, of course, endoderm nuclei are somehow much more sensitive to damage in their own cytoplasm than they are in egg cytoplasm.)

3. While the original endoderm transfers usually lead to a variety of types of development, this is not always so. In one experiment (Fig. 6) we observed only two classes of embryos, which would be hard to account for on the basis of chance injury to the nuclei.

4. In the majority of clones there was no evidence of chromosome changes such as might be expected to result from nuclear damage.

On the basis of this evidence we may assume that the restrictions in the capacity of endoderm nuclei to promote differentiation are real and not artificially induced. Other points about which definite statements can be made are (1) that the nuclear changes are highly stabilized, as shown by the serial transplantation experiments, and (2) that they do not occur in all cells at once. Rather it appears that in the late gastrula the endoderm nuclei fall into three general classes: (1) undifferentiated nuclei, (2) nuclei restricted to varying degrees in their capacity to promote normal post-gastrula development, particularly of ectodermal derivatives, and (3) nuclei incapable of participating in the formation of chorda mesoderm, resulting in arrest at gastrulation. In later stages of development the number of nuclei in class (1) (undifferentiated) decreases while those showing restrictions of differentiation-promoting capacity increase. This indicates that a progressive and "irreversible" nuclear change occurs during differentiation. Whether in any given cell this restriction in differentiating-promoting ability occurs slowly or rapidly, continuously or in distinct steps, we do not know, although a study of nuclear changes during the post-blastula development of the clones might eventually give answers to some of these questions. Also, it is unknown which of the nuclear or peri-nuclear structures are involved. Control experiments have shown that the endoderm cytoplasm by itself is incapable of modifying the differentiation of normally nucleated eggs. However, we cannot yet determine whether it is the nucleus itself or some replicating peri-nuclear organelle which is responsible for the restricted developmental potencies.

Finally, we should consider briefly the question of the specificity of the nuclear changes in endoderm cells. We have seen that these changes result first in a loss of the capacity to promote normal differentiation of ectodermal derivatives, and presumably later the ability to promote differentiation of chorda mesoderm is also lost. Thus, the nuclear changes are consistent with the fact that the nuclei are derived from endoderm. But whether they are specific for endoderm is uncertain. In order to settle this point it would be necessary to explore the capacity for various types of differentiation by appropriate grafting experiments with parts of the arrested endoderm embryos, and the same sort of analysis would have to be done on embryos containing other types of nuclei. Now that the nuclear changes in endoderm cells are known to be highly stabilized and to give a fairly uniform type of development in the clones, this central problem of specificity may be attacked.

Summary

Nuclei of late gastrula endoderm, transplanted to enucleated eggs (*Rana pipiens*) promote the following general types of de-

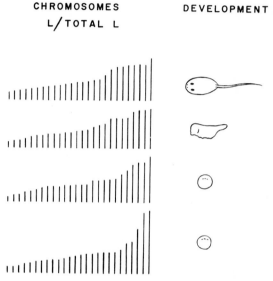

CHROMOSOMES
L/TOTAL L   DEVELOPMENT

Fig. 11. Relative lengths of chromosomes were measured on a total of 78 metaphase plates from 14 endoderm embryos and 6 controls. The results shown above for endoderm embryos are representative. Differences in relative lengths, from embryo to embryo, are not significant being within the range observed in different plates from single embryos. The one exception, in which the range in relative lengths is greater than normal, is plotted at the bottom of the figure.

velopment: (1) arrest at gastrula stages, (2) normal gastrulation followed by deficient development in later stages, especially in the ectodermal derivatives, (3) normal development throughout.

In order to determine if the nuclear changes responsible for the deficient development are stable, serial transfers of endoderm nuclei were carried out. Individual nuclei were transplanted to enucleated eggs, which cleaved and produced blastulae. In a given test, one of

TABLE 2. Chromosome numbers of donor embryos used in serial transplantation experiments

Type of Donor	Development of Test Eggs	No. of Embryos	No. of Metaphase Plates	Exact Chromosome Counts								Approximate Counts		
				12	13	20	23	24	25	26	27	13–14	21–28	35–45
Endoderm Nuclei														
Original donors (last gast.)	Variable	8	33		4					17			12	
Clonal donors (blastulae)	Normal	10	43	1	3				2	29			8	
	Abnormal: post-neurula arrested blastulae and gastrulae	14	55		2		1			34			13	5
	arrested blastulae and gastrulae*	14	73		1	1	1	2	2	44	1	5	16	
	arrested blastulae and gastrulae*	7	26							26				
Blastula Nuclei														
Original and clonal donors (blastulae)	Normal	20	75					1		59			15	
	Abnormal: post-neurula	2	15		2							8	5	

Original donors—late gastrulae: Donor cells taken from presumptive anterior midgut. For reasons of technical convenience chromosome counts were done on squashes of archenteron roof.

Clonal donors: Embryos derived from eggs injected with endoderm nuclei, sacrificed at blastula stage to provide nuclei (animal hemisphere) for establishment of clones. Counts done on part of animal hemisphere of these donors. In the table donors are grouped according to type of development observed in the derived clones.

* Listed separately are 7 blastulae which were not used as donors. They were taken from the 4th blastula generation of two clones which consistently showed arrest in late blastula or early gastrula stage.

Controls: Original donors and clonal donors, both in blastula stage, grouped together.

For further description see text and Figs. 10 and 11.

these blastulae was sacrificed to provide nuclei for transfer to a new group of eggs. Such a group represents a clone, all members of which are nucleated by descendants of one original endoderm nucleus. One member of such a clone may be sacrificed at the blastula stage to provide nuclei for transfer to a new group of enucleated eggs, giving in effect a second blastula generation of the clone. The same process may be repeated to provide several generations.

Analysis of the development of 18 clones revealed the following: Whereas test eggs containing different endoderm nuclei developed in the different ways mentioned above, eggs within one clone developed much more uniformly. In some clones all embryos were arrested at gastrula stage, in others they displayed a fairly uniform set of deficiencies in post-gastrula development, and in a few clones almost all embryos developed normally throughout. Furthermore, within any given clone the development in the second and later generations was generally of the same type as that observed in the first generation. In a few clones the deficiencies became more severe in the later generations, but no case of reversal to a more normal type of development was noted.

Chromosome studies on donor embryos in the clonal experiments showed that chromosome number generally remained unchanged at the diploid value (26). In three clones, all consisting of embryos arresting at early gastrula stage, a few small ring chromosomes were present. Otherwise, no chromosome changes were detected even though the clones exhibited quite different types of development.

These experiments show that descendants of individual endoderm nuclei have a fairly uniform expression with respect to differentiation, which does not reverse to a more normal expression in the course of the serial transfers. In other words, compared with nuclei of undifferentiated cells, the endoderm nuclei show stabilized changes in capacity to promote differentiation. How these changes arise, whether they are specific, and which

of the nuclear or peri-nuclear structures are involved, are problems remaining to be worked out.

ACKNOWLEDGEMENTS

We wish to thank Dr. Jack Schultz for the benefit derived from many discussions we have had with him on problems of differentiation. We also wish to acknowledge the assistance of Miss Marie DiBerardino, who carried out the chromosome studies described in this paper and provided valuable assistance in many other ways as well.

REFERENCES

Beermann, W., 1956, Nuclear differentiation and functional morphology of chromosomes. *Cold Spr. Harb. Symp. Quant. Biol.* **21:** 217–232.

Briggs, R., E. U. Green, and T. J. King, 1951, An investigation of the capacity for cleavage and differentiation in *Rana pipiens* eggs lacking "functional" chromosomes. *J. Exp. Zool.* **116:** 455–500.

Briggs, R., and T. J. King, 1952, Transplantation of living nuclei from blastula cells into enucleated frogs' eggs. *Proc. Nat. Acad. Sci. Wash.* **38:** 455–463.

————, 1953, Factors affecting the transplantability of nuclei of frog embryonic cells. *J. Exp. Zool.* **122:** 485–506.

Comandon, J., and P. DeFonbrune, 1939, Greffe nucleaire totale, simple ou multiple, chez une *Amibe. Compt. rend. soc. biol.* **130:** 744–748.

Danielli, J. F., I. J. Lorch, M. J. Ord., and E. C. Wilson, 1955, Nucleus and cytoplasm in cellular inheritance. *Nature, Lond.* **176:** 1114–1115.

Ephrussi, B., 1951, Remarks on cell heredity. In: *Genetics in the 20th Century.* New York, Macmillan Company, pp. 241–262.

————, 1953, *Nucleo-cytoplasmic relations in microorganisms.* Oxford, Clarendon Press.

Fankhauser, G., 1934a, Cytological studies on egg fragments of the salamander *Triton.* IV. The cleavage of egg fragments without the egg nucleus. *J. Exp. Zool.* **67:** 349–394.

————, 1934b, Cytological studies on egg fragments of the salamander *Triton.* V. Chromosome number and chromosome individuality in the cleavage mitoses of merogonic fragments. *J. Exp. Zool.* **68:** 1–57.

Glueksohn-Waelsch, S., 1954, Some genetic aspects of development. *Cold Spr. Harb. Symp. Quant. Biol.* **19:** 41–49.

Grobstein, C., 1952, Effects of fragmentation of mouse embryonic shields on their differentiative behavior after culturing. *J. Exp. Zool.* **120**: 437–456.

Grobstein, C., and E. Zwilling, 1953, Modification of growth and differentiation of chorioallantoic grafts of chick blastoderm pieces after cultivation at a glass-clot interface. *J. Exp. Zool.* **122**: 259–284.

Hadorn, E., 1948, Gene action in growth and differentiation of lethal mutants of *Drosophila*. *Symposia Soc. Exp. Biol.* **2**: 177–195.

——, 1956, Patterns of biochemical and developmental pleiotropy. *Cold Spr. Harb. Symp. Quant. Biol.* **21**: 255–382.

Hämmerling, J., 1934, Über genomwirkungen und Formbildungsfähigkeit bei *Acetabularia*. *Arch. Entwick-mech. Org.* **132**: 424–462.

——, 1953, Nucleo-cytoplasmic relationships in the development of *Acetabularia*. *Intern. Rev. Cytol.* **2**: 475–498.

Holtfreter, J., 1933, Die totale Exogastrulation, eine Selbstablösung des Ektoderms vom Entomesoderm Entwicklung und funktionelles Verhalten nervenloser Organe. *Arch. Entwick-mech. Org.* **129**: 669–793.

——, 1938, Differenzierungspotenzen isolierter Teile der Anurengastrula. *Arch. Entwick-mech. Org.* **138**: 657–738.

Hungerford, D. A., 1955, Chromosome numbers of ten-day fetal mouse cells. *J. Morph.* **97**: 497–510.

King, T. J., and R. Briggs, 1954, Transplantation of living nuclei of late gastrulae into enucleated eggs of *Rana pipiens*. *J. Embryol. Exp. Morph.* **2**: 73–80.

——, 1955, Changes in the nuclei of differentiating gastrula cells, as demonstrated by nuclear transplantation. *Proc. Nat. Acad. Sci. Wash.* **41**: 321–325.

Lederberg, J., 1956, Infection and heredity. *Growth Symp.* **13**: 101–124. Princeton Univ. Press.

Lehman, H. E., 1955, On the development of enucleated *Triton* eggs with an injected blastula nucleus. *Biol. Bull.* **108**: 138–150.

——, 1956, Nuclear transplantation, a tool for the study of nuclear differentiation. *AAAS Symp.*

Loeb, J., 1894, Über eine einfache Methode, zwei oder mehr zusammengewachsene Embryonen aus einem Ei hervorzubringen. *Pflüger's Arch.* **55**: 525–530.

Lorch, I. J., and J. F. Danielli, 1950, Transplantation of nuclei from cell to cell. *Nature, Lond.* **166**: 329–333.

Moore, J. A., 1955, Abnormal combinations of nuclear and cytoplasmic systems in frogs and toads. *Adv. Genet.* **7**: 139–182.

Niu, M. C., and V. C. Twitty, 1953, The differentiation of gastrula ectoderm in medium conditioned by axial mesoderm. *Proc. Nat. Acad. Sci. Wash.* **39**: 985–989.

Porter, K. R., 1939, Androgenetic development of the egg of *Rana pipiens*. *Biol. Bull.* **77**: 233–257.

Poulson, D. F., 1945, Chromosomal control of embryogenesis in *Drosophila*. *Amer. Nat.* **79**: 340–363.

Rostand, J., 1943, Essai d'inoculation de noyaux embryonnaires dans l'oeuf vierge de grenouille. *Rev. sci.* **81**: 454–456.

Schultz, J., 1952, Interrelations between nucleus and cytoplasm: problems at the biological level. *Exp. Cell Res. Suppl.* **2**: 17–43.

Sonneborn, T. M., 1954, Patterns of nucleocytoplasmic integration in *Paramecium*. *Proc. 9th Intern. Congress Genetics.* Caryologia, suppl. 1954: 307–325.

Spemann, H., 1914, Über verzögerte Kernversorgung von Keimteilen. *Vergandl. deut. zool. Ges.*, 1914: 16–221.

——, 1938, *Embryonic Development and Induction.* New Haven, Yale Univ. Press, p. 211.

Stauffer, E., 1945, Versuche zur experimentallen Herstellung haploider Axolotl-Merogone. *Rev. suisse zool.* **52**: 231–327.

Subtelny, S. S., 1956, Personal communication.

Sze, L. C., 1953, Changes in the amount of desoxyribonucleic acid in the development of *Rana pipiens*. *J. Exp. Zool.* **122**: 577–601.

Tartar, V., 1953, Chimeras and nuclear transplantations in ciliates, *Stentor coeruleus* × *S. polymorphus*. *J. Exp. Zool.* **124**: 63–103.

Waddington, C. H., and E. M. Pantelouris, 1953, Transplantation of nuclei in newt's eggs. *Nature, Lond.* **172**: 1050.

Weisz, Paul B., 1951, A general mechanism of differentiation based on morphogenetic studies in ciliates. *Amer. Nat.* **85**: 293–311.

Wilson, E. B., 1925, *The Cell in Development and Heredity.* 3rd ed. New York, Macmillan Company.

DISCUSSION

BALINSKY: The persistence of the same types of development in each of the different clones makes it plausible that there are differences in the nuclei propagating in each clone. Do you have any suggestion as to why the initial nuclei used to start each clone could have been different, seeing that they were all taken originally from the same part of the embryo, the floor of the archenteron of a late gastrula stage?

KING: The embryological evidence for the determination of late gastrula endoderm is based on explantation and transplantation experiments which involved large groups of cells. We cannot distinguish whether this determination depends upon differentiation of the individual cells or is to be regarded as a property of the mass as a whole. Grobstein (1952) and Grobstein and Zwilling (1953), working with cultured explants of mouse embryonic shield and chick blastoderm, find that the extent of differentiation depends upon the degree to which the explant cells are dispersed. Large explants will differentiate into neural tissue, but if these explants are divided into eighths or sixteenths the differentiation fails to occur or is poorly expressed. Thus it appears that in chick and mouse embryos organ determination occurs while the individual cells are still undifferentiated or in various states of differentiation. The same situation may exist in the amphibian gastrula.

Another source of heterogeneity is suggested by Holtfreter's (1933) observation that the midgut contains "lethal" cells, as well as cells which later form the gut epithelium. In urodeles the lethal cells can be seen to degenerate in the gut lumen during late embryonic life. However, we could find no evidence of cell lethality in the developing gut of the anuran (*R. pipiens*) used in our experiments.

STERN: It has been suggested that if embryonic nuclei from prospective germ cells were transplanted they would demonstrate unrestricted potentialities in development. This expectation implies the belief that the genetic totipotency of the nuclei of germ cells at the time of their presence in mature germ cells is equivalent to developmental totipotency of these nuclei at other stages. However, it may well be that nuclei of immature germ cells are just as restricted developmentally as those of somatic cells, while on the other hand, developmentally restricted nuclei of somatic cells may be totipotent genetically.

KING: We would agree with Dr. Stern's comment, especially since we do not yet know what part of the nuclear complex is involved in the changes reported in this paper, and whether these changes might not be reversible under different conditions than those existing in our experiments.

MARKERT: The range of variation in developmental capacity shown by nuclei taken from a restricted area would seem to support the concept that the state of differentiation of a tissue reflects the average state of differentiation of its constituent cells. These cells apparently do not undergo synchronous transformations but gradually differentiate as variable members of a complex population. Such a process of tissue differentiation based on the additive individual contributions of diverse, although related, cells should be relatively "well-buffered" against transitory abnormal influences to which the embryo might be exposed during development. Only those influences which persisted long enough to transform a substantial number of cells with initially different degrees of sensitivity could effectively alter the course of tissue differentiation. Over any short period of time that fraction of the tissue cells in any particular phase of development would be dispensable so far as the development of the entire tissue was concerned.

The Role of the Nucleus in Differentiation Especially in Acetabularia*

J. HAEMMERLING

I. EFFECTS OF ENUCLEATION

(1) Morphogenesis

The uninucleate photosynthetic organisms belonging to the genus *Acetabularia* (Chlorophyceae) produce an upright stalk at the anterior end of which are formed whorls of deciduous laterals and finally a persistent cap. In *A. mediterranea* the stalk reaches a length from 3–5 cm. within 3 months and the cap a diameter up to 1 cm. in a further month. The nucleus is located in the rhizoid so that anucleate parts are readily produced by cutting this off. The morphogenetic capacities as well as some other activities of such parts are summarized in Fig. 1.

As is well known, anucleate parts still possess marked morphogenetic capacities and are able to form a new stalk, several whorls and even a healthy growing cap. This is especially so if the anucleate part is cut from a plant which is about to produce a cap. The morphogenetic capacity is greatest in anterior parts but nearly lacking in posterior parts.

Thus, morphogenesis can proceed in the absence of the nucleus but it is nevertheless *basically* nucleus controlled. The best demonstration of this fact has come from recent darkening experiments, which have proved to be useful also for study of the problem of cytoplasmic RNA synthesis.[19–21]

Non-growing posterior parts with rhizoids, that is, with nuclei, were kept in darkness. They then acquired marked morphogenetic capacities which were realized when the rhizoid was cut off and the now anucleate part re-illuminated. In darkness there is no growth.

Symposia of the Society for Experimental Biology, XVII, 127–137, 1963. Reprinted with permission.

* Since a more extensive review dealing with this and related problems [appeared] in the *Ann. Rev. Plant Physiol.* 14 (1963), no other references will be given here. The superior numerals in this paper refer to the reference number in this review.

Moreover, the dry weight in both the cell and the nucleus decrease and therewith the contents of protein[45] and RNA.[46, 47] But one fundamental nuclear activity continues in darkness: the release from the nucleus into the cytoplasm of compounds which induce morphogenesis after re-illumination. We have called such substances "morphogenetic substances." The extent of morphogenesis depends on the length of the dark period, that is, on the amount of morphogenetic substances released from the nucleus. Furthermore, these substances are accumulated at the anterior end of the darkened cell part, as is shown by special experiments. The results are essentially the same when an isolated nucleus, washed several times, is implanted into an anucleate part.[21] Hereby the possibility is ruled out that it is only a matter of substances present in the rhizoid immigrating into the stalk.

The results obtained with pre-darkened parts confirm definitely the conclusions drawn already for normally illuminated anucleate parts: first, that the extent of morphogenesis depends on the amount of morphogenetic substances present at the moment of enucleation in the cytoplasm, secondly that these substances are released from the nucleus and, thirdly, that they are accumulated at the anterior stalk end.[6] Only morphogenesis itself requires light, whereas release of the morphogenetic substances from the nucleus and the formation of their apical–basal concentration gradient proceed also in darkness.

From further evidence it can be concluded that precursors of the morphogenetic substances are released in darkness and that they are converted to the active stage by light.[9, 24]

(2) Synthetic Activities

Nearly all compounds examined exhibit a *de novo* synthesis in anucleate parts which leads to a considerable increase of their

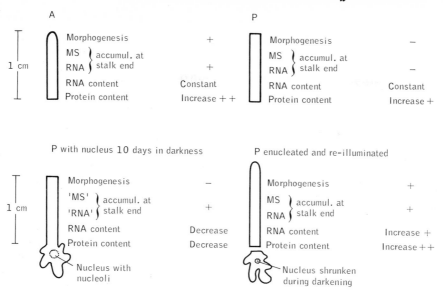

Fig. 1. Upper row: activities of normally illuminated anucleate parts. Lower row: results of the darkening experiment. A, anterior stalk part; P, posterior stalk part; MS, morphogenetic substances; 'MS,' precursors of morphogenetic substances; 'RNA,' substances inducing cytoplasmic RNA synthesis.

amount, i.e. carbohydrates,[39, 41, 42] the different phosphorus fractions (excluding RNA phosphorus);[40] lipids,[40, 43] free amino acids,[44] and protein.[6, 39]

Protein increase takes place in the plastids as well as in the rest of the cytoplasm.[49] An increase in amount can be assumed with high probability also for at least two enzymes, phosphorylase[52] and invertase.[53] Furthermore, total protein synthesis can proceed for 2 weeks as fast as in nucleate parts (but never faster as assumed by Brachet[2, 39]). Later it decreases but can continue for more than 4 weeks.[48]

If total protein synthesis is related to the growth performances of anucleate parts, a positive correlation is found. Thus, if anucleate parts of the same length but with different growth performances are compared, it is found that protein increase is smaller the smaller the growth. This does not mean that protein does not increase in non-growing parts, e.g., in posterior parts. On the contrary, these still produce considerable amounts of protein. This means that protein synthesis can be dissociated from growth or, in other words, growth is not the automatic consequence of protein increase at least in *Acetabularia*.[56]

With RNA a surprising situation has been found. In nucleate parts the RNA content increases continuously but enucleation, in marked contrast to its effect on other compounds, causes a sudden stop in this increase. This was found first by Richter,[46] and was recently confirmed by Schweiger and Bremer.[47] It was also confirmed on two other occasions in the laboratory of Brachet,[57, 58] who originally believed that RNA would increase also.[39]

As to the reasons why the RNA increase stops immediately after enucleation, two very different possibilities exist. First, it could be that one or more RNA fractions increase at the expense of others.[46] This point was taken up by Naora, Naora and Brachet.[58] They assumed that plastid RNA increases in approximate proportion to the decrease in other cytoplasmic fractions but actually the problem remains unsolved (see the detailed discussion by Haemmerling, 1963).

Another possibility is that all RNA is transferred from the nucleus to the cytoplasm and stays there without increasing. It was clearly shown by Schweiger and Bremer[47] that this is not the case and, moreover, that anucleate cytoplasm is capable of considerable net syn-

TABLE 1. *Acetabularia mediterranea:* examples of cytoplasmic RNA synthesis (after table III in [47])

RNA Content	Darkness: Day 0 (%)	Enucleation and Re-illumination: Day 10 (%)	10 Days Re-illumination: Day 20
Experiment 5	100	−42.0	+132.2 (+34.3)
4	100	−31.5	+108.1 (+42.6)
Control 5	100	−30.4	+ 22.5 (−14.7)
4	100	− 9.0	− 17.3 (−24.7)

Experiment: nucleate 1.5 cm. posterior parts darkened, enucleation and re-illumination after 10 days, RNA contents after further 10 days (determination also on day 0 without rhizoid). Control: anucleate posterior parts darkened and re-illuminated. RNA contents on day 20 related to day 10 (in parentheses to day 0); absolute RNA-P contents on day 0 experiment and control 5: 2.04 μg./100 parts; experiment and control 4: 3.24 μg./100 parts.

thesis of RNA if only the right conditions obtain (Table 1). These are the conditions in the darkening experiment described above. As already mentioned, the RNA contents of darkened nucleate parts drop considerably, the maximum decrease within 10 days being 42%. But if these parts are enucleated and the now anucleate parts re-illuminated for a further 10 days, they show a marked increase in RNA contents, the maximum increase observed being 132% relative to that on the day of re-illumination. The same treatment of parts which have been anucleate from the beginning leads likewise to an RNA decrease but in this case there is no increase, or only a small one, not more than 25%, after re-illumination. The results of studies on the incorporation of ^{32}P into individual nucleotides have made it highly probable that we are faced with a *de novo* synthesis (Table 2).

TABLE 2. Incorporation of ^{32}P-orthophosphate into the four cytoplasmic RNA nucleotides of *Acetabularia mediterranea* (after table IV in [47])

	CMP	AMP	GMP	UMP
	(10^{-3} c./min./100 parts)			
Experiment	102	104	108	77
Control	34	35	36	30

Experiment: nucleate 1.5 cm. posterior parts darkened for 10 days, activated for 24 hr. immediately after enucleation and re-illumination. Control: same treatment of anucleate parts. The incorporation of ^{32}P is in accordance with the RNA base composition. The degree of incorporation into the parts which contained a nucleus during the darkening period is comparable with the increase of RNA contents shown in Table 1.

This first report of net synthesis of cytoplasmic RNA is not only interesting because the synthesis takes place in the absence of the nucleus, but still more because it demonstrates at the same time that cytoplasmic RNA synthesis is nevertheless strongly nucleus controlled: it must be concluded that in darkness substances are released from the nucleus and stored in the cytoplasm, and that these induce RNA synthesis in the light.

These substances are, apparently, consumed in the light. Thus it is conceivable that normally illuminated and actively growing cells do not contain any great store of these substances and consequently in general are not able to increase their RNA contents after enucleation.

There is a striking parallel between the substances which induce RNA synthesis and those which induce morphogenesis. Both are released from the nucleus in the dark and both exert their action only in the light. Presumably the correspondence is even greater. Particular findings[15] indicate that the substances inducing RNA synthesis are concentrated at the anterior end of the stalk during the darkening period and this also holds, as we saw, for the precursors of the morphogenetic substances.

A second parallel is constituted by the fact that in the light it is not only the active morphogenetic substances which are concentrated at the anterior end of stalk end but also a highly polymerized RNA, as shown by Werz with cytochemical methods.[59] Moreover, both

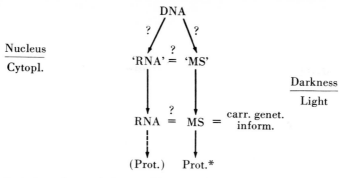

Fig. 2. Tentative scheme of the possible relations between morphogenetic substances and RNA and their precursors. (For the conclusion that the MS are carriers of genetic information and determine the mode of membrane formation, see part II of the text). 'RNA,' substances released from the nucleus and inducing cytoplasmic RNA synthesis; RNA, RNA synthesized in the cytoplasm, which is assumed to obtain genetic information via 'RNA'; 'MS,' precursors of morphogenetic substances released from the nucleus; MS, active morphogenetic substances; darkness, processes taking place also in darkness; light, processes taking place presumably only in light. The parallels between the left and the right side of the scheme depend on the results of independent studies. It must be tested by further experiments whether or not the parallel sequence of events means physical identities. *, Enzyme systems for species-specific membrane formation (stalk, whorl, cap).

show the same behavior under all conditions; if RNA appears at the end of the stalk end so do the morphogenetic substances; if RNA disappears the morphogenetic substances also disappear.

Thus the question arises as to whether this double parallelism means a physical identity (Fig. 2). The answer must be left for further studies.

With respect to the fairly widespread idea that all, or the main part, of cytoplasmic RNA comes from the nucleus, it is now established that this is probably wrong, at least for *Acetabularia* under the conditions examined; the former idea that the nucleus is the only or the main center of protein synthesis is now regarded as incorrect and could be regarded as doubtful since the first results obtained on anucleate *Acetabularia*.[17] But even the highest rates of cytoplasmic RNA synthesis would not exclude the possibility that some RNA is transferred from the nucleus into the cytoplasm. Here the situation is not so clear as it seems at first sight.

The results of the now numerous labeling experiments on various cell types are certainly consistent with the assumption of a transfer of RNA from the nucleus. They all show the appearance of labeled RNA first in the nucleus

and only later in the cytoplasm. The problem is whether *post hoc* necessarily means *propter hoc:* there is no case in which the product leaving the nucleus is defined as RNA beyond doubt. Ingenious objections along these lines have also been made recently by Harris and Watts[66] and by Plaut[65] who was the first to start this type of indirect study (using the best method available: injecting a labeled nucleus into non-labeled cytoplasm).

As a result of these objections, Werz tried to tackle the problem by direct observation, but it must be said that this method too has so far failed to give final evidence.

As to *Acetabularia* it is safe to state that the living nucleus extrudes RNA under suboptimal conditions, e.g., after isolation in artificial media such as sucrose. Actually the nucleus extrudes bubbles. These contain RNA as shown by their ultraviolet absorption maximum and other cytochemical characteristics. Such nuclei implanted in anucleate parts induce normal morphogenesis. Nevertheless, it cannot be excluded that isolated nuclei undergo reversible changes during the isolation period. The indirect observations made in situ on fixed and stained cells under different experimental conditions are consistent with the view that the RNA extrusion by isolated nuclei is a normal physiological process. But under normal conditions, that is, by observation of the living untreated cell, RNA transfer could not be demonstrated. This might well be due to conditions of light refraction within the cell but, whatever the reason, a final positive conclusion seems impossible.[60]

Lastly, another type of direct examination will be discussed. By using an ultraviolet-television-microscope, Werz observed directly a transfer of nuclear RNA into the cytoplasm in epidermis cells of *Allium cepa* bulb and in ovary cells of *Gasteria*. The cells were living and examined in thin preparations. The nuclei extrude substances, the absorption maximum of which corresponds to nucleic acids, into the cytoplasm. These substances were determined as RNA applying the usual cytochemical methods. Nevertheless, these cases again give no final roof that the RNA transfer is a normal physiological process. It could be provoked by the ultraviolet irradiation or other damaging factors. In normal light no transfer was observed, as in *Acetabularia*. There is, however, another finding, which strongly supports the assumption that we are dealing with a normal process: if untreated cells were fixed and stained *in toto* similar pictures were found as observed on the ultraviolet irradiated cells.[69] A direct observation under normal conditions can be expected only on the premise that the RNA is released in the form of particles; in *Gasteria* it takes place as a process of diffusion as shown in the ultraviolet light; in Acetabularia it is in the form of particles, but only under suboptimal conditions.

To summarize all these findings, we can state that the labeling experiments are consistent with the assumption of RNA transfer; that the direct and indirect observations on *Acetabularia* make a transfer seem probable; and that it is still more probable in *Gasteria* and *Allium*. But in spite of high probability there is as yet no final direct evidence. Furthermore, it is highly probable that not all cytoplasmic RNA is released from the nucleus, at least in *Acetabularia* under the conditions examined. Under the right conditions a considerable RNA synthesis takes place in the cytoplasm. This synthesis is due to substances inducing RNA synthesis which are released from the nucleus.

Both circumstances are of interest in connection with the problem of the transfer of genetic information from DNA to cytoplasmic proteins via RNA.

1. Although there can be little doubt that in the specificity transfer chain (DNA→RNA→ protein) the cytoplasmic carrier of genetic information is in fact RNA, the *physical* base of RNA transfer from the nucleus into the cytoplasm is not established as yet; the problem of the source of cytoplasmic DNA and DNA-RNA hybrids is unsolved.

2. Provided that the RNA synthesized in the cytoplasm, or part of it, obtains genetic information, not all RNA can be loaded with information within the nucleus. The introduction of a further intermediate, standing between chromosomal DNA and that RNA, would be necessary. It is unknown whether this intermediate would correspond to the substances inducing cytoplasmic RNA synthesis and still more uncertain whether these substances are a special type of RNA (but if this RNA were a carrier of genetic information it could not be messenger RNA, because it would not act directly in specific protein synthesis). The speculative parts of this and the foregoing discussion (which is summarized in Fig. 2) may show the lines to be followed in further studies.

A survey of the morphogenetic and synthetic activities of various cells other than *Acetabularia* is given elsewhere (Hammerling, 1963). This survey shows that in many cases single capacities of enucleated cells are not different from those of *Acetabularia*. If they are different this can be attributed to special circumstances. It seems that the principles of nuclear action on the cytoplasm which have been outlined are general ones.

II. Interspecific Systems

The problem of nuclear control of differentiation may be studied in *Acetabularia* in another way, namely, by making interspecific systems. As already mentioned, the nucleus can be isolated in artificial media. It can be cleaned by several washings and, in contrast to the very susceptible nuclei of amoebae and amphibia, it survives for several minutes. If such nuclei are implanted in anucleate stalk parts they often induce complete morphogenesis. If, now, a nucleus of species A is implanted in an anucleate stalk of species B, eventually an A cap is formed and in the reciprocal implant a B cap; the same holds for stalk and whorls if suitable species are used (unpublished). By this method the former conclusion is confirmed that the "morphogenetic substances" released from the nucleus are species specific (at least, part of them), that is, that they are carriers of genetic information. The former conclusion was based on the results obtained with transplants, that is, grafting of a whole rhizoid with the nucleus A on to an anucleate B part and vice versa.[18] However, in such transplants considerable amounts of living A cytoplasm are always transplanted together with the A nucleus. From the congruent results obtained with the implants it follows that the co-transplantation or co-implantation of A cytoplasm can be neglected. This conclusion is not based on the assumption that an implanted nucleus is always completely free from some adherent cytoplasmic particles but on the time factor. Even though some cytoplasmic particles may be always co-implanted and survive, they could not be multiplied in time to such an extent that they could participate from the very beginning in species specific morphogenesis appropriate to the species from which the nucleus was taken.

The described activities of anucleate parts lead likewise to the conclusion that they are due to DNA controlled cytoplasmic carriers of genetic information. In *Escherichia coli* these carriers are unstable.[105] In *Acetabularia* they are stable: morphogenesis of anucleate parts can proceed up to 4 weeks; sometimes it begins only after 1–2 months.[17] The combination of anucleate aged A pieces with B nuclei leads to the same conclusion: transitory intergrades showing not only B but also A characters can be formed (unpublished; for fresh pieces see[18]).

Plurinucleate interspecific systems have also been made, but, because of the implanta-

tion difficulties, at present only by means of transplantation. The complete sequence of two to four nucleated systems between the species *crenulata* and *mediterranea* has been examined: $cren_{2-4}$, $cren_3med_1$, $cren_2med_1$, $cren_1med_1$ and $cren_2med_2$, $cren_1med_2$, $cren_1med_3$, and med_{2-4}. (The suffixes indicate the number of nuclei.) The morphology of the caps formed by these transplants changes gradually from nearly pure *cren* type to nearly pure *med* type, corresponding to the ratio of nuclei, that is, to the ratio of both kinds of morphogenetic substances. If this is true the $cren_1med_1$ and $cren_2med_2$ transplants should form the same cap type. This is the case. The caps formed by the intraspecific transplants are pure *cren* or *med* types.[89]

It is clear that neither in uninucleate nor in plurinucleate interspecific systems of *Acetabularia* could persisting specific influences of the cytoplasm foreign to the acting nucleus or nuclei be detected. This, of course, does not exclude the possibility that they exist but are too small to be detectable. On the other hand, it seems worthwhile to point out that it may be wrong to assume that different species always *must* differ not only in a part of their nuclear genes but also in plasmagenes. Species differ, of course, in their cytoplasms but the cytoplasmic differences may be due to different nuclear genes or plasmagenes, or both.

Persisting specific cytoplasmic influences have been found, in addition to nuclear control, in the well-known transfers of nuclei made by Danielli between *Amoeba proteus* and *discoides*.[109] However, this is by no means a contradiction of the results obtained with *Acetabularia*. The different results given by the amoebae and the species of *Acetabularia* permit only one general conclusion: the conclusions to be drawn from one type of interspecific system must not be generalized. The fate of a given system will depend on the biochemistry of the nucleus or the cytoplasm or both. There is a third case which seems to resemble or even match the *Acetabularia* results reported by Moore[106] as found by Sambuichi.[107] Sambuichi transferred blastula nuclei of a variety A of *Rana nigromacula* into enucleated eggs of another one, B, and got a tadpole which showed the characters of the variety A. Finally, an interspecific system will break down if the nucleus is not compatible with the foreign cytoplasm. In such cases it would suffice that only one essential process could not proceed due to the wrong constitution of cytoplasm and nucleus. Cases of breakdown have been found in the transfer experiments made by Fischberg and colleagues[108] and Moore[106] between distantly related species of amphibia. Interspecific systems between two *Stentor* species also die off, according to Tartar's experiments.[80]

It is of special interest that those *Acetabularia* systems which form intergrade caps belong to both the compatible and incompatible systems according to their cytological state. The non-dividing primary nucleus is fairly well compatible with foreign cytoplasm. But the situation changes completely if the dividing secondary nuclei come into play.[89] These are formed from the primary nucleus after the cap has reached its maximum size. They divide by many mitotic divisions while still in the rhizoid and are transported into the cap by protoplasmic streaming. There the cysts are formed which later produce the gametes.[12] Apparently, division and transport of the secondary nuclei proceed normally in interspecific systems which form an *intergrade cap*. But in most cases cyst formation is highly disturbed in such caps and progeny was never produced except in one case with a few germinating zygotes. Now, formation of an intergrade means not so much that the system contains both kinds of cytoplasm as that it contains—we will restrict ourselves here to plurinucleate systems—both kinds of nuclei. Therefore, we have to conclude that the cytoplasm A 'kills' the B secondary nuclei and vice versa. To understand these effects we have to consider the fact that the secondary nuclei are both morphologically and physiologically different from the primary nucleus.[11] Possibly the reason for this incompatibility is still simpler: for reasons which cannot be discussed here, it can be regarded as a possibility that the *persisting* presence of cytoplasm foreign to the nuclei leads to the initiation of chromosomal breakages already within the primary

nucleus (but not disturbing its function) and consequently to the formation of secondary nuclei with unbalanced chromosome sets.

It must be pointed out, however, that a uninucleate system A_1B_0 which forms a *pure* A cap corresponding to the acting nucleus A, forms normal cysts and normally copulating gametes which give rise to a normal A progeny. The same holds for the reciprocal B_1A_0 systems.[18] We have to conclude that such systems no longer contain foreign cytoplasm disturbing the processes necessary for the attainment of a complete life cycle.

In conclusion two other findings may be described. Werz[99, 100] detected by cytochemical means network or clot-like structures at the tip of the stalk. These are clearly different between the species and are dependent on the nucleus. In binucleate transplants between *A. mediterranea* and *crenulata* an intermediate structure is formed, whereas in both kinds of uninucleate transplants with a *med* or a *cren* nucleus, structures usually appear which correspond to the acting nucleus.

The structures contain acid polysaccharides which are probably sulphated. The same holds for the membrane. As yet it is not known whether the polysaccharides differ chemically in different species. But it might be that they are involved in membrane formation. Besides general considerations there are special facts which support this assumption. It may be pointed out here that it is the *mode* of membrane formation which causes the eventual morphological differences between stalk whorls and caps within and between the species. This requires the formation of different enzyme systems (cf. Fig. 2).

Individual proteins have also been examined. By means of starch gel electrophoresis it was found by Clauss[103 and unpublished] that acid phosphatase and some non-specific esterases differ in certain species. In various binucleate interspecific transplants both kinds of enzymes appear, whereas in the uninucleate transplants, after a transition period, are found only the enzymes corresponding to the acting nucleus. Thus, the differences between these enzymes are apparently controlled by species specific nuclear actions as are also the morphogenetic substances and the structures described. (There is, however, still one puzzling case. This concerns the behavior of acid phosphatase in the *mediterranea–acicularia* systems.[103, 104] This is in need of further study.)

REFERENCE

Haemmerling J. (1963). *Annu. Rev. Plant Physiol.* **14**, 65.

5

Chromosome Differentiation

THE CHROMOSOME is a complex structure whose organization is poorly understood. It consists of strands or loops of DNA in association with protein and RNA. It has at least two regions of specialization, the kineticore or point of spindle attachment, and a site at which nucleolar RNA is synthesized. The amount of RNA associated with DNA varies and probably depends upon the activities of the cell at the time the chromosome is examined (Swift 1962). Little is known about the distribution of protein along the DNA chain. A physicochemical description of the DNA protein complex has been given by Zubay and Doty (1959). A number of questions might be asked about the character and function of the proteins associated with DNA in the chromosomes.

Does each functional gene or cystron have a unique protein or a unique combination of proteins associated with it? Is the heterochromatic region of the chromosome, which is classically the heavily staining condensed region, functionally inactive because of the presence of a protein cover, and is the euchromatic region which stains lightly the portion which is actively transcribing? Much recent attention has been directed to the histone proteins which are associated with DNA (Huang and Bonner 1962; Izawa, Alfrey, and Mirsky 1963; Bonner and Ts'o 1964) but there is no evidence yet that they are gene repressors, in fact they seem to lack DNA regional specificity (Johns and Butler 1964). Equally likely candidates are the residual proteins or the neutral salt soluble proteins also found in the nucleus (Mirsky and Osawa 1961).

The chromosomes of one organism generally differ from one another in length and location of the centromere; in many forms sex chromosomes have been distinguished morphologically from autosomes. Giant chromosomes have a distinctive pattern of banding over their entire length.

Beermann (1963) * discovered that puffs and rings of the chromosomes of Chironomus occur at specific loci in each tissue. He interprets puffing as evidence of differential gene activation. He and his co-workers have also shown that unique sequences of puffing occur during development of one tissue. In the last period of larval life when the imaginal discs begin to develop under the stimulus of the hormones of pupation, changes are observed in giant chromosomes of the salivary glands. New puffs make their appearance and those which have been present during the life of the larva disappear. The hormone responsible for changes in the pattern of puffing is ecdysone (Clever and Karlson 1960). Whether it acts directly at the level of the chromosome or whether indirectly through an undefined metabolic sequence is not known.

* Italicized references indicate articles which appear in this book.

Both the puff and the ring are thought to be uncoiled segments of the chromosome. Coiling or uncoiling of specific loci might constitute in part a mechanism for regulation of transcription. Chromosomal segments which are uncoiled would then be the only ones which are genetically active. Both the puffs of the dipteran chromosome and the loops of the amphibian chromosome notably reflect regions where DNA is being transcribed.

It has been suggested that the Balbiani ring (a giant puff that differs from the normal puff only in size) may arise through local reduplication of an already polytene chromosome.

Although the giant chromosome of the dipteran is polytene that of the amphibian oocyte has only a small number of DNA strands. In cells of higher organisms, generally, it is possible that the DNA is no more than double stranded (Taylor 1963) although a multistranded condition has also been pointed out (Ris 1957).

Practically the entire genome of the amphibian oocyte may be functioning during oogenesis. Most loops appear uniformly labeled 12–18 hours after administration of H^3 uridine (Gall and Callan 1962). This means that as many as 10^5 to 10^6 different messages might be made during oogenesis since there are about 10^4 loops each having an average of 10^2 cistrons. Possibly at no other time during the life of the organism is so large a number of cistrons functioning simultaneously. The major steps of early development might be executed through the use of many templates which are synthesized during oogenesis, used during different stages of development and never made again. At the end of oogenesis the synthetic machinery for both RNA and protein is shut down; the chromosome becomes quiescent and awaits activation by the sperm. Both transcription and translation must be controlled at various stages since (1) genes must be activated during oogenesis, (2) m-RNA must be protected for later use after it is made, and (3) genes must be repressed until after fertilization. To what extent the structural organization of the chromosome might assist in controlling gene expression is yet unknown.

REFERENCES

1. Bonner, J., and P. Ts'o (1964). *The Nucleohistones*, Holden-Day, Incorporated, San Francisco.
2. Clever, U., and P. Karlson (1960). Induktion von Puff-Veranderungen in den Speicheldrusenchromosomen von *Chironomus tentans* durch Ecdyson. *Exptl. Cell Res.* **20**:623–626.
3. Clever, U. (1964). Actinomycin and puromycin: effects on sequential gene activation by Ecdysone. *Science* **146**:794–795.
4. Gall, J. G., and H. G. Callan (1962). H^3 uridine incorporation in lampbrush chromosomes. *Proc. Natl. Acad. Sci.* **48**:562–570.
5. Huang, R. C., and J. Bonner (1962). Histone, a suppressor of chromosomal RNA synthesis. *Proc. Natl. Acad. Sci.* **48**:1216–1230.
6. Izawa, M., V. G. Allfrey, and A. E. Mirsky (1963). Composition of the nucleus and chromosomes in the lampbrush stage of the newt oocyte. *Proc. Natl. Acad. Sci.* **50**:811–817.
7. Johns, E. W., and J. A. V. Butler (1964). Specificity of the interactions between histones and deoxyribonucleic acid. *Nature* **204**:853–855.
8. Mirsky, A., and S. Osawa (1961). The interphase nucleus. In J. Brachet and A. Mirsky (eds.), *The Cell*, Vol. II, Academic Press, New York, pp. 677–770.
9. Ris, H. (1957). Chromosome structure. In W. McElroy and B. Glass (eds.), *The Chemical Basis of Heredity*, Johns Hopkins Press, Baltimore, pp. 23–69.
10. Swift, H. (1962). Nucleic acids and cell morphology in dipteran salivary glands. In J. M. Allen (ed.), *The Molecular Control of Cellular Activity*, McGraw-Hill, New York, pp. 73–125.
11. Taylor, J. H. (1963). Control mechanisms for chromosome reproduction in the cell cycle. In R. J. C. Harris (ed.), *Cell Growth and Cell Division*, Vol. 2, Academic Press, New York, pp. 161–177.
12. Zubay, G., and P. Doty (1959). The isolation and properties of deoxyribonucleoprotein particles containing single nucleic acid molecules. *J. Mol. Biol.* **1**:1–20.

Cytological Aspects of Information Transfer in Cellular Differentiation

WOLFGANG BEERMANN

The embryonic development of higher, multicellular organisms, especially animals, offers some of the most striking examples of cellular specialization. The diverse forms and functions of cells, all of which by virtue of their common descent from the zygote must contain identical sets of genes, demonstrate that, at least in the higher organisms, very effective control mechanisms exist which must be capable of activating some of the genetic potencies of the cell and of suppressing others. More specifically, since the structural as well as the functional character of a cell will ultimately depend on its protein composition, differentiation may be described as a controlled process whereby cells of identical genetic constitution develop different protein patterns. This view has some obvious implications from the point of view of biochemical genetics. Since we know that the structural information for the synthesis of proteins is laid down in a coded form in the nucleotide sequences of the informational DNA units of the genome (the classical "genes") we are led to postulate the existence of a mechanism which reads the genetic information differentially in different types of cells. In looking for mechanisms which, on the basis of a given genotype, would bring about the development of different protein patterns, several possibilities may be envisaged. The transfer of information from the DNA of the gene to the protein involves two main steps: first, the transcription of the nucleotide sequences of the DNA into nucleotide sequences of RNA molecules (synthesis of "messengers") and, secondly, the transcription of the nucleotide sequences of the RNA messengers into the amino acid sequences of the protein. The first of these processes, messenger synthesis, would have to take place at the site of the genes themselves.

American Zoologist, 3:23–32 (1963). Reprinted with permission.

The second could take place anywhere in the cell, most probably at the site of the ribosomes in the cytoplasm. With respect to the regulation and control of these processes, we are therefore left with several possibilities. One could take the extreme stand of those embryologists who, in the past, tended to ignore entirely the nucleus and the Mendelian factors in assuming that there is no differentiation at the level of the chromosomes, or, in modern terms, that all genes are producing messenger molecules at the same rate all the time. Under these circumstances a change in the pattern of protein synthesis can only be produced by a specific inhibition or activation of specific messengers, or by a differential self-reproduction of some species of messenger molecules. Both types of control would meet with certain *a priori* limitations from the theoretical standpoint, that is they could only be effective to a limited extent. The drastic changes accompanying the actual differentiation of cells seem to require a direct involvement of the genes in the control mechanism such that the initial production of the messengers can be regulated. The well known results of Jacob and Monod (1961) show that this type of gene regulation is actually realized in bacteria. In the course of our own work on dipteran giant chromosomes we have collected data of a quite different nature which, however, lend further support to the hypothesis of differential gene control as outlined above.

VISIBLE DIFFERENTIATION OF GIANT POLYTENE CHROMOSOMES IN INTERPHASE

Giant interphase chromosomes occur in the highly differentiated giant cells of dipteran larval and imaginal tissues. They attain a length of at least 10 times, and a cross section of up to 10,000 times that of normal univalent interphase chromosomes. According to the generally accepted views of Koltzoff (1934), Bauer (1935), and Bridges (1935), these chromosomes are to be considered as being "polytene," i.e., multivalent in a cable-like fashion, as a result of progressive replication of the chromatids without mitotic splitting. The most conspicuous feature of the polytene chromosomes is their banding pattern which, according to the concept of polyteny, reflects the ultimate chromomeric organization of the mitotic chromosomes of the individual. In other words, it is commonly taken for granted that the "phenotype" of the giant chromosomes—in most instances salivary gland chromosomes—is directly representative of the underlying genetic organization of the constituent strands and is not subject to phenotypic variation. However, if one actually studies the banding pattern of homologous chromosomes in different tissues of the same individual it is quite obvious that the statement of constancy needs further specification. Although it is not true that the pattern varies in the sense of actual variations in the number, the distance, and the arrangement of the bands relative to each other, specific differences can be observed with respect to the fine structure of individual bands in different tissues. The same band may appear as a sharply defined disc of considerable density and DNA

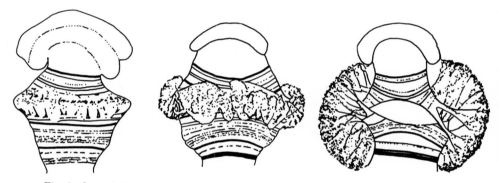

Fig. 1. One of the three large puffs ("Balbiani's rings") of the 4th chromosome characteristic for all salivary gland nuclei of *Chironomus tentans* and *Chironomus pallidivittatus*. Three different stages of puffing are shown. Magnification approximately 1000.

concentration or it may have the appearance of a "puff." Sometimes the puffing may be rather inconspicuous, with the locus in question still forming a band-like coherent structure of only slightly changed texture and dimensions. In other cases a single band may be blown up into a huge ball-like, diffusely staining structure, called a Balbiani-ring (Fig. 1). From our investigations on *Chironomus,* where polytene chromosomes in four different tissues may be studied on a comparative basis, one elementary fact emerged quite early (cf., Beermann 1956, 1959). The variations in the puffing behavior of the bands are not random but strictly correlated to cellular differentiation. Different tissues are characterized by different puffing patterns in their chromosomes, and developmental changes are always paralleled by characteristic changes in the puffing pattern as well. The statement is therefore justified that cellular differentiation regularly involves chromosomal differentiation, at least on the morphological level. Before we go on from here to discuss the possible physiological meaning of the observed chromosomal differentiation, the process of puffing as such needs to be defined in terms of chromosome fine structure and chemistry. The unchanged chromomere, i.e., the ultimate unit composing each band, may be considered as a tightly folded-up portion of the constituent DNA-histone fiber of the chromatid. Puffing in terms of the single chromomere would mean the unfolding, or uncoiling, of the DNA-histone fiber into a long, loop-like thread. This has actually been observed to be so in the case of Balbiani's rings, both by light and by electron microscopy (Beermann and Bahr, 1954). The cytochemistry of puffing strengthens the structural interpretation. The intensity of the Feulgen reaction diminishes as the puffing of a band increases. The diffuse, peripheral regions of large puffs no longer show any visible Feulgen reaction. This would be expected on the basis of a progressive unfolding of the DNA which is equivalent to a structural dilution. On the other hand, cytochemistry shows the presence in large amounts of non-histone proteins in the puffs. The role of these proteins in the formation of puffs, i.e., in the unfolding of the chromomeric DNA fiber, may be a decisive one but has not yet been elucidated. All puffs contain RNA, but it is doubtful whether RNA plays any structural role at all. As will be seen presently, the RNA of the puffs seems to be exclusively concerned with genic activity.

On cytochemical as well as structural criteria, about 10% of all the bands appear to be in a more or less puffed condition in each tissue but, as has been already pointed out, as a rule these are not the same bands, the puffing pattern being specifically different from tissue to tissue and from stage to stage. Even the size attained by any one puff is usually quite characteristic for the cell type studied, the most outstanding example being Balbiani's rings which are characteristic for the polytene chromosomes of the salivary glands in all Chironomids. It has actually been demonstrated that puffing is a completely reversible phenomenon and does not involve any permanent change in the structure of the chromosome. Mention should be made, however, of an exceptional situation found in some puffs of polytene chromosomes of *Sciarid* flies. Here, in a few loci, puffing is always accompanied by the accumulation of large amounts of DNA (Rudkin and Corlette, 1957). If, as it seems, extra replications of the constituent chromomeres are involved, this may indeed lead to an irreversible structural and functional change of the locus.

PUFFING PATTERNS AS PATTERNS OF GENIC ACTIVITY, IN TERMS OF RNA SYNTHESIS

A priori, there is little doubt that the chromosomal differentiation observed in polytene chromosomes is primarily a functional phenomenon. A fruitful working hypothesis may be based on the assumption that puffing is an expression of, or the actual mechanism which causes enhanced genic activity whatever this may mean in precise biochemical terms. For, if we consider the puffs to be activated gene loci, then the observed differentiation with respect to puffing patterns would be equivalent to differentiation with respect to patterns of genic activity—in other words, it is exactly what one would expect if differential gene activation occurred in embryonic development. This interpretation implies that those loci which are puffed in any one tissue, or stage of development, contain genetic information which is of special importance to the cells under consideration. One should expect, for instance, that the bands forming the giant puffs of the Balbiani ring type in the salivary glands contain genes which specifically control the structure or the function of the salivary glands, the more so since the same bands are not found in a puffed condition in other tissues of the *Chironomus* larva. Before we furnish direct genetic proof for this hypothesis, let us see what general physiological arguments we can adduce in favor of an interpretation of puffing in terms of genic activity.

On account of their large size, the polytene chromosomes lend themselves to autoradiographic studies. If radioactive (tritium-labeled) precursors of the nucleic acids or of the proteins are injected into *Chironomus* larvae, and if after a short incubation period the salivary glands are dissected, fixed, and squashed, then covered with autoradiographic stripping film, the following results are obtained. Tritiated thymidine is exclusively incorporated into the DNA during the endomitotic replication of the chromosomes. On the average only 2 out of 50 cells are found in the replication phase, the chromosomes of all other cells remaining unlabeled. The pattern of labeling in the case of thymidine exactly reflects the pattern of banding as demonstrated by the Feulgen reaction. The results are radically different if tritiated uridine, a precursor of RNA, is injected. Fifteen minutes after injection, appreciable amounts of labeled RNA are found in all nuclei of the salivary glands, whereas little or none is found in the cytoplasm. Within the nucleus the labeled RNA shows a highly characteristic distribution: it is almost exclusively located in the puffed regions of the chromosomes and in the nucleolus. The radioactivity of these regions increases when longer incubation times are used, but the topography remains essentially unchanged. With longer incubation times the cytoplasmic RNA will also become labeled, indicating a transfer of labeled RNA from the nucleus, that is, from the puffed chromosome regions and from the nucleolus to the cytoplasm. Such a transfer is also indicated by the fact that the amount of label in the puffs cannot be increased indefinitely by prolongation of the incubation period. A maximal value is very soon reached (after 2 hours) while the activity of the cytoplasm still increases over the next 12 hours. The relationship is, however, not entirely clear because most of the cytoplasmic RNA label could also be derived not from the puffs but from the nucleolus. That non-nucleolar RNA from the nucleus is actually transported into the cytoplasm can only be inferred from an independent study of lethal embryos lacking the nucleolus-organizing regions (Beermann, 1960).

The incorporation studies with tritiated uridine show that puffs are active centers of chromosomal RNA synthesis. Since, in addition to RNA, large amounts of protein always occur in the puffed regions, one might expect to find a similar situation with respect to protein synthesis or turnover in the puffs. However, there is no indication of a rapid and strictly localized incorporation of tritiated amino acids into the chromosomes or the nucleolus of *Chironomus* salivary gland nuclei. In fact, the autoradiograph of a salivary gland cell one hour after injection of tritiated leucine looks almost like a negative of a uridine autoradiograph; no label in the nucleus and heavy incorporation in the cytoplasm. Although these observations by no means exclude nuclear and chromosomal protein synthesis as a possibility, they seem to rule out protein synthesis as a major function of the puffed chromosome regions. We are therefore left with the conclusion that the activity of the puffed chromosome regions consists entirely in the synthesis of RNA; in other words, the puffing pattern of the polytene chromosomes represents the pattern of RNA synthesis along the chromosomes. Are we justified in considering this type of a chromosomal activity pattern as being equivalent to a pattern of "genic activity" in the sense of a differential reading of the genetic information? In a very general sense this question can be answered in the affirmative since, as is well known from modern biochemical studies on protein synthesis, RNA molecules play a central role in the transfer of information from the DNA to the protein, as "messengers" or "templates" and, in the case of the so-called soluble RNA, as specific vehicles for the amino acids to direct them into their correct position on the templates. However, in order to prove the point directly, one would have to characterize the RNA produced in the puffs chemically and demonstrate that it actually plays one or the other decisive role in protein synthesis. A first attempt to characterize the RNA of the puffs of *Chironomus* polytene chromosomes has been made in collaboration with Dr. Edström from Gothenburg, Sweden.

The largest puffs (the Balbiani rings) of the salivary gland chromosomes of *Chironomus tentans* are very suitably located in the short fourth chromosome which can easily be isolated with glass needles from the nuclei of formalin-fixed glands. These chromosomes are collected, individually placed on coverslips, and left to dry. They can then be cut into three pieces, each containing one of the three giant Balbiani-ring puffs. The RNA from a

TABLE 1. Base composition of the RNA extracted from different components of Chironomus salivary gland cells, as molar proportions in per cent of the sum (From Edström and Beermann, 1962)

	Adenine	Guanine	Cytosine	Uracil	A/U.	G + C%	n
Chromosome 1	29.4 ± 0.5	19.8 ± 1.0	27.7 ± 0.8	23.1 ± 0.6	1.27	47.5	4
Chromosome 4							
Proximal (BR 1)	35.7 ± 0.6	20.6 ± 1.7	23.2 ± 1.2	20.8 ± 0.8	1.72	43.8	5
Median (BR 2)	38.0 ± 0.6	20.5 ± 0.6	24.5 ± 0.6	17.1 ± 0.6	2.22	45.0	6
Distal (BR 3)	31.2 ± 2.2	22.0 ± 2.0	26.4 ± 1.9	20.2 ± 1.4	1.54	48.4	3
Nucleolus	30.6 ± 0.8	20.1 ± 0.5	22.1 ± 0.6	27.1 ± 0.6	1.13	42.2	13
Cytoplasm	29.4 ± 0.4	22.9 ± 0.3	22.1 ± 0.4	25.7 ± 0.3	1.14	45.0	7
A/G ratio for DNA							
Chromosome 1	37.8	12.2				24.4	
Chromosome 4	35.9	14.1				28.2	

number of homologous pieces, i.e., RNA which practically represents the specific RNA of one single puff, is extracted by repeated RNAase digestion and then subjected to a microanalytic procedure involving hydrolysis in micropipettes, electrophoresis on a rayon fiber of 25 μ diameter, and UV microphotometry of the fractions separated on the fiber (cf. Edström, 1960). The sensitivity of the method is about 10^{10} g RNA per analysis. This quantity roughly corresponds to 50 Balbiani rings, or 5 nucleoli, or half the cytoplasm of one salivary gland cell in *Chironomus*. The method leads to a characterization of the cellular RNA fractions in terms of their base ratios (adenine + uracil + cytosine + guanine = 100%). The results are shown in Table 1.

The information gained from base ratios is, of course, limited. Base ratios do not tell us anything about the size of the RNA molecules analyzed, nor do they reflect their nucleotide sequence. In our case, we cannot even decide whether we are dealing with pure RNA fractions; our fractions might be mixtures of several molecular species. Therefore, the observed similarity between the nucleolar and the cytoplasmic RNA's might be spurious although it agrees nicely with the idea that the structural ribosomal RNA in the cytoplasm is of nucleolar origin. However, if large, significant differences in the base composition are consistently found between the nucleolar and the cytoplasmic RNA's on the one hand, and the chromosomal and puff RNA's on the other, the idea of one being the precursor of the other becomes less likely. More specifically,

our data speak against the possibility that the RNA produced at the puffs is collected in the nucleolus and/or is stored in the cytoplasm in the form of ribosomal stationary RNA. It could, however, represent a short-lived messenger type of RNA, or, perhaps, soluble transfer RNA, or a mixture of both. If we consider this chromosomal RNA as a direct copy of the chromosomal DNA, the specific way in which it differs in its base composition from the other RNA fractions becomes highly significant. The DNA molecules are generally known to be double-stranded, with the base composition of one strand complementary to the other, so that the ratios thymine/adenine and cystosine/guanine both equal 1. If both strands of the DNA molecules in the puffs were copied by the RNA at the same rate, then, obviously, one should obtain a mixture of two types of single-stranded RNA molecules complementary to each other, with an over-all base composition where uracil/adenine and cytosine/guanine again both equal 1. But this type of symmetry is approached only in the nucleolar and the cytoplasmic RNA fractions. The chromosomal RNA fractions are extremely asymmetric, with A/U more than 2 in the case of the Balbiani rings, and with large deviations from 1 also in the ratio G/C, especially in chromosome 1. It should be pointed out that RNA fractions of such an extreme asymmetry have never been detected before. If, as is very likely, we are dealing with copies of the chromosomal DNA we are faced with the following possibilities: (1) The DNA in the puffs may be effectively single-stranded so that only one type of RNA molecule is produced; this single-strandedness could have either a structural or a functional (enzymatic) basis. (2) The two complementary types of RNA copies are both actually formed, but one of the two is immediately removed from the site of synthesis, either by enzymatic destruction or by rapid transport mechanisms. In any case it would appear that either the production or the selection of only one, and a specific one, of the two possible RNA copies of the genic DNA is a necessary prerequisite for an unambiguous information transfer mechanism. Our data, then, support the hypothesis that the RNA of the puffs is either the messenger itself or its complementary counterpart, the "anti-messenger." This conclusion, in turn, once more strengthens our original view that the puffing pattern of the polytene chromosomes is an expression of differential gene activation.

Genetic Characterization of a Specific Puffed Region in Salivary Gland Chromosomes

In *Chironomus* the salivary glands continuously produce a mucopolysaccharide secretion which hardens under water and enables the larvae to build from mud particles the tubes in which they live and feed. The protein moiety of the secretion rapidly incorporates radioactive amino acids. The rate of synthesis of the secretion protein must be high as compared to the rates of synthesis of any other cellular proteins. If there is any quantitative relationship between the rate of messenger production and the rate of protein synthesis at all, one should expect the locus, or loci, containing the information for the synthesis of secretion protein to be especially, and exclusively, active in the salivary glands. As judged by their giant size and their synthetic activity with respect to RNA, the Balbiani rings of the salivary gland chromosomes seem to represent such loci. The bands forming Balbiani rings are always few in number (2–5), and those forming Balbiani rings in the salivary glands

never seem to form a puff in any other tissue. Moreover, whenever one lobe of the gland differs from the others in the composition of the secretion which it produces—as is the rule in Chironomid salivary glands—this differentiation on the level of cellular function is invariably accompanied by a differentiation on the chromosomal level, with respect to the pattern of bands forming Balbiani rings. This differentiation is often mutually exclusive so that different bands are transformed into Balbiani rings in different regions of the gland. In other instances the cells of the gland may all share two or three Balbiani rings, but specialized regions of the gland may have chromosomes with additional Balbiani rings of their own. If the general views outlined above are correct, a lobe-specific Balbiani ring would furnish the genetic information necessary for the production of a lobe-specific component of the secretion. Any change, genetic or other, which would prevent a lobe-specific Balbiani ring from being developed should, on our hypothesis, lead to the loss of a lobe-specific secretion component. We have been able to verify this correlation by cytogenetic methods (Beermann, 1961).

In *Chironomus pallidivittatus* and in many other *Chironomus* species a small specialized sector of the larval salivary gland, usually consisting of four cells, produces a secretion which, in contrast to the clear secretion of the major part of the gland, is granular in character. However, in *Chironomus tentans*, the closest relative of *C. pallidivittatus*, the granular component is not present in the secretion of the special cells. This difference between the two species does not seem to be due to a loss of structural differentiation in the salivary glands of *C. tentans*, since the special cells in the latter maintain the same fine structural details which characterize them in *C. pallidivittatus*, e.g., a cytoplasmic secretion zone of the brush border type which is not found in the normal gland cells of both species. The difference between the two species, then, must be due to the loss of a specific synthetic function from the special cells of *C. tentans*. The chromosomal situation is exactly what one would expect: In both species there are three Balbiani rings which are shared by all the cells of the glands, all in the small 4th chromosome, as mentioned earlier. In *C. pallidivittatus,* where the special cells regularly produce secretion granules, the small 4th chromosome always shows an additional Balbiani ring close to its centromeric end (Fig. 2). In *C. tentans,* on the other hand, there is no lobe-specific Balbiani ring so that, concomitant with the loss of the major, and distinctive, function of the special cells the only major distinguishing character on the chromosomal level is also lost. We may formulate the hypothesis, therefore, that the genetic information necessary for the production of the secretion granules is entirely or partially located in the band which forms the lobe-specific Balbiani ring in *C. pallidivittatus,* and that the transfer of this information to the cellular synthetic sites depends on the actual formation of the Balbiani ring in question. These postulates can be put to test by classical gene localization techniques. *C. tentans* and *C. pallidivittatus* produce fertile hybrids, and their chromosomes are marked by a number of species specific rearrangements, mainly in-

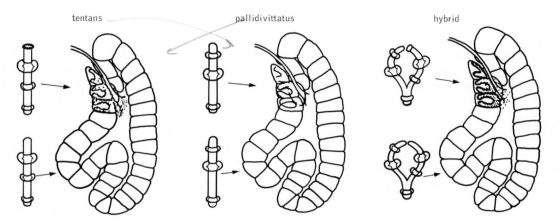

Fig. 2. The pattern of Balbiani rings in the two functionally different portions of the salivary gland in *Chironomus tentans, pallidivittatus,* and their hybrid. See text for further details.

versions, which prevent crossing-over in most chromosome regions. It was found that the "mutant character" in question, namely, the inability to produce secretion granules, is recessive, and that it is inherited as a simple Mendelian factor whose pattern of inheritance closely follows the inheritance of the 4th chromosome of *C. tentans.* Its location within the 4th chromosome was determined by crossing-over tests and found to coincide with the location of the lobe-specific Balbiani ring. In heterozygotes, the two allelic segments behave visibly differently so that the allelic segments originally furnished by *C. pallidivittatus* form the Balbiani ring whereas the homologous segment furnished by *C. tentans* fails to do so in the same nucleus. This per-

mits a parallel scoring of crossovers both on the chromosomal level and on the level of the phenotype, always with identical results. Moreover, some exceptional cases have been observed in these hybridization experiments where the formation of the lobe-specific Balbiani ring was suppressed by modifying genetic factors. In all these instances a parallel decrease was observed in the amount of secretion granules in the special lobe of the salivary glands.

Apart from demonstrating that our interpretation of the puffing phenomenon is basically correct, these results also illustrate another general point, namely, the possibility of purely "operational" mutations as opposed to informational ones. No visible deficiency is present at the locus of the mutant which distinguishes *C. tentans* from *C. pallidivittatus*. Thus, it is conceivable that the mutation did not involve the informational content of the locus at all but only its operational properties. These might be determined by a special segment immediately adjacent to the informational one, just as the operation of bacterial genes is controlled via a special "operator" site (Jacob and Monod, 1961). At any rate, since we know now that puffing is an operational phenomenon, we are in a position to use this phenomenon to define operational units or "operons" in polytene chromosomes. The question may then be raised whether or not the units thus defined always coincide with the units defined by other means, morphological as well as genetic ones. We will probably have to revise the statement that a puff as a rule represents only a single band which in turn could be considered as an informational unit. A combined study of position effects and puffing may throw further light on this problem.

The Induction and Control of Puffing

The existence of different activity patterns of the genes in different types of cells and in different stages of development must be due to the action of specific triggering and controlling factors in development. Unfortunately, the mechanism of puff formation as such is at present a complete mystery. When a puff is formed, the most conspicuous change from a chemical standpoint is the incorporation of large amounts of nonbasic proteins, presumably in an organized fashion. The same protein must be incorporated also whenever chromosomal replication occurs in a place where a puff is already present. With radioactive precursors, however, we have not been able to find evidence for a substantial net synthesis of protein, nor for that matter, for any kind of turnover during puff formation or puff growth. Probably the proteins are made elsewhere in the cells and become subsequently attached to the site of puff formation. The properties of this protein are not known in

detail, nor do we know whether the protein is the same in all puffs. An attractive hypothesis would be that the protein represents RNA polymerase. As regards RNA, we have seen earlier that the bulk of the RNA in the puffs seems to be involved in information transfer but we can by no means exclude the presence in puffs of small amounts of RNA with an "inductive" function.

In the present state of ignorance about the puffing mechanism, the search for inducing or controlling agents is largely determined by the view that agents known to be effective as inducers in animal development might act via the activation of genes. This idea is generally supported by the fact that unspecific physical and chemical factors which are able to bring about specific changes in development, such as temperature or ionic strength of the medium, can also evoke specific responses in the puffing pattern of the chromosomes (Becker, 1959; Ritossa, 1962; personal communication). A much better clue to the understanding of the puffing mechanism should, of course, be derivable from the use of biological agents such as the hormones, which are known to be extremely specific both in their action and their chemical structure. In insects the molting process is initiated and can be experimentally induced by the molting hormone, "ecdysone," a product of the prothoracic glands. This hormone has been highly purified, but not yet chemically identified by Karlson (1956); there are indications that it is a cholesterol derivative. Clever (1961) in our laboratory has found that the injection of minimal doses of this hormone into *Chironomus* larvae leads within 30 minutes to the formation of a puff at a specific site in chromosome 1, and 30 minutes later to the formation of another puff in chromosome 4. The hormone, as judged by the puffing reaction, is active in concentrations as low as 10^{-7} μg/mg larval weight in the case of the first puff, and 10^{-6} μg/mg in the case of the second puff. These values are equivalent to a few hundred molecules per single chromatid in each nucleus. After molting has been induced, the first puff stays on until after the molting process is completed—as it should, since ecdysone is constantly present in the hemo-lymph during the molting period, owing to an induction of hormone production in the animals themselves. The second puff, however, invariably regresses after 2 days, a process which must be due to the action of a specific "repressor." The formation of the two primary puffs is followed, in normal development as well as in the experiments, by a chain of secondary puffing reactions, the amplitude of which does not, however, depend on the hormone concentration as it does in the case of the primary puffs. These data indicate that the hormone acts as a direct inducer of activity in two loci, an activity which in its turn triggers off the whole chain of secondary events which may include the production of several new enzymes. That the primary puffs probably only act as recipients for the developmental signal is further indicated by the fact that they are formed not only in the salivary glands but also in the Malpighian tubules and probably in all tissues. Jacob and Monod (1961) think that inducers, or repressors, of gene activity exert their function as co-factors by forming a molecular complex with an internal "apo-repressor," thereby changing its stereochemical affinity to the "operator" in the operon involved. It is possible that the hormone in our case is just such an "effector."

The fact that, in the case of the ecdysone, a hormone has been found to act as a specific inducer of puffing at a specific site of the chromosomes does not, of course, justify generalization in one way or the other. Neither must all hormones of necessity act as gene inducers, nor can the majority of substances that act in gene regulation be considered as hormones. On the contrary, the very fact that cellular differentiation can take place in a multicellular organism shows that most of the specific inducers or repressors of gene activities must remain limited in their effects to the cell in which they are produced. It is the search for these substances that may, in the future, prove to be the most illuminating approach to the problem of cellular differentiation.

REFERENCES

Bauer, H. 1935. Der Aufbau der Chromosomen aus den Speicheldrüsen von *Chironomus Thummi* Kiefer (Untersuchungen an den Riesenchromosomen der Dipteren I). *Z. Zellforsch.* 23:280–313.

Becker, H. J. 1959. Die Puffs der Speicheldrüsenchromosomen von *Drosophila melanogaster*. 1. Mitteilung. Beobachtungen zum Verhalten des Puffmusters im Normalstamm und bei zwei Mutanten, *giant* und *giant-lethal-larvae*. *Chromosoma* (Berlin) 10:654–678.

Beermann, W. 1956. Nuclear differentiation and functional morphology of chromosomes. *Cold Spr. Harb. Symp. Quant. Biol.* 21:217–232.

———. 1959. Chromosomal differentiation in insects. p. 83–103. In D. Rudnick (ed.), *Developmental Cytology*. Ronald, New York.

———. 1960. Der Nukleolus als lebenswichtiger Bestandteil des Zellkerns. *Chromosoma* (Berlin) 11:263–296.

———. 1961. Ein Balbiani-Ring als Locus einer Speicheldrüsen-Mutation. *Chromosoma* (Berlin) 12:1–25.

Beermann, W., and G. F. Bahr. 1954. The submicroscopic structure of the Balbiani-ring. *Exptl. Cell Res.*, 6:195–201.

Bridges, C. B. 1935. The structure of salivary chromosomes and the relation of the banding to the genes. *Am. Naturalist* 69:59.

Clever, U. 1961. Genaktivitäten in den Riesenchromosomen von *Chironomus tentans* und ihre Bezichungen zur Entwicklung. I. Genaktivierungen durch Ecdyson. *Chromosoma* (Berlin) 12:607–675.

Edström, J. E. 1960. Extraction, hydrolysis, and electrophoretic analysis of ribonucleic acid from microscopic tissue units (microphoresis). *J. Biophys. Biochem. Cytol.* 8:39–46.

Edström, J. E., and W. Beermann. 1962. The base composition of nucleic acids in chromosomes, puffs, nucleoli, and cytoplasm of *Chironomus* salivary gland cells. *J. Cell Biol.* 14:371–379.

Jacob, F., and J. Monod. 1961. Genetic regulatory mechanisms in the synthesis of proteins. *J. Mol. Biol.* 3:318–356.

Karlson, J. 1956. Chemische Untersuchungen über die Metamorphose-hormone der Insekten. *Ann. Sci. nat. Zool.* 11:125–137.

Koltzoff, N. K. 1934. The structure of the chromosomes in the salivary glands of Drosophila. *Science* 80:312–313.

Rudkin, G. T., and S. L. Corlette. 1957. Disproportionate synthesis of DNA in a polytene chromosome region. *Proc. Natl. Acad. Sci.* (U.S.) 43:964–968.

Chromosomes and Cytodifferentiation

JOSEPH G. GALL*

It is now widely believed that ribonucleic acid (RNA) transmits genetic information from the deoxyribonucleic acid (DNA) of the chromosomes to the sites of protein synthesis in the cytoplasm. For technical reasons much of our knowledge on the relationships between nucleic acids and proteins is derived from studies on microorganisms, although such important information as the details of hemoglobin synthesis has come from higher animals. Again for technical reasons it is generally impossible to relate specific gene functions to visible changes in the chromosomes. In most cells RNA synthesis is at a peak during the interphase stage when the chromosomes are least amenable to study by present-day techniques. Two exceptions are known, however: the giant polytene chromosomes found in larval Diptera and the even larger lampbrush chromosomes characteristic of a variety of oocytes. This paper will review recent studies on these giant chromosomes with emphasis on the morphological and cytochemical changes associated with RNA metabolism.

I. STRUCTURAL CONSIDERATIONS

We may begin our discussion of the lampbrush and polytene chromosomes with a brief statement of their similarities and differences. More detailed information is available in several recent reviews (Gall, 1958; Beermann, 1959; Callan and Lloyd, 1960a; Callan, 1962; Swift, 1962). Both kinds of giant chromosome are considerably "unwound" relative to the condensed condition typical of a mitotic chromosome. Whether there has been

In *Cytodifferentiation and Macromolecular Synthesis* (Michael Locke, ed.), Academic Press, 119–143, 1963. Reprinted with permission.

* The original studies reported here were supported by research grants from the National Science Foundation and the National Cancer Institute, U.S. Public Health Service.

intercalary growth with consequent elongation of the basic chromosome strands is not clear. But it is certain that the lampbrush chromosomes have attained their large size without replication beyond that normal for meiotic chromosomes; that is, they consist of four chromatids in two sets of two. On the other hand, the polytene chromosomes have undergone some 10 to 15 replications without separation of strands, and therefore consist of a thousand or more units comparable to a mitotic chromatid. In neither case, however, are the strands thought to be completely unwound. The chromomeres of the lampbrush chromosomes and the bands of the polytene chromosomes presumably represent areas of more tightly coiled thread, although this supposition is difficult to establish unequivocally from electron micrographs. The tightly wound condition apparently corresponds to the inactive state, as evidenced by lack of isotope incorporation or RNA accumulation in these regions. On the other hand, the threads can unravel to produce a "puff" (in the polytene chromosomes) or a "loop" (in the lampbrush chromosomes). These regions actively incorporate RNA precursors and accumulate cytochemically demonstrable RNA. In fact, the typical loop or puff is visible only because of its ribonucleoprotein matrix; the DNA is so dispersed in these regions that a Feulgen reaction is not usually detectable. The much discussed DNA puffs, which so far have been found in a few species only, are exceptional in showing a disproportionate increase in DNA (Breuer and Pavan, 1955; Rudkin and Corlette, 1957; Stich and Naylor, 1958; Swift, 1962). Figures 1–4 show diagrammatically the postulated structure of the loops and puffs. From these diagrams one can see that puffing and loop formation are similar phenomena, the one occurring in a multistranded chromosome, the other in a two-stranded, prophase chromosome.

The nature of the strands which form the "backbone" of the puffs and loops is of considerable importance to our understanding of chromosome activity. Since the loops are structurally simpler than the puffs, the problem is obviously easier to attack in the lampbrush chromosomes. Several years ago Callan and Macgregor (1958) showed that lampbrush chromosome loops, although Feulgennegative, are extensively fragmented by deoxyribonuclease (DNAase) (Figs. 5–9). This observation is of great interest in showing that

Fig. 1. A segment of *Chironomus* salivary gland chromosome showing a moderately developed puff (Balbiani ring). From Beermann (1952a).

DNA occurs in the loops and indeed is involved in maintaining structural continuity of the loop. The observation by itself does not prove that DNA forms a continuous fiber throughout the length of the loop; however, it is significant that ribonuclease (RNAase) and several proteases do not cause fragmentation (Macgregor and Callan, 1962). It seems possible that the looped fibers which traverse the puffs in the polytene chromosomes also contain DNA, since the puff forms at the "expense" of a DNA band, and a DNA band is reconstituted when the puff regresses (Beermann, 1952a).

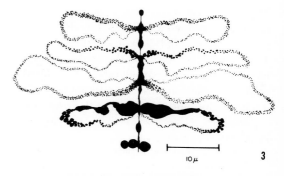

Fig. 2. Diagram of the chromosome fibrils in the region of a puff. The chromosome would actually contain several thousand fibrils instead of the eight shown here. From Beermann (1952a).

Callan and Macgregor (1958) also noticed that the delicate fiber connecting successive chromomeres in the lampbrush chromosome is attacked by DNAase. Consequently, the enzyme not only fragments the loops but also reduces the chromosome to a number of shorter segments (Figs. 5 and 6). If the inter-

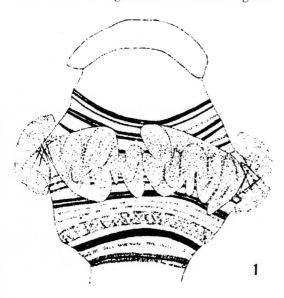

Fig. 3. A segment of lampbrush chromosome from an oocyte of the newt, *Triturus*. Pairs of lateral loops project from an axis of Feulgen-positive granules.

Fig. 4. Postulated structure of a pair of lampbrush chromosome loops. The loop consists of ribonucleoprotein matrix surrounding a very delicate DNA fibril.

pretation given in Fig. 4 is correct in its essentials, we should expect that breakage of the interchromomeric fiber would involve enzymatic attack on two chromatids, whereas breakage of a loop would involve only one chromatid.

Recently an effort has been made to clarify these points by making a kinetic analysis of the DNAase fragmentation (Gall, 1963). The lampbrush chromosomes provide excellent material for such a study since they can be isolated unfixed into the enzyme solution. As the material fragments, one can count the pieces and analyze the number of breaks as a function of time. If we assume that the chromosome consists of n longitudinal subunits which are attacked independently and with equal probability by the enzyme, then breakage should follow the equation:

$$b = k_1 t^n \qquad (1)$$

in which b is the observed number of breaks, k_1 is a proportionality constant, and t is time. The determination of n, the number of subunits, is made by plotting the data in the form:

$$\log b = n \log t + k_2 \qquad (2)$$

Here n will be the slope of the line obtained by plotting $\log b$ against $\log t$. It was found that n for the loops averaged 2.6 (23 determinations), whereas for the interchromomeric regions the value was 4.8 (19 determinations). The simplest interpretation of these data would seem to be that there are two independently attacked subunits in the loop, but four in the interchromomeric regions. The data are certainly not consistent with the assumption of 1 and 2 or 4 and 8 subunits in these regions, respectively, although we have

no experimental reason to rule out the possibility of odd numbers or non-integers.

The nature of the subunits cannot be deduced from the breakage kinetics, but only from what is known of the specificity of the enzyme. The enzyme used, DNAase 1 from beef pancreas, probably breaks the two polynucleotide chains of the DNA molecule independently, as shown by kinetic analysis of DNA degradation in solution (Schumaker *et al.*, 1956; Thomas, 1956). If the enzyme behaves in the same fashion when digesting the DNA of the chromosome, then the data suggest that the DNA of the chromatid exists as one double helix. Our information does not distinguish between one very long molecule in the loop or a series of shorter molecules connected end to end. It is possible, of course, that orientation of the DNA in the chromosomes is such as to insure preferential attacks by the enzyme, in which case the observed value of n would be smaller than the true number of polynucleotide chains.

The number of polynucleotide strands cannot be very large, however, since the loop axis —the delicate thread on which the ribonucleoprotein matrix is accumulated—is no more than 60–80 Å in diameter (Figs. 10 and 11). The double helix of the DNA molecule is about 20 Å in diameter and is presumably associated with protein in the chromosome.

It is much more difficult to make statements about the thousand or more threads of the polytene chromosomes. Heitz and Bauer (1933) long ago noticed that the interband regions of the salivary gland chromosomes are faintly Feulgen-positive. Recently Swift (1962) has made an attempt to correlate the intensity of Feulgen staining in the interband regions with the intensity expected for various degrees of DNA strandedness. He used the large chromosomes of *Sciara* and the Azure A-Feulgen technique, which gives considerably darker staining than the conventional Feulgen. On the assumption that continuous DNA fibers span the interband regions, and knowing the level of polyteny in the cells examined, he concluded that there could be only one or two DNA double helices in each of the chromosome fibers. Since we do not know that

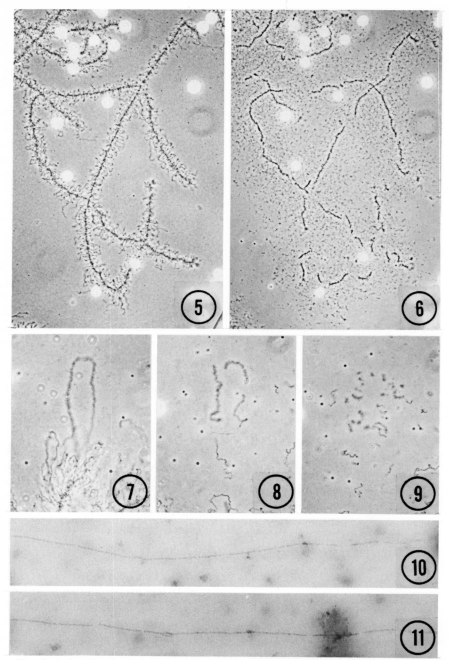

Fig. 5. A lampbrush chromosome (bivalent), unfixed, 10 minutes after being isolated in a DNAase solution (0.02 mg/ml). Phase contrast, 200 ×. Fig. 6. The same chromosome, after 30 minutes in DNAase. Note that the loops have been extensively fragmented, and that the main chromosome axis is broken in a number of places. Phase contrast, 200 ×. Figs. 7–9. Three photographs of the same loop taken 5, 13, and 16 minutes after isolation in DNAase (0.02 mg/ml). Fragmentation of the loops occurs without noticeable decrease in width of the pieces. Phase contrast, 300 ×. Figs. 10 and 11. Electron micrographs of the fibril which forms the axis of the loop and which is responsible for maintaining structural continuity of the loop. It is presumed that this fibril consists of DNA and associated protein; its diameter is about 60–80 Å. 75,000 ×. (Micrographs furnished by Dr. O. L. Miller, Oak Ridge National Laboratory.)

the DNA is continuous we must accept these results with caution. They do render unlikely any model of the chromosome which postulates large numbers of polynucleotide chains in each chromatid (cf. also the discussion in Taylor, 1963).

II. Loops, Puffs, and Genes

Extensive studies during the past decade have shown that puffing of the chromosome bands is a highly specific phenomenon, a given tissue being characterized by unique patterns of puffing during the course of its development (Beermann, 1952a,b, 1956; Breuer and Pavan, 1953, 1955; Mechelke, 1953; Becker, 1959; Kroeger, 1960). The chromosomes of *Chironomus, Sciara,* and their close relatives have been favorite objects of study because of their large size, but the same conclusions hold for *Drosophila* and probably for other genera as well.

Beermann has argued that the time- and tissue-specific puffing of certain bands should be interpreted as cytological evidence of differential gene activation. A summary statement of his views may be found in an earlier volume of the Growth Symposia (Beermann, 1959). Recently he has described a case in which the correlation between puffing and gene activity is quite clear (Beermann, 1961). In *Chironomus tentans* the salivary secretion lacks a special kind of granule which is found in *Chironomus pallidivittatus* and in all other species examined. These granules are produced by four special cells near the duct of the salivary gland (Fig. 12). Crosses between *C. tentans and C. pallidivittatus* show that the inability to produce the granules (SZ granules, named after their production in "Sonderzellen") is inherited as a simple recessive Mendelian character. The locus of the *sz* gene was shown to be in chromosome IV, either in its distal region or directly adjacent to the centromere. The localization was done by conventional cytogenetic techniques making use of inversions as markers. Immediately next to the centromere, that is, in one of the two possible locations of the gene, a conspicuous puff

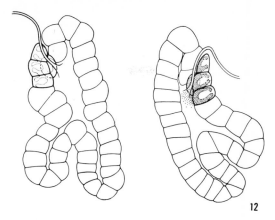

Fig. 12. The salivary glands of *Chironomus tentans* (left) and *C. pallidivittatus* (right). Note the four special cells ("Sonderzellen") in *C. pallidivittatus,* which produce a granular secretion. The production of secretion is controlled by the *sz* gene located in chromosome IV. Individuals lacking the secretion are *sz/sz,* while those producing secretion are *sz+/sz+* or *sz+/sz.* From Beermann (1961).

(Balbiani ring) is found, but only in the four special gland cells of *C. pallidivittatus* which produce the SZ granules. The puff is absent from the rest of the salivary gland cells in *C. pallidivittatus* and from all the cells of *C. tentans* (Fig. 13). In hybrid individuals

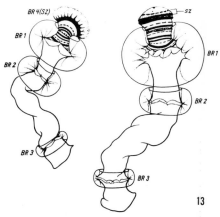

Fig. 13. Left: chromosome IV from a special cell of an individual capable of producing the secretion (*sz+/sz+*). Note the puff labeled BR 4(SZ) at the tip of the chromosome. Right: chromosome IV from the same individual (*sz+/sz+*), but from one of the normal cells which does not produce the granular secretion. The tip of the chromosome shows normal banding. From Beermann (1961).

the puff is "heterozygous"; that is, only the chromosome carrying the dominant allele, sz^+, shows a puff. These observations constitute the most compelling evidence now available that puffing is a visible manifestation of gene activity.

As Beermann has pointed out, it would be of the greatest interest to know just what biochemical steps lead to the production of the special salivary secretion and how many of these steps are controlled by the sz locus. Conceivably the sz locus is concerned with the production of only one protein, which is needed in relatively large amounts by the cells producing the secretion. On the other hand, the locus could be complex and involve a whole series of ordered reactions. Further genetic analysis will be difficult because of the lack of suitable allelic forms, but valuable information can probably be obtained from chemical studies on the salivary secretion itself.

It has not yet been possible to correlate the appearance of a particular loop pair in the lampbrush chromosomes with a known gene. Certain attributes of the loops, however, parallel those of the "classical" gene, and these may be briefly mentioned. On a chromosome of average length in *Triturus* there are of the order of 1000 loop pairs. Despite their long physical length, therefore, each corresponds to a relatively short segment of the genetic material. The loops are morphologically heterogeneous, and they have individually distinctive rates as well as patterns of precursor uptake (see Section IV). Callan and Lloyd (1956, 1960a,b) have shown that loops at a given position on the chromosome can exist in alternative forms distinguishable by specific morphological features. A given individual can be homozygous or heterozygous for a particular loop morphology and individual peculiarities of loop morphology are transmitted in a regular Mendelian fashion to the offspring. Callan and Lloyd (1960a,b) have also shown that within a natural population of newts the relative numbers of individuals homozygous or heteroxygous for particular loop forms are consistent with the Hardy-Weinberg relationship.

III. HETEROGENEITY OF NUCLEAR RNA

The idea that RNA is concerned in the transfer of the genetic code from the DNA of the chromosomes is a major tenet in nearly all recent theories of gene action (see various papers in Frisch, 1961). In general at least three types of RNA are recognized: soluble or transfer RNA, of relatively low molecular weight and specific for the different amino acids; messenger RNA, distinguished by high metabolic rate and by possessing base ratios similar to the DNA of which it is presumably a copy; and ribosomal RNA, whose role is still unclear. Ribosomal RNA makes up the bulk of the cytoplasmic RNA on a weight basis.

Considerable evidence is now at hand to indicate that much of the cell's RNA is made in the nucleus. No attempt will be made here to review the literature, which is well covered in the article of Prescott (1960). The incorporation studies, on which this evidence is largely based, suggest a heterogeneity of the nuclear RNA, but they have not permitted precise characterization of the several fractions.

If we are to relate the various nuclear RNA fractions to specific cytological areas, it is necessary either to use bulk isolation techniques for the components of the nucleus, or, conversely, so to refine the analytical techniques that studies may be made on small portions of single nuclei. The first approach has been used recently by Sibatani *et al.* (1962), who have isolated several RNA fractions from thymus nuclei, including one whose base ratios are rather similar to the base ratios of the DNA (making the usual substitution of uracil for thymine) and which they believe may represent the messenger. The second approach has been made possible by the elegant technique of microphoresis developed by Edström (1960a). Base ratio analyses are possible on samples containing as little as 100 $\mu\mu g$ of RNA. The RNA is extracted enzymatically from the sample, subjected to hydrolysis in a microdrop, and finally placed on a delicate cellulose fiber for electrophoresis. The

TABLE I. Base composition of RNA from nucleolus and cytoplasm of five animal species[a, b]

	Tegenaria (Spider) Oocyte		*Asterias* (Starfish) Oocyte		*Chironomus* (Fly) Salivary Gland		*Triturus cristatus* (Newt) Oocyte		*Triturus viridescens* (Newt) Oocyte	
	N[c]	C[c]	N	C	N	C	N	C	N	C
Adenine	25.2	25.1	23.7	23.5	30.6	29.4	18.1	20.1	21.5	23.7
Guanine	29.8	30.2	33.4	31.9	20.1	22.9	31.7	27.2	29.3	28.0
Cytosine	22.9	21.9	24.3	24.8	22.1	22.1	28.7	29.5	30.1	27.7
Uracil	22.2	22.9	18.5	19.7	27.1	25.7	21.7	23.0	19.1	20.7

[a] Mean values of molar proportions in percent of the sum.
[b] Data from Edström and co-workers (Edström, 1960a,b; Edström and Beermann, 1962; Edström and Gall, 1963; Edström *et al.*, 1961).
[c] N = nucleolus; C = cytoplasm.

separated components are photographed in ultraviolet light and their amount estimated photometrically. The sample may be a small bit of material collected with a microneedle from a fixed tissue slice or squash.

A. Nucleoli

Base ratio analyses of nucleolar RNA have been made by Edström and his co-workers on material from oocytes of a spider (Edström, 1960b), a starfish (Edström *et al.*, 1961), and two species of newt (Edström and Gall, 1963), and on the nucleoli from *Chironomus* salivary gland cells (Edström and Beermann, 1962). These RNA samples differ conspicuously from one another, as shown in Table I. An extremely interesting relationship emerges, however, when one compares the cytoplasmic RNA from the same cells, also shown in Table I. In each case the cytoplasmic RNA tends to have a composition similar to the RNA of the nucleolus. This can be seen by plotting the

molar proportion of each base in the cytoplasm against the molar proportion of the same base in the nucleolus (Fig. 14). The RNA analyzed in these cases is simply that which remains in the nucleolus or cytoplasm after fixation in Carnoy's fluid or formaldehyde. The cytoplasmic RNA represents for the most part ribosomal RNA. The original papers should be consulted for a cautious consideration of the errors inherent in the technique.

B. Chromosomes

Although nucleoli usually represent the most obvious accumulation of RNA in the nucleus, RNA is also found in the nuclear sap and the chromosomes. In the amphibian oocyte, for instance, the chromosomes and sap together contain more RNA than the nucleoli. Non-nucleolar RNA similarly makes up a large fraction in the other cells analyzed by Edström. Base ratios have been determined

TABLE II. Base composition of chromosomal RNA from oocytes of the newt *Triturus cristatus* and salivary gland cells of *Chironomus tentans*[a, b]

	Triturus[c] All Chromosomes Together	*Chironomus* Chromosome I	Chrosome IV Upper	Chrosome IV Middle	Chrosome IV Lower
Adenine	26.3	29.4	35.7	38.0	31.2
Guanine	20.7	19.8	20.6	20.5	22.0
Cytosine	24.7	27.7	23.2	24.5	25.4
Uracil	28.3	23.1	20.8	17.1	20.2

[a] Excludes nucleolar and nuclear sap RNA. Expressed as molar proportions in percent of the sum.
[b] Data from Edström and Beermann (1962) and Edström and Gall (1963).
[c] In *Triturus* the DNA composition is: A = T = 28.8; G = C = 21.2

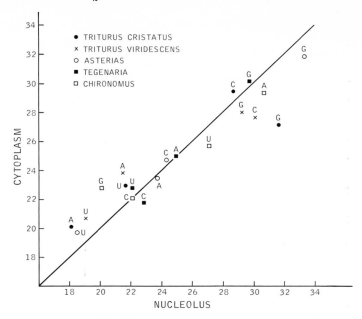

Fig. 14. Graph to illustrate the similarity in composition of cytoplasmic and nucleolar RNA in five different animal species. The scale on the axes gives the molar proportion of purine or pyrimidine in per cent of the sum; each point represents one base in one species. (A, G, C, U = adenine, guanine, cytosine, uracil). If the cytoplasmic and nucleolar RNA were identical, points would fall along the straight line. Data from Edström and co-workers (see Table I).

for pooled chromosomal RNA from oocytes of two species of newt and for individual chromosomes and parts of chromosomes of *Chironomus*. The results of these analyses are shown in Table II. In the two species of *Triturus* it is clear that the pooled chromosomal RNA is quite unlike the RNA of the nucleoli or cytoplasm. However, the base ratios are rather similar to the DNA base ratios of the same species, substituting uracil for thymine. The DNA base ratios were determined from red blood cell nuclei.

In the salivary glands of *Chironomus*, Edström and Beermann (1962) have made a direct demonstration of RNA heterogeneity between parts of the same chromosome. The small chromosome IV of *Chironomus tentans* has three conspicuous puffs which together account for a large fraction of the total RNA of this chromosome (Fig. 13). By collecting several hundred chromosomes and cutting them into three pieces, Edström and Beermann have

been able to analyze the RNA of relatively small parts of the genome. They also analyzed the total RNA of chromosome I. The RNA extracted from chromosome I differed significantly from that found in the segments of chromosome IV, and the latter differed significantly between each other (Table II).

Any generalizations to be made from these data must be tentative because of the small number of cases examined. It seems probable that the chromosomal RNA is heterogeneous, as shown by the analyses between and within chromosomes. These differences might be referable to heterogeneity at the individual locus level, although as yet the smallest fraction analyzed represents about $\frac{1}{3}$ of the smallest chromosome of *Chironomus*. The pooled chromosomal RNA in *Triturus* resembles the DNA more closely than it does other RNA fractions. Nevertheless the two differ significantly and it is not possible to say that the one is a complete copy of the other. The cytoplasmic RNA does not resemble the chromosomal RNA at all closely. It must, therefore, represent either a very small fraction of the chromosomal RNA, or something else entirely. Because of its close similarity to nucleolar RNA we may postulate that the cytoplasmic RNA (ribosomal RNA) is primarily a product of the nucleolus.

The nucleolus, as a conspicuous and nearly universal component of cells, has received considerable attention in all discussions of RNA metabolism (see reviews of Vincent, 1955; Swift, 1958). Basically two ideas have been entertained about its function: that it represents a storehouse into which material from all parts of the chromosomes is dumped before being transmitted to the cytoplasm; or that it represents the specific product of one genetic locus. The first of these, as attractive as it is on many grounds, is difficult to reconcile with the base ratio analyses. Nor is it supported by certain tracer studies, which seem to show an independent metabolic pathway for RNA synthesis in the nucleolus (McMaster-Kaye and Taylor, 1958; McMaster-Kaye, 1962). The postulate that the primary function of the nucleolus is the production of ribosomes fits the base ratio analyses, which show a close correspondence between nucleolar and cytoplasmic RNA; and also agrees with the well-known observation that nucleoli contain small particles which are morphologically similar to the ribosomes (Fig. 15). It also helps to explain why the nucleolus should be of very nearly universal occurrence in animal and plant cells, and why its elimination leads ultimately to death (McClintock, 1934; Elsdale *et al.*, 1958; Beermann, 1960).

According to current notions the ribosomes must become "loaded" with messenger RNA before they are functional in protein synthesis. If the ribosomes are produced in the nucleolus, then we must ask where and under what circumstances they become associated with the chromosomal RNA. Conceivably this association could take place before the ribosomes leave the nucleolus for the cytoplasm, or it could occur in the cytoplasm, both ribosomes and chromosomal RNA traveling independent paths out of the nucleus. Some of the conflicting evidence regarding precursor pathways in the nucleus (Harris, 1959; Fitzgerald and Vinijchaikul, 1959; Amano and Leblond, 1960; McMaster-Kaye, 1962) might be resolved if the nucleolus at times is actively engaged in the synthesis of new RNA (ribosomal) and at other times is receiving RNA from the chromosomes. Such a view would be a compromise between the "storehouse" and "gene-product" theories of the nucleolus.

IV. RNA Synthesis in Lampbrush Chromosome Loops

Morphological studies on the lampbrush chromosomes, culminating in the important monograph of Callan and Lloyd (1960b), have shown that the loops come in a wide variety of forms. All have one feature in common: one end of the loop is an extremely thin thread, often barely discernible by phase contrast microscopy, whereas the rest of the loop is broader (Fig. 3). Some loops may be gourdlike with very marked asymmetry, while others are more slender and tapering. The majority of loops are of nearly uniform diameter, 1 or 2 μ throughout most of their length. Added to these differences in asymmetry are marked differences in the texture of the ribonucleoprotein making up the bulk of the loop. Hence individual loops may be easily recognized and mapped.

Several years ago it was suggested (Callan, 1956; Gall, 1955) that loop asymmetry might be explained on two assumptions: (1) the loop is formed by the spinning out of a thread from the parent chromomere, and (2) synthesis of ribonucleoprotein occurs on this thread, but is not accompanied by immediate release of the product. On these assumptions the loop would be spinning out at the thin end, which had consequently had less time to accumulate ribonucleoprotein matrix than the older, thick end.

We have recently tried to test this hypothesis by following the incorporation of H³-uridine in the chromosomes of two species of newt, *Triturus cristatus* and *T. viridescens* (Gall and Callan, 1962, and unpublished observations). Chromosomes may be labeled either by injecting the radioactive compound directly into the animal or by placing bits of the ovary into a dish containing the isotope. The second method makes it easy to obtain high activity in the chromosomes and to study short term incorporation. Within an hour or two after isotope administration, the majority of loops become labeled along their whole length. There are marked variations in intensity of label from one loop to the next, suggesting a heterogeneity of metabolic rates (Fig. 16). A very few loops remain unlabeled after such brief exposure, and these have proved of considerable interest.

Two such nonlabeling loops have been examined in detail, one in each of the two species. When H^3-uridine is injected into the coelomic cavity, these loops begin to show labeling after about a day, but the radioactivity in every case is limited to a short region near the *thin* end of the loop. During the course of about 10 days the area of labeling extends from the thin end toward the thick, so that eventually the whole loop is labeled (Fig. 17).

Labeling with H^3-phenylalanine follows a different course. Here all loops, including the ones which label sequentially with uridine, are labeled along their entire length after 1 day.

In the experiment with uridine one must distinguish between an actual movement of materials from one side of the loop to the other, and a wave of synthesis starting at the thin end and passing over the loop. Theoretically, one should be able to distinguish these alternatives by diluting out the precursor at a suitable time and noting the change in the pattern of incorporation. Unfortunately, we have not been able to affect the pattern of incorporation either by injecting nonradioactive uridine or by transferring a labeled ovary to a cold animal. Nevertheless, it seems unlikely that we are dealing with a wave of synthesis, since all cases showed labeling first at the thin end of the loop. If waves of synthesis were passing over the loops, we should have found oocytes in different phases at the time of isotope administration. That is, in some cases the initial labeling should have appeared at intermediate points along the loop.

For the sake of argument, let us accept that sequential labeling results from a movement of material from one side of the loop to the other. There are still two alternatives: the DNA loop axis is stationary while the ribonucleoprotein matrix moves along it, or the axis and matrix move together like a conveyor belt. Both models would result in the observed sequential labeling. In the first case only a very short region of the DNA fiber would be concerned (continuously) in the production of RNA. In the second model, the loop would be spinning out all the time, each new segment of fiber being engaged in RNA synthesis for a short time. The second hypothesis requires the subsidiary assumption that the loop axis is reeling in at the thick end of the loop and that material is being shed from the thicker regions of the loop. We have had circumstantial evidence for a long time that material is shed from the loops (Duryee, 1950; Gall, 1955; Callan, 1956). It is also clear that the loop eventually spins back in during the later stages of oogenesis, when all the loops regress; and the loop axis contracts into the chromomere when the ribonucleoprotein matrix is removed experimentally (Gall, 1956; Macgregor and Callan, 1962). Hence, it seems reasonable to suppose that the loop could be spinning out continuously on one side and back in on the other side.

On either model (stationary or moving loop axis) the asymmetry of the loop would be explained by the continuing protein synthesis. As already mentioned, phenylalanine incorporation occurs throughout the length of the loop. Presumably then, the matrix material synthesizes protein during its 10-day journey from one side of the loop to the other.

What are we to say of the majority of loops which do not show sequential uridine labeling? Obviously uridine incorporation in these loops is not localized and we cannot use its

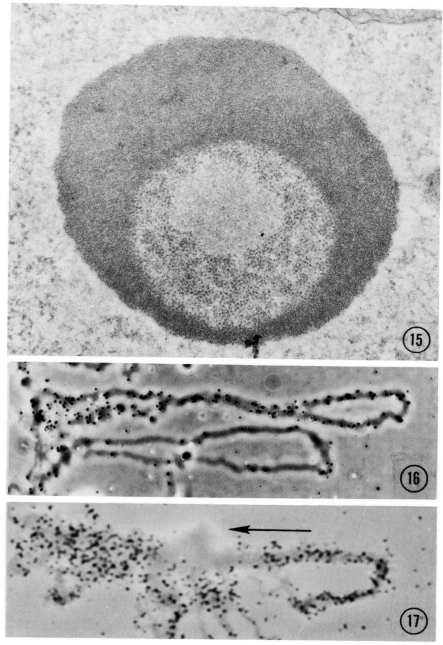

Fig. 15. Electron micrograph of a nucleolus from the oocyte of *Triturus viridescens*. A dense peripheral area surrounds a central cluster of ribosomelike particles. Such particles are found in a wide variety of nucleoli. Section of OsO_4-fixed oocyte stained with UO_2. 30,000 ×. (Micrograph furnished by Dr. O. L. Miller, Oak Ridge National Laboratory. See also Miller, 1962.)

Fig. 16. Autoradiograph of two adjacent loops on the same chromosome showing marked difference in isotope incorporation. From oocyte of *Triturus* injected 26 hours previously with H^3-uridine. 1500 ×. Fig. 17. The large loop on chromosome I of *Triturus viridescens* which labels sequentially with H^3-uridine. Autoradiograph of the loop and adjacent chromosome region from an individual injected 3 days previously. The labeling began at the thin end of the loop (below right) and is proceeding in the direction of the arrow. The thick end of the loop is the large mass of unlabeled material in the center of the photograph. About 1500 ×.

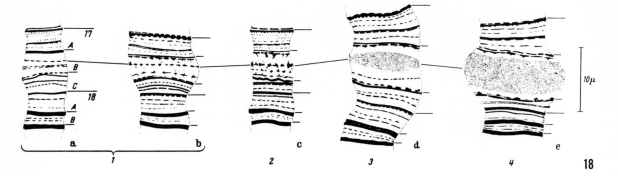

Fig. 18. Various degrees of puffing at band I-17-B in *Chironomus; a-c* from untreated control animals, *d* and *e* from larvae which had been injected with the hormone ecdysone. From Clever (1961).

translocation as a measure of loop movement. However, it does not follow that the majority of loops are stationary. On the contrary, the asymmetry of the loops itself suggests that movement is the usual situation, the thicker end of the loops being the older. In these cases we have to postulate that both RNA and protein synthesis go on continuously as the material moves along. We believe that what is special about the loops with sequential labeling is not that they move while others are stationary, but rather that their movement is detectable because of unusually restricted RNA synthesis.

V. CONTROL OF CHROMOSOMAL SYNTHESIS

During larval development in *Chironomus* or *Drosophila* the chromosomes of a given organ go through a regular sequence of puffing and regression at specific loci. The lampbrush chromosomes, too, exhibit changes during oocyte enlargement, as carefully detailed by Callan and Lloyd (1960b). Certain conspicuous loops which are present in the later stages of oocyte development are not evident in earlier stages; and other loops slowly change their morphology during the long period of oocyte enlargement. If these changes do indeed represent differential activity of genes or groups of genes, then study of the factors affecting puff and loop forma-

tion might well provide information on genetic control mechanisms.

In his study of salivary gland puffs of *Drosophila* Becker (1959) showed that glands isolated into a salt solution may continue their normal sequence of puff formation and regression for at least an hour. In this case the changes which occur may well be ones which were "triggered" before the gland was isolated, and the relative autonomy of the system be related to the short duration of the experiment. The observation is important in showing that experimental manipulation of isolated organs is possible. It would be interesting to know, for instance, if various simple compounds added to the external medium could cause recognizable new puffs or regression of old ones.

External factors, on the other hand, certainly do influence puffing and loop formation. The most thorough study of the control of puffing has been carried out by Clever (1961), who has examined the effects of the insect hormone ecdysone on the salivary gland puffs of *Chironomus* (Fig. 18). When a small amount of the hormone is injected into a larva of the proper stage, pupation occurs within a few days, even though the animal would not ordinarily pupate for a week or more. Externally no morphological changes are evident for some time after the injection. Clever has shown, however, that the hormone has an almost instantaneous effect on the puffing pattern of the chromosomes. Within 15–30 minutes after injection of the hormone a new puff appears at locus I-18-C. This is followed within about an hour by a new puff at locus IV-2-B. Eventually a whole series of puffs occur in a regular order. The sequence of puffing which precedes the induced molting is similar to the sequence which occurs at the time of normal pupation. Clever postulates that the hormone has its primary effect on the gene at locus I-18-C, and this locus in turn activates still other genes in a chain reaction. In this way a relatively simple external influence may trigger a complex series of intranuclear reactions leading eventually to the physiological changes associated with molting.

In terms of the schemes discussed by Jacob and Monod (1961), the hormone might act by combining with a repressor inside the cell. This would lead in turn to the derepression of a given gene, in this case I-18-C. Further activation of genes would result either from the direct action of the ribonucleoprotein product of gene I-18-C or by the action of smaller molecules produced under its influence. It would appear that the salivary gland chromosomes offer exceptionally good experimental material for further studies on regulator mechanisms in cells of higher organisms.

Two other cases of altered chromosome activity may be mentioned. Kroeger (1960) has transplanted nuclei from larval salivary glands of *Drosophila* into the cytoplasm of the egg. He has reported that certain puffs regress whereas other new ones arise, the effects being dependent upon the developmental stage of the eggs used.

Macgregor (1963) has followed the changes in lampbrush chromosomes from oocytes of *Triturus cristatus* after injection of gonadotropic hormone. Several quite striking alterations in loop morphology occur, as well as changes in the consistency of the nuclear sap. In this instance, no "target" chromosome locus has been discovered comparable to band I-18-C in Clever's study. Another intriguing effect of gonadotropic hormone is to speed up the rate of H³-uridine incorporation in the sequentially labeled loops (Gall and Callan, 1962). Whereas total labeling occurs after about 10 days in normal animals, those given the hormone show completely labeled loops after four days.

VI. DISCUSSION

The major concern of this paper has been to define, in morphological and cytochemical terms, the nature of the units in the chromosome concerned with RNA synthesis. These units are the loops of the lampbrush chromosome and the puffs of the polytene chromosome. One of their most striking features is their size. The threads which make up the larger puffs or Balbiani rings are some 5 μ or more in length; the loops of the lampbrush chromosomes average perhaps 50 μ, exceptional cases reaching 200 μ or more. The DNA, or DNA-protein fiber which maintains structural continuity in a lampbrush chromosome loop, is, however, less than 100 Å in diameter, and may contain only one Watson-Crick double helix.

A DNA fiber of these dimensions is not what the geneticist usually has in mind when he speaks of a gene, in the sense of a cistron. Benzer (1961) has estimated that the A cistron in the *rII* region of phage T4 may consist of several hundred nucleotide pairs. A DNA fiber 1000 nucleotide pairs in length (sufficient to specify a protein of 333 amino acids on the basis of a triplet code), would be slightly more than 0.3 μ in length.

There are several ways to reconcile the large size of the chromosome units with the suggested dimensions of the cistron: (1) The units we are dealing with in the chromosome are complex, perhaps consisting of an integrated series of different cistrons; (2) the chromosome units are highly repetitive, there being many copies of the same cistron; (3) there is a great deal of DNA not concerned with coding but in some unknown way essential to the activity of the unit; or (4) the DNA segments are short and interspersed with long segments of protein or other material.

We can rule out the last of these alternatives on the grounds that DNAase reduces the loops to extremely short segments, most of which are on the borderline of visibility in the light microscope or smaller. This observation does not necessarily imply that the DNA is continuous, but it does tell us that there are no very long segments which are free of DNA.

Among the other alternatives we cannot at the moment make any certain decision and the actual situation may involve a combination of the choices. The extraordinary length of the lampbrush chromosome loops in *Triturus* is probably correlated with another peculiarity of salamanders. This is the exceptionally high DNA content of their diploid cells, first recognized in the DNA measurements of Mirsky and Ris (1951). The content per diploid nucleus in various urodeles ranges from about 7 to 30 times that in a typical mammal such as the mouse or rat (Mirsky and Ris, 1951; Gall, 1962). This fact is usually explained by assuming that the chromosomes of urodeles have a higher degree of polyteny than the chromosomes of mammals; that is, they consist of more strands, but the strands themselves are similar in length. The DNAase experiments render this interpretation unlikely. More probably the chromosome length varies from organism to organism and approximates or equals the total length of the contained DNA. The very high DNA content of the urodeles might have been derived by serial replication of units along the chromosome strand, rather than by piling up of a large number of strands. Such a process, with its consequent redundancy of genetic information, could have led to the great length of the lampbrush chromosome loops. In the course of evolution the various replicated subunits might diverge by mutation and lead to greater genetic variability.

Whatever may be the fine structure of the units with which we are dealing, we do know that they are involved in RNA synthesis and that their periods of synthetic activity can be correlated, as shown so elegantly by Beermann and others, with functional changes in the cell.

Most of the cytochemical problems of chromosomal RNA synthesis lie ahead of us. Can it be shown, for instance, that the RNA made at each point on the chromosome is unique and specific for that point? If the microphoresis technique of Edström could be improved in sensitivity by a factor of 10, or better 100, perhaps by combining it with radioisotopes, then it should be possible to obtain base ratio analyses on single loops and the smaller puffs.

In the discussion of the RNA of the chromosome, we should not lose sight of the fact that the bulk of the material on the loops and puffs is protein, most of which may be synthesized in place. Is this some kind of "carrier" protein necessary for the transport of RNA to the nucleolus or to the cytoplasm? Or is it a more specific product of the locus itself? Conceivably this question could be approached through the use of the fluorescent antibody technique.

If the DNA of the loop is laid out in single file, as we now believe, it should be possible to study the type of connection between molecules, the state of the molecule at the time of RNA synthesis, and similar problems. A number of enzymes are now available which might give insight into such structural questions. Finally, if it becomes possible to obtain RNA synthesis by the chromosomes after isolation from the nucleus, the way would be open for a wide variety of studies relating to the mechanism of gene action.

All these approaches would be of general interest to problems of differentiation, since the control of gene action appears to be closely linked with cellular differentiation. At present we know only one agent, the insect hormone ecdysone, which has a specific regulatory action on a chromosome puff. Hopefully, other such substances will be found and eventually help us to identify the nature of the intranuclear control mechanisms.

VII. Concluding Remarks

The purpose of this paper has been to make the following statements seem reasonable. They are intended more as hypotheses for future work than as rigorous conclusions from available evidence.

a. The chromosomes of higher organisms are composed of one, or at most a few, DNA double helices that may extend the length of the chromatid.

b. The functional units, in terms of RNA synthesis, are DNA segments up to 50 μ or more in length (the loops of the lampbrush chromosomes and the puffs of the polytene chromosomes). These units must consist of many cistrons.

c. The units are polarized. RNA synthesis begins at one end of the unit and proceeds sequentially to the other.

d. The chromosomal RNA is heterogeneous. It is probably equivalent to the messenger RNA of bacteria.

e. The ribosomal RNA is produced in the nucleolus.

f. Cellular differentiation is associated with differential activation of the chromosomal units.

REFERENCES

Amano, M., and C. P. Leblond (1960). Comparison of the specific activity time curves of ribonucleic acid in chromatin, nucleolus and cytoplasm. *Exptl. Cell Research* **20**, 250–253.

Becker, H. J. (1959). Die Puffs der speicheldrüsenchromosomen von *Drosophilia melanogaster*. *Chromosoma* **10**, 654–678.

Beermann, W. (1952a). Chromomerenkonstanz und spezifische Modifikationen der Chromosomenstruktur in der Entwicklung und Organdifferenzierung von *Chironomus tentans*. *Chromosoma* **5**, 139–198.

Beermann, W. (1952b). Chromosomenstruktur und Zelldifferenzierung in der Speicheldrüse von *Trichocladius vitripennis*. *Z. Naturforsch.* **7b**, 237–242.

Beermann, W. (1956). Nuclear differentiation and functional morphology of chromosomes. *Cold Spring Harbor Symposia Quant. Biol.* **21**, 217–232.

Beermann, W. (1959). Chromosomal differentiation in insects. In *Developmental Cytology*, Growth Symposium No. 16 (D. Rudnick, ed.), pp. 83–103. Ronald Press, New York.

Beermann, W. (1960). Der Nukleolus als lebenswichtiger Bestandteil des Zellkernes. *Chromosoma* **11**, 263–296.

Beermann, W. (1961). Ein Balbiani-Ring als Locus einer Speicheldrüsenmutation. *Chromosoma* **12**, 1–25.

Benzer, S. (1961). On the topography of the genetic fine structure. *Proc. Natl. Acad. Sci. U.S.* **47**, 403–415.

Breuer, M. E., and C. Pavan (1954). Salivary chromosomes and differentiation. *Proc. 9th Intern. Congr. Genetics, Florence, Italy, 1954* (Suppl. of *Caryologia* **6**), Part II, p. 778.

Breuer, M. E., and C. Pavan (1955). Behavior of polytene chromosomes of *Rhynchosciara angelae* at different stages of larval development. *Chromosoma* **7**, 371–386.

Callan, H. G. (1956). Recent work on the structure of cell nuclei. In Symposium on the Fine Structure of Cells, Leiden. *Intern. Union Biol. Sci. Publ.* **B21**, 89–109.

Callan, H. G. (1963). The nature of lampbrush chromosomes. *Intern. Rev. Cytol.* **15**, 1–34.

Callan, H. G., and L. Lloyd (1956). Visual demonstration of allelic differences within cell nuclei. *Nature* **178**, 355–357.

Callan, H. G., and L. Lloyd (1960a). Lampbrush chromosomes. In *New Approaches in Cell Biology* (P. M. B. Walker, ed.), pp. 23–46. Academic Press, New York.

Callan, H. G., and L. Lloyd, (1960b). Lampbrush chromosomes of crested newts *Triturus cristatus* (Laurenti). *Phil. Trans. Roy. Soc.* **B243**, 135–219.

Callan, H. G., and H. C. Macgregor (1958). Action of deoxyribonuclease on lampbrush chromosomes. *Nature* **181**, 1479–1480.

Clever, U. (1961). Genaktivitäten in den Riesenchromosomen von *Chironomus tentans* und ihre Beziehungen zur Entwicklung. 1. Genaktivierung durch Ecdyson. *Chromosoma* **12**, 607–675.

Duryee, W. R. (1950). Chromosomal physiology in relation to nuclear structure. *Ann. N.Y. Acad. Sci.* **50**, 920–953.

Edström, J.-E. (1960a). Extraction, hydrolysis, and electrophoretic analysis of ribonucleic acid from microscopic tissue units (microphoresis). *J. Biophys. Biochem. Cytol.* **8**, 39–46.

Edström, J.-E. (1960b). Composition of ribonucleic acid from various parts of spider oocytes. *J. Biophys. Biochem. Cytol.* **8**, 47–51.

Edström, J.-E., and W. Beermann (1962). The base composition of nucleic acids in chromosomes, puffs, nucleoli, and cytoplasm of *Chironomus* salivary gland cells. *J. Cell Biol.* **14**, 371–380.

Edström, J.-E., and J. G. Gall (1963). The base composition of ribonucleic acid in lampbrush chromosomes, nucleoli, nuclear sap, and cytoplasm of *Triturus* oocytes. In preparation.

Edström, J.-E., E. Grampp, and N. Schor (1961). The intracellular distribution and heterogeneity of ribonucleic acid in starfish oocytes. *J. Biophys. Biochem. Cytol.* **11**, 549–557.

Elsdale, T. R., M. Fischberg, and S. Smith (1958). A mutation that reduces nucleolar number in *Xenopus laevis*. *Exptl. Cell Research* **14**, 642–643.

Fitzgerald, P. J., and K. Vinijchaikul (1959). Nucleic acid metabolism of pancreatic cells as revealed by cytidine-H^3 and thymidine-H^3. *Lab. Invest.* **8**, 319–328.

Frisch, L., ed. (1961). *Cold Spring Harbor Symposia Quant. Biol.* **26**.

Gall, J. G. (1955). Problems of structure and function in the amphibian oocyte nucleus. *Symposia Soc. Exptl. Biol.* **9**, 358–370.

Gall, J. G. (1956). On the submicroscopic structure of chromosomes. *Brookhaven Symposia in Biol.* **8**, 17–32.

Gall, J. G. (1958). Chromosomal differentiation. In *The Chemical Basis of Development* (W. D. McElroy and B. Glass, eds.), pp. 103–135. Johns Hopkins Press, Baltimore, Maryland.

Gall, J. G. (1962). Unpublished observations.

Gall, J. G. (1963). The kinetics of DNAase action on chromosomes. *Nature* **198**, 36–38.

Gall, J. G., and H. G. Callan (1962). H^3-uridine incorporation in lampbrush chromosomes. *Proc. Natl. Acad. Sci. U.S.* **48**, 562–570.

Harris, H. (1959). Turnover of nuclear and cytoplasmic ribonucleic acid in two types of animal cell, with some further observations on the nucleolus. *Biochem. J.* **73**, 362–369.

Heitz, E., and H. Bauer (1933). Beweise für die Chromosomenstruktur der Kernschleifen in den Knäuelkernen von *Bibio hortulanus* L (cytologische Untersuchungen an Dipteran, I). *Z. Zellforsch.* **17**, 67–82.

Jacob, F., and J. Monod (1961). Genetic regulatory mechanisms in the synthesis of proteins. *J. Mol. Biol.* **3**, 318–356.

Kroeger, H. (1960). The induction of new puffing patterns by transplantation of salivary gland nuclei into egg cytoplasm of *Drosophilia*. *Chromosoma* **11**, 129–145.

Macgregor, H. C. (1963). Physiological variability in the oocytes of the crested newt. In preparation.

Macgregor, H. C., and H. G. Callan (1962). The actions of enzymes on lampbrush chromosomes. *Quart. J. Microscop. Sci.* **103**, 173–203.

McClintock, B. (1934). The relation of a particular chromosomal element to the development of the nucleoli in *Zea mays*. *Z. Zellforsch.* **21**, 294–328.

McMaster-Kaye, R. (1962). The metabolism of nuclear ribonucleic acid in salivary glands of *Drosophilia repleta*. *J. Histochem. and Cytochem.* **10**, 154–161.

McMaster-Kaye, R., and J. H. Taylor (1958). Evidence for two metabolically distinct types of ribonucleic acid in chromatin and nucleoli. *J. Biophys. Biochem. Cytol.* **4**, 5–11.

Mechelke, F. (1953). Reversible Strukturmodifikationen der Speicheldrüsenchromosomen von *Acricotopus lucidus*. *Chromosoma* **5**, 511–543.

Miller, O. L. (1962). Studies on the ultrastructure and metabolism of nucleoli in amphibian oocytes. *Proc. 5th Intern. Congr. on Electron Microscopy, Philadelphia, 1962* NN-8.

Mirsky, A. E., and H. Ris (1951). The desoxyribonucleic acid content of animal cells and its evolutionary significance. *J. Gen. Physiol.* **34**, 451–462.

Prescott, D. (1960). Nuclear function and nuclear-cytoplasmic interactions. *Ann. Rev. Physiol.* **22**, 17–44.

Rudkin, G. T., and S. L. Corlette (1957). Disproportionate synthesis of DNA in a polytene chromosome region. *Proc. Natl. Acad. Sci. U.S.* **43**, 964–968.

Schumaker, V. N., E. G. Richards, and H. K. Schachman (1956). A study of the kinetics of the enzymatic digestion of deoxyribonucleic acid. *J. Am. Chem. Soc.* **78**, 4230–4236.

Sibatani, A., S. R. deKloet, V. G. Allfrey, and A. E. Mirsky (1962). Isolation of a nuclear RNA fraction resembling DNA in its base composition. *Proc. Natl. Acad. Sci. U.S.* **48**, 471–477.

Stich, H., and J. Naylor (1958). Variation of desoxyribonucleic acid content of specific chromosome regions. *Exptl. Cell Research* **14**, 442–445.

Swift, H. (1958). Studies on nucleolar functions. In *Symposium on Molecular Biology* (R. E. Zirkle, ed.), pp. 266–303. Univ. of Chicago Press, Chicago, Illinois.

Swift, H. (1962). Nucleic acids and cell morphology in dipteran salivary glands. In *The Molecular Control of Cellular Activity* (J. M. Allen, ed.), pp. 73–125. McGraw-Hill, New York.

Taylor, J. H., ed. (1963). Molecular models for organization of DNA into chromosomes. In *Molecular Genetics*, Vol. I, Chapter II. Academic Press, New York.

Thomas, C. A. (1956). The enzymatic degradation of desoxyribose nucleic acid. *J. Am. Chem. Soc.* **78**, 1861–1868.

Vincent, W. S. (1955). Structure and chemistry of nucleoli. *Intern. Rev. Cytol.* **4**, 269–298.

6

Genetic Control of Differentiation

CLASSICAL GENETICS has left us with the axiom that the morphological, functional, and biochemical characteristics of an organism are dependent on its genetic constitution (Stern 1955; Hadorn 1961). Recent experiments continue to confirm this concept.

Although distant from cells which are discussed ordinarily in the context of differentiation, T4 phage has provided a fine example of gene control of morphogenesis (*Epstein, et al. 1963*).* Through studies of many mutants of two types (Edgar, Denhardt, and Epstein 1964) a series of linearly related genes has been shown to be responsible for determination of a set of phenotypic characteristics. Each gene is concerned with a particular developmental feature of the phage. Although so far 37 genes are involved in morphogenesis only 20 different proteins have been detected in the phage. Are the other 17 genes "morphogenetic genes" which may be needed for combination of the proteins of the phage into a macromolecular super structure? If they are, how do they function? Possibly they code for enzymes or other "helper" proteins which weave or condense structural proteins and other subunits into higher-order structures. The helper proteins could, but need not, form part of the final structure.

It might be useful to speculate that helper proteins are used in higher organisms for gastrulation, neurulation, and other activities concerned with the developmental disposition of cells. They might assist in controlling surface properties and in general properties of cell organelles which could affect cell size, shape or cell movement. Such proteins might be needed in only very small amounts to do their jobs.

The requirement of a specific genetic background for a particular cytodifferentiation is exemplified in the development of the thymus since thymic rudiments will differentiate in homologous but not in heterologous hosts (*Auerbach 1961*). The possibility that a strain-specific, lymphocyte promoting substance (a helper protein?) is required for lymphoid differentiation is an attractive one. The effect of such a factor may be similar to that of viral antigen produced on the fibroblast cell surface by infection with Rous sarcoma virus (Vogt and Rubin 1962). The result in both cases is loss of "contact inhibition" (see Introduction, Chapter 1), but by what mechanism is still obscure.

In the life cycle of the frog there may be at least five different genes concerned with the synthesis of hemoglobin (*Baglioni and Sparks 1963*). Some of the genes are activated during early development of the tadpole; others at the time of metamorphosis. How quickly one set of genes is turned on and the other off is not known. Detection of tadpole hemoglobins in metamorphosing tadpoles does not

---

* Italicized references indicate articles which appear in this book.

mean that these proteins are still being made. It is possible that the switch from tadpole to adult hemoglobin occurs abruptly, that is, when genes for adult proteins are activated, those for tadpole proteins are simultaneously repressed. It is not yet known whether the tadpole and adult proteins can be made by the same cell or whether the stimulus to make adult protein acts only on stem cells which have not yet begun to make hemoglobin.

The stimulus to switch from tadpole to adult hemoglobin is probably hormonal. It is likely that thyroxin is involved, but it is not known how. It should be possible to induce synthesis of adult hemoglobins in premetamorphosing tadpoles by administration of hormone. This would resolve the question of whether the transition from tadpole hemoglobins to adult hemoglobins is controlled internally within the tissue or externally by the hormone which throws the switch.

REFERENCES

1. Edgar, R. S., G. H. Denhardt, and R. H. Epstein (1964). A comparative genetic study of conditional lethal mutations of bacteriophage T4D[1]. *Genetics* 49:635–648.
2. Hadorn, E. (1961). *Developmental Genetics and Lethal Factors*, Methuen, London.
3. Stern, Curt (1955). Gene action. In B. Willier, P. Weiss, and V. Hamburger (eds.), *Analysis of Development*, Saunders, Philadelphia, pp. 151–169.
4. Vogt, P., and H. Rubin (1962). The cytology of Rous sarcoma virus infection. *Cold Spring Harbor Symposia on Quantitative Biology*, Vol. XXVII, pp. 395–405, The Biological Laboratory, Cold Spring Harbor, New York.

Genetic Control of Thymus Lymphoid Differentiation*

ROBERT AUERBACH†

As our knowledge of the functional and pathological aspects of lymphoid systems in their central role in immunity and leukemia increases, the lack of understanding of the primary differentiative mechanism leading to the formation of such systems becomes limiting. Thus we find that theories of antibody formation as well as of leukemia etiology hinge ultimately on hypothetical differentiative mechanisms which are neither established from lymphoid systems nor generally valid for any differentiating system as yet analyzed in multicellular organisms.

We have recently reported that the embryonic mouse thymus, isolated as an epithelial rudiment prior to lymphoid differentiation, can develop into a lymphoid system upon isolation in tissue culture[1] as well as after transplantation to the anterior chamber of adult mouse eyes.[2] The present paper concerns itself entirely with grafts grown for seven days in the anterior eye chamber, and takes into consideration the genetic constitution of donor and host tissues. The experiments demonstrate that in contrast to other embryonic systems the developmental direction of the thymus can be profoundly and rapidly influenced, typical lymphoid differentiation depending on donor-host compatibility.

The unique nature of the results is inter-

Proceedings of the National Academy of Sciences, 47, No. 8, 1175–1181 (August, 1961). Reprinted with permission.

* Supported by research funds from the National Institutes of Health (C-3985) and funds administered by the Research Committee of the University of Wisconsin.

† With the technical assistance of William D. Ball and E. Mattie Morin.

preted as manifestation of a release from tissue-level control mechanisms normally associated with differentiation in multicellular organisms. The operational feasibility of both directive and selective influences in lymphoid differentiation is discussed. Finally, a hypothesis is developed which states that the thymus represents the primary rudiment of the mammalian immunological system.

MATERIALS AND METHODS

Mice of strains C_3H, Bagg albino C, and AKR/Lw were used. Embryonic age was determined by observation of vaginal plugs. Thymus rudiments were obtained from 12-day embryos of C_3H, C, and F_1 (C ♀ × C_3H ♂) matings, and from 13-day (12-day equivalent) embryos of AKR matings, lung rudiments from the same embryos serving as source of control material when required. With a few exceptions in transplants to AKR mice, recipients were adult male mice of 2–5 months' age. Normally, each mouse received only one graft, but in experiments in which lung and thymus morphogenesis were compared, both eyes were utilized, one receiving lung, the other receiving thymus. Grafts were made into nembutal-anaesthetized animals in standard fashion,[3] recovered after seven days, fixed in Bouin's, sectioned at 5–7 μ, and stained with hematoxylin and eosin.

RESULTS

As previously reported, when an F_1 (C × C_3H) thymus rudiment is transplanted into F_1 (C × C_3H) host eye, the rudiment develops rapidly into a lymphoid structure, and within one week becomes histologically similar to the thymus of a newborn animal.[2,4] Preliminary studies on the sequence of events show that after two days the graft is well established and growing, that after four days it is clearly shifting in a lymphoid direction, and that in the next three days rapid growth and lymphopoiesis occur. The timing parallels the differentiation of thymus *in situ*, where lymphocytes appear in 15- to 16-day embryos, and reach *ca.* 12 million in the newborn (19-day)

mouse.[5] While there is considerable variation in the size attained by implants, the histological differentiation seen seven days after transplantation is characteristic and consistent. The graft is almost exclusively lymphoid, with a few scattered epithelial foci and dispersed stromal material.

The initial rationale in the transplantation experiments to be reported (Table 1 and Figs. 1–4) was that in view of the known role of the thymus in AKR-strain leukemia[6] an effect of AKR environment on the differentiation of thymus rudiments from nonleukemic strains might be expected. F_1 (C × C_3H) rudiments were transplanted into AKR mouse eyes, grafts into F_1 (C × C_3H) mice serving as controls; grafts were recovered after one week. Control grafts behaved in a typical manner. Grafts implanted into AKR eyes had become established and well vascularized and had grown considerably, although somewhat less than control grafts. The histological appearance of the grafts was, however, strikingly different from the control grafts. In place of the expected lymphoid differentiation, these grafts had grown into a large, somewhat disorganized mass of epithelial and fibrous material interspersed with vesicles and some debris. The total amount of lymphoid material varied from little to none, and where found, it seemed restricted to the areas furthest removed from the host-donor tissue interfaces; furthermore, such lymphoid areas appeared to be undergoing regression or alteration.

The experiments were repeated, using lung rudiments as control tissue. F_1 (C × C_3H) lung tissue growing in AKR mice was indistinguishable from similar tissue growing in F_1 (C × C_3H) mice. On the other hand, F_1 (C × C_3H) thymus growing in AKR mice again showed the predominantly nonlymphoid direction of differentiation.

Reciprocal experiments were now performed, in which AKR thymus rudiments were transplanted into AKR and F_1 (C × C_3H) hosts, lung tissue again serving as control. The results were comparable. AKR lung tissue grew well in both types of hosts, and no distinction was seen between the two groups. On the other hand, while AKR thymus

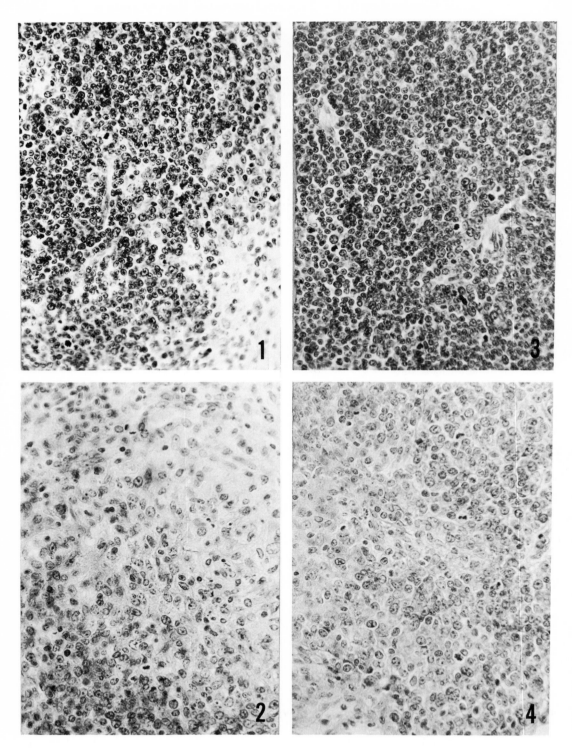

Figs. 1–4. 12-day embryonic thymus rudiments grown for 7 days in the anterior eye chamber of adult male mice. Fig. 1. C_3H thymus rudiment in F_1 (C × C_3H) host eye. Fig. 2. F_1 (C × C_3H) thymus rudiment in AKR host eye. Fig. 3. AKR thymus rudiment in F_1 (AKR × C_3H) host eye. Fig. 4. C_3H thymus rudiment in C host eye.

TABLE 1. Lymphoid differentiation as a function of donor-host compatibility

| Donor Strain | Predominant Differentiation | | | |
| | Lymphoid | | Nonlymphoid | |
	Host Strain	Number	Host Strain	Number
C_3H	C_3H	5/5	C	10/12
	$F_1(C \times C_3H)$	11/11		
C	C	4/4	C_3H	10/10
	$F_1(C \times C_3H)$	5/5		
$F_1(C \times C_3H)$	$F_1(C \times C_3H)$	100 + /100 + [a]	C	4/4
			C_3H	6/7
			AKR	37/41[b]
AKR	AKR	8/8[c]	$F_1(C \times C_3H)$	6/8
	$F_1(C_3H \times AKR)$	9/9		

[a] Standard control used in numerous experiments in addition to the ones reported in this paper.[2,4]

[b] Includes 14 severely leukemic mice.

[c] Includes four severely leukemic mice.

rudiments developed into typical lymphoid grafts when transplanted into isologous AKR hosts, they developed into characteristic nonlymphoid type grafts when grown in F_1 (C × C_3H) hosts.

At this point it was felt that the transplantation effect might well be independent of the leukemic properties of the AKR strain, so that a large number of graft combinations were made using C_3H, C, AKR, F_1 (C × C_3H) and F_1 (C_3H × AKR) mice. The results, summarized in Table 1, were consistent. In all situations involving the implantation of inbred-line thymus into its own strain (three types) or into an F_1 hybrid of that strain (three types) typical lymphoid differentiation ensued. No readily recognizable differences in growth or histological differentiation between implants into the strain of origin and implants into F_1 hybrids were observed. In all situations involving the implantation of thymus from one inbred line into a different inbred line (three types) lymphoid differentiation generally failed to ensue. In transplants of an F_1 hybrid into either of the parental strains nonlymphoid differentiation was predominant.

Finally, two preliminary experiments may be reported. In the first, F_1 (C × C_3H) tissue was grafted into AKR mice, F_1 (C × C_3H) mice serving as control hosts; grafts were recovered after two, four, and seven days. Dif-

ferences between the two groups were apparent after four days in 3 out of 4 cases. In a second experiment, F_1 (C × C_3H) tissue was grafted into 2-week-old C_3H mice (in 4 cases). In this instance the grafts grew well, became lymphoid, and were indistinguishable from control grafts.

DISCUSSION

The anterior chamber of the eye has been considered refractory to early immunological phenomena as evidenced by the ready maintenance and growth for two or more weeks of highly heterologous combinations such as human or mouse tissues in rat eye or chick tissues in mouse eye.[3,4,7] Yet in the present experiments the results parallel those that would be expected on the basis of transplantation compatability, lymphoid differentiation being restricted to a compatible host-donor relationship. On the other hand, the rapidity of the effect would be unusual even for adult tissues grown in immunologically active transplantation sites. Furthermore, the response is limited to the lymphoid elements; for growth and vacularization of the implant is not prevented, and there is no general graft rejection.

Whether the process involved in the results is actually immunological, i.e., a specific host response to donor tissue which is lymphocyte-inhibiting in effect, is open to conjecture.

Experimentally, the same results would be expected if specific lymphocyte-promoting substances, subject to genetic control, were required for lymphoid differentiation. Tissue culture experiments aimed at distinguishing between these possibilities are in progress.

In view of the contrast between the results obtained with thymus transplants and those obtained with other systems it becomes essential to examine critically the properties and functions of the developing thymus lymphoid system. One striking feature of thymus differentiation is the loss of tissue cohesion concomitant with the appearance of lymphoid cells. Whereas reticular, stromal, and epithelial cells are firmly bound to the thymus tissue architecture, the lymphoid series of cells is essentially nonadhesive. Since cellular adhesion is normally an adjunct of embryonic systems, and since intercellular materials are becoming increasingly implicated as controlling elements in differentiative events,[8-10] the change in adhesion accompanying lymphoid differentiation may represent a key factor in our results. Loss of adhesiveness may signify that the normal developmental-control mechanisms are bypassed or play a relatively minor role, and that different control mechanisms can under these conditions become operative or manifest. This rationale suggests that certain other systems such as germ-cell differentiation, would behave in a similar fashion; transplantation experiments to test this point are contemplated.

Although the functions of specific cells in the lymphoid series are not clear, it seems likely that the lymphoid system plays a leading role in immune phenomena. Recent theories of antibody-forming mechanisms[11] have tended to emphasize selection or directed differentiation of certain cells in response to antigen (or antibody). In this connection the present results and preceding discussion seem significant. The transplantation results indicate that the thymus lymphoid differentiating system is subject to genetically-determined external controls. In addition to the directive (or permissive) nature of the host environment, selective models can be designed, e.g., a situation in which cells from two strains are mixed prior to transplantation; the significance of such models remains to be determined. The rationale that the present results are related to loss of tissue cohesion is attractive in this connection, for it permits the application of principles developed for unicellular organisms for this system in distinction to other multicellular differentiating systems.

The experiments focus attention on the lack of information concerning thymus function. Since the thymus represents the dominant lymphoid rudiment of the early embryo and since it differentiates during the period of development when the embryo is most sensitive to external modifications of the immunological system,[12] it seems appropriate to suggest that the thymus represents the major rudiment of the mammalian immunological system.[13] Implicit in this suggestion is the assumption that lymphoid cells which arise in the thymus subsequently become disseminated in a selective fashion. That thymic lymphoid cells originate *in situ* from nonlymphoid cells has been recently demonstrated by transplantation and tissue culture studies;[4] the presence of a lymphocyte circulation has been shown;[14] and the selective nature of thymus cell localizations in other lymphoid regions has been established.[15] The precision of selective settling of thymic lymphoid cells is seen in the regional intrasplenic distribution of thymic cells introduced into lethally irradiated animals;[16] and this conforms well with the demonstrated depression of spleen germinal center activity following thymectomy.[17]

A summary of the points of discussion leads to the presentation of a unified view of thymus function, lymphocyte differentiation, and the development of immune systems. Initially the thymus is subject to typical inductive tissue interactions, but during development the loss of tissue adhesion leads to the establishment of a new set of controlling and directing elements. Cells selected and/or directed toward lymphoid differentiation then develop into thymic lymphoid cells which migrate from the thymus into specific areas of the developing spleen. Here, in their new environment they directly or indirectly become foci for production of antibody-forming cells.

The hypothesis, though speculative, is attractive in being readily amenable to testing. One would predict that embryonic thymectomy would lead to a reduction of the antibody-forming capacity; this experiment can be performed in lower vertebrates. One would expect that heterotypic combinations of embryonic spleen and thymus would lead to complex differentiation not attainable by these rudiments individually. And finally, one would hope that such heterotypic combinations involving the differentiation simultaneously of spleen and thymus in tissue culture would lead to the formation of a system competent to perform immunological reactions *in vitro*.

SUMMARY

Thymus rudiments from 12-day-old mouse embryos of C, C_3H, and C ♀ × C_3H ♂ matings and from 13-day (12-day equivalent) embryos of AKR matings were grown for 7 days in the anterior eye chamber of adult male C, C_3H, AKR, F_1 (C × C_3H) and F_1 (C_3H × AKR) mice.

In all situations involving the implantation of inbred-line thymus in its own strain or in an F_1 hybrid of that strain, as well as of F_1 hybrid thymus in a similar F_1 hybrid host, typical lymphoid differentiation occurred. In all combinations in which the thymus from one strain was implanted into an unrelated strain or in which thymus from an F_1 hybrid was implanted into either parental strain or into an unrelated strain, lymphoid differentiation was reduced. Instead, grafts developed into disorganized, large masses of fibrous and epithelial material.

It is suggested that the explanation may lie in the loss of tissue adhesion concomitant with lymphoid differentiation, that this constitutes a release from tissue-level control mechanisms normally associated with differentiation, and that this permits different control mechanisms to become operative or manifested.

A hypothesis is developed which states that the thymus may represent the major primordium of the mammalian immunological system.

[1] Ball, W. D., and Auerbach, R., *Exptl. Cell Research*, **20**, 245 (1960).

[2] Auerbach, R., *Dev. Biol.*, **2**, 271 (1960).

[3] Greene, H. S. N., *Cancer Res.*, **3**, 809 (1943).

[4] Auerbach, R., *Dev. Biol.*, **3**, 336 (1961).

[5] Ball, W. D., and Auerbach, R. (unpublished observations).

[6] McEndy, D. P., Boon, M. C., and Furth, J., *Cancer Res.*, **4**, 377 (1944).

[7] Browning, H. C., *Cancer*, **2**, 646 (1949).

[8] Grobstein, C., *Exptl. Cell Research*, **13**, 575 (1957).

[9] Auerbach, R., "The organization and reorganization of embryonic cells," in *Self-Organizing Systems* (New York: Pergamon Press, 1960).

[10] Moscona, A., "Patterns and mechanisms of tissue reconstruction from dissociated cells," in *Developing Cell Systems and Their Control*, ed. D. Rudnick (New York: Ronald Press Co., 1960).

[11] E.g., *Mechanisms of Antibody Formation* (Prague: Publishing House of the Czechoslovakiau Academy of Science, 1960); "Symposium on Antibodies," *J. Cellular Comp. Physiol.*, **50**, suppl. 1 (1957); "Cellular Aspects of Immunity," in *Ciba Foundation Symposium on Cell Metabolism* (Boston: Little, Brown and Co., 1960).

[12] Billingham, R. E., and Brent, L., *Proc. Roy. Soc. (London)*, **B242**, 439 (1959).

[13] Cf. Ruth, R. F., *Federation Proc.*, **19**, 579 (1960).

[14] Yoffey, J. M., Everett, N. B., and Reinhardt, W. O., "Cellular migration streams in the hemopoietic system," in *The Kinetics of Cellular Proliferation*, ed. F. Stohlman, Jr. (New York: Grune and Stratton, 1959).

[15] Fichtelius, K. E., *Acta Anat.* (Suppl.), **19**, 1 (1953).

[16] Congdon, C. C., Makinodan, T., Gengozian, N., Shekarchi, I. C., and Urso, I. S., *J. Natl. Cancer Inst.*, **21**, 193 (1958).

[17] Metcalf, D., *Brit. J. Haematol.*, **6**, 324 (1960).

A Study of Hemoglobin Differentiation in
Rana catesbeiana

CORRADO BAGLIONI

CHARLES E. SPARKS

INTRODUCTION

Many biochemical changes are known to occur as amphibians undergo metamorphosis (Frieden, 1961). Among these, the developmental changes of body proteins are of considerable interest; the changing body proteins can be analyzed at the molecular level by available chemical methods, and this analysis may throw some light on molecular mechanisms of differentiation.

Physiological differences between tadpole and frog hemoglobin have been reported by McCutcheon (1936) and Riggs (1951). *Rana catesbeiana* tadpole hemoglobin is characterized by a greater oxygen affinity and by the absence of a detectable Bohr effect; frog hemoglobin shows a Bohr effect and lower affinity for oxygen.

Multiple forms of hemoglobins are known to occur in many vertebrate species (see review by Gratzer and Allison, 1960). Herner and Frieden (1961) have studied the hemoglobin pattern of *R. catesbeiana* by paper electrophoresis; they have reported that frog and tadpole hemoglobins are heterogeneous and that marked differences exist between them. Chieffi *et al.* (1960) have reported that the hemoglobins of *R. esculenta* are separated by starch-gel electrophoresis into well-defined bands and that differences in electrophoretic mobility between tadpole and frog hemoglobins are clearly demonstrated by this technique.

In the present investigation the hemoglobin pattern of *R. catesbeiana* has been studied by the sensitive technique of starch-gel electrophoresis. A well-defined and reproducible pattern of hemoglobins has been shown. These hemoglobins have been isolated and characterized by fingerprinting (Ingram, 1958).

Developmental Biology, 8, 272–285 (1963). Reprinted with permission.

MATERIALS AND METHODS

Tadpoles and frogs (*Rana catesbeiana*) were obtained from the Connecticut Valley Supply Company, Valley Road, Southampton, Massachusetts. Frogs of medium size were generally used; very large frogs were occasionally examined. Tadpoles at different stages were used; tadpoles with evidence of forelimbs were discarded. The tadpoles were kept in distilled water containing 0.5 gm of NaCl per liter. To induce metamorphosis, thyroxine, dissolved in diluted alkali, was added to the final concentration of 5×10^{-7} M.

Blood was obtained from tadpoles by dissecting and cutting the bulbus arteriosus at the point where it branches. This allowed the heart to pump out blood while the tadpole was held over a small beaker containing 4% citrate (Riggs, 1951). The red cells were then immediately washed with 4% citrate three times; tadpole red cells were washed within a short period of time since they showed a tendency to lyse even in isotonic solutions. The packed red cells were hemolyzed by adding three volumes of distilled water and freezing.

Blood was obtained from the frogs by inserting a hypodermic needle containing 4% citrate into the common carotid artery. The red cells were washed with 0.8% NaCl and hemolyzed with three volumes of distilled water.

The lysed cells were thawed and centrifuged at 10,000 g. The clear supernatant was dialyzed overnight against 0.001 M phosphate buffer pH 7.0. Some hemoglobin was precipitated during dialysis. The hemoglobin was transformed into cyanomethemoglobin according to Allen *et al.* (1958), and the precipitated hemoglobin became soluble. Globin was prepared from hemoglobin solutions by the method of Rossi-Fanelli *et al.* (1958).

Hemoglobin preparations were examined by starch-gel electrophoresis in a horizontal apparatus; the discontinuous buffer system of Poulik (1957) was used. The gels were cut into identical halves; one half was stained with the benzidine reagent and the other with amido black (Smithies, 1959). Electrophoresis in urea-containing gels was carried out according to the method of Poulik (1961). Preparative block electrophoresis was performed following the method of Kunkel (1954), using Pevikon C-870 (Fosfatbolaget, Stockholm) instead of starch; 700–800 mg of hemoglobin was applied to each block.

Hemoglobin was hydrolyzed with trypsin according to Ingram (1958). The tryptic hydrolyzates were then analyzed by fingerprinting, following the method of Ingram (1958) as modified by Baglioni (1961). Each hemoglobin was fingerprinted at least eight times. The fingerprints were stained as previously indicated (Baglioni, 1961).

To prepare sucrose gradients, the two chambers of a constant mixing device were filled with 5% and 20% solutions of sucrose in 0.001 M phosphate buffer pH 7.0, respectively. The phosphate buffer contained 10 mg of KCN per liter; 0.12 ml of hemoglobin solution was layered on top of the gradient. The gradient was run in the SW-39 rotor for 14 hours at 38,000 rpm. The content of the tube was drained from the bottom by piercing the centrifuge tube with a hypodermic needle. Fractions of 4 drops were diluted with 1 ml of distilled water and read at 410 mμ. Fractions to be examined by starch-gel electrophoresis were pooled and concentrated by ultrafiltration.

RESULTS

Hemoglobin Patterns

The hemoglobins of several tadpoles and frogs were individually examined by starch-gel electrophoresis. Three distinct hemoglobins were consistently observed in all the tadpoles examined (Fig. 1). Four hemoglobins were consistently observed in frogs (Fig. 1); one of these, the fastest-running one, is present in minute amount. A diagram of the starch-gel pattern of tadpole and frog hemoglobin is reproduced in Fig. 2. One of the major frog hemoglobins (indicated as *2* in column *b* of Fig. 2) appears to have the same electrophoretic mobility as the slowest-running tadpole hemoglobin.

The hemoglobin pattern of tadpoles during metamorphosis has been studied. Metamorphosis was induced by thyroxine (see Methods). The tadpoles began to lose their tails and show forelimbs within 1 week after thyroxine administration. The tadpoles were killed at this time, and their hemoglobins were examined by starch-gel electrophoresis. The tadpole during metamorphosis appears to have both the hemoglobins characteristic of tadpoles and those characteristic of adult frogs (Fig. 2, column *c*).

The hemoglobins of very large, and presumably older, frogs were occasionally studied; two additional slow-moving bands were observed by starch-gel electrophoresis (Fig. 2*d*). A similar pattern was observed in samples of frog hemoglobin kept for a few days before starch-gel electrophoresis. The presence of these bands is probably caused by polymerization of hemoglobin molecules.

Preparation of Hemoglobins

Tadpole hemoglobin, 700 mg, was separated by preparative block electrophoresis into four fractions (Fig. 3), designated T-1, T-2, T-3, and T-4. These fractions were eluted and analyzed by starch-gel electrophoresis (see Fig. 4). Fractions T-2 and T-3, which were found to be not sufficiently pure, were purified by a second preparative block electrophoresis. The hemoglobins isolated were concentrated to a volume of few milliliters by ultrafiltration; globin was then routinely prepared from the purified hemoglobin fractions. Frog hemoglobin, 800 mg, was separated by preparative block electrophoresis into four fractions (Fig. 3, designated F-1, F-2, F-3, and F-4. Fraction F-1 was obtained in very poor yield, and it has not been possible to characterize it further. The other hemoglobin fractions were examined by starch-gel electrophoresis (Fig. 4). Fraction F-2 was found to be not sufficiently pure and was purified by

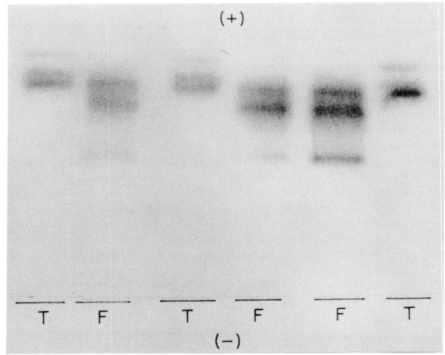

Fig. 1. Photograph of a starch-gel electrophoresis at pH 8.6 of the hemoglobins of three tadpoles (T) and of three frogs (F).

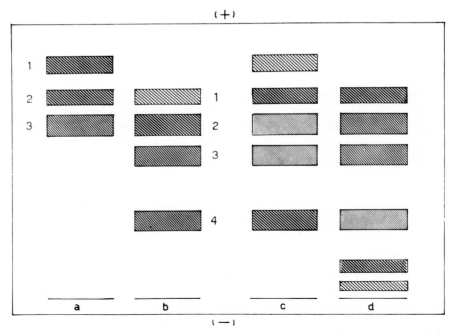

Fig. 2. Diagrammatic representation of the starch-gel electrophoresis pattern of the hemoglobins of tadpoles (a), frogs (b), metamorphosing tadpoles (c), and older frogs (d).

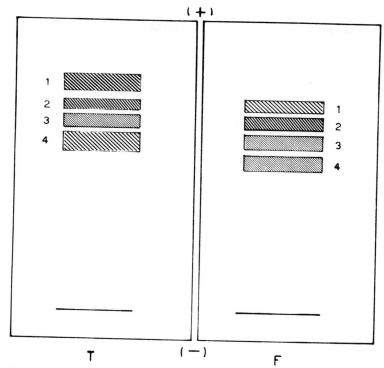

Fig. 3. Diagrammatic representation of preparative block electrophoresis patterns of tadpole (*T*) and frog (*F*) hemoglobins.

a second preparative block electrophoresis. Fraction F-3 was separated by starch-gel electrophoresis into two bands of very different electrophoretic mobility, one corresponding to a band of intermediate electrophoretic mobility of the frog hemoglobin pattern and the other to the slowest-moving band. Further purification by preparative block electrophoresis did not resolve fraction F-3, which gave consistently a single band in block electrophoresis and two bands in starch-gel electrophoresis. Fraction F-4 was obtained in sufficiently pure form after preparative block electrophoresis.

The peculiar separation of fraction F-3 into two bands by starch-gel electrophoresis made us suppose that the slow-moving hemoglobin is a polymer of the fast-moving hemoglobin. It is indeed known that in starch-gel electrophoresis the starch gel acts as a molecular sieve; protein molecules are separated according to their electrophoretic charge and

to their molecular size (Smithies, 1959). In preparative block electrophoresis, the conditions are approached instead of free boundary electrophoresis, where molecular size plays a much less important role and proteins are separated mainly according to their charge.

To test our hypothesis, the unfractionated frog hemoglobin was centrifuged in a sucrose gradient. Fractions were collected by piercing the bottom of the centrifuge tube, and the optical density of the fractions was determined (see Methods). The result of this experiment is shown in Fig. 5. Frog hemoglobin separated incompletely into two peaks; fractions from each peak were pooled and concentrated. They were then analyzed by starch-gel electrophoresis. Peak *1* showed by starch-gel electrophoresis only one component, corresponding in electrophoretic mobility to the slowest-moving component of frog hemoglobin. Peak *2* showed three hemoglobin components, namely all the fast-running frog

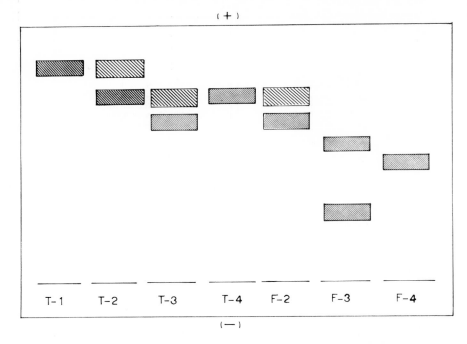

Fig. 4. Diagrammatic representation of the starch-gel electrophoresis pattern of the hemoglobin fractions isolated by preparative block electrophoresis. *T-1*, *T-2*, *T-3*, and *T-4* are fractions isolated from tadpole hemoglobin; *F-2*, *F-3*, and *F-4* are fractions isolated from frog hemoglobin.

hemoglobins. It thus seems likely that fraction F-3, isolated by preparative block electrophoresis, contains two components of identical electrophoretic charge—as shown by the lack of separation in the preparative block

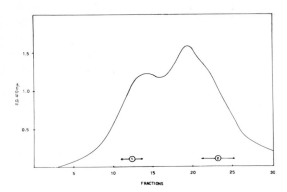

Fig. 5. Sucrose density gradient sedimentation pattern of frog hemoglobin. *1* and *2* indicate the fractions of each peak that have been combined for analysis by starch-gel electrophoresis. In *1*, only the hemoglobin *4* of Fig. 2b is present; in *2* are present all the other frog hemoglobins.

electrophoresis—and of different molecular size—as shown by the separation in starch-gel electrophoresis and by the results of the sucrose gradient centrifugation.

Human hemoglobin was centrifuged in the sucrose gradient along with frog hemoglobin as a standard. Peak *2* of frog hemoglobin occupied the same position in the sucrose gradient as human hemoglobin. Trader *et al.* (1963) have reported that sedimentation patterns of *R. catesbeiana* hemoglobin show two components, a 4.3S component and a 7.0S component. It may thus be supposed that the three fast-running frog hemoglobins (in starch-gel electrophoresis) correspond to the 4.3S component of Trader *et al.* (1963), while the slowest-running hemoglobin corresponds to the 7.0S component. This hemoglobin seems likely to be a dimer of frog hemoglobin 3 (Fig. 2, column *b*) on the basis of its molecular weight and of its electrophoretic mobility in preparative block electrophoresis.

Analysis of Hemoglobins

The hemoglobins isolated by preparative block electrophoresis were analyzed by "fingerprinting" (Ingram, 1958). Photographs of the fingerprints are reproduced in Figs. 6 and 7. The fingerprints of the tadpole hemoglobins (Fig. 6), although similar, exhibit distinctive differences. Some of these differences are indicated by arrows in Fig. 6. More differences were detected by specific staining reactions (see Baglioni, 1961) for given amino acids. However, the only common feature of these tadpole hemoglobin fingerprints is the absence of peptides containing either methionine or cysteine, as shown by the negative reaction with the platinic iodide reagent. The tadpole fingerprints showed three peptides containing tryptophan in corresponding position, five to six peptides containing arginine, six peptides containing histidine, and four to five peptides containing tyrosine.

In frog hemoglobin fingerprints (Fig. 7), one or two peptides containing methionine or cysteine are present in the neutral band. The frog fingerprints show two peptides containing tryptophan, six to eight peptides containing arginine, seven to nine peptides containing histidine, and four to five peptides containing tyrosine. The fingerprints of the different frog hemoglobins appear to be similar; the similarity in the case of hemoglobin F-3 and F-4 is striking. Hemoglobin F-2 shows more differences with the other frog hemoglobins, while it has some peptides in common with tadpole hemoglobins.

Tadpole and frog globins were examined by electrophoresis in starch gels containing 8 *M* urea. At this concentration of urea, protein molecules dissociate into individual peptide chains. Each tadpole and frog hemoglobin separated, in starch gels containing urea, into two distinct bands (Fig. 8). Reduction with mercaptoethanol and alkylation with iodoacetamide (Poulik, 1961) did not alter this pattern. It is thus likely that each tadpole and frog hemoglobin is made up of two types of peptide chains, which, as in mammalian hemoglobins, are not linked by —S—S— bonds.

DISCUSSION

The electrophoretic analysis and the fingerprinting analysis indicate that the *R. catesbeiana* tadpole possesses four hemoglobins and that the frog possesses four other hemoglobins. The fingerprinting analysis is necessary to interpret correctly the electrophoretic patterns. A tadpole hemoglobin (band 3 in Fig. 2, column *a*), which has the same electrophoretic mobility in starch-gel electrophoresis at pH 8.6 as a frog hemoglobin (band 2 in Fig. 2, column *b*), shows a completely different pattern of peptides by fingerprinting.

Both tadpole and frog hemoglobins appear to be made up of two types of peptide chains, similar to mammalian hemoglobins. Mammalian hemoglobins are made up of two pairs of peptide chains and have a molecular weight around 65,000. No information about the molecular weight of tadpole hemoglobin has been sought. This information may be necessary in order to explain some of the discrepancies between electrophoretic mobility in preparative block electrophoresis observed with tadpole hemoglobin T-4. Trader *et al.* (1963) have reported that a small amount of a component with a sedimentation constant smaller than 4.3S is observed in unfractionated *R. grylio* hemoglobin; this component may have a molecular weight half that of other tadpole hemoglobins.

The present observations indicate that all frog hemoglobins but one sediment in a sucrose density gradient with human hemoglobin and have thus a molecular weight similar to that of mammalian hemoglobins. They are presumably made up of four peptide chains. One frog hemoglobin has a higher molecular weight (band 4 in Fig. 2, column *b*) and is presumably an aggregate of eight peptide chains. It seems likely that this hemoglobin is formed from a frog hemoglobin that has a tendency to polymerize (fast component of fraction F-3; see Fig. 4), and that it is a dimer of this hemoglobin. There are indications that this hemoglobin may polymerize further *in vivo* and possibly *in vitro*. It

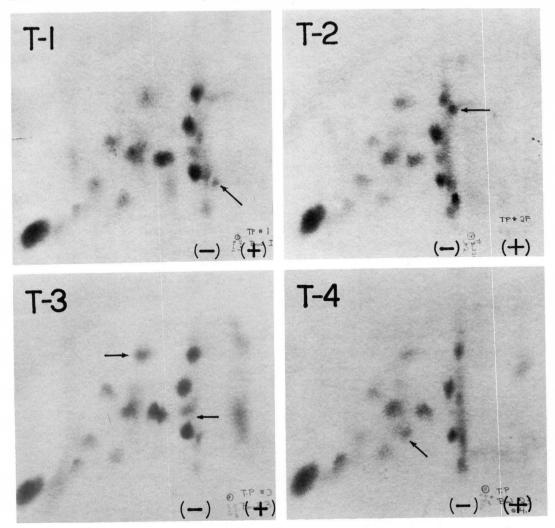

Fig. 6. Photographs of fingerprints of tadpole hemoglobins. *T-1*, *T-2*, *T-3*, and *T-4* refer to the fractions separated by preparative block electrophoresis and shown in Figs. 3 and 4. The arrows point out peptides which are peculiar to some hemoglobins.

is not clear whether this polymerization is caused by physiological changes associated with aging of the frogs. There is a smaller amount of dimer present in metamorphosing tadpoles and froglets than in adult frogs. Moreover, polymers of higher molecular weight seem to be formed in older frogs only.

More hemoglobins have been shown in tadpoles and adults of *R. catesbeiana* than have been described so far in other amphibian and vertebrate species. In order to form all the hemoglobins observed in tadpoles and frogs,

the manufacture of several different types of peptide chains is required. It is difficult, however, to estimate how many different peptide chains combine to form the hemoglobins of *R. catesbeiana*. A more detailed chemical analysis of the hemoglobins of tadpoles and frogs is required to determine exactly how many different peptide chains comprise these hemoglobins. However, the tadpole hemoglobins are made up of at least three types of peptide chains, and the frog hemoglobins are also made up of at least three types of peptide

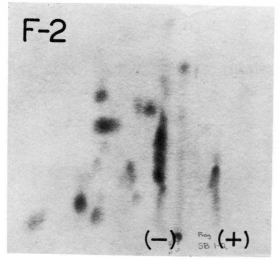

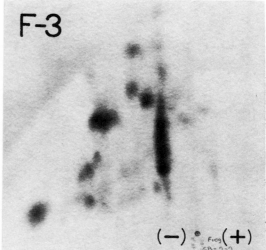

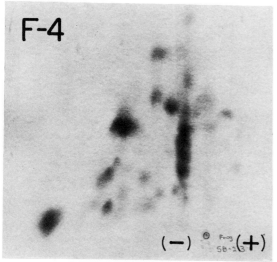

Fig. 7. Photographs of fingerprints of frog hemoglobins. *F-2*, *F-3*, and *F-4* refer to the fractions separated by preparative block electrophoresis and shown in Figs. 3 and 4.

chains, one of which may be identical with a tadpole peptide chain. This is the minimal number of peptide chains that can form the observed hemoglobins by aggregating in all the possible combinations.

If the amino acid sequence of each peptide chain is determined by a different structural gene, as is the case in man (see for references Baglioni, 1963), we have to assume that several genes are involved in determining the hemoglobin peptide chains of *R. catesbeiana*. Since the tadpole hemoglobins show a close similarity by fingerprinting, it may be supposed that the genes for tadpole hemoglobin peptide chains have originated from a com-

mon ancestor gene through duplication and divergent evolution. This type of argument has been developed in great detail by Ingram (1961) to interpret the similarities that exist between human hemoglobin peptide chains. Also the frog hemoglobins are similar, and the corresponding genes may have a common origin.

The differentiation of hemoglobin during the life cycle of mammals, like man and sheep, can be compared to that of the amphibian *R. catesbeiana*. In man (see for references Baglioni, 1963) and in sheep (Muller, 1961), one hemoglobin peptide chain is present only during fetal life. In *R. catesbeiana*

(—)

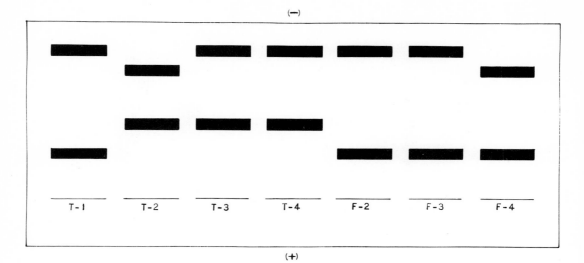

T-1   T-2   T-3   T-4   F-2   F-3   F-4

(+)

Fig. 8. Diagrammatic representation of the electrophoretic pattern of tadpole and frog globins in starch gels containing 8 M urea (see Methods); amido black stain.

there are two or three peptide chains present only in tadpoles, but not in frogs. This suggests that the tadpole hemoglobin structural genes are under a common regulatory control and that they are switched off at once when the frog hemoglobin genes are switched on.

Summary

The hemoglobins of tadpole, metamorphosing tadpole, and frog (*Rana catesbeiana*) have been studied. Starch-gel electrophoresis has shown the presence of three hemoglobins in tadpoles and four different hemoglobins in frogs; metamorphosing tadpoles have both tadpole and frog hemoglobins.

Hemoglobins have been isolated and characterized by fingerprinting and by electrophoresis in urea-containing starch gels. The hemoglobins examined are made up of two types of peptide chains, like mammalian hemoglobins. All frog hemoglobins but one have a molecular weight around 65,000; one frog hemoglobin of molecular weight around 130,000 has been separated by sucrose density gradient centrifugation. This hemoglobin is presumably formed by dimerization of a frog hemoglobin which shows a tendency to polymerize, with the aging of the frogs, to polymers of even higher molecular weights.

This investigation has been supported by grants of the Medical Foundation, Boston, Massachusetts, and of the National Science Foundation to the senior author (C. B.). The authors thank Dr. Vernon M. Ingram for discussions and criticism of the manuscript.

REFERENCES

Allen, D. W., W. A. Schroeder, and J. Balog (1958). Observations on the chromatographic heterogeneity of normal adult and fetal human hemoglobin: A study of the effect of crystallization and chromatography on the heterogeneity and isoleucine content. *J. Am. Chem. Soc.* **80**, 1678–1684.

Baglioni, C. (1961). An improved method for the fingerprinting of human hemoglobin. *Biochim. Biophys. Acta* **48**, 392–396.

Baglioni, C. (1963). Correlations between genetics and chemistry of human hemoglobins. In *Molecular Genetics* (H. Taylor, ed.), pp. 405–475. Academic Press, New York.

Chieffi, G., M. Siniscalco, and M. Adinolfi (1960). Modificazioni del comportamento elettroforetico dell'emoglobina durante la metamorfosi di *Rana esculenta*. *Atti Accad. Nazl. Lincei Rend. Classe Sci. Fis. Mat. Nat.* **28**, 233–235.

Frieden, E. (1961). Biochemical adaptation and anuran metamorphosis. *Am. Zool.* **1**, 115–149.

Gratzer, W. B., and A. C. Allison (1960). Multiple hemoglobins. *Biol. Rev.* **35**, 459.

Herner, A. E., and E. Frieden (1961). Biochemical changes during anuran metamorphosis. VIII. Changes in the nature of red cell proteins. *Arch. Biochem. Biophys.* 95, 25–35.

Ingram, V. M. (1958). Abnormal human hemoglobins. I. The comparison of normal and sickle-cell hemoglobins by "fingerprinting." *Biochim. Biophys. Acta* 28, 539–545.

Ingram, V. M. (1961). Gene evolution and the haemoglobins. *Nature* 189, 704–708.

Kunkel, H. G. (1959). Zone electrophoresis. *Methods Biochem. Anal.* 1, 141–170.

McCutcheon, F. H. (1936). Hemoglobin function during the life history of the bull-frog. *J. Cellular Comp. Physiol.* 8, 63–81.

Muller, C. J. (1961). A comparative study on the structure of mammalian and avian haemoglobins. Doctoral thesis, University of Groningen.

Poulik, M. D. (1957). Starch gel electrophoresis in a discontinuous system of buffers. *Nature* 180, 1477–1479.

Poulik, M. D. (1961). Structural differences among antibodies of different specificities. *Proc. Natl. Acad. Sci. U.S.* 47, 1751–1758.

Riggs, A. (1951). The metamorphosis of hemoglobin in the bullfrog. *J. Gen. Physiol.* 35, 23–40.

Rossi-Fanelli, A., E. Antonini, and A. Caputo (1958). Studies on the structure of hemoglobin. I. Physiological properties of human globin. *Biochim. Biophys. Acta* 30, 608–615.

Smithies, O. (1959). Zone electrophoresis in starch gels and its application to studies of serum proteins. *Advan. Protein Chem.* 14, 65–112.

Trader, C. D., J. S. Wortham, and E. Frieden (1963). Hemoglobin: molecular changes during anuran metamorphosis. *Science* 139, 918–919.

Physiological Studies of Conditional Lethal Mutants of Bacteriophage T4D

R . H . E P S T E I N
A . B O L L E
C . M . S T E I N B E R G
E . K E L L E N B E R G E R
E . B O Y D E L A T O U R

R . C H E V A L L E Y
R . S . E D G A R
M . S U S M A N
G . H . D E N H A R D T
A . L I E L A U S I S

INTRODUCTION

Following infection of a sensitive bacterium with a phage, a characteristic series of intracellular events occur. In the case of the virulent phage T4, these events include both the cessation of synthesis of many macromolecular constituents characteristic of the growing bacterial cell, and the establishment of a new biosynthetic pattern directed toward the growth and reproduction of the phage. In this new pattern of events, one set of synthetic activities follows another in temporal sequence. For example, a series of enzymes concerned with the synthesis of phage-specific DNA are formed during the first ten minutes following infection while the protein com-

Cold Spring Harbor Symposia on Quantitative Biology, 28, 375–394, 1963. Reprinted with permission.

ponents of the phage particles are synthesized later (see, for example, Kellenberger, 1961). These events are due to the introduction of the phage genome into the bacterial cell and it becomes, therefore, of basic interest to understand how the phage genome is implicated in these processes. This problem which is of importance for our understanding of bacteriophage as a biological entity, has relevance to the general question of the genetic control of growth and development. The special technical advantages of experiments with bacteriophage recommend their use in an attack on this latter problem.

Studies with defective mutants of phage lambda (Jacob *et al.*, 1957; Campbell, 1961) have shown that mutations in the phage genome profoundly affect the pattern of events which occur as a consequence of infection. Yet little is known about what functions are performed by particular phage genes, the distribution of these genes in the phage genome, or the nature of the interactions between these genes. Although for T4 and T2 we have inferential evidence regarding the functions of host range (Streisinger and Franklin, 1956), co-factor (Brenner, 1954), and osmotic shock resistant mutants (Brenner and Barnett, 1959), the function of only one gene, the endolysin gene of T4 (Streisinger *et al.*, 1961),

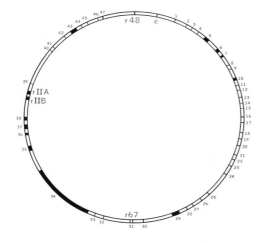

Fig. 1. A map showing the distribution of genes in T4D. The extent of some genes is indicated by the filled areas in the circle. The scale is 10° of arc = 15% recombination. The map, taken from Edgar *et al.* (in preparation) is based upon observed recombination distances, uncorrected for negative interference.

is known with complete assurance. In large part, the inability to correlate the genetic structure of the phage with the functions it performs stems from the lack of suitable mutants for such studies.

The establishment of the relationship between a gene and its expression depends upon the isolation of mutants of the gene which affect its activity in a manner that produces an observable change of phenotype. For technical reasons having to do with genetic analysis of the mutants, it is also useful if they are selective. A class of mutations that offer special advantages in these regards are conditional lethal mutations. Recently, two types of conditional lethal mutants in bacteriophage

T4D have been described and genetically characterized; temperature sensitive (*ts*) mutants which form plaques at 25°C but not at 42°C (Edgar and Lielausis, in preparation), and amber mutants (*am*) which form plaques on *Escherichia coli* CR63 but not on *E. coli* B (Epstein, Steinberg, Bolle, in preparation). Neither temperature nor host, under the conditions employed, affect the plaque-forming ability of wild type T4. Thus, each type of mutant behaves as a lethal under one set of conditions that we shall refer to as restrictive, while under a second set of conditions the mutant phenotype resembles wild type. Both classes of mutations can occur at only a restricted number of sites within a gene, but may occur in a large number of different genes.

The sites of both types of mutations are widely distributed in the genome of the phage. A comparative genetic study of the two systems (Edgar, Denhardt, Epstein, in preparation) has resulted in a map combining both *ts* and *am* mutants (see Fig. 1). Many *am* and *ts* mutations occur in the same genes. It is probable that the genes already identified represent an appreciable fraction of the total number of genes in the T4 genome. From the genetic analysis of these systems, it appears likely that additional genes will be revealed by further mutant isolations.

These mutants are especially useful in the study of gene function because, under restrictive conditions, mutant infections are abortive. By comparing a given feature of abortive mutant growth with that of wild type under comparable conditions, it is possible to obtain information relating to the step in development at which the mutation exerts its effect and thus to infer something about the function of the affected gene. Our purpose in the studies reported here is to investigate, in a preliminary way, to what extent various functions initiated by the infecting phage are carried out by different *am* and *ts* mutant phages. We have chosen to study a large number of mutants, thus our study is necessarily a superficial one. It concerns the ability of the various mutants to induce, under restrictive conditions, (1) nuclear breakdown, (2) synthesis of

DNA, (3) spontaneous lysis of infected cells, (4) synthesis of tail fiber antigen and (5) the synthesis of phage-related morphological components identifiable in the electron microscope.

As we shall show, in most cases the phenotypes of the various mutants can be described in a qualitative way by the ability or inability of the mutant complex to carry out successfully the above-mentioned processes. The distribution of phenotypes of genes around the genome, when defined in this manner, is strikingly nonrandom.

MATERIALS AND METHODS

In some cases the materials and methods used in the studies of the amber and temperature sensitive mutants differ. In these cases we have usually described the techniques employed in a section concerning the temperature sensitive mutants (Pasadena) and separately, those features which differ for the amber mutants (Geneva).

Phage Strains. (Pasadena) T4D wild type, various *ts* mutants (Edgar and Lielausis, in preparation), and the standard plaque morphology mutants *r*67 and the *r*II mutant *r*73 were used. The preparation of stocks of these strains will be described elsewhere (Edgar and Lielausis, in preparation).

(Geneva) T4D wild-type, various *am* mutants (Epstein *et al.*, in preparation), and the plaque morphology mutants *r*48, and the *r*II mutant *r*61 were used.

Bacterial Strains. (Pasadena) *Escherichia coli* strain B, or a one-step mutant B/5,1, were used as host for experiments. *E. coli* strain S/6, or its one-step mutant S/6/5,1, were used as plating indicator. In some of the serum blocking experiments strain F(λ) (Steinberg and Edgar, 1962) was used as plating indicator. (The method of preparing plating bacteria is given by Edgar and Lielausis, in preparation.) The preparation of host cells for the experiments described here is as follows: A saturated overnight culture of B (or B/5,1) made in SFH broth was diluted 100 times in SFH broth and grown with aeration for 2½ hr at 30°C (to a titer of

about 10^9 cells/ml). The cells were centrifuged and resuspended in H broth and adjusted to a concentration of about 2×10^{10} cells/ml.

(Geneva) *E. coli* B was used as host for experiments. Platings were made on the indicator strains *E. coli* S/6 and *E. coli* CR63. Strain K112–12 (λ) of *E. coli* was used in some experiments involving calibration of the serum blocking test. Plating bacteria and host cells for experiments were prepared by diluting an inoculum from a saturated overnight culture 100-fold in prewarmed (37°C) H broth. This culture was then grown with vigorous aeration for 2 hr, centrifuged, and the pellet resuspended in fresh H broth. Bacteria to be used for plating were concentrated ten-fold; the concentration of bacteria which were to serve as hosts in experiments was adjusted during resuspension to give 4×10^8 cells/ml.

Media. (Pasadena and Geneva) H broth, SFH broth (H broth without NaCl) and SPH broth (H broth with one-tenth the amount of NaCl present in H broth) were used as growth media for bacteria and bacteria infected with phage. For plating, EHA top layer agar and EHA bottom agar were used. (The recipes for these media can be found in Steinberg and Edgar, 1962.)

Basic Experimental Design. (Pasadena) One ml of host bacteria at a concentration of 2×10^{10} cells/ml was equilibrated at 39.5°C. Five ml of phage (also equilibrated at 39.5°C) at a concentration of about 10^{10} phage/ml in H broth was added to the bacteria. After 2 min the total six ml was transferred to 50 ml of SFH broth also equilibrated at 39.5°C. This growth tube now contained bacteria at a concentration of 10^8/ml infected with an average of 2.5 phage. The initial incubation under concentrated conditions and in the presence of NaCl permits the adsorption of at least 99% of the phage in the 2 min period. Further adsorption is greatly reduced by the low amount of NaCl in the growth tube. The growth tube was aerated by vigorous bubbling and maintained at 39.5°C (± 0.2°C). (In some experiments a temperature of 40.5°C was used.) Samples taken at 10, 20, and 40 min were assayed for infective centers and mature phage. Other samples were taken at various times for measurements described below.

(Geneva) As above except that appropriate volumes of bacteria and phage, each at 30°C were mixed so that the final titer of bacteria was 2×10^8 cells/ml and the multiplicity of infection about five. Samples for the determination of unadsorbed phage and infected bacteria titers were taken at 10 min after infection. All cultures were lysed at 60 min after infection and were assayed for progeny of both *am* and *am*+ genotypes.

Cytological Observations. (Pasadena) Samples of infected cells were added to an equal volume of a 40% solution of polyvinylpyrrolidone (PVP) containing 10% formaldehyde. Within 10 min after the addition of the formaldehyde to the cells the samples were observed with a phase contrast microscope under oil immersion (mag. × 1250). As in a previous study using gelatin (Mason and Powelson, 1956), the PVP is used to provide a refractive index in the medium surrounding the cells which permits visualization of cell nuclei. The formaldehyde serves to fix the cells. The cells do not change their optical properties for about 15 min at which time they become opaque. (Even before 15 min, 10 to 50% of the cells are opaque.) Cells infected with wild type phage pass through three clearly distinguishable phases which correspond to (1) uninfected cells with nuclei of normal appearance, (2) nuclear disruption and (3) a stage of general transparency which normally corresponds to the development of the pool of vegetative phage DNA.

(Geneva) As above, except that formaldehyde fixation was omitted and all samples were examined within 2 min of preparation. In some determinations a gelatin suspension of appropriate concentration was used in place of PVP.

DNA Determinations. (Pasadena) The total amount of DNA in samples of the cultures taken at various times was measured by the Keck modification of the Ceriotti method (Keck, 1956). 2.5 ml samples from the infected cultures were added to 2.5 ml of a 0.1 M HCl and 0.001 M indole solution. These samples were heated at 96°C for 10 min and then shaken successively with four equivalent volumes of amyl acetate and the aqueous phase retained. The OD of the samples was then measured in a Beckman DU spectrophotometer at 490 mμ. The blank was a control sample of growth medium (SPH broth) treated identically to the growth tube samples.

(Geneva) A number of determinations were made by the Ceriotti method described above. In other measurements of DNA synthesis a slight modification of the method of Burton (1956) was employed. Four ml aliquots containing 2×10^8 infected bacteria/ml were taken from an experimental culture and transferred to centrifuge tubes containing one ml ice cold 70% perchloric acid (PCA). After two hr in the cold, the mixture of infected bacteria and PCA was centrifuged for 15 min at $6{,}000 \times g$, the supernatant discarded, and the pellet resuspended in one ml of 0.5 N PCA. The resuspended samples were hydrolyzed at 75°C for a period of 25 min, cooled, and then centrifuged a second time at $6{,}000 \times g$ for 15 min. The supernatant was carefully decanted and 0.7 ml added to 0.3 ml of 0.5 N PCA and the resulting one ml sample mixed with two ml of diphenylamine reagent, and incubated at 30°C for 16 hr. The extent of reaction with the reagent was determined as the optical density at 590 mμ. The instrument used for these measurements was a Meunier colorimeter.

Diphenylamine reagent: 1.5 gm of diphenylamine was dissolved in a solution containing 100 ml of concentrated acetic acid and 1.5 ml of concentrated sulfuric acid. This solution was stored in the dark and just before use, 0.25 ml of aqueous acetaldehyde (0.07 M) was added to the solution for each 40 ml of reagent required.

Lysis Measurements. (Pasadena) Lysis of the infected cultures was determined from measurements of the optical density of samples taken at different times. The OD was determined at 450 mμ in a Bausch and Lomb Spectronic colorimeter. The OD of the control (*r*67) cultures drops by at least a factor of two, beginning at about 25 min after infection.

(Geneva) Lysis of most cultures was confirmed by simple visual observation. In a number of cases, lysis was also measured by bacterial counts in a Petroff-Hauser counting chamber; in others, the lysis of a culture was followed by changes in optical density as a function of time. Measurements of optical density at 590 mμ were made with a Meunier colorimeter.

Preparation of Lysates. (Pasadena and Geneva) Most mutant-infected cells lyse within 40 min after infection. At 40 min (60 min in Geneva) the lysates were sterilized by the addition of chloroform and debris centrifuged out at low speed (1000 $\times$ g for 20 min). However, some mutant infected cultures do not lyse, even after incubation for as long as 2 hr. Lysates of these complexes were obtained by the addition of egg-white lysozyme (10 gamma/ml) and versene (0.1 M). Lysis of the cells of such a treated culture was checked by microscopic observation. These lysates were then sterilized with chloroform and centrifuged to remove large debris.

Serum Blocking Antigen Measurements. (Pasadena) Measurements for the presence of serum blocking antigen were performed essentially by the method of De Mars (1955). The anti-T4 rabbit serum was used at a dilution which gave a k value of 5×10^{-2}/min. For each experimental series a calibration curve was also made. The serum was calibrated using an rII mutant (r73) or in some cases ultraviolet inactivated phage. The results of these two calibrations did not differ. Various diluted samples of the ts mutant lysates were mixed with serum and incubated at 48°C for 18 hr. At this time about 5×10^5 r67 "tester phage" were added and the tubes incubated for another 2 hr. Samples were then plated on F(λ) and the plates incubated at 42°C so that only the tester phage would form plaques. Inactivation of the tester in the absence of serum is negligible. The serum blocking titer of the lysate was calculated on the basis of at least two different dilutions of the mutant lysate which gave tester phage survival on the linear portion of the calibration curves.

(Geneva) Assay and calibrations were the same as in the Pasadena tests except for the following modifications. In most tests the reaction mixtures were incubated at 30°C for 14 hr. Tester phage (wild type) were added at a concentration of 6×10^7 and incubation at 30°C was continued for another 2½ hr. Tester phage survival was measured by plating on S/6. For each series of determinations a few points on the calibration curve were repeated.

Electron Microscopy. (Pasadena) Most lysates were examined by two methods. *Method A:* Grids were prepared according to the agar filtration method of Kellenberger and Arber (1957). Polystyrene latex spheres were added to the lysate samples for counting purposes. The concentration of the spheres was determined by calibration against control lysates of wild type phage. Grids were shadowed with gold-platinum-palladium alloy. In many cases the shadow angle was too large (45°) to give good visualization of tail components. Counts were made from photographs of fields chosen on the basis of even dispersion of the spheres. Areas of clumping or streaking of spheres were avoided. Preparations with large holes in the supporting film were also rejected. Only preparations in which the background appeared clean, and in which microsomal particles were clearly visible, were counted. Sufficient counts were made to include at least 50 spheres. This corresponded to 50 phage particles in control lysates. *Method B:* Lysates were treated with DNAase and RNAase and concentrated 100-fold by centrifugation at 40,000 $\times$ g for 30 min. Samples were resuspended in either phosphate buffer or 2% ammonium acetate. Neutralized 1% phosphotungstate acid (PT) with added sucrose (1%) was added to an equal volume of the phage lysate. Samples were placed on grids with parlodion films and the excess liquid removed by the application of filter paper to the edge of the grid. In many cases, more than one preparation was made of a given lysate and for a number of cases, preparations from different lysates of the same mutant (or wild type) were examined. The results of acceptable repeated determinations were similar.

Observations were made with an RCA EMUII or a Philips EM 120 microscope.

(Geneva) The agar filtration method was employed for the preparation of lysates for electron microscopic observation. Latex spheres at known concentration were added to all preparations. Grids carrying the supporting film and sample were shadowed at an angle of 30° with gold-platinum-palladium alloy. For each preparation, grids were examined with an RCA II electron microscope and ten fields of view were photographed at a magnification of 3500 ×. Films from grids judged to be acceptable with respect to the distribution of latex spheres and of objects were counted. At least 70 but most often 200 or more latex spheres (about 15 to 30 per field) and at least 200 phage-related morphological entities (when present in normal amounts) were counted for each preparation.

From the known latex concentration, the counts of various phage morphological components, and the measurements of infected bacteria used in the preparation of the lysates, the number of equivalents per bacterium for each category of object was calculated. From repeated determinations of the same lysate we estimate that, on the average, two separate determinations will differ from each other by less than a factor of two. The relative amounts of the various components were more reproducible.

In some cases, lysates of mutant-infected cells were also examined in PT preparations; the procedure followed was that described in Brenner and Horne (1959).

RESULTS

With both *am* and *ts* mutants, the general experimental design was as follows: Bacteria were infected with a given mutant phage under restrictive conditions. A control culture (wild type or *r*48) was, in most cases, also included in each experimental set. The vast majority of the mutants produce less than 1% of the viable phage produced by a control culture under comparable conditions. Samples of the infected bacteria were taken at various times during the course of the infectious cycle. On these samples, various determinations were made which are described below.

In general, the results of our studies were unambiguous in the sense that for a given determination, the mutant infected cultures were either comparable to the control or markedly defective. For this reason, we have chosen to

present our experimental results in summary form in a table. In Table 1 the mutants studied are grouped by genes and the genes are listed in the order in which they occur in the linkage structure. The finding in a particular test is reported either as a plus, indicating a result comparable to the control, or as a zero, indicating that the mutant infected culture was defective as compared to the control. Following each description of a particular determination below, we indicate the criteria for the designations plus and zero used in the table.

Tests and Criteria for Judging Results

1. Nuclear Breakdown. One to three min after infection the nucleus of the bacterium is disrupted. This disruption, termed nuclear breakdown, which has been investigated by electron microscopic studies (Kellenberger, Sechaud, and Ryter, 1959) is also demonstrable under special conditions in phase contrast microscopy (see Materials and Methods). All *am* and *ts* mutants studied initiate nuclear breakdown. With some mutants (*am*N82 in gene 44, *am*N116 in gene 39, and *am*N130 in gene 46) the ability to initiate nuclear breakdown has been confirmed by studies of sectioned material in the electron miscroscope. Since this process occurs in all mutant infected cells, these results have been omitted from the table. In passing, we should note that in all cases, including the mutant complexes in which DNA synthesis is not initiated, the infected bacteria lose the capacity to form colonies.

2. DNA Synthesis. Shortly after infection, the total amount of DNA in the cell begins to increase. The increase in DNA is linear with time and reaches, at the end of the latent period, a value 2.5 to 5 times the amount of DNA in the cell at the time of infection. Total DNA was measured in samples taken at early times, before any increase in DNA is observed in controls (one to five min), and at late times, just before or after lysis occurs in the controls (25 to 60 min). Increases in the amount of DNA by a factor of two or more between early and late samples is considered normal and is entered in the table as a plus. Mutant infected cultures which show an in-

TABLE 1. Phenotypic classification of *am* and *ts* mutants

Gene	Mutant	Viable Phage/Cell	Lysis	DNA	Serum Blocking Antigen	Normal Particles	Contracted Particles	Heads	Tails
—	Control Geneva	150	+	+	+	+	0	+	+
	Control Pasadena	200	+	+	+	+	0	0	0
1	amB24	0.03	0	0	0	0	0	0	0
	amA494	0.005	0	0	0	0	0	0	0
2	amN51	2	+	+	+	0	0	+	+
3	tsA2	0.01	+	+	+	0	0	+	+
4	amN112	2	+	+	+	0	0	+	+
5	tsA28	0.4	+	+	+	0	0	+	0
	tsB49	0.01	+	+	+	0	0	+	0
	amN135	0.008	+	+	+	0	0	+	0
	amB256	0.006	+	+	+	0	0	+	0
6	tsA25	0.01	+	+	+	0	0	+	0
	amN102	0.08	+	+	+	0	0	+	0
	amB251	0.002	+	+		0	0	+	0
	amB254	0.03	+			0	0	+	0
	amB274	0.02	+			0	0	+	0
7	tsB98	0.01	+	+	+	0	0	+	0
	amB16	0.003	+	+	+	0	0	+	0
	amN115	0.009	+			0	0	+	0
	amB23	0.002	+	+		0	0	+	0
8	tsB25	0.01	+	+		0	0	+	0
	amN132	0.02	+	+	+	0	0	+	0
9	tsN11	1.0	+	+	+	0	+	0	0
	tsL54	10				+	+	0	0
10	tsA10	0.5	+	+	+	0	0	+	0
	tsB64	0.02	+	+	+	0	0	+	0
	tsB12	0.02	+	+		0	0	+	0
	amB255	0.03	+	+	+	0	0	+	0
11	tsL140	<0.01	+	+		0	0	+	0
	amN93	0.07	+		+	+	+	+	0
	amN128	0.02	+	+	+	+	0	+	+
12	tsA13	0.02	+	+	+	+	+	+	+
	tsB60	0.05	+	+	+	+	+	+	+
	amN69	0.003	+	+	+	0	+	+	+
	amN104	0.01	+			+	+	+	+
	amN108	0.02	+			+	+	+	+
13	tsN49	1.0	+	+	+	0	0	+	+
14	amN71	0.1	+			0	0	+	+
	amB20	0.01	+	+	+	0	0	+	+
	amE351	0.1	+	+	+	0	0	+	+
15	tsN26	0.02	+	+	+	0	0	+	+
	amN133	1.0	+	+	+	0	0	+	+

TABLE 1 (continued)

Gene	Mutant	Viable Phage/Cell	Lysis	DNA	Serum Blocking Antigen	Normal Particles	Contracted Particles	Heads	Tails
16	amN66	0.01	+	+		0	0	+	+
	amN88	0.8	+	+	+	0	0	+	+
17	tsL51	2.0	+	+		0	0	+	+
	amN56	0.002	+		+	0	0	+	+
18	tsA38	0.4	+	+	+	0	0	+	+
19	tsN3	0.01	+	+	+	0	0	+	0
	tsB31	0.05	+	+		0	0	+	0
20	tsA23	0.01	+	+	+	0	0	0	+
	amB8	0.43	+			0	0	0	+
	amN83	0.002	+	+		0	0	0	+
	amN50	0.007	+	+	+	0	0	0	+
21	tsN8	0.03	+	+		0	0	0	+
	amN80	1.0	+	+		0	0	0	+
	amN121	0.3	+			0	0	0	+
	amN90	0.3	+	+	+	0	0	0	+
22	tsL147	0.5	+	+		0	0	0	+
	amB270	0.001	+	+	+	0	0	+[1]	+
23	tsL65	0.1	+	+		0	0	+	+
	tsN37	1.0	+	+	+	0	0	+	+
	amB17	0.04	+	+	+	0	0	0	+
	amB272	0.006	+	+	+	0	0	0	+
24	tsN29	0.02	+	+	+	0	0	0	+
	amN65	0.01	+	+	+	0	0	0	+
	amB26	0.007	+	+	+	0	0	0	+
25	amN67	1.0	+		+				
	amN61	1.0	+	+	+	0	0	+	0
26	amN131	0.01	+	+	+	0	0	+	0
27	tsN34	0.5	+	+	+	0	0	+	0
	amN120	0.002	+	+	+	0	0	+	0
28	amA452	0.1	+	+	+	0	0	+	0
29[4]	amB7	<0.001	+	+	+	0	0	+	0
	amN85	0.01	+	+	+	0	0	+	0
	tsL103	0.5	+	+		0	0	+	0
30	tsN7	0.5	+	+	+	0	0	0	+
	tsB20	0.01	+	+		0	0	0	+
31	amN54	0.02	+	+	+	0	0	0	+
	amN111	0.005	+	+	+	0	0	0	+
32	amA453	<0.001	0	0	0	0	0	0	0
33	amN134	0.006	0[2]	+	0	0	0	0	0
34	tsA20	0.1	+	+	+	+	0	0	0
	tsN1	0.04	+	+	+	+	0	0	0
	tsB3	0.03	+	+	+	+	0	0	0
	tsB22	0.3	+	+	+	+	0	0	0
	tsB57	0.01	+	+	+	+	0	0	0

TABLE 1 (continued)

Gene	Mutant	Viable Phage/Cell	Lysis	DNA	Serum Blocking Antigen	Normal Particles	Contracted Particles	Heads	Tails
	tsA44	0.02	+	+	+	+	0	0	0
	amN58	0.1	+	+	0	+	0	+	+
	amB25	0.04	+	+	0				
	amB258	0.07	+		0				
	amB288	0.03	+		0				
	amB265	0.03	+		0				
35	tsN30	0.1	+	+	+	+	0	0	0
	amB252	0.1	+	+	+	+	0	+	+
36	tsN41	1.0	+	+	+	+	0	0	0
	tsB6	1.0	+	+	+	+	0	0	0
37	tsB78	0.01	+	+	+	+	0	0	0
	tsB32	0.05	+	+	+	+	0	0	0
	tsN5	2.0	+	+	+	+	0	0	0
	amN52	0.03	+	+	0	+	0	+	+
	amN91	0.003	+		0	+	0	+	+
	amB280	0.06	+		0	+	0	+	+
38	amN62	1.2	+		0[1]	+	0	+	+
	amB262	0.1	+	+	0[1]	+	0	+	+
39	tsA41	~50	+[3]	+[3]					
	tsG41	~50	+[3]	+[3]	+				
	amN116	37	+[3]	+[3]	+[3]	+	0	+	+
40	tsL177	0.01	+[2]	+					
41	tsA14	0.01	0	0	0	0	0	0	0
	amN57	0.07	0	0	0	0	0	0	0
	amB15	0.05	0	0					
42	tsG25	5.0	0	0	0				
	amN122	0.007	0	0	0	0	0	0	0
43	tsL91	5.0	0	0	0				
	tsG37	10.0	0	0	0				
	tsL141	0.5	0	0	0				
	tsL56	0.4	0	0	0				
	tsL107	0.1	0	0	0	0	0	0	0
	amB22	0.08	0	0	0	0	0	0	0
	amN101	16	0	+[3]	+	+	0	+	+
44	amN82	0.001	0	0	0	0	0	0	0
	tsB110	0.01	0	0					
45	tsL159	1.0	0	0					
46	tsL109	1.0	0	+[3]					
	amN130	2.6	0	+[3]	+	+[1]	0	+	+
	amN94	0.9				0	0	+	+
	tsL166	0.01	0	+[3]					
47	tsL86	1.0	0	+[3]					
	tsB10	1.0	0	+[3]					

[1] Present in low but significant amount.

[2] Lysis is incomplete but facilitated by chloroform.

[3] Phenotype abnormal, see text.

[4] Note added in proof: More recent $am \times ts$ complementation tests show that gene 29 is actually composed of two separate genes; the sites of amB7 and tsL103 are in one of these genes, the site of amN85 in the other.

crease of less than a factor of two are considered to be defective and the results are scored as zero. Where DNA synthesis was defective, the measurements have been repeated with many samples taken at different times during the course of the infection. In a number of cases, no appreciable DNA increase was detected despite the fact that several phage per bacterium were produced (e.g., *ts* G25 of gene 42). This is possibly due to conversion of bacterial DNA to phage DNA, resulting in no net synthesis. In some instances, DNA synthesis is detected but is clearly abnormal in kinetics. These cases will be discussed later.

3. Serum Blocking Antigen. Antibody prepared against phage particles neutralizes phage primarily by complexing with tail fibers (Franklin, 1961). The presence of tail fiber antigen in lysates can be detected by its ability to combine with neutralizing antibody resulting in a decrease in the neutralizing power of the serum when subsequently tested (De Mars, 1955). We have used this technique to detect tail fiber antigen in lysates of mutant infected cells. Control lysates produce over 50 equivalents of serum blocking power per infected bacterium. Experiments with mutant infected lysates are scored as plus if over 50 equivalents are produced per infected cell. Mutants defective in the production of tail fiber antigen produce less than 15 equivalents per cell and are designated by a zero in the table.

4. Lysis. Although synthesis of the endolysin commences shortly after that of phage DNA, the onset of cell lysis does not occur until a later time. The spontaneous lysis of the infected culture indicates that the endolysin is synthesized and the mechanism triggering the lytic mechanism is operative. Although control cultures infected with *r*48 or *r*67 lyse spontaneously, wild type infected cultures do not lyse spontaneously under concentrated conditions due to lysis inhibition induced by the phage released from early lysing cells. In most cases mutant infected cultures produce too few progeny phage to induce lysis inhibition. Clearing of these cultures indicates an operative lytic mechanism (+). Lack of clearing in cases where no phage are released indicates a defect in the lytic mechanism (0). Cultures which do not lyse but which produce several infective particles per cell may show no lysis due to lysis inhibition rather than to defects in the lytic mechanism. In these cases, an operative lytic mechanism is indicated if lysis occurs when antiserum is added to the culture to prevent lysis inhibition, or where lysis of the cells can be induced with chloroform. (Chloroform appears to induce lysis of cells only if endolysin is present.)

5. Synthesis of Morphological Components. Lysates of the mutant infected cells were examined in the electron microscope for the presence of structures identifiable as components of phage particles. We are largely concerned with the presence or absence of: (a) phage head membranes, (b) tail cores with or without surrounding sheaths but with attached endplates, and (c) complete phage particles. Although other phage related structures have been observed in some preparations, they have not been included in the table. In a later section, we shall comment on some of the special observations.

In Geneva, appreciable numbers of free heads and tails as well as complete particles are found in control lysates, while under the conditions employed in Pasadena, the ratio of intact phage to unassembled components was usually more than ten to one. This difference is unexplained. In the *ts* mutant lysates, if the amount of a given component (particles, head membranes, etc.) was comparable to the amount of complete particles in the controls, we conclude that a given component is present in normal quantity and the mutant is scored as plus in the appropriate column. Due to technical difficulties, it was not always possible to get reliable counts on the frequencies of tail cores with attached endplates. For this reason, all lysates which did not have a normal number of intact particles were concentrated by centrifugation and examined in PT. In these preparations, plus means that an abundance of tails were observed in PT preparations, while a zero means that few if any tails were observed.

In Geneva, in almost all shadowed preparations, both free heads and tails could be readily seen. The number of equivalents per infected cell for each component was calculated. Where the number of equivalents was comparable to that observed in control preparations, the mutant is scored as a plus for that character. If less than 15 equivalents per bacterium of a given component were found in the lysate, the mutant was scored as a zero. In general, as in the case of the other determinations, the distinctions were unambiguous. Mutant lysates classified as defective contain no more than 20% and generally considerably less of a given component than those classified as normal.

In shadowed preparations and, more often, in PT preparations free phage heads which contain electron dense material, presumably DNA, are occasionally seen. The fact that the majority of the free head membranes are empty we interpret as due to the loss of DNA from the head during processing for electron microscopic observation. It is likely that all empty head membranes contain DNA at some stage in their production (see Kellenberger *et al.*, 1959).

GENERAL REMARKS AND OBSERVATIONS

From an examination of the table it is apparent that, with few exceptions, mutations in the same gene give the same general result. This indicates that the phenotype we observe reflects the mutational loss of function of a particular gene under restrictive conditions. We conclude that the differences between a particular mutant and wild type are gene specific and do not represent some property common to the *am* or *ts* mutants as a whole.

In Fig. 2 we have summarized the results of the table, representing each gene by a single symbol indicating its phenotype when mutant. It is clear from the figure that the distribution of the genes throughout the genome is not random with respect to our designated phenotypes. Rather, the genes appear to show a highly clustered arrangement according to function. We will describe below the general phenotypic features of each cluster

and additional observations not included in the table.

As a first approximation, the genes appear to fall in two major classes. One class (genes 1, 32, and 39 to 47) exhibits defects in DNA synthesis, the second class (genes 2 to 31 and 33 to 38) exhibits defects in maturation. These two major groups of genes occupy two non-overlapping regions of the genome (although we should point out that the endolysin gene (Streisinger *et al.*, 1961) lies between genes 47 and 1). The DNA defective genes are classified in the following manner.

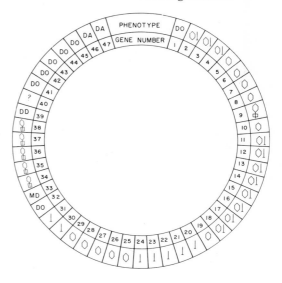

Fig. 2. Mutant phenotypes of genes containing conditional lethals. Genes are given in their map order. Some mutant phenotypes are symbolized by letters, the meanings of which are described in the text. The symbol designations of the rest of the genes represent the major morphological component present in mutant lysates.

DD Gene (39). There is a delay in the onset of DNA synthesis after which DNA synthesis proceeds normally. Tail fiber antigen synthesis shows a corresponding delay, active phage are eventually formed, and the complexes finally lyse if serum is present.

DO Genes (1, 32, and 41 to 45). No detectable DNA synthesis occurs. (One mutant of gene, 43, *am*N101, shows some DNA synthesis and probably is a "leaky" mutant.) In no case was tail fiber antigen, particle components, or lysis of the infected cells de-

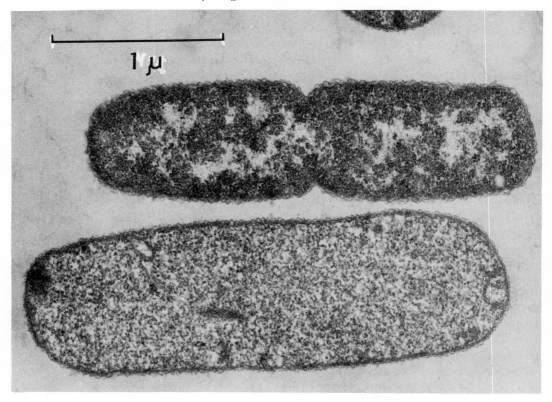

Fig. 3. A micrograph of sectioned cells from an *am*N122 (gene 42) infected culture. The culture was fixed (formaldehyde, 2%, osmium tetroxide, 1%) after 45 min of incubation at 32°C. Note the homogeneous distribution of ribosomes and absence of a DNA pool in the infected cell (lower cell). For purposes of comparison we have chosen a field containing a cell (upper cell) which appears to be uninfected.

tected. The infected cells lose the ability to form colonies.

DA Genes (46 and 47). DNA synthesis is initiated normally but ceases after a short interval; few active phage but various phage-related components are synthesized. Cultures clear at least partially if treated with chloroform.

Gene 40 has been incompletely studied. DNA is synthesized but it is not yet known if the kinetics or amount of DNA formed is aberrant. The cells lyse with chloroform indicating the presence of the endolysin.

In a few cases, observations were made on the intracellular morphology of bacteria infected with mutants defective in DNA synthesis. Samples from mutant infected cultures were taken at various times during the infectious cycle and thin sections of fixed and embedded cells were examined in the electron microscope. The observations which have been made are in accord with the results of the determinations just discussed. Cells infected with a DA mutant, *am*N130, contain condensates (Kellenberger *et al.*, 1959) indicating that maturation is not completely blocked. Sections of cells infected with *am*N116, a DD mutant, contain condensates in samples taken at late times (46 min after infection) but at earlier times no condensates are observed, although they are present in comparable control infected bacteria. For *am*N122 and *am*N81, both DO mutants, no evidence of phage maturation is observed in the sections and further, the characteristic DNA pool is not formed although nuclear breakdown does occur. The appearance of cells infected with *am*N122 is shown in Fig. 3.

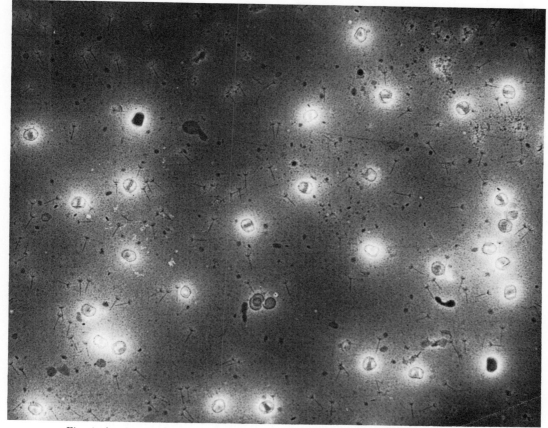

Fig. 4. A micrograph of a lysate of *ts*A38 (gene 18). As described in Materials and Methods the lysate was concentrated by centrifugation and prepared by the PT method. Note empty heads and free cores with attached endplates.

The second class of mutants are those which exhibit defects in maturation. In most respects the pattern of events after infection is normal. DNA synthesis is normal and the infected cultures lyse at the same time as controls. However, almost no viable phage are produced and only certain morphological components are found in the lysates. As a first approximation, the mutants can be divided into several categories based upon the components present in normal amounts in the lysates: (1) normal appearing but inactive particles; (2) particles with contracted sheaths; (3) head membranes and free tails (see Fig. 4); (4) head membranes only; (5) tails only; and (6) few if any components. All of the mutants which lyse normally and synthesize DNA normally fall into one of these 6 categories.

The Tail Fiber Genes (34 to 38). Cells infected with all mutants of these genes produce normal-appearing particles. Free heads and tails are also present in *am* lysates but not in *ts* lysates. However, as pointed out earlier, this difference between the results found in Geneva and Pasadena also occurs for the controls. In the case of certain *am* mutants, it appears likely that the particles do not have tail fibers. In no case are these non-infectious particles capable of killing bacteria and preliminary studies suggest that they cannot attach normally to bacteria. *am* Mutants from genes 34 and 37 do not initiate synthesis of tail fiber antigens, while for *am* mutants of gene 38 the level is low. *ts* Mutants from all these genes result in normal levels of tail fiber antigen. Mapping experiments have indicated that mutations affecting the co-factor requirement (Brenner, 1957) are located in gene 34 (Edgar *et al.*, in preparation), while the host range character (Streisinger, 1956) is probably located in or near gene 37. These observations, taken as a whole, indicate that these genes are involved in the synthesis and assembly of the tail fibers and that in the absence of their formation inactive particles lacking tail fibers are formed.

The MD (Maturation Defective) Gene (33). While DNA synthesis appears to be normal, the cells show only partial lysis which is facilitated with chloroform. The lysates contain few if any morphological components and tail fiber antigen is absent. While the phenotype suggests a general defect in maturation, more work is required to characterize the nature of the block for this gene.

The Head Genes (20 to 24 and 30 and 31). These two groups of genes are characterized by the absence of heads in lysates from mutant infected cells and thus would appear to be involved in head synthesis or assembly. In one case (gene 23) heads are formed by the *ts* but not by *am* mutants in the gene. The osmotic shock resistant mutants (Brenner and Barnett, 1959) map in the neighborhood of gene 23.

Sectioned material from bacteria infected with mutants from genes 20–24 provide further information about the defects produced. While lysates of mutants *am*N50 and *am*N90, from genes 20 and 21 respectively, do not contain head membranes, sections of bacteria infected with these mutants contain structures which may be related to head membranes. In the case of *am*N90, head-like structures are observed against the limiting membrane of the bacterium, but very few of these structures are found in the interior of the cell (see Fig. 5). In bacteria infected with mutant *am*N50, long cylinders (polyhead) which in cross-section have dimensions similar to phage heads are present in large quantity (see Fig. 6). The fact that these objects are not found in abundance in the lysates is most easily explained by loss during the centrifugation employed in the preparation of lysates for electron microscopic observation.

Sections of cells infected with *am*B17 (gene 23) and *am*N65 (gene 24) show neither condensates nor aberrant structures similar to those found in the case of *am*N90 or *am*N50.

Less can be said about the rest of the maturation defective mutants. We have characterized the phenotypes of these genes in the figure as resulting in the formation of heads only (genes 5–8, 10, 19 and 25–29), unassembled heads and tails (genes 2–4, 11–18) or contracted phage (gene 9). The head and tail classification includes mutants (genes 11 and 12) which give appreciable numbers of complete but inactive particles in the lysates. The proportion of these complete particles varies from mutant to mutant and preparation to preparation. This variability is most easily explained by the formation of particles susceptible to breakdown. The majority of the particles produced by mutants of gene 9 have contracted sheaths although the heads remain filled.

The particular morphological components scored in the lysates were chosen because observation can be made with reasonable confidence. Certain other morphological components have been observed in some mutant lysates but have not been included in our characterization of the mutants because quantitative observations are more difficult. For example, free cores without endplates have been observed in lysates of *am*B274 (gene 6). It should also be noted that no distinction has been made in reporting our results between the presence or absence of a sheath surrounding the free tail cores. Differences between the various mutants exist in this regard but more work is required to ascertain the distributions of these phenotypes among the mutants.

Of particular interest is the observation that, in most lysates which contain incomplete particles, cylinders of varying lengths and with widths approximately that of contracted sheath are frequently observed (Figs. 7 and 8). Electron microscopic studies of this material (Boy de la Tour and Kellenberger, in preparation) show that these cylinders (which we shall refer to as polysheath) are composed of sheath material.

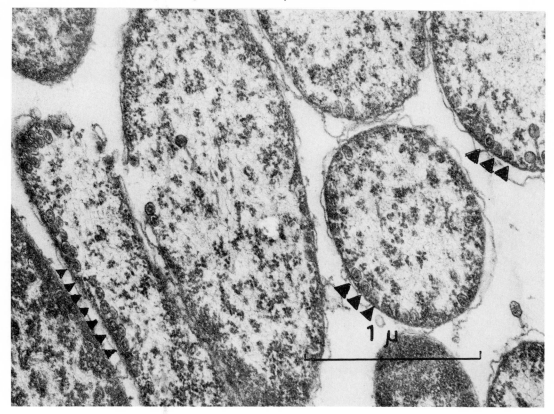

Fig. 5. *am*N90 (Gene 21) infected *E. coli* B. Cells were fixed after incubation for 40 min at 32°C. Note the abnormal heads arranged along the cytoplasmic membrane (arrows).

DISCUSSION

The Nature of *am* and *ts* Mutations

Although most *am* and *ts* mutants located within the same gene present the same phenotypes, there are instances in which the *am* and *ts* phenotypes are dissimilar. Gene 34 is one example of such dissimilarity. While particle morphology, bacterial killing ability and attachment behavior of the *am* and *ts* mutants of gene 34 are very similar, tail fiber antigen is absent in all *am* lysates and present in all *ts* mutant lysates. The observations hold for *am* and *ts* mutants at a variety of sites within the gene. The assumption that *am* mutations prevent the formation of protein (or permit only the synthesis of a grossly altered molecule) while the *ts* mutations do not, provides a simple explanation for the differences observed. Thus, we imagine that

in *ts* mutant lysates the protein coded by gene 34 is present as an altered and functionally defective molecule which nevertheless has antigenic activity, but that no gene 34 protein is present in the *am* mutant lysates. It is of interest, in this connection, that a preliminary investigation of the particles in the *am* lysates indicates that they lack tail fibers.

The explanation suggested is also supported by a study of a second gene in which dissimilarities exist between the phenotypes of *am* and *ts* mutants. On the basis of the *am* phenotypes we have assumed that gene 23 is involved in the formation of the phage head membrane. Head membranes, however, are present in the *ts* lysates although absent in *am* lysates. Sarabhai and Brenner (personal communication) recently demonstrated that gene 23 is the structural gene for head protein. The study includes the observation that the mu-

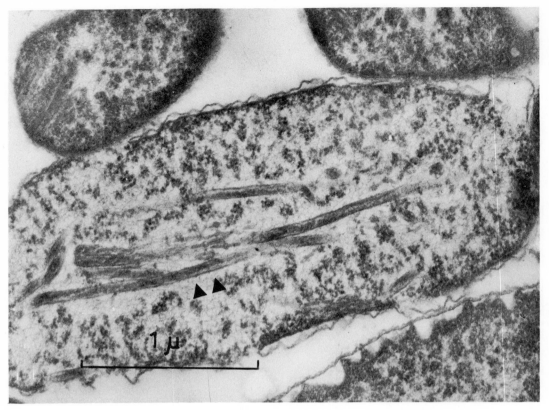

Fig. 6. *am*N50 (Gene 20) infected *E. coli* B. Cells were fixed after incubation for 40 min
at 32°C. Note the long cylinders (polyhead) in the interior of the cell (arrows).

tant *am* 17 in this gene prevents the formation of head protein.

Arguments presented elsewhere (Epstein *et al.*, in preparation; Edgar and Lielausis, in preparation; Edgar *et al.*, in preparation) concerning the nature of *am* and *ts* mutants lend additional support to our interpretation of the major difference between these two mutant types.

The Arrangement of Genes with Related Phenotypes

One of the most striking results of our study is that genes with various functions, as inferred from our phenotypic tests, are not randomly distributed in the genome but are grouped into regions within which all genes have similar phenotypes and presumably related functons. Genes which appear to be involved in the early functions of growth (mutations affecting DNA synthesis) form

one major region of the genome separate from the second major group of genes which are concerned with late functions (e.g., the maturation of phage). Each of the two major regions can be further subdivided into subregions or clusters of genes with similar phenotypes. Since our operational definition of a gene (based upon the complementation properties of the mutants) (Edgar *et al.*, in preparation) is in accord with that used in genetic studies with other organisms, a cluster is, by this criterion, composed of a number of genes and not just one gene. In support of this contention is the finding that mutations in one gene but not in others in the same cluster result in the absence of specific phage-induced proteins. Mutations in gene 42 not only affect the synthesis of dCMP hydroxymethylase but in certain instances modify its structure (Wiberg *et al.*, 1962; Dirksen *et al.*, 1963; Wiberg, personal communication).

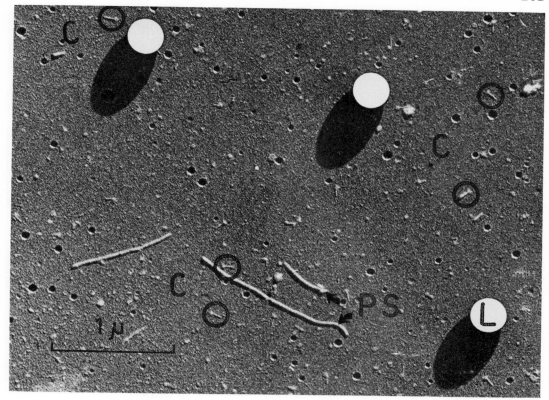

Fig. 7. A shadowed preparation of a lysate of *am*B17 infected *E. Coli* B. This field is taken from a micrograph used for particle counts. Note latex spheres (L), polysheath (PS), and cores with attached endplates (circled).

As mentioned earlier, there is now evidence that gene 23 specifically controls the structure of the head protein. In both cases these proteins are unaffected by mutations in other genes in the same cluster.

Since a significant proportion, perhaps as much as half, of the genes of the phage have been studied, the clustered arrangement appears to be a general feature of the genome. There are a small number of exceptions, single genes bounded by genes of dissimilar phenotype (e.g., 1, 9, 10, 19, 32, 33, 39, 40). The exceptions may, however, represent single representatives of as yet unidentified clusters, or cases in which the observed phenotype is not diagnostic of the primary gene function.

The cluster pattern bears an obvious resemblance to the operons of bacteria (Jacob and Monod, 1961), and it is tempting to suggest that the phage genome is organized into 10–20 operons. It should be emphasized that the clustering itself is, at present, the only evidence that the operon is a basic unit of organization of phage genes. None of the mutants we have isolated has been demonstrated to have a control function. Although regulator genes analogous to the *i* gene controlling the β-galactosidase operon of *E. coli* may be present in our collection of mutants, our methods of analysis, at present, would probably not permit their identification. Operator mutants, because of their *cis*-dominant phenotypes, should have been revealed by the complementation tests referred to above, yet none were found among more than 400 *am* and *ts* mutants examined. The studies of operator mutants in bacteria suggest that the operator does not function through a transcribed gene product (see Attardi *et al.*, 1963) but rather it is a region of the DNA which is acted upon

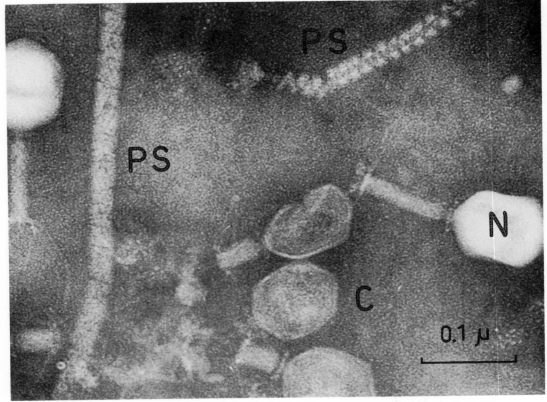

Fig. 8. Phage stock of *am*N90 (gene 21) made on *E. coli* CR63. The micrograph, a PT preparation, shows polysheath (PS), normal (N) and contracted (C) phage. It should be noted that growth of *am*N90 on CR63 is partially defective.

by a product of a regulator gene. The absence of operator mutants in our set may therefore be due to the fact that the conditional lethal phenotypes of the *am* and *ts* mutants are made manifest only through the transcription process, thus restricting these mutants to regions of the DNA which produce a gene product.

Gene Interaction

In mutant infected cells in which no detectable DNA synthesis occurs, none of the genes which are involved in the production of components of the mature particle, or the endolysin, are activated. It could be imagined that, in the absence of DNA synthesis, there are not sufficient gene copies in the cell to support the production of late proteins. However, Cohen (1948) and Koch and Hershey (1959) have shown that the rate of protein synthesis in the infected cell is constant over the normal growth cycle; only the type, but not the quantity, of protein differs at different times. For this reason, it is possible that the lack of activity of the genes involved in late function is a direct consequence of the failure of a mutant gene of the DNA negative class to carry out its function. Wiberg *et al.* (1962) observed that in cells infected with DNA negative mutants, the synthesis of all the early enzymes which were studied continues instead of being arrested shortly after infection as is the case in cells infected with wild type or with *am* mutants not exhibiting defective DNA synthesis. These results indicate that mutations blocking DNA synthesis affect the regulation of development in the infected cell such that phage growth cannot proceed past an early stage. The activation of late gene expression may thus require the attainment of a certain cytoplasmic state. The notion that this state may involve the onset of DNA synthesis, or some event associated with it, is supported by experiments with other mutants defective in DNA synthesis. Cells infected with *am*N116 (gene 39) exhibit a net increase in DNA only after some delay. A comparable delay is observed for the synthesis of tail fiber antigen, the appearance of the first infectious phage progeny, and the onset of cell lysis. In cells infected with *am*N130 (gene 46) although DNA synthesis is arrested after a normal onset of synthesis, synthesis of tail-fiber antigen occurs and the pattern of early enzyme synthesis (Wiberg *et al.*, 1962) is normal.

It is worth noting that this particular type of phenotypic interaction may not be characteristic of all phages. Jacob *et al.* (1957) found a number of defective mutants of phage lambda which, while blocked in genome replication, and presumably in phage specific DNA synthesis, nevertheless did permit the expression of some of the late functions such as the lytic mechanism and coat protein synthesis. Furthermore, lambda complexes, incapable of DNA synthesis due to a block in thymine synthesis, nevertheless synthesize endolysin and coat protein (Weigle, personal communication; Karamata *et al.*, 1962).

The functional interaction between genes affecting DNA synthesis and those concerned with phage maturation defines two groups of genes which we have called early genes and late genes. These two major groups of gene clusters defined from the point of view of functional interaction have also a physical counterpart in their arrangement in the genetic structure (note that genes 1 and 32 are exceptions). If future investigations support the interpretation of each cluster as a separate operon, the possibility must be considered that operons themselves may sometimes be physically grouped into higher order units of functional significance.

The Morphogenesis of Phage Particles

The problem of the construction of finished phage particles does not end with an understanding of the synthesis of the individual protein subunits of which the particle is composed. The manner in which these subunits are assembled is of interest and may be considered as a special case of the broader question of the mode of assembly of cell organelles.

Studies on the aggregation properties of the subunits of the tobacco mosaic virus (TMV) have suggested that the form of the protein shell of the virus is largely determined by the properties of the subunits themselves. The protein subunits can spontaneously aggregate to give the helical form of the virus and complete virus particles may be reconstituted *in vitro* from these subunits and viral RNA (Schramm *et al.*, 1955; Fraenkel-Conrat and Williams, 1955).

While TMV is a simple rod composed of only a single species of protein, the T4 phage is a more intricate structure composed of a number of different kinds of protein subunits organized in a complex manner (Brenner *et al.*, 1959). Although we have little information concerning the specific mode of assembly of T4 virus particles, it would appear likely that maturation involves the interdependent assembly of many components. This is suggested, for example, by the formation of polysheath by most mutants which give incomplete particle assembly. We might imagine that cores, delimited by endplate and some other element, serve as a matrix for the crystallization of normal sheath. In the absence of this matrix, sheath material might crystallize in a contracted form of indeterminate length.

However, mechanisms only involving interdependent successive crystallization of the various subunits are probably insufficient to account for maturation. We have found 37 genes involved in the morphogenesis of the phage particles, and it is likely that more genes of this type exist. On the other hand, although the phage particle has an intricate structure, it seems unlikely that there are more than 20 species of protein in the particle itself. Thus we might imagine that many of the genes involved in maturation of the phage do so indirectly, playing a role in the assembly rather than in the synthesis of protein subunits which compose the mature particle.

A number of observations suggest that some genes involved in maturation do act in such an indirect manner. The phenotypes of the mutants in genes 20–24 suggest that they are involved in head membrane formation. Sarabhai's observations indicate that head protein is formed by mutants in all of these genes except gene 23. Our preliminary investigations of the intracellular morphology of bacteria infected with mutants from genes 20 and 21 of this region suggest that although head protein is formed, assembly of head structures is aberrant, leading to either polyhead or head-like structures bound to the cell membrane. One interpretation of these observations is that the products of genes 20 and 21 are essential factors in head membrane formation but not in the usual sense of making a material contribution to the finished structure.

If the suggested roles for maturation genes are correct, the phage particle represents a structure whose morphogenesis cannot be conceived of as simple crystallization from subunits, as may be the case with TMV. Thus, the study of those genes with functions ancillary to genes coding for structural proteins of T4 are of great interest as models for "morphogenetic" genes.

ACKNOWLEDGMENTS

The work performed in Geneva was supported by a grant from the U.S. Public Health Service (contract no. E4267). The work performed in Pasadena was aided by a grant from the National Foundation and by a U.S. Public Health Service Grant (no. RG-6965). Part of this work was performed while one of us (R.H.E.) was a U.S. Public Health postdoctoral fellow at the California Institute of Technology. R.H.E. is also greatly indebted to the Department of Bacteriology, University of California at Los Angeles for providing support and facilities for part of this research, and in particular to Mr. F. Eiserling for help with some of the earlier electron microscope studies.

REFERENCES

Attardi, G., S. Naono, J. Rouvière, F. Jacob, and F. Gros. 1963. Production of Messenger RNA and regulation of protein synthesis. *Cold Spring Harbor Symp. Quant. Biol.* **28**:363–372.

Brenner, S. 1957. Genetic control and phenotypic mixing of the adsorption cofactor requirement in bacteriophages T2 and T4. *Virology* **3**: 560–574.

Brenner, S. and L. Barnett. 1959. Genetic and chemical studies on the head protein of bacteriophages T2 and T4. *Brookhaven Symp. Biol.* **12**: 86–94.

Brenner, S. and R. W. Horne. 1959. A negative staining method for high resolution electron microscopy of viruses. *Biochim. Biophys. Acta* **34**: 103–110.

Brenner, S., G. Streisinger, R. W. Horne, S. P. Champe, L. Barnett, S. Benzer, and M. W. Rees. 1959. Structural components of bacteriophage. *J. Mol. Biol.* **1**: 281–292.

Burton, K. 1956. A study of the conditions and mechanism of the diphenylamine reaction for the colorimetric estimation of deoxyribonucleic acid. *Biochem. J.* **62**: 315–323.

Campbell, A. 1961. Sensitive mutants of bacteriophage λ. *Virology* **14**: 22–32.

Cohen, S. S. 1948. The synthesis of bacterial viruses. I. The synthesis of nucleic acid and protein in *Escherichia coli* B infected with T2r+ bacteriophage. *J. Biol. Chem.* **174**: 281–293.

De Mars, R. I. 1955. The production of phage-related materials when bacteriophage development is interrupted by proflavine. *Virology* **1**: 83–99.

Dirksen, M., J. C. Hutson, and J. M. Buchanan. 1963. Host dependent synthesis of altered early enzymes after infection of *E. coli* with some amber mutants of bacteriophage T4. *Cold Spring Harbor Symp. Quant. Biol.* **28**: 392–394.

Fraenkel-Conrat, H. and R. C. Williams. 1955. Reconstitution of active tobacco mosaic virus from its inactive protein and nucleic acid components. *Proc. Natl. Acad. Sci.* **41**: 690–698.

Franklin, N. C. 1961. Serological study of tail structure and function in coliphages T2 and T4. *Virology* **14**: 417–429.

Jacob, F., C. Fuerst, and E. Wollman. 1957. Recherches sur les bactéries lysogènes défectives. *Ann. Inst. Pasteur* **93**: 724–753.

Jacob, F. and J. Monod. 1961. Genetic regulatory mechanisms in the synthesis of proteins. *J. Mol. Biol.* **3**: 318–356.

Karamata, D., E. Kellenberger, G. Kellenberger, and M. Terzi. 1962. Sur une particule accompagnant le développement du coliphage λ. *Path. Microbiol.* **25**: 575–585.

Keck, K. 1956. An ultramicro technique for the determination of deoxypentose nucleic acid. *Arch. Biochem. Biophys.* **63**: 446–451.

Kellenberger, E. 1961. Vegetative bacteriophage and the maturation of virus particles. *Adv. in Virus Res.* **8**: 1–61.

Kellenberger, E. and W. Arber. 1957. Electron microscopical studies of phage multiplication. I. A method for quantitative analysis of particle suspensions. *Virology* 3: 245–255.

Kellenberger, E., J. Séchaud, and A. Ryter. 1959. Electron microscopical studies of phage multiplication. IV. The establishment of the DNA pool of vegetative phage and the maturation of phage particles. *Virology* 8: 478–498.

Koch, G. and A. D. Hershey. 1959. Synthesis of phage-precursor protein in bacteria infected with T2. *J. Mol. Biol.* 1: 260–276.

Mason, D. J. and D. M. Powelson. 1956. Nuclear division as observed in live bacteria by a new technique. *J. Bact.* 71: 474–479.

Schramm, G., G. Schumacher, and W. Zillig. 1955. Über die Struktur des Tabakmosaikvirus. III. Mitt.: Der Zerfall in alkalischer Lösung. *Z. Naturforsch.* 10b: 481–492.

Steinberg, C. M. and R. S. Edgar. 1962. A critical test of a current theory of genetic recombination in bacteriophage. *Genetics* 47: 187–208.

Streisinger, G. 1956. The genetic control of host range and serological specificity in bacteriophages T2 and T4. *Virology* 2: 377–387.

Streisinger, G. and N. Franklin. 1956. Mutation and recombination at the host range genetic region of phage T2. *Cold Spring Harbor Symp. Quant. Biol.* 21: 103–109.

Streisinger, G., F. Mukai, W. J. Dreyer, B. Miller and S. Horiuchi. 1961. Mutations affecting the lysozyme of phage T4. *Cold Spring Harbor Symp. Quant. Biol.* 26: 25–30.

Wiberg, J. S., M. Dirksen, R. H. Epstein, S. E. Luria, and J. M. Buchanan. 1962. Early enzyme synthesis and its control in *E. coli* infected with some amber mutants of bacteriophage T4. *Proc. Natl. Acad. Sci.* 48: 293–302.

7

Isozymes

It has been suggested (Cahn *et al.* 1962) that the shift in the chicken from heart (LDH_1) to muscle (LDH_5) lactic dehydrogenase during development of breast muscle is related to the change in physiological requirements of the tissue. *In ovo* lactic acid is removed more efficiently in the presence of LDH_1 than in the presence of LDH_5. LDH_1 is strongly inhibited by pyruvate and can channel the latter into the Kreb's cycle more effectively than LDH_5. The changeover to LDH_5 in the chick comes just before hatching and probably when the chorioallantoic membrane begins to dry up and the metabolism of more actively contracting breast muscle becomes more anerobic.

Hence LDH_1 is required where tissues are well oxygenated; LDH_5, where tissues are less well oxygenated. At the beginning of avian development LDH_1 predominates where as at the beginning of mammalian development LDH_5 does. During embryogenesis each tissue achieves an optimum proportion of isozymes (*Markert 1963*) [*] probably in accordance with its physiology.

It seems quite clear that an isozyme consists of 4 polypeptide chains only 2 of which may be different. Given two different chains which may combine as tetramers it is possible to have only 5 isozymes: 1111, 1115, 1155, 1555, 5555 where 1 stands for LDH_1 and 5 for LDH_5.

Evidence that the two monomers are products of two distinct genes is convincing. There are greater differences between heart and muscle LDH than between beef heart and chicken heart LDH (Kaplin and Ciotti 1961). Independent variations during development and in different tissues also argue that muscle LDH and heart LDH are regulated by different genes. The amino acid compositions and the peptide patterns of the two enzymes are different.

Malate dehydrogenase like lactic dehydrogenase isozymes seem to consist of two types of subunits also organized into five different tetramers. The distribution of malate dehydrogenase isozymes in different tissues or in different blastomeres of the developing sea urchin as reported by *Moore and Villee (1963)* can be explained in at least two ways. The final distribution of the isozymes may be the result of a sorting-out process whereby molecules present in the egg are divided up among daughter cells, such that some species go to one cell and others go to another cell. Or the final distribution can result from the synthesis of some isozymes by "small" cells and the synthesis of other isozymes by "large" cells. It should be possible to distinguish between these alternatives in the sea urchin by labeling the embryos with isotopic protein precursors just prior to separations of blastometers in sucrose. If the isolated enzyme is radioactive, then obviously synthesis as well as distribution

[*] Italicized references indicate articles which appear in this book.

would be judged asymmetrical. If each kind of sea urchin blastomere (large or small) makes different MDH's, there must be controls which result in the selective assembly of two gene products, since two and only two genes seem to be involved in synthesis of all five isozymes.

REFERENCES

1. Cahn, R. D., N. O. Kaplan, L. Levine, and E. Zwilling (1962). Nature and development of lactic dehydrogenases. *Science* 136:962–969.

2. Kaplan, N. O., and M. M. Ciotti (1961). Evolution and differentiation of dehydrogenases. *Ann. N.Y. Acad. Sci.* 94:701–722.

Epigenetic Control of Specific Protein Synthesis in Differentiating Cells

CLEMENT L. MARKERT

The recognition of the chromosomal basis of inheritance some sixty years ago immediately posed a dilemma which has not yet been resolved and which in fact sums up what may be the fundamental problem of embryonic development. It was observed that during cell division each daughter cell received an identical set of chromosomes, presumably therefore an identical set of hereditary potentialities. Yet these daughter cells commonly followed their own independent pathways of development until finally at late stages of differentiation they exhibited very different phenotypes. Thus the dilemma: identical genotypes give rise to very different phenotypes—as different as nerve, and muscle, and pigment cells. With the tremendous expansion of our knowledge of genetics and biochemistry, of the structure and function of genes, of deoxyribonucleic acid (DNA), ribonucleic acid (RNA), and protein, and of their complementary structural and chemical relationships, this basic dilemma has become sharper and its solution so much the more important for our understanding of cell differentiation and embryonic development.

In *Cytodifferentiation and Macromolecular Synthesis* (Michael Locke, ed.), Academic Press, 65–84, 1963. Reprinted with permission.

We know now that the metabolic machinery of a cell is largely regulated by enzymes and that the structure of enzymes, like other proteins, is ultimately encoded in the DNA of the chromosomes and probably also in RNA. So far as we can presently judge, the cells of a metazoan have constant identical supplies of DNA, but their enzymatic composition varies enormously. In fact the enzymatic content of a cell is the principal feature by which we assess the biochemical state of differentiation of the cell. Clearly some mechanism must regulate gene expression and this mechanism, whatever it may be, should provide the key to our dilemma and simultaneously elucidate the most basic problems of development. In searching for a mechanism that could selectively and differentially control gene expression in terms of the enzymes produced, we might profitably examine each step leading to the synthesis of an enzyme from the DNA to messenger RNA to ribosome to released enzyme. A limitation imposed anywhere along this sequence could regulate the enzymatic repertory of a cell and thus specify its state of differentiation. However, the problems of control seem to enlarge rapidly as the distance from the chromosome increases.

At the level of the chromosome we can

easily imagine a single molecule activating or inhibiting a gene, turning it on or off, as it were. But at all later steps many molecules in many locations would be required to stifle the enzymatic expression of a functioning gene. Effective control of the enzyme molecules themselves would seem to involve enormous logistic problems and constitute a profligate drain on the resources of the cell, but then, perhaps the cell does not view economy the way we do. It should be remembered that the titer of any given enzyme per cell may range from many millions of molecules to none so far as we can tell, or at least to a number so low as to have no physiological significance for the cell. Turning the gene off seems to be the most satisfactory method of completely preventing the appearance of a particular enzyme in the cell. But what of the problem of regulating the amount of enzyme produced once the gene is turned on? Again the problem seems easiest to solve at the gene itself, but we have few facts to guide us in constructing a hypothesis of molecular regulation of the quantity of gene function. Taking a cue from the exciting work on the regulation of bacterial genes summarized by Jacob and Monod (1963), we might assume that the quantitative control of gene function is determined by the duration of gene activation which in turn is a function of the abundance of unstable activating molecules. The more abundant the activator, the greater would be the time during which the activator and gene were associated, and thus the more numerous would be the gene products.

In our efforts to formulate a mechanism for regulating gene function, it is important to bear in mind that the mechanism cannot be an autonomous expression of the genome of any particular cell. The mechanism is clearly dependent upon external influences. Transplanting an embryonic cell from one tissue environment to another will commonly change the fate of the transplanted cell to conform with its new location. Thus gene expression is dependent upon the extracellular environment, although more immediately upon the environment within the cell. Obviously a cyclical, dynamic interaction between

the genome and its environment occurs, so that the environment specifies which part of the genome is to function and to what degree, and the functioning genome in turn modifies the environment. This reciprocal interplay of genome and environment drives the cell along the path of differentiation and is basically responsible for embryonic development.

Perhaps the most important, and certainly the most neglected, portion of this cycle is the chromosomes themselves—particularly the structural and chemical changes which occur in them as their function changes (Gall and Callan, 1962; Beermann, 1961; Clever, 1961). Our knowledge of chromosome change as related to function is still meager, but other parts of this cycle of interaction, particularly the synthesis of specific proteins, can more profitably be reviewed today. The mechanisms—genetic and epigenetic—that bring about the synthesis of protein molecules can best be studied by focusing on a specific protein. The enzyme lactate dehydrogenase (LDH) has been extensively investigated by many laboratories, and now provides a rich source of information for analyzing problems of protein synthesis. This oxidoreductase is ubiquitous in vertebrate tissues and is found in many other organisms as well. It catalyzes the interconversion of pyruvate and lactate and simultaneously of $NADH_2$ and NAD.* Lactate appears to have little metabolic importance other than as a temporary storage reservoir for hydrogen during periods of relative anaerobiosis. Pyruvate, of course, occupies a key position in carbohydrate metabolism.

ISOZYMES

From our understanding of the gene control of enzyme synthesis, the encoding of a single protein by a single gene would lead us to suppose that all the molecules of LDH within a single individual should be identical, except possibly for rare accidents. We were

* NAD = nicotinamide-adenine dinucleotide, replacing DPN (diphosphopyridine nucleotide); $NADH_2$ = dihydronicotinamide-adenine dinucleotide, replacing DPNH (diphosphopyridine nucleotide, reduced form).

surprised, therefore, a few years ago (Markert and Møller, 1959), to find that LDH exists in several distinct molecular varieties, five in fact, in the tissues of vertebrates. These multiple molecular forms, or isozymes, of LDH, present in a sharp fashion the problems involved in the genetic and also in the epigenetic control of specific protein synthesis in differentiating cells.

The fact that LDH exists in more than one molecular variety in a single organism was first recognized by Meister (1950) and later confirmed by Neilands (1952). Using zone electrophoresis, Wieland and Pfleiderer (1957) and Pfleiderer and Jeckel (1957) were later able to demonstrate additional molecular varieties of LDH and to show that they existed in tissue- and species-specific patterns. Other enzymes have also been shown to exist in multiple molecular forms, but generally the early observations were considered, at best, to be biochemical curiosities or, at worst, evidence of defective preparative procedures leading to artifacts in the form of partially degraded but still active enzyme molecules. A full appreciation of the fact that many enzymes normally exist in several different isozymic forms depended upon the development of analytical procedures that permitted a direct assay of the isozymic content of tissues with a minimum of manipulation and without the use of conventional preparative procedures.

The development of techniques (Smithies, 1955) for the resolution of protein mixtures by electrophoresis in starch gels provided the basic analytical procedure. The employment of histochemical staining techniques to visualize enzymes separated on starch gels (Hunter and Markert, 1957) provided a simple procedure for direct analysis of enzymes in tissue homogenates. By these methods the isozymes of numerous enzymes, particularly those of LDH, were readily separated and identified (Markert and Møller, 1959). These stained starch strips (Fig. 1), or zymograms, revealed the existence of five isozymes of LDH in all the mammals so far examined (Fig. 2).

The common occurrence of the same num-

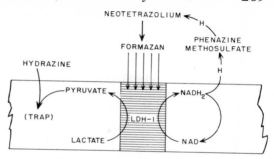

Fig. 1. Diagram of the reactions involved in visualizing the isozymes of LDH after resolution by starch gel electrophoresis. The method essentially provides a colorimetric test for the production of $NADH_2$.

ber of LDH isozymes in different mammals suggested that the isozymes probably had biological significance. This conclusion became obvious when a variety of different tissues were analyzed. Nearly every tissue contained all five isozymes of LDH in precise relative proportions—that is, the zymogram of each tissue showed a characteristic constant pattern of isozymes. These patterns are very stable and are not easily modified by procedures commonly employed in the pu-

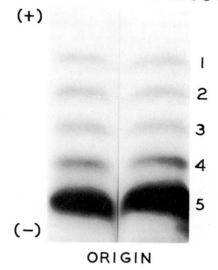

Fig. 2. Photograph of zymograms of two independent preparations of mouse LDH from skeletal muscle. Note that all five isozymes are present. Electrophoresis occurred at pH 7.0 at room temperature for about 6 hours at a voltage gradient of 6 V/cm.

rification of enzymes. Homogenizing different tissues together resulted in zymograms that showed merely the summation of the patterns of the constituent tissues. Neither inhibition nor activation of individual isozymes occurred. Moreover, during the several steps involved in purification the isozymic pattern remains essentially constant. From these observations it seems clear that isozyme patterns, as seen on zymograms, reflect conditions within the tissue and are definitely not artifacts of the analytic procedures.

Since these analyses were performed on tissues that were, of course, composed of heterogeneous populations of cells, it seemed possible that the pattern of isozymes observed represented a corresponding pattern of cell types, each contributing a single isozyme to the total. Two lines of investigation provided at least a partial answer to this possibility. First, a single cell type—mouse erythrocytes—was obtained in pure form. These erythrocytes were separated from the cells of the blood by centrifugation, washed thoroughly in physiological saline solution, lysed in distilled water, and the resulting solution electrophoresed. This single cell type produced a complex pattern of several isozymes. Thus, one might conclude that a single cell can synthesize more than one isozyme, although these observations do not preclude the possibility that the erythrocytes themselves are a heterogeneous population in terms of isozymic content. This reservation seems unlikely in view of the work of Nace *et al.* (1961). By using fluorescent labeled antibodies to different LDH isozymes of the frog, these investigators were able to demonstrate the presence of three isozymes in the egg of the frog *Rana pipiens*. It seems probable, therefore, that single cells do produce more than one isozyme. However, the diverse cells composing a tissue do not make identical contributions to the isozyme pattern of the tissue. This is easily demonstrated by dividing a complex organ, such as the stomach, into distinct parts and analyzing each of these separately. Quite different isozyme patterns are commonly obtained from these different parts of an organ. The pattern of any organ

or tissue is merely the summation of the patterns of its constituent parts.

It is obvious from an examination of the zymograms (Fig. 3) of the different tissues of the mouse that the specific characteristics of each tissue or organ is based upon the specific proportions of the several isozymes present in the tissue and not upon the presence or absence of an isozyme (Markert and Ursprung, 1962). The concept of a tissue-specific isozyme is entirely inappropriate. Furthermore, all of the isozymes appear to be equally important. Although LDH-5 predominates in many mouse tissues, each isozyme is the most abundant in some tissue. Nearly all tissues contain measurable amounts of all five isozymes, and the few exceptions probably represent cases in which the titer of the isozyme is too low to be detected by these techniques. The range of variation on a zymogram from the faintest to the darkest band represents about a hundredfold difference in isozyme titer.

The fact that each cell can synthesize more than one isozyme raises the question as to where these isozymes may be located within the cell. Reliance must be placed on cytochemical techniques for identifying the location of enzymes within cells. Such techniques are difficult to apply to LDH because of the ready solubility of this enzyme. However, some progress has been made. Allen (1961) demonstrated that LDH is not uniformly distributed throughout the cell and, in fact, different cell types show characteristic distributions of the LDH. His results did not permit the identification of the different isozymic forms of LDH but only located the enzymatic activity. However, the use of fluorescent labeled antibodies (Nace *et al.*, 1961) against individual isozymes did permit localization to individual cells, and even intracellular location could be ascertained with some accuracy, particularly in large cells such as the frog egg. Nace and his associates eluted fluorescent labeled antibodies from precipitin bands in Ouchterlony plates. With these antibodies they then stained tissue sections and demonstrated the differential location of individual isozymes. For example, LDH-1 was identified

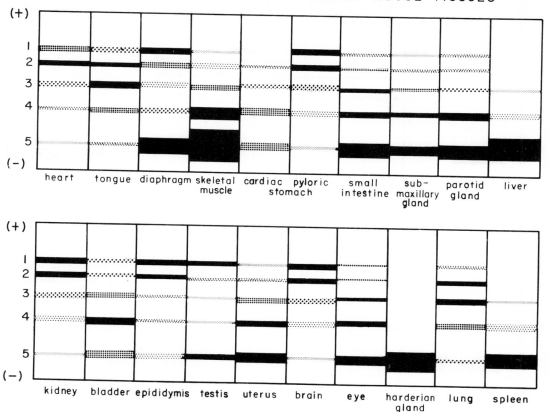

Fig. 3. Diagrammatic representation of the LDH zymogram patterns from 20 tissues or organs of the adult mouse. The darkness of the isozyme bands is a rough indication of the amount of enzyme activity in the band. (From *Develop. Biol.*, **5**, 363–381.)

on yolk platelets of the egg and in the connective tissue of the oviduct. LDH-3 was found in the egg cytoplasm and in certain cells of the oviduct epithelium and in jelly-secreting glands of the oviduct. The location of LDH-2 in the egg was not determined but it was found in certain cells of the oviduct epithelium. Walker and Seligman (1963) have also described precise intracellular localizations of LDH activity which were characteristic for different cell types, although the techniques used by these investigators do not resolve the individual isozymes. All these data suggest that each isozyme may be located in a prescribed site in the cell. Presumably the difference in net charge by which we are able to separate the isozymes electrophoretically is an important molecular property in allow-

ing each isozyme to be held at specific sites in the cell.

The specificity of isozyme distribution in the various tissues of vertebrates strongly implies biological significance. Moreover, since the patterns of adult tissues are different, it follows that these patterns must have arisen during the course of embryonic development. Direct analysis of tissues at successive steps in development shows this to be so. The adult patterns gradually emerge and in so doing exhibit remarkable regularities of change from the embryonic precursor patterns (Fig. 4). In the mouse, the most extensively investigated mammal, the largest part of the pattern change occurs during early neonatal existence, although progressive changes also occur during embryonic life. Once adulthood is reached,

ONTOGENY OF LDH ISOZYME PATTERNS IN MOUSE TISSUES

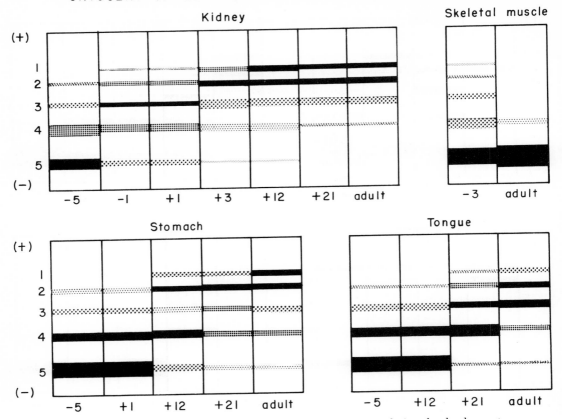

Fig. 4. Diagrammatic representation of changing LDH patterns during the development of several mouse tissues. Note that patterns do not change synchronously. The numbers along the abscissa indicate days before (−) or after (+) birth. (From *Develop. Biol.*, **5**, 363–381).

no further change is observed, even in very old mice. All embryonic tissues first exhibit a predominance of LDH-5. As development proceeds a gradual shift in pattern occurs so that enzyme activity is progressively transferred toward the LDH-1 end of the spectrum. The extent of this shift varies enormously in different tissues. In skeletal muscle, for example, very little change in pattern occurs, nearly all LDH activity being in LDH-5, both in the embryo and in the adult. Heart muscle exhibits quite another picture. In this tissue enzyme activity is progressively shifted from LDH-5 toward LDH-1. In the adult heart nearly all LDH activity is found in isozymes LDH-1 and LDH-2 with almost none remaining in the previously dominant LDH-5. Yet other tissues show intermediate degrees of change from the embryonic emphasis on

LDH-5 to the increased abundance of LDH-1 generally characteristic of adult tissues.

This progressive transposition of enzyme activity from one end of the spectrum of isozymes to the other does not occur synchronously throughout the developing mouse. Some tissues mature faster than others so far as their isozyme patterns are concerned. At the same stage of development, for example, the kidney shows a more nearly adult pattern than does the heart, even though the heart functions in the embryo much as it does in the adult. Each tissue evidently matures at its own characteristic rate, largely independently of other tissues.

The pattern changes characteristic of mouse development are paralleled in the development of the chick (Lindsay, 1962) but with certain conspicuous and instructive exceptions.

LDH-5 is not the principal isozyme in the chick embryo as it is in the mouse, but rather LDH-1 first appears. In certain tissues such as breast muscle, LDH activity is gradually shifted along the spectrum of isozymes until in the adult only LDH-5 is detected. No change occurs in the chick heart pattern; LDH-1 remains predominant throughout life. Thus adult patterns in the chick are similar to those of the adult mouse, but the starting patterns in the embryo are quite different and therefore the sequence of pattern change is also different. As will be discussed later these differences between chick and mouse are probably related to the availability of oxygen during embryonic development.

PHYSICOCHEMICAL NATURE OF LDH

A full appreciation of the biological significance of isozymes depends upon a detailed knowledge of the physical and chemical differences among them. Accordingly we have undertaken to analyze the physicochemical nature of the LDH isozymes (Markert and Appella, 1961). Highly purified, crystalline preparations of LDH have been made from beef, pig, mouse, and chicken muscle. The most extensive analysis has been made with beef LDH (Table I) but the same general results also seem to apply to LDH from the other organisms.

Beef LDH has a molecular weight of 135,000 as determined from measurements with the ultracentrifuge and by light scattering. In the ultracentrifuge crystalline preparations from beef skeletal muscle, containing all five isozymes, show a single symmetric peak. This monodisperse behavior in the ultracentrifuge suggests that all five isozymes are the same size. By contrast, free boundary electrophoresis or zone electrophoresis in starch gels reveals five distinct molecular species. Thus the net charge on each isozyme is different. At pH 7.0 the isozymes are equally spaced along the starch gel after electrophoresis. This arrangement suggests that each isozyme differs from the next in the series by the same increment of charge. A plausible molecular basis for such regularity will be discussed later. Each of these isozymes may be separated from the crystalline preparation by electrophoresis in a column of cellulose powder followed by elution with buffer. Such purified isozymes have the same molecular weight as the crystalline preparations containing several isozymes. Thus the possibility that isozymes are polymers is excluded. They are all the same size. They are not equally stable, however. The curves depicting the course of denaturation by heat for beef LDH-1 and LDH-5 reveal that LDH-5 is noticeably less stable. This fact suggests that the tertiary structure of the two molecules might be significantly different. The tertiary structure relies heavily upon hydrogen bonds to hold the molecule in a stable configuration. Agents that rupture hydrogen bonds might then reveal differences among isozymes if indeed the differences lie in the tertiary structure.

SUBUNIT HYPOTHESIS

When hydrogen bonding reagents such as 12 M urea and 5 M guanidine hydrochloride were added to solutions of the isozymes, they were readily denatured; all enzymatic activity disappeared, as was expected. However, more important was the fact that the molecule was

TABLE I. Physicochemical properties of LDH isozymes[a]

Physicochemical Property	LDH-1	LDH-5
Molecular weight	135,000	135,000
Sedimentation coefficient ($S_{20, w}^{0} \times 10^{-13}$ cm/sec)	7.0	7.0
Diffusion coefficient ($D_{20, w} \times 10^{-7}$ cm²/sec)	5.10	5.10
Partial specific volume (W_{20} ml/gm)	0.750	0.750
Isoelectric point	4.5	9.5
Subunit size	35,000	35,000
Electrophoretic mobility (pH 7.2, 0.1 ionic strength phosphate buffer)	−4.90	+0.63

[a] From beef tissues.

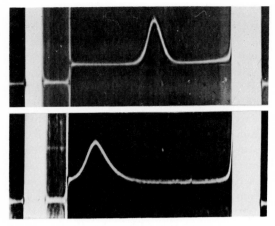

Fig. 5. Schlieren photographs taken at the same time after the beginning of ultracentrifugation. Upper photo is of intact LDH preparation; lower photo is after dissociation of LDH into subunits. The difference in sedimentation constants indicates that the subunits are one-fourth the size of the intact molecule. Note that each preparation is monodisperse.

split into four polypeptide chains of equal size as shown by measurements in the ultracentrifuge (Fig. 5). Low pH will also dissociate the LDH molecule into its constituent polypeptides. These polypeptides have no enzyme activity and may be separated into at least two electrophoretically distinct forms. The subunits obtained from LDH-1 and from LDH-5 each appear to be electrophoretically homogeneous but different from each other. The subunits of LDH-2, -3, and -4 all appear to be mixtures of the two kinds of subunits found in LDH-1 and -5. Complex crystalline preparations containing several isozymes also dissociate into two kinds of subunits. Assorting these two kinds of subunits in all possible combinations of four would yield five distinct molecular varieties (Appella and Markert, 1961). It is surely more than coincidence that five LDH isozymes are found in nearly all mammalian tissues so far examined. If the two subunits are designated A and B, then the formulas for the five isozymes can be written A^0B^4, (LDH-1); A^1B^3 (LDH-2); A^2B^2 (LDH-3); A^3B^1 (LDH-4); A^4B^0 (LDH-5). This hypothesis (Markert, 1962; Appella and Markert, 1961), which owes much to our knowledge of hemoglobin composition and synthesis, not only provides a plausible explanation for the structure of isozymes, but is readily subject to experimental test. At least three tests are apparent. (1) Recombination of equal numbers of the dissociated subunits of LDH-1 and LDH-5 should produce all five isozymes in the ratio of 1:4:6:4:1. The major difficulty in this approach is to discover the conditions required to promote reassociation of the subunits. Some success has been achieved but satisfactory completion of this test will require more experimentation. (2) Total amino acid analyses of LDH-1, LDH-3, and LDH-5 should demonstrate whether LDH-3 has an amino acid composition that could be formed by equal numbers of the subunits found in LDH-1 and LDH-5 as the hypothesis predicts. The results of this test will be presented below. (3) If each type of subunit is antigenic, then immunochemical tests should demonstrate that LDH-1 and LDH-5 are not cross-reactive but that each is cross-reactive with LDH-2, -3, and -4. Such tests have been conducted in several laboratories and the results are consistent with the hypothesis (Plagemann *et al.*, 1960a; Cahn *et al.*, 1962; Lindsay, 1962; Markert and Appella, 1963).

Recombination of dissociated subunits to form new isozymes is the most critical test. Although this test is not yet complete it is interesting to note that most of the patterns of isozymes as seen in zymograms of mouse tissues (Fig. 3) could be produced by a random assortment of subunits, provided that the proportions of the subunits were fixed at an appropriate ratio (Fig. 6). Thus in mouse skeletal muscle the ratio of A to B should be about 30:1, in kidney about 1:10, and in adult heart about 1:3. At about the time of birth the mouse heart should contain equal numbers of subunits A and B, thus producing mostly LDH-3. The few exceptions to the possibility of randomly generated patterns, such as the diaphragm, can be attributed to the heterogeneity of the tissue components, each contributing a quite different isozyme composition to the overall pattern of the organ.

Analysis of the isozyme patterns in fragments of the stomach (Fig. 3) demonstrates the local heterogeneity that can exist in complex organs or tissues. It is perhaps surprising that the organ patterns agree as closely as they do with patterns predicted upon the basis of random assortment of subunits. The fact that the spectrum of isozymes in any tissue is continuous is also in accord with the subunit hypothesis. No isozymes are skipped in the series and the quantities of each generally follow a smooth gradient of diminution from the most abundant to the least. These charac-

teristics of the distribution pattern would be predicted from the subunit hypothesis, provided the subunits were assorted at random.

CHEMICAL COMPOSITION

By investigating the chemical composition of isozymes some insight may be obtained into their synthesis and perhaps into their function. Two general approaches are avail-

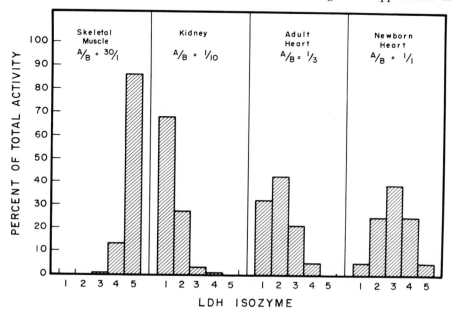

Fig. 6. Relative abundance of each LDH isozyme in tissues as predicted on the assumption of a random assortment of different initial numbers of the polypeptide subunits A and B.

able: determination of total amino acid composition by means of an amino acid analyzer and determination of peptide patterns ("fingerprinting") after trypsin digestion. Both procedures have been applied to crystalline preparations containing several isozymes and also to pure preparations of LDH-1 and LDH-5 from beef tissues. The amino acid composition of these preparations is shown in Table II. It is obvious that LDH-1 and LDH-5 differ considerably although they appear to be related proteins. Moreover the differences correspond with the electrophoretic behavior of these isozymes. At pH 7.0 LDH-1 has a greater net negative charge than LDH-5 and accordingly is richer in aspartic and glu-

tamic acids, but poorer in the basic amino acids, arginine, lysine, and histidine. The basic amino acids are all more abundant in LDH-5. The subunit hypothesis predicts that the amino acid composition of LDH-3 should be equal to one-half the sum of the amino acids of LDH-1 and LDH-5. Unfortunately, pure preparations of LDH-3 in sufficient quantity to provide a critical test of this hypothesis have not yet become available, and preliminary results with small quantities have been ambiguous.

Since the amino acid compositions of LDH-1 and LDH-5 are different, their peptide patterns should also be different, and this is so. Peptides are obtained by digesting the

TABLE II. Amino acid composition of LDH isozymes from beef muscle

| Amino Acid | Number of Amino Acid Residues per Molecule of Enzyme[a] | |
	LDH-1	LDH-5
Lysine	94	95
Histidine	25	34
Arginine	34	52
Aspartic acid	123	104
Threonine	56	62
Serine	92	61
Glutamic acid	124	135
Proline	42	63
Glycine	91	100
Alanine	72	122
Valine	135	82
Methionine	32	20
Isoleucine	86	73
Leucine	130	118
Tyrosine	26	35
Phenylalanine	19	26

[a] Based upon a molecular weight of 135,000 (including 12 residues of cysteine and 30 residues of tryptophan in each isozyme).

LDH with trypsin, which splits the molecule at each arginine and lysine residue. The resulting peptides are resolved on paper by chromatography and electrophoresis and visualized with the aid of ninhydrin. Such peptide patterns show that some of the peptides from LDH-1 and LDH-5 appear to be the same. The N-terminal residue appears to be threonine in both LDH-1 and -5 and the C-terminal residue is aspartic acid for both isozymes. These similarities argue for a common origin during the biochemical evolution of these isozymes. The two different genes which presumably encode the constituent polypeptides of LDH probably arose by duplication from a single precursor gene and then diverged through the accumulation of spontaneous mutations.

The peptide analysis also tends to confirm the subunit hypothesis. The number of arginine + lysine residues found in LDH-1, for example, is about 130. If only a single long polypeptide were involved, then digestion with trypsin should yield approximately 130 peptides. However, only about one-fourth this number is actually observed (Fig. 7)—a result to be expected if the molecule is composed of four identical subunits. It is interesting to note that four molecules of NAD are bound to each molecule of LDH, presumably one per subunit, although once dissociated the subunits do not bind NAD.

IMMUNOCHEMICAL PROPERTIES

Recently Lindsay (1962) and Cahn *et al.* (1962) have completed extensive immunochemical analyses of LDH isozymes obtained principally from the chicken. These studies show that LDH-1 and LDH-5 are immunochemically distinct although both are related to LDH-2, -3, and -4. Antisera to either LDH-1 or LDH-5 will precipitate LDH-2, -3, and -4 as well as the immunizing antigen, but will not precipitate the isozyme at the opposite end of the spectrum. These results are consistent with the assumption that the polypeptides A and B are distinct antigens. It would then follow that the immunochemical properties of the intact LDH molecule would be a function of its subunit composition. In fact Lindsay's (1962) analysis indicates that one antibody molecule is sufficient to inhibit one enzyme molecule. Thus complete inactivation of LDH-2, -3, and -4 by antisera to either LDH-1 or -5 is to be expected. The data on quantitative precipitin tests by Cahn *et al.* (1962) also supports this expectation. Earlier studies of the immunochemical properties of LDH isozymes of the rabbit (Plagemann *et al.*, 1960a) and frog (Nace *et al.*, 1961) can also be fitted into this general analysis although the subunit hypothesis was not considered in this work. These investigators tended to picture each isozyme as distinct, as indeed it is, but not necessarily in the qualitative sense implicit in their discussions.

Recent immunochemical investigations of beef, pig, and mouse LDH isozymes (Markert and Appella, 1963) also support the conclusions drawn from the work with chick LDH. Isozymes from these different species did not cross-react in agar gel diffusion analyses, but such species specificity is not surprising. During the long course of evolution the genes

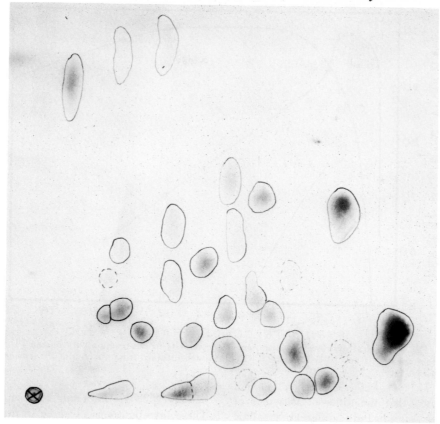

Fig. 7. Peptide pattern of LDH-1 from beef heart. Isozyme digested with trypsin and peptides resolved on paper by electrophoresis and chromatography. The peptide pattern of LDH-5 is conspicuously different. Note that the number of peptides is about 30 or one-fourth of the number of arginine + lysine residues in the intact enzyme molecule.

encoding the structure of LDH in different species would surely become different in some degree. In fact the electrophoretic behavior of the LDH isozymes of different species is commonly different, and the different mobilities indicate a difference in amino acid composition—that is, in the primary structure of the constituent polypeptide chains. This species specificity opens up the possibility of a fruitful examination of the synthesis of LDH. The favored hypothesis of LDH synthesis assumes that two nonallelic genes produce two different polypeptides which, assorting at random in groups of four, produce the five isozymes observed. A hybrid between two species would possess four such genes, each producing a different polypeptide. Assorting four different polypeptides in all possible combinations

of four would give rise to 35 different molecular varieties of LDH. Thus an examination of LDH patterns in hybrid tissues should prove very instructive.

FUNCTION OF ISOZYMES

From the point of view of cell function it seems strange that a cell should synthesize precise patterns of isozymes, all performing exactly the same catalytic function. One type of molecule would seem sufficient. However, a detailed examination of the catalytic properties of the LDH isozymes shows that they are not identical although each exhibits the basic properties of LDH. The extensive work of Kaplan and his associates (Kaplan *et al.*, 1960; Kaplan and Ciotti, 1961) has clearly

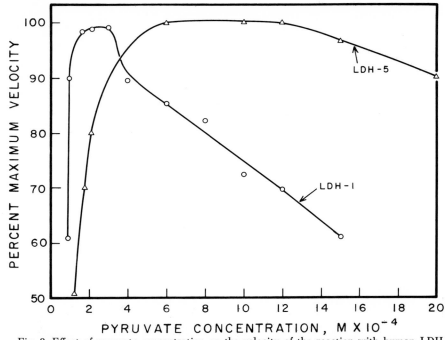

Fig. 8. Effect of pyruvate concentration on the velocity of the reaction with human LDH isozymes LDH-1 and LDH-5 at pH 7.0. (Redrawn and modified from the data of Plagemann *et al.*, 1960.)

demonstrated that the different isozymes of LDH have significantly different catalytic efficiencies, particularly when various NAD analogs are substituted for the normal coenzyme in the assay mixture. This behavior of the isozymes *in vitro* with abnormal substrates probably reflects differences in their normal behavior *in vivo*, although no direct test of this assumption has been made. It seems quite likely that the fundamental role of LDH is to regulate the ratio of NAD to $NADH_2$ with the production of lactate as only an essential by-product of this activity. The $NAD/NADH_2$ ratio is of critical importance in regulating numerous biochemical reactions in the cell. Each isozyme may serve to regulate this ratio at specific locations in the cell where that particular isozyme is bound by virtue of its unique charge.

The catalytic efficiency of the different isozymes has been measured in the presence of different concentrations of the normal substrates, lactate and pyruvate, by several investigators (Plagemann *et al.*, 1960b; Kaplan and Ciotti, 1961; Lindsay, 1962; Cahn

et al., 1962; Markert and Ursprung, 1962). These investigations all agree in demonstrating that high pyruvate concentrations inhibit LDH (Fig. 8). However, the substrate optimum for LDH-1 is much lower than for LDH-5, and with increasing concentrations of pyruvate LDH-1 activity is inhibited long before LDH-5 activity is depressed. This behavior has interesting physiological implications and provides a metabolic rationale for the existence of LDH isozymes. Mammalian skeletal muscle, for example, is rich in LDH-5. During periods of vigorous activity this muscle produces large quantities of pyruvate that are then reduced to lactate by LDH-5 with a simultaneous oxidation of $NADH_2$ to NAD. This reaction enables the muscle to use glucose as a source of energy even after oxygen is exhausted, because essential supplies of NAD can be regenerated from $NADH_2$ by transferring the hydrogen to pyruvate (to yield lactate) rather than to oxygen. Thus lactate can serve as a temporary hydrogen storage reservoir until increased oxygen supplies become available. However, at high levels of lactate, muscle function is impaired. This is not usually serious in skeletal muscle but it might be fatal in heart muscle. Since heart muscle contains principally LDH-1, large quantities of lactate are not likely to accumulate during rapid metabolism of glucose because the enzyme would be increasingly inhibited by the increased concentration of pyruvate. Thus in heart muscle, lactate production should be maintained at a relatively constant low level even in the face of fluctuating pyruvate concentrations. Only tissues capable of tolerating relatively anaerobic conditions are rich in isozymes at the LDH-5 end of the spectrum. Other tissues are equipped principally with LDH-1 or LDH-2. It is interesting to note that mammalian embryos have a preponderance of LDH-5 in accord with their relatively anaerobic environment. The tissues of chick embryos, on the other hand, appear to be as well oxygenated as adult tissues and these embryonic tissues synthesize mostly LDH-1. Only later in adult tissues subject to anaerobiosis, such as skeletal muscle, does LDH-5 become a prominent part of the enzymatic repertory.

These observations not only give meaning to the existence of isozymes, but suggest that the epigenetic control of their synthesis may in some way involve the oxygen tension in the cell. The metabolic mechanisms which bring about the differential function of genes still remain one of the greatest mysteries in biology, but it does seem clear that regulation of the relative levels of function of two genes for the A and B polypeptides is sufficient to account for the LDH isozymic patterns observed in adult tissues, as well as the changing patterns apparent during embryonic development.

Whether differential gene function is a plausible explanation for the origin of the isozymic forms of enzymes other than LDH, only further investigation will reveal. Although the isozymes of any enzyme carry out the same catalytic function, their distinguishing physical properties may enable them to be integrated into distinct metabolic pathways in different locations in the cell. This arrangement should permit a more precise and sensitive control of cell metabolism and thus should have proved biologically advantageous during the course of evolution. The large number of enzymes which have so far been demonstrated to exist in multiple molecular forms indicates that organisms have frequently exploited the advantages of synthesizing isozymes. These specialized forms of an enzyme must now be accorded a position of general biological significance. Further study of the nature of isozymes and of the genetic and epigenetic mechanisms that regulate their synthesis will surely advance our understanding of the processes of cellular differentiation, and may even bring a solution of the dilemma posed by different phenotypes arising from the same genotype.

ACKNOWLEDGMENTS

The work from the author's laboratory reviewed here has been supported by grants from the National Science Foundation, the American Cancer Society, and by contracts with the Atomic Energy Commission. Most of the research was carried out in collaboration with Drs. Ettore Appella and H. Ursprung. The skillful assistance of Joanne Yundt and Sheila Hutman is gratefully acknowledged.

REFERENCES

Allen, J. M. (1961). Multiple forms of lactic dehydrogenase in tissues of the mouse: Their specificity, cellular localization, and response to altered physiological conditions. *Ann. N. Y. Acad. Sci.* **94,** 937–951.

Appella, E., and C. L. Markert (1961). Dissociation of lactate dehydrogenase into subunits with guanidine hydrochloride. *Biochem. Biophys. Research Communs.* **6,** 171–176.

Beermann, W. (1961). Ein Balbiani-Ring als Locus einer Speicheldrüsenmutation. *Chromosoma* **12,** 1–25.

Cahn, R. D., N. O. Kaplan, L. Levine, and E. Zwilling (1962). Nature and development of lactic dehydrogenases. *Science* **136,** 962–969.

Clever, U. (1961). Genaktivitäten in den Riesenchromosomen von *Chironomus tentans* und ihre Beziehungen zur Entwicklung. I. Genaktivierungen durch Ecdyson. *Chromosoma* **12,** 607–675.

Gall, J. G., and H. G. Callan (1962). H^3-Uridine incorporation in lampbrush chromosomes. *Proc. Natl. Acad. Sci. U.S.* **48,** 562–570.

Hunter, R. L., and C. L. Markert (1957). Histochemical demonstration of enzymes separated by zone electrophoresis in starch gels. *Science* **125**, 1294–1295.

Jacob, F., and J. Monod (1963). Regulation of protein synthesis in bacteria as a model for genetic repression, allosteric inhibition and differentiation. In *Cytodifferentiation and Macromolecular Structure* (Michael Locke, ed.), Academic Press, 1963, pp. 30–64.

Kaplan, N. O., and M. M. Ciotti (1961). Evolution and differentiation of dehydrogenases. *Ann. N. Y. Acad. Sci.* **94**, 701–722.

Kaplan, N. O., M. M. Ciotti, M. Hamolsky, and R. E. Bieber (1960). Molecular heterogeneity and evolution of enzymes. *Science* **131**, 392–397.

Lindsay, D. T. (1962). Developmental patterns and immunochemical properties of lactate dehydrogenase isozymes from the chicken. Thesis, Johns Hopkins University, Baltimore, Maryland.

Markert, C. L. (1962). Isozymes in kidney development. In *Hereditary, Developmental, and Immunologic Aspects of Kidney Disease* (J. Metcoff, ed.), pp. 54–63. Northwestern Univ. Press, Evanston, Illinois.

Markert, C. L., and E. Appella (1961). Physicochemical nature of isozymes. *Ann. N.Y. Acad. Sci.* **94**, 678–690.

Markert, C. L., and E. Appella (1963). Immunochemical properties of lactate dehydrogenase isozymes. *Ann. N.Y. Acad. Sci.* **103**, 915–929.

Markert, C. L., and F. Møller (1959). Multiple forms of enzymes: Tissue, ontogenetic, and species specific patterns. *Proc. Natl. Acad. Sci. U.S.* **45**, 753–763.

Markert, C. L., and H. Ursprung (1962). The ontogeny of isozyme patterns of lactate dehydrogenase in the mouse. *Develop. Biol.* **5**, 363–381.

Meister, A. (1950). Reduction of α, γ-diketo and α-keto acids catalyzed by muscle preparations and by crystalline lactic dehydrogenase. *J. Biol. Chem.* **184**, 117–129.

Nace, G. W., T. Suyama, and N. Smith (1961). Early development of special proteins. *Symposium on Germ Cells and Development (Inst. Intern. Embryol. and Fondazione A. Baselli), 1960,* pp. 564–603.

Neilands, J. B. (1952). Studies on lactic dehydrogenase of heart—purity, kinetics, and equilibria. *J. Biol. Chem.* **199**, 373–381.

Pfleiderer, G., and D. Jeckel (1957). Individuelle Milchsäuredehydrogenasen bei verschiedenen Säugetieren. *Biochem. Z.* **329**, 370–380.

Plagemann, P. G., K. F. Gregory, and F. Wróblewski (1960a). The electrophoretically distinct forms of mammalian lactic dehydrogenase. I. Distribution of lactic dehydrogenases in rabbit and human tissues. *J. Biol. Chem.* **235**, 2282–2287.

Plagemann, P. G., K. F. Gregory, and F. Wróblewski (1960b). The electrophoretically distinct forms of mammalian lactic dehydrogenase. II. Properties and interrelationships of rabbit and human lactic dehydrogenase isozymes. *J. Biol. Chem.* **235**, 2288–2293.

Smithies, O. (1955). Zone electrophoresis in starch gels: Group variations in the serum proteins of normal human adults. *Biochem. J.* **61**, 629–641.

Walker, D. G., and A. M. Seligman (1963). The use of formalin fixation in the cytochemical demonstration of DPN and TPN dependent dehydrogenases in mitochondria. *J. Cell. Biol.* **16**, 455–469.

Wieland, T., and G. Pfleiderer (1957). Nachweis der Heterogenität von Milchsäuredehydrogenasen verschiedenen Ursprungs durch Trägerelektrophorese. *Biochem. Z.* **329**, 112–116.

Malate Dehydrogenase: Multiple Forms in Separated Blastomeres of Sea Urchin Embryos

RICHARD O. MOORE

CLAUDE A. VILLEE

Abstract. *Sea urchin embryos at the 64-cell stage were dissociated by treatment with trypsin and separated by centrifugation on a sucrose gradient. The large blastomeres have two and the small blastomeres have three bands of L-malate dehydrogenase activity, which are separated by disk microelectro-*

Reprinted from *Science* **142**, No. 3590, 389–390 (October 18, 1963). Copyright © 1963 by the American Association for the Advancement of Science.

phoresis on polyacrylamide gel, whereas un-fertilized eggs have five.

Changes in the number and amounts of the multiple forms of enzymes in a given tissue, during the latter part of embryonic development, have been demonstrated for lactate dehydrogenases (1, 2) and for malate dehydrogenases (2). The relationship of this phenomenon of multiple molecular forms of an enzyme to the "one gene-one enzyme" theory and to the problem of cellular differentiation is of interest. All the tissues of adult echinoderms that have been tested contain malate dehydrogenases which have characteristic ratios of activity with nicotinamide-adenine dinucleotide (NAD) and its analogs (3). Electrophoresis on either starch granules or gel, or adsorption to and elution from diethylaminoethanol (DEAE) cellulose columns, revealed three to five molecular forms of malate dehydrogenase in these tissues (4, 5). Unfertilized eggs of the sea urchin, *Arbacia*, have five NAD-malate dehydrogenases, 6-hour embryos have three, and 12- to 48-hour embryos have four. We have now investigated the multiple forms of malate dehydrogenase in separated blastomeres of early embryos.

Eggs and sperm, collected by electric shocks (10 v), were washed and diluted for fertilization. Embryos were grown at 25°C to the 64-cell stage, collected by gentle centrifugation and frozen briefly. They were suspended in a small volume of $0.53M$ NaCl containing $2 \times 10^{-3}M$ ethylenediamine tetraacetate, pH 5.0, for 3 minutes at 37°C to remove the egg membranes and jelly. Two volumes of $0.265M$ Tris buffer, pH 7.9, containing 0.01 percent recrystallized trypsin were added and the mixture was placed in a glass homogenizer in a water bath maintained at 37°C. Gentle movements of the pestle were continued until miscroscopic examination revealed that the blastomeres were completely dissociated. The dissociated blastomeres were layered on a 0.29 to $0.87M$ sucrose gradient and centrifuged at 750g for 25 minutes. The large blastomeres formed a pellet at the bottom of the tube and the small blastomeres formed a

layer between the 0.29 and $0.87M$ sucrose. The layers were separated and examined microscopically, then the cells were disintegrated by ultrasonic techniques to make the enzymes soluble.

The resulting preparations were assayed spectrophotometrically for the rate of reaction of malate dehydrogenase with NAD and its analog, by means of a Beckman DB spectrophotometer and a recording potentiometer (5). Aliquots of each preparation were subjected to disk microelectrophoresis on polyacrylamide gels for 70 minutes at 5 mA in tris-glycine buffer, pH 8.6. Positions of malate dehydrogenase activity were located by staining the gels in 10 ml of a solution containing: $0.05M$ L-malate; $0.001M$ NAD; $0.002M$ KCN; $0.0005M$ $MgCl_2$; $0.05M$ glycyl glycine; 0.05 mg/ml phenazine methosulfate; and 0.3 mg/ml nitro blue tetrazolium. The pH of the solution was 7.4.

The ratio of the rates of reaction of malate dehydrogenase with acetylpyridine-adenine nucleotide (APAD) compared with NAD is 0.68 in unfertilized eggs, but rises during the early embryonic period and reaches 2.2 in 48-hour embryos (5). In the preparations from blastomeres separated at the 64-cell stage, the APAD/NAD ratio for malate dehydrogenase activity was 1.4 in preparations

TABLE 1. Malate dehydrogenase (MDH) activity in eggs and embryos of the sea urchin. *Arbacia punctulata*, as determined by spectrophotometry (column 2) and electrophoresis (column 3)

Stage of Development	Ratio of Activity with APAD/NAD	Bands of MDH Activity	
		With NAD	With APAD
Unfertilized eggs	0.68	5	8
Whole embryos (6 hours)	0.63	3	
Whole embryos (48 hours)	2.2	4	
Small blastomeres	$1.4 \pm 0.13*$	3	2
Large blastomeres	$2.3 \pm 0.20*$	2	1

* The mean value of eight experiments $\pm$ standard error.

from small blastomeres and 2.3 in preparations from large blastomeres (Table 1).

Staining of the acrylamide gels revealed a slowly migrating band of NAD-malate dehydrogenase activity in small blastomeres which is not present in preparations from large blastomeres. The small cells have a total of three NAD-malate dehydrogenases which are separable by electrophoresis and the large cells have two (Fig. 1). Two of the bands in

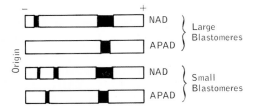

Fig. 1. Bands of activity of L-malate dehydrogenase with NAD and APAD, separated by disk electrophoresis on polyacrylamide gel and stained with nitro blue tetrazolium.

the small cells appear to be identical to the two bands seen in preparations from large blastomeres. Preparations from small blastomeres subjected to electrophoresis show two bands of APAD-malate dehydrogenase activity whereas preparations from large blastomeres show only one. The additional band of APAD-malate dehydrogenase in the small blastomeres moves slowly and remains near the anode, but it is not identical with the additional band of NAD-malate dehydrogenase. Material obtained from unfertilized eggs by homogenization or ultrasonication and subjected to disk electrophoresis on polyacrylamide gels showed five bands of malate dehydrogenase activity with NAD, and eight with APAD. Thus, as development proceeds from the egg to the 64-cell embryo, the number of malate dehydrogenases which are separable by electrophoresis decreases from five to three in small blastomeres, and to two in large blastomeres.

The method of separating small and large blastomeres in quantities large enough for chemical analysis makes possible studies of the development of biochemical differences in cells during early embryonic development.

Later in development the differences in the size and density of the cells are too small to permit separation. The present experiments with the multiple forms of malate dehydrogenase provide an example of the differentiation of enzymes early in development, and indicate the feasibility of a study of the genetic and biochemical mechanisms controlling the formation of enzymes during development, analogous to the classic experiments in microorganisms (6).

The finding that there are as many as five forms of NAD-L-malate dehydrogenase might suggest that these are tetramers of two types of subunits, and that the five forms represent the five possible combinations of the two subunits, as suggested for mammalian lactate dehydrogenases (7). Vertebrate tissues have only two malate dehydrogenases which are separable by electrophoresis (2). The fundamental genetic control of malate dehydrogenase may be similar to that postulated for lactate dehydrogenase—that is, two genes, one for each type of subunit; but the two types of subunits may be prevented from forming hybrids in vertebrates although this is possible in the echinoderm system (8).

REFERENCES AND NOTES

1. C. L. Markert and F. Møller, *Proc. Natl. Acad. Sci. U.S.* 45, 753 (1959); L. B. Flexner, J. B. Flexner, R. B. Roberts, G. DeLaHaba, *Develop. Biol.* 2, 313 (1960); N. O. Kaplan and M. Ciotti, *Ann. N.Y. Acad. Sci.* 94, 701 (1961).
2. B. O. Wiggert and C. A. Villee, *Science* 138, 509 (1962).
3. N. O. Kaplan, M. Ciotti, M. Hamolsky, R. E. Bieber, *Science* 131, 392 (1960); C. A. Villee, *Biol. Bull.* 119, 298 (1960).
4. R. O. Moore and C. A. Villee, *Biol. Bull.* 121, 398 (1961).
5. ———, *Comp. Biochem. Physiol.* 9, 81 (1963).
6. F. Jacob and J. Monod, *Cold Spring Harbor Symp. Quant. Biol.* 26, 193 (1961).
7. E. Appella and C. L. Markert, *Biochem. Biophys. Res Commun.* 6, 171 (1961); R. D. Cahn, N. O. Kaplan, L. Levine, E. Zwilling, *Science* 136, 962 (1962).
8. Aided by grants A 4241 and C 2400 from the National Institutes of Health and by grants from the Association for the Aid of Crippled Children, the Charles and Marjorie King Fund, and the Lalor Foundation.

8

Enzyme Regulation

MOST OF THE ENZYMES which have been studied in the cells of higher organisms have been shown to be constitutive. That is, their formation is not "electively provoked by a substrate" (Jacob and Monod 1961). In fact, in cells other than microorganisms there are no unequivocal examples of substrate induction. Although levels of activity of a number of enzymes have been shown to be increased by addition of specific substrates (Knox and Mehler 1951; Greengard and Feigelson 1961; Schimke 1962; and Hiatt and Bojarski 1961), it seems likely that these results can be accounted for by enzyme stabilization, that is, by control of the rate of enzyme degradation, which is substrate mediated, rather than by an actual change in the synthetic rate of the enzyme. This is now clear in the case of tryptophan pyrrolase (Schimke, Sweeney, and Berlin 1964). During apparent substrate induction (Knox and Mehler 1951) of this enzyme new enzyme molecules are being added to the system since an inhibitor of protein synthesis, puromycin, prevents increase in activity (Greengard, Smith, and Acs 1963). Addition of new enzyme has been demonstrated by use of specific immunologic reactions (Feigelson and Greengard 1962). Hence enzyme increases through *de novo* synthesis rather than activation. Schimke, Sweeney, and Berlin (1964) have shown, however, that synthesis is *not* enhanced by addition of tryptophan but that enzyme is stabilized.

Agents other than substrate can result in enhanced enzyme activity. Hormones, for example, have been shown to stimulate production of enzyme (Shor and Frieden 1958 and Knox 1961). Similarly, dietary factors can enhance the level of activity of a number of liver enzymes (Pitot and Cho 1961). So can removal of an embryonic tissue from the normal environment and thus from the regulatory controls which are ordinarily imposed by the organism result in an increase of enzyme activity (*Kirk and Moscona 1963*).* The dramatic increase, and later decrease, in activity of thymidine kinase in the course of a developmental sequence (*Hotta and Stern 1963*) has been shown to be related to the formation of RNA and is blocked by appropriate inhibitors. The nature of the "enzyme inducer" in this system remains unknown, and it is not clear whether the stimulus is exogenous or endogenous in origin. Further work will show whether the observed increases of both glutamine synthetase (*Kirk and Moscona 1963*) and thymidine kinase (*Hotta and Stern 1963*) might be attributable to enzyme stabilization.

Another example of appearance and subsequent disappearance of an enzyme in the course of a developmental sequence has been provided recently by Sussman and Osborn (1964), who show that UDP-galactose polysaccharide transferase which is absent in vegetative cells of the cellular slime mold and appears relatively late in development disappears when the fruiting body is formed. Enzyme activity could not be demonstrated in morphologically deficient mutants which do not synthesize the mucopolysaccharide.

* Italicized references indicate articles which appear in this book.

It will be recalled that the appearance of sulfating enzymes in the somite signals the onset of chondrogenesis (Chapter 2), but there is no indication yet on how genes for the enzymes are activated. Further, the appearance of hatching enzymes (Kaighn 1963) or of lysosomal enzymes in limb tissues during the course of normal limb development seem more likely the result of an interaction between the environment and the genome than the result of an internal genetic clock unwinding.

An example of end-product repression is provided in the work of *Walker* (*1963*), who has shown that transamidinase can be repressed *in ovo* for long periods by the administration of creatine.

Subtle variations, e.g., periodic fluctuations in levels of activity or synthesis of enzymes, other proteins, or protein precursors, may occur during development. (Goodwin 1963 and Chance 1964). Stern (1961) has observed periodic variations of DNAse in the maturing lily anther, and Tanzer and Gross (1964) find oscillations in the proline pool which have a period of 1–4 hours. Although the significance of these observations is still obscure, new evidence that rhythmic processes occur in developing and other systems continues to accumulate.

Hormonal and other triggers may prove more significant than substrates in affecting appearance, disappearance, and levels of activity of enzymes during development.

REFERENCES

1. Chance, B., R. W. Estabrook, and A. Ghosh (1964). Damped sinusoidal oscillations of cytoplasmic reduced pyridine nucleotide in yeast cells. *Proc. Natl. Acad. Sci.* **51**:1244–1251.

2. Feigelson, P., and O. Greengard (1962). Immunochemical evidence for increased filters of liver tryptophan pyrrolase during substrate and hormonal enzyme induction. *J. Biol. Chem.* **237**:3714–3717.

3. Goodwin, B. C. (1963). *Temporal Organization in Cells*, Academic, New York.

4. Greengard, O., and P. Feigelson (1961). The activation and induction of rat liver tryptophane pyrrolase *in vivo* by its substrate. *J. Biol. Chem.* **236**:153–157.

5. Greengard, O., M. A. Smith, and G. Acs (1963). Relation of cortisone and synthesis of ribonucleic acid to induced and developmental enzyme formation. *J. Biol. Chem.* **238**:1548–1551.

6. Hiatt, H., and T. Bojarski (1961). The effects of thymidine administration and thymidylate kinase activity and on DNA synthesis in mammalian tissues. *Cold Spring Harbor Symposia on Quantitative Biology*, Vol. XXVI, pp. 367–369, The Biological Laboratory, Cold Spring Harbor, New York.

7. Jacob, F., and J. Monod (1961). Genetic regulatory mechanisms in the synthesis of proteins. *J. Mol. Biol.* **3**:318–356.

8. Kaighn, M. E. (1964). A biochemical study of the hatching process in *fundulus heteroclitus*. *Develop. Biol.* **9**:56–80.

9. Knox, W. E. (1961). The adaptive control of enzyme activity in animals. In D. Rudnick (ed.), *Synthesis of Molecular and Cellular Structure*, Ronald, New York, pp. 13–33.

10. Knox, W. E., and A. H. Mehler (1951). The adaptive increase of the tryptophan peroxidase-oxidase system of liver. *Science* **113**:237–238.

11. Pitot, H., and Y. Cho (1961). Studies on the mechanism of enzyme induction in rat liver. *Cold Spring Harbor Symposia on Quantitative Biology, Vol. XXVI*, pp. 371–377, Cold Spring Harbor, New York.

12. Schimke, R. T. (1962). Adaptive characteristics of urea cycle enzymes in the rat. *J. Biol. Chem.* **237**:459–468.

13. Schimke, R., E. Sweeney, and C. Berlin (1964). An analysis of the kinetics of rat liver tryptophan pyrrolase induction: the significance of both enzyme synthesis and degradation. *Biochem. Biophys. Res. Comm.* **15**:214–219.

14. Shor, J. M., and E. Frieden (1958). Induction of tryptophan peroxidase of rat liver by insulin and alloxan. *J. Biol. Chem.* **233**:612–618.

15. Stern, H. (1961). Periodic induction of deoxyribonuclease activity in relation to the mitotic cycle. *J. Biophys. Biochem. Cytology* **9**:271–277.

16. Sussman, M., and M. Osborn (1964). UDP-galactose polysaccharide transferase in the cellular slime mold, *dictyostelium discoideum:* appearance and disappearance of activity during cell differentiation. *Proc. Natl. Acad. Sci.* **52**:81–87.

17. Tanzer, M., and J. Gross (1964). Collagen metabolism in the normal and lathyritic chick. *J. Exptl. Med.* **119**:275–289.

End-Product Repression in the Creatine Pathway of the Developing Chick Embryo

JAMES B. WALKER

INTRODUCTION

Model systems for the study of controls governing enzyme levels in intact higher animals are at present quite limited in number. Many of the animal enzymes examined appear to be constitutive, resistant to exogenous manipulations. However, the levels of certain key enzymes in metabolic pathways which bear relatively heavy traffic do vary in a manner which suggests that nutritional adaptation is a physiological control mechanism in animals as well as bacteria.[1-6] On the other hand, there may be but little selective advantage in controlling the enzyme levels in pathways carrying relatively light molecular traffic.[7] Liver, as the organ most concerned with smoothly integrating the synthesis and breakdown of large quantities of carbohydrates, lipids, and proteins, is a logical focus of metabolic control processes.

Desirable attributes of a model control system might include the following: (1) a highly specific relationship between a controlling compound and its target enzyme; (2) a rapid and pronounced response of the tissue level of the target enzyme to its controlling compound; (3) an extent of response which is proportional to the concentration of the controlling compound; (4) a relatively long half-life *in vivo* of the controlling compound; (5) permeability of the tissue cells to the controlling compound; (6) experimental evidence that the control system is of physiological importance to an individual organism and occurs in a number of tissues of various species; (7) ability of the control system to function relatively free from other influences, i.e. in the absence of intestinal flora and functioning hormones; and (8) the possibility of studying the system in rapidly growing embryonic tissues as well as in adult tissues in a steady-state of enzyme synthesis and breakdown.

We believe that the control system we shall discuss in this paper possesses many of these attributes. This system consists of a negative feedback control of the level of arginine-glycine transamidinase by its ultimate biosynthetic end product, creatine, in the liver of the developing chick embryo. At the outset, however, it might be helpful to describe some of the background events which preceded our investigation of the chick embryo system.

BIOSYNTHESIS OF CREATINE IN HIGHER ANIMALS

Over 50 years ago Folin,[8] impressed by the constancy of creatinine excretion in man, proposed that creatinine formation was a measure of the body's endogenous metabolism, whereas urea was a measure of its exogenous metabolism. Since that time Borsook and Dubnoff,[9, 10] Bloch and Schoenheimer,[11] and Cantoni and Vignos[12] have defined the reactions by which creatine is synthesized (Reactions 1 and 2).

$$\text{Arginine} + \text{glycine} \rightleftarrows \text{ornithine} + \text{guanidinoacetate} \quad (1)$$

$$\text{Guanidinoacetate} + \text{S-adenosylmethionine} \rightarrow \text{S-adenosylhomocysteine} + \text{creatine} \quad (2)$$

It is now believed that the constant rate of creatinine formation in man reflects a non-enzymic first order degradation of a relatively constant body pool of phosphorylcreatine.[13] It has been estimated that approximately 2 per cent of a total body pool of 120 g of creatine is converted to creatinine each day.[14] Since this pool of phosphorylcreatine must be continually replenished by newly synthesized creatine, it is apparent that the rate of creatine biosynthesis must be carefully controlled.

Advances in Enzyme Regulation, 151–168, 1963. Reprinted with the permission of the author and Symposium Publications, a division of Pergamon Press, Ltd.

In recent years our laboratory has been concerned with determining the nature and extent of these physiological controls.

As a prerequisite for such investigations we have found it necessary to determine where creatine is synthesized in the body, a requirement not encountered by investigators studying metabolic controls in microorganisms. From *in vitro* studies of the organ distributions of the enzymes catalyzing Reactions 1 and 2, we have found that the potential sites of synthesis vary with the species. Although data are not yet complete, our findings suggest that creatine can be synthesized *de novo* from its three precursor amino acids, at physiologically significant rates, in the following tissues: frog liver;[15] chick liver;[16] pancreas of dog, cow,[17] rat, and man;[18] and liver of monkey and man.[18] A number of other tissues have significant levels of only one of the necessary enzymes. For example, kidneys of all mammals examined thus far have arginine-glycine transamidinase activity,[9] while mammalian livers[10, 12] and testis[19] have significant levels of guanidinoacetate methylferase activity. Our most surprising findings were (1) the extremely high levels of transamidinase activity occurring in pancreatic acinar cells of the larger mammals,* and (2) the fact that livers of primates, in marked contrast to livers of a number of lower mammals, have physiologically significant levels of transamidinase. Our *in vitro* studies with human tissues are consistent with the conclusions of Sandberg, Hecht, and Tyler,[21] who employed catheterized human volunteers, that in man most of the body creatine is synthesized *de novo* in the liver. They are consistent, that is, if compartmentalization in the liver protects enough of the creatine precursor, arginine, from degradation by the large amounts of arginase present in liver. However, human pancreas, which has a high level of transamidinase but

* Levels are lower in the pancreas of rodents such as the rat, guinea pig, and rabbit. Pancreatic acinar cells rather than islet cells appear to contain the enzyme, since we found no difference between enzyme levels in the head and tail of dog pancreas, even though these areas have markedly different islet populations.[20]

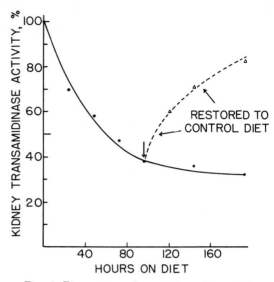

Fig. 1. Time-course of repression of rat kidney arginine-glycine transamidinase, when adult rats are fed a complete diet containing 3 per cent creatine. Derepression occurs promptly when creatine is removed from the diet. Enzyme activities in this and subsequent figures are expressed as μmoles of hydroxyguanidine formed from arginine and hydroxylamine/ hr g tissue (wet wt.).[16]

only a low level of arginase, may also play an important role in creatine biosynthesis. Sandberg *et al.* did not measure creatine or guanidinoacetate levels in the portal vein, and therefore *in vivo* contributions of human pancreas to creatine biosynthesis could not be evaluated.

END-PRODUCT CONTROL OF KIDNEY TRANSAMIDINASE LEVELS IN WEANLING AND ADULT RATS

From our studies of the distribution of enzymes involved in creatine biosynthesis in various species, it was apparent that a number of experimental systems might be employed in the search for metabolic control mechanisms. The rat offers certain experimental advantages which need not be enumerated here, and indeed our first published report on control mechanisms concerned our finding that when creatine was added to the diet of rats the level of kidney transamidinase decreased with time[22] (Fig. 1). Suitable control experiments established that this decrease in activity could not be attributed to inhibition by creatine or any other readily dissociable inhibitor. It therefore appeared that we were dealing with a repression of transamidinase synthesis by its ultimate biosynthetic end product, creatine, or a metabolite or conjugation product[23,24] derived from creatine. Control of enzyme synthesis by end-product repression had been extensively documented in the enteric bacteria,[24–27] but documented examples in intact higher animals were, and still are, rare. However, DeMars[28] had previously reported a marked repression of glutamine transferase activity in HeLa cell cultures by added glutamine. Important studies on feedback systems in intact animals which might involve enzyme repressions have been carried out for a number of years in the pathways of cholesterol[29–32] and bile acid[32,33] synthesis in mammalian liver. It is significant that in both the creatine and cholesterol pathways (1) the feedback control acts on the first pathway-specific enzyme,[16,31] and (2) the controlled enzyme decreases markedly during periods of fasting.[30,34] The rates at which these changes occur are also important. If changes in enzyme levels are to be effective control mechanisms in adult organisms, it is essential that the enzymes involved have a relatively short half-life.

Our work with rats[22] established that dietary creatine lowers the kidney transamidinase level not only in rapidly growing weanlings, but also in adult rats in a physiological steady-state in which the rate of synthesis of tissue enzymes equals the rate of degradation, a situation quite different from that encountered in unicellular cultures in the log phase of growth. This work has been confirmed and extended by Fitch, Hsu, and Dinning[35–37] working with kidneys of rats and rabbits, Coleman[38] working with mouse kidneys, and Van Pilsum and Canfield[39] with rat kidney transamidinase. It should be noted that most of these investigators prefer not to describe the activity decrease as a repression. In fact, Fitch *et al.*[37] propose that glycine is a necessary inducer of transamidinase synthesis, and

dietary creatine acts by antagonizing this induction. If this is true, it is difficult to reconcile with their finding that glycine added to an arginine-enriched diet *lowers* the transamidinase level.[37] Van Pilsum and Canfield[39] have observed a partial reversal of the creatine effect by the addition of large amounts of arginine to the diet. The significance of these data is not apparent in view of the fact that Fitch *et al.* found that 5 per cent arginine lowered the transamidinase level,[37] and our finding that in the closed system of the chick embryo, arginine enhances repression.[40] As for other rat tissues, we have also observed a repression of rat pancreatic transamidinase by dietary creatine, but this tissue is less convenient to work with than kidney. Rat liver cannot be employed for repression studies because this tissue does not contain transamidinase.[18,41] Although the rat kidney system has certain experimental advantages, it is not the most sensitive system, as subsequent events have shown.

END-PRODUCT CONTROL OF LIVER TRANSAMIDINASE LEVELS IN THE GROWING CHICK

The system which has proved most desirable from our standpoint is the chick liver system.[16,34] The level of chick liver arginine-glycine transamidinase, initially somewhat higher than that of rat kidney, is much more responsive to dietary creatine than is rat kidney transamidinase, in terms of effective creatine concentrations required and extent and rate of repression (Fig. 2, lower curve). The level of guanidinoacetate methylferase is not affected by dietary creatine. From the physiological standpoint, it appears that liver is the main site of creatine biosynthesis in the chick, and therefore the site at which physiological controls should operate. On the other hand, Sandberg *et al.*[21] found that the kidneys, of man at least, do not contribute significantly to the *in vivo* synthesis of guanidinoacetate or creatine; this finding casts doubt upon the physiological significance of repression of the mammalian kidney enzyme. It should be

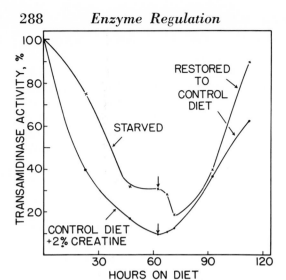

Fig. 2. Lower curve: Time-course of repression of chick liver transamidinase activity and subsequent derepression. Upper curve: Changes in transamidinase activity which occur during fasting and refeeding. Chicks were 10-days old at start of experiment. The total transamidinase activity per chick in the fasted birds is much lower than would appear from the curve of activity per gram of liver, because of liver atrophy. The initial drop in specific activity on refeeding reflects fat accumulation at this time and not a decrease in total organ transamidinase.

pointed out, in the context of this Symposium, that chick liver for our purposes is more closely related to human liver than is the biochemists' more popular tissue analogue, rat liver. Both chick[16] and human livers[18] have comparable levels of transamidinase, whereas rat liver[18, 41] has no detectable transamidinase activity. Although we have carried out extensive experiments with chicks from 1 to 3 weeks of age, in the discussion to follow we shall be primarily concerned with our more recent studies on the control of enzyme levels in the liver of the developing chick embryo and the newly hatched chick.

End-Product Control of Liver Transamidinase Levels in the Developing Chick Embryo

We have observed that livers of newly hatched chicks have very low levels of arginine-glycine transamidinase activity. Within 6 days after hatching, liver transamidinase increases 10-fold to its adult level, if chicks are fed a complete diet.[40] If chicks are fed a complete diet containing creatine, a decrease rather than an increase, occurs; if chicks are not fed, the level decreases to zero activity. Several possible explanations for this behavior were considered: (1) Creatine is synthesized by the hen and secreted into the egg, where it represses embryonic liver transamidinase until birth. After birth, transamidinase is derepressed as excess creatine is transferred from the liver to the muscles,[42] or excreted[43, 44] in the urine. (2) Transamidinase is repressed by creatine synthesized by the developing embryo in excess of its pre-hatch needs. Post-hatch uptake of creatine by newly active muscles derepresses the enzyme. (3) Chicks at the end of the incubation period have exhausted certain nutrients, and the low enzyme level is analogous to that observed in fasting chicks (Fig. 2, upper curve). This, of course, does not explain why fasting *per se* should lower the transamidinase level. (4) Birth triggers the synthesis of an adult form of transamidinase by an unknown mechanism. (5) Transamidinase synthesis is dependent upon neural and humoral factors activated after birth. To help distinguish among these possibilities, chick embryos in various stages of development were assayed for creatine-synthesizing enzymes. Both enzymes were found to be present in liver of the developing chick embryo. It appears that creatine can be synthesized *de novo* during development, and need not be furnished preformed in the egg.[40, 45, 46]

Liver transamidinase activity is high early in development and then declines to a low value a few days before hatching. If this decline were due to repression by an excess of endogenously synthesized creatine, it should be possible to repress liver transamidinase throughout development by injecting creatine into the egg, and this has proved to be the case. The upper curve in Fig. 3 shows the normal level of liver transamidinase at various stages of development, with a characteristic decline in activity prior to hatching. The lower curve shows that injection of creatine completely represses liver transamidinase.

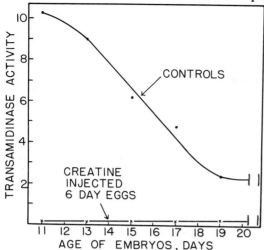

Fig. 3. Transamidinase activity of embryonic chick liver during development. Upper curve: Normal pattern, showing characteristic decline in activity per gram of liver during later stages of development. As a result of liver growth during this period,[45] the total transamidinase activity per embryo does not decrease. Bottom curve: Repression of embryonic transamidinase by creatine injected into eggs on 6th day of incubation.

Repression also occurs when precursors of creatine are injected into the egg. Creatine precursors proximal to the repressible enzyme, citrulline and arginine (but not ornithine), repress transamidinase 35–50 per cent; these repressions are potentiated in the presence of non-repressing levels of glycine. On the other hand, guanidinoacetate, which is metabolically distal to the repressible enzyme, is as effective as creatine itself (Fig. 4). Efforts made to determine if guanidinoacetate must be first converted to creatine before serving as a repressor, by injecting competing methyl group acceptors into the egg, have given inconclusive results.

Numerous experiments have demonstrated that the specificity between target enzyme and controlling compound is quite good. Guanidinoacetate methylferase is not repressed by injected creatine, nor are several other metabolically unrelated enzymes. Among the compounds found to be inactive as repressors were possible degradation products of guanidinoacetate or creatine, methylguanidine, N,N-dimethylguanidine, N-methylglycine, and a large number of amino acids and related

compounds. Slight repression by injected creatinine can be attributed to non-enzymic conversion to creatine during the experimental period. As for the rapidity of repression by creatine, it was found that embryonic liver transamidinase was repressed to 40 per cent of the control level 1 day after injection, and to the 11 per cent level 2 days after creatine injection. It should be noted that repression of transamidinase by creatine is not due to a toxic effect; embryos from eggs injected with creatine appear normal and weigh the same as control embryos injected with water.

We would like to think that our manipulations serve to exaggerate a normal metabolic control mechanism prevailing during development, as suggested in the second possibility listed earlier, but this remains to be proved. However, the data of Sendju,[46] which came to our attention after the above work was performed, do lend independent support to this suggestion. Sendju analyzed for creatine in the egg of the developing chick embryo, and, although his analytical method for creatine lacked specificity, he concluded that only small amounts of creatine are present up to

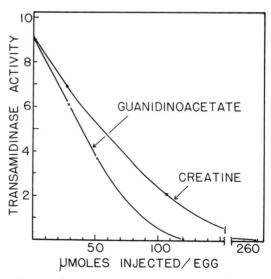

Fig. 4. Quantitative relationship between repressor concentration and extent of repression. Compounds were injected on the 7th day of incubation, and livers were harvested on the 13th day. The higher concentrations of guanidinoacetate inhibit embryo growth somewhat; creatine is relatively non-toxic at all levels tested.

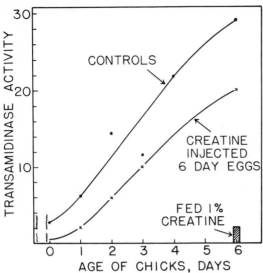

Fig. 5. Transamidinase activity per gram of liver during early post-hatch period, when chicks are fed a complete diet. Continuation of experiment of Fig. 3. Repression is not permanent; derepression of the transamidinase level of creatine-injected chicks results in a 40-fold increase in 6 days. Creatine added to the diet of controls prevents normal increase in activity following birth.

the 14th day of incubation. From 14 days on, the creatine content of the embryo increases sharply in linear fashion.[45,46] As can be seen from Fig. 3, this period of increasing creatine content coincides with the period of rapid decline in liver transamidinase activity, as though endogenous repression were indeed occurring. In collaboration with Mr. Guy Fain, an attempt was made to enhance any such endogenous repression by feeding laying hens for 20 days a diet containing 2 per cent creatine and 0.5 per cent guanidinoacetate. However, no dramatic lowering of transamidinase levels was observed in eggs obtained from these hens.

The net question which arose concerned the degree of permanency of experimental transamidinase repression in the embryo. Would the maintenance of near-zero levels of transamidinase over a major portion of development affect in any way the post-hatch levels of this enzyme? Figure 5 shows that liver transamidinase activity of both creatine-injected and control chicks increases after birth at approximately the same rate. In the chicks

previously injected with creatine, liver transamidinase increases 40-fold in the first 6 days following birth. Even when eggs were injected at minus 1 day of incubation, the chicks that hatched had normal transamidinase levels at 1 week of age. Repression of transamidinase by creatine therefore appears to be reversible in all systems studied to date.

ENZYME REPRESSION AND DIFFERENTIATION

We have seen that differentiated animal tissues contain markedly different levels of transamidinase. We have also seen that a tissue normally containing a high level of transamidinase can be converted into a tissue containing very little transamidinase by adding a single compound to its environment. This phenotypic change is reversible, in contrast to the apparent irreversibility of differentiation. However, this does not mean that enzyme repressions do not play a role in establishing and maintaining tissue specific enzyme patterns. Knox,[47] among others, has emphasized that a series of individually reversible changes could result in relatively irreversible differentiation. More specifically, Monod and Jacob,[48] using hypothetical circuits composed of known control elements, have described how interlocking, individually reversible, repressions might combine to give essentially irreversible differentiation. In some of their circuits a single transient event would determine subsequent enzyme patterns. In experimental support of this concept, instances are known where exposure to a single compound profoundly influences subsequent development.[49-52] Hormones, of course, are well known examples of compounds which affect enzyme patterns in target tissues of adult organisms. In higher animals, cross repressions between different metabolic pathways may well be more prevalent than end-product repression of the type described in this paper. During development, not only might individual gene function be modulated by cross repressors or end-product repressors, but also whole groups of genes may be turned on or off by the action of histones,[53] hormones, interlocking repressor systems, or mechanoenzymes associated with certain areas of a chromosome.

Knowledge of the site at which the transamidinase repressor acts might aid in an understanding of why different tissues have different levels of this enzyme. Since a relatively small molecule like actinomycin D can combine with[54] and inhibit information transfer from DNA in general,[55] there is no *a priori* reason why creatine or phosphorylcreatine might not combine with and inhibit information transfer from a particular DNA or RNA molecule. On the other hand, a coupling enzyme, whose synthesis is directed by a regulator gene, might catalyze the addition of creatine or phosphorylcreatine to another moiety to form the actual repressor. Various tissues might then have different transamidinase levels as a result of differences in their permeability to creatine, their content of ATP:creatine phosphoryltransferase, or their content of the coupling enzyme. Some of the other possible sites of repressor action in the creatine-transamidinase system have been discussed elsewhere.[56] The general problem of differentiation is, of course, much more complex and involves several levels of organization.[57]

Physiological Significance of Transamidinase Repression

The physiological significance of a metabolic control system is in part reflected by the extent of its distribution in nature. It might be expected that ineffective systems would be eliminated by natural selection. In this context, it is of interest that end-product repression of transamidinase has been observed in each of several animal species examined, in both adult and embryonic tissues, and in tissues as diverse as liver, kidney, and pancreas. Transamidinase repression by creatine has been demonstrated in nongrowing tissues in the steady state, in growing tissues in the log phase of growth, and in slowly growing tissues in which the transamidinase level normally exhibits a differential rate of increase. Repression has been shown in the closed system of the developing chick embryo, where repressor concentration is reproducible and can be controlled, in the absence of intestinal flora, and under conditions where hormonal activities are somewhat minimized. In all the above systems there is no parallel or coordinate repression of guanidinoacetate methylferase, and in all of the systems derepression of transamidinase occurs upon removal of the repressor. Since creatine and transamidinase do not occur in bacteria, it seems unlikely that this represents a vestigial control system. On the contrary, the creatine-transamidinase control system must have evolved relatively late in evolution. This consideration, together with the widespread distribution of this feedback control in higher animals, suggests that it has survival value for at least some of the species involved.

Figure 6 illustrates some metabolic relationships which should prove helpful in describing our current thoughts on the physiological significance of the creatine-transamidinase feedback control system. The diverse biosynthetic responsibilities of the amino acid precursors of creatine, arginine, glycine, and methionine, are depicted in this diagram. The situation is most clear cut in the case of chicks, ducks,[34] and perhaps birds in general. For example, it would appear particularly important that the chick not synthesize creatine in excess of its needs, since all three of the amino acid precursors of creatine must be supplied in the diet.[58] Experimentally, dietary creatine has been found to spare a portion of the arginine and glycine requirements of chicks.[59-61] Since creatine does not inhibit the catalytic activity of either of its synthesizing enzymes, the mechanism of the creatine sparing effect very likely involves end-product repression of transamidinase synthesis as described in this paper and illustrated in Fig. 6. Carnivorous birds should find this sparing action particularly advantageous, since the creatine content of muscle is sufficient to repress transamidinase to a significant extent.[16]

However, the survival advantage of this negative feedback system may be most pronounced during periods of food deprivation, which occur when food is scarce, during migratory flights, hibernation, or parenthood (some species). According to this theory, in the absence of food, creatine released from muscle and nerve reservoirs, along with newly synthesized creatine not utilized by these tissues, accumulates in the blood and liver, and differentially represses the synthesis of transamidinase relative to other liver enzymes. Enzyme degradation, proceeding at the normal or an increased rate, then lowers the enzyme level in a first order reaction. The upper curve of Fig. 2 lends experimental support to this view. The maximal rate of de-

crease of liver transamidinase activity is the same whether the chick is fasting or being fed a complete diet containing creatine. Furthermore, the maximal rate of decrease in both cases is very nearly the same as the maximal rate of increase during derepression. These observations are consistent with the view that creatine unbalances a steady state of equal rates of enzyme synthesis and degradation by repressing enzyme synthesis. As the first pathway specific enzyme, the level of transamidinase acts as a valve regulating metabolic flow between synthesis of creatine and the other compounds. During fasting, then, a portion of the amino acid precursor

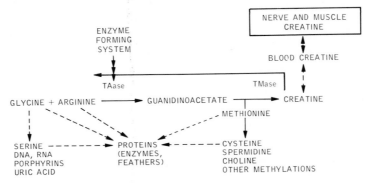

Fig. 6. Diagram showing alternative metabolic pathways available to the amino acid precursors of creatine. Growing chicks require all 3 amino acids in their diet. Transamidinase functions as a valve which regulates metabolic flow along the creatine pathway. The level of transamidinase is in turn regulated by the concentration of its remote end product, creatine.

pool is diverted away from synthesis of creatine, now in excess, for use in more essential biosyntheses (Fig. 6). For example, glycine is essential for the synthesis of the uric acid required to remove ammonia released during the gluconeogenesis of fasting; methionine methyl groups are required to minimize fatty liver during fasting; and all three amino acids are required for synthesis of essential enzymes, serum proteins, protein hormones, and feathers. The continued synthesis of feathers is especially important to birds, and during adult life represents a substantial portion of the dietary amino acid requirements.[60, 62] The extreme vulnerability of the chick to arginine deficiencies, well documented in the literature,[58-61] is now believed to result in part from excessive degradation by arginase.[61] A low kidney threshold for

plasma creatine also appears to contribute to the problem.[43, 61] Since chicks cannot synthesize citrulline,[58] each mole of creatine or urea excreted represents a mole of arginine which must be furnished by the diet.

It should be emphasized that transamidinase control of creatine synthesis may not be absolute during fasting. In many cases, some creatine continues to be synthesized, even during prolonged fasting. However, data reported elsewhere[16] suggest that creatine synthesis would be very nearly completely repressed in livers of fasting carnivorous birds. Carnivorous birds, with a diet containing 0.4 per cent creatine, are in a state of partial repression with respect to liver transamidinase.[16] On fasting, the transamidinase level decreases from the steady-state level at the start of the fast, whether this is the repressed level[16] or the derepressed[34] level. Therefore creatine synthesis would be most nearly completely shut off in carnivorous birds, such as sea-gulls, pelicans, and vultures, after several days without food.

Creatine appears to be a particularly effective controlling compound because of its limited metabolic fates and long half-life *in vivo*. End-product repression rather than end-product inhibition of transamidinase has been selected as the metabolic feedback control probably because of the large pools of creatine which exist in the body. As a result of the presence of these large reservoirs, minute to minute regulation of creatine synthesis, as by end-product inhibition, is not necessary. However, during relatively long term changes in food availability, end-product repression enables the organism to adjust its rate of creatine biosynthesis according to its needs.

The fact that metabolic control of creatine biosynthesis has survival value implies that creatine itself plays a significant role in animal metabolism. Speculation concerning this role has been advanced by many eminent biochemists over the years.[45, 63-66] The importance of creatine in metabolism appears to be due, at least in part, to its unique role in smoothly buffering the ATP levels of tissues such as nerve and muscle, tissues characteristic of animals. The ATP concentration must be precisely controlled because of the large number of reactions in which ATP participates; the rate of each such reaction has its own characteristic dependence upon the ATP concentration. Precise regulation of both impulse initiation and conduction and muscle contraction may well be dependent upon a properly functioning creatine-phosphorylcreatine system.

In the past, there has been a tendency to equate metabolic controls in higher animals to hormonal controls. It is of interest, therefore, that certain analogies can be drawn between creatine and hormones. Like the hormones, creatine is synthesized in one tissue and transported in the blood to its target organs, primarily muscle and nerves, where it influences the metabolism of those tissues. Moreover, as in the case of the hormones, an excess of creatine in the blood acts via a negative feedback control mechanism to limit the rate of its biosynthesis. Whether or not these analogies can be extended further remains to be seen.

SUMMARY

Negative feedback systems are believed to be operative in higher animals in physiologically important processes ranging from formation of tropic hormones to maintenance of organ size. However, model systems for the study of such controls at the molecular level in intact animals are quite rare, and are limited to two biosynthetic pathways: the cholesterol-bile acid pathway, and the creatine pathway. In this paper the properties of the latter model system are described in detail. Two enzymes are involved in the biosynthesis of creatine. The second enzyme appears to be constitutive, whereas the steady-state level of the first enzyme, arginine-glycine transamidinase, is responsive to the tissue concentration of creatine. This process has been operationally termed end-product repression, by analogy with bacterial systems, until its mechanism can be more completely elucidated. Creatine repression of transamidinase has been observed in the rat, mouse, rabbit, chick, and duck, in tissues as diverse as kidney, pancreas, and liver. More recently, repression has been studied in the liver of the developing chick embryo and the newly hatched chick. Virtually complete repression of embryonic liver transamidinase can be maintained throughout development by a single injection of creatine into the egg. Derepression occurs in the first week following birth, when chicks are fed a normal diet. Numerous experiments have shown that there is a highly specific relationship between the target enzyme and the controlling compound. Creatine precursors proximal to the target enzyme repress 35–50 per cent while the precursor distal to the target enzyme represses completely. In the closed system of the egg, repression of the target enzyme can be readily shown to be proportional to repressor concentration. Moreover, this system permits the demonstration that repression can occur in the absence of intestinal flora, and under conditions of minimal hormonal influences. The normal pattern of change of transamidinase activity during embryonic and neonatal development is consistent with a repression by endogenous creatine prior to birth, followed by a post-hatch derepression, but other explanations are also entertained.

Evidence is cited in support of the thesis that the creatine-transamidinase control system has survival value for birds, and perhaps reptiles and amphibians. It is suggested that liver transamidinase of carnivorous birds is normally in a partially repressed state, as a result of the 0.4 per cent creatine content of ingested muscle tissue, whereas transamidinase of herbivorous birds is normally derepressed. Experimentally it has been demonstrated that fasting lowers the activity of both the repressed and derepressed enzymes. At least part of this decrease can be attributed to a repression by endogenous creatine which appears in increased concentration in the blood, liver and kidneys of most higher animals during fasting. During fasting, then, the decrease in transamidinase activity permits diversion of a portion of the dietary essential amino acids, arginine, glycine, and methionine, from the synthesis of creatine, now in excess, to more immediately essential biosyntheses. For example, glycine is essential for synthesis of the uric acid required to remove amino groups arising from the gluconeogenesis of fasting; methionine methyl groups are required for the increased lipid transport of fasting; and all three amino acids are needed for synthesis of essential enzymes, protein hormones, and feathers.

In addition to the foregoing, the implications of the occurrence of a repressible system during embryonic development for the problem of the establishment and maintenance of tissue specific enzyme levels are discussed.

Acknowledgments

It is a pleasure to acknowledge the collaboration of Margaret Skorvaga Walker in much of this work. Our experiments were supported by grants from the U.S. Public Health Service, and from the Robert A. Welch Foundation, Houston, Texas. The author is a Research Career Development Awardee of the U.S. Public Health Service.

REFERENCES

1. G. Weber, Pathology of glucose-6-phosphate metabolism; a study in enzyme pathology, *Rev. Can. Biol.* **18**, 245–282 (1959).
2. R. A. Freedland and A. E. Harper, Metabolic adaptations in higher animals. V. The study of metabolic pathways by means of metabolic adaptation, *J. Biol. Chem.* **234**, 1351–1354 (1959).
3. J. Tepperman and H. M. Tepperman, Effects of antecedent food intake pattern on hepatic lipogenesis, *Am. J. Physiol.* **193**, 55–64 (1958).
4. W. M. Fitch and I. L. Chaikoff, Extent and patterns of adaptation of enzyme activities in livers of normal rats fed diets high in glucose and fructose, *J. Biol. Chem.* **235**, 554–557 (1960).
5. G. Weber and H. Macdonald, Role of enzymes in metabolic homeostasis. I. Depletion and restoration of liver enzymes involved in glycolysis, glucogenesis, and hexosemonophosphate shunt in normal and hypophysectomized rats, *Exp. Cell. Res.* **22**, 292–302 (1961).
6. R. T. Schimke, Adaptive characteristics of urea cycle enzymes in the rat, *J. Biol. Chem.* **237**, 459–466 (1962).
7. A. C. Wilson and A. B. Pardee, Regulation of flavin synthesis by *Escherichia coli*, *J. Gen. Microbiol.* **28**, 283–303 (1962).
8. O. Folin, A theory of protein metabolism, *Am. J. Physiol.* **13**, 117–138 (1905).
9. H. Borsook and J. W. Dubnoff, Formation of glycocyamine in animal tissues, *J. Biol. Chem.* **138**, 389–403 (1941).
10. H. Borsook and J. W. Dubnoff, Formation of creatine from glycocyamine in liver, *J. Biol. Chem.* **132**, 559–574 (1940).
11. K. Bloch and R. Schoenheimer, Biological precursors of creatine, *J. Biol. Chem.* **138**, 167–194 (1941).
12. G. L. Cantoni and P. J. Vignos, Enzymatic mechanism of creatine synthesis, *J. Biol. Chem.* **209**, 647–659 (1954).
13. H. Borsook and J. W. Dubnoff, The hydrolysis of phosphocreatine and the origin of urinary creatinine, *J. Biol. Chem.* **168**, 493–510 (1947).
14. K. Bloch, R. Schoenheimer, and D. Rittenberg, Rate of formation and disappearance of body creatine in normal animals, *J. Biol. Chem.* **138**, 155–166 (1941).

15. J. B. Walker, Arginine-X transamidinases, *Federation Proc.* **18**, 346 (1959).

16. J. B. Walker, Metabolic control of creatine biosynthesis. I. Effect of dietary creatine, *J. Biol. Chem.* **235**, 2357–2361 (1960).

17. J. B. Walker and M. S. Walker, The formation of creatine from guanidioacetate in pancreas, *Proc. Soc. Exp. Biol. Med.* **101**, 807–809 (1959).

18. J. B. Walker, Formamidine group transfer in extracts of human pancreas, liver, and kidney, *Biochim. Biophys. Acta*, in press.

19. F. Salvatore and F. Schlenk, A new assay of guanidinoacetate methyltransferase, *Biochim. Biophys. Acta* **59**, 700–702 (1962).

20. S. A. Benscosme, E. Liepa and S. S. Lazarus, Glucagon content of pancreatic tissue devoid of alpha cells, *Proc. Soc. Exp. Biol. Med.* **90**, 387–392 (1955).

21. A. A. Sandberg, H. H. Hecht, and F. H. Tyler, Studies in disorders of muscle. X. The site of creatine synthesis in the human, *Metabolism, Clin. and Exptl.* **2**, 22–29 (1953).

22. J. B. Walker, Repression of arginine-glycine transamidinase activity by dietary creatine, *Biochim. Biophys. Acta* **36**, 574–575 (1959).

23. L. Szilard, The control of the formation of specific proteins in bacteria and in animal cells, *Proc. Nat. Acad. Sci. U.S.* **46**, 277–292 (1960).

24. H. J. Vogel, Control by repression, in *Control Mechanisms in Cellular Processes*, Ronald, New York, 1961, pp. 23–65.

25. A. B. Pardee, The control of enzyme activity, in *The Enzymes*, Vol. 1, Academic Press, New York, 1959, pp. 681–716.

26. A. C. Wilson and A. B. Pardee, Comparative aspects of metabolic control, in *Comparative Biochemistry*, Vol. VI, Academic Press, New York, in press.

27. H. S. Moyed and H. E. Umbarger, Regulation of biosynthetic pathways, *Physiol. Rev.* **42**, 444–466 (1962).

28. R. DeMars, The inhibition by glutamine of glutamyl transferase formation in cultures of human cells, *Biochim. Biophys. Acta* **27**, 435–436 (1958).

29. G. M. Tomkins, H. Sheppard and I. L. Chaikoff, Cholesterol synthesis by liver. III. Its regulation by ingested cholesterol, *J. Biol. Chem.* **201**, 137–141 (1953).

30. N. R. L. Bucher, Alterations of cholesterol biosynthesis in liver cell fractions from rats in various experimental conditions, *Ciba Fndn. Symposium on Biosynthesis of Terpenes and Sterols*, Little, Brown, Boston, 1959, pp. 46–60.

31. M. D. Siperstein, The homeostatic control of cholesterol synthesis in liver, *Am. J. Clin. Nutrition* **8**, 645–649 (1960).

32. W. T. Beher, G. D. Baker and W. L. Anthony, Feedback control of cholesterol biosynthesis in the mouse, *Proc. Soc. Exp. Biol. Med.* **109**, 863–868 (1962).

33. S. Bergstrom and H. Danielsson, On the regulation of bile acid formation in the rat liver, *Acta Physiol. Scand.* **43**, 1–7 (1958).

34. J. B. Walker, Metabolic control of creatine biosynthesis. II. Restoration of transamidinase activity following creatine repression, *J. Biol. Chem.* **236**, 493–498 (1961).

35. C. D. Fitch, C. Hsu and J. S. Dinning, Some factors affecting kidney transamidinase activity in rats, *J. Biol. Chem.* **235**, 2362–2364 (1960).

36. C. D. Fitch, C. Hsu and J. S. Dinning, The mechanism of kidney transamidinase reduction in vitamin E-deficient rabbits, *J. Biol. Chem.* **236**, 490–492 (1961).

37. C. D. Fitch, C. Hsu and J. S. Dinning, Partial reversal of creatine inhibition of transamidinase by dietary glycine, *Biochem. Biophys. Acta* **52**, 194–195 (1961).

38. D. L. Coleman, Effects of dietary creatine and glycine on transamidinase activity in dystrophic mice, *Arch. Biochem. Biophys.* **94**, 183–186 (1961).

39. J. F. Van Pilsum and T. M. Canfield, Transamidinase activities, *in vitro*, of kidneys from rats fed diets supplemented with nitrogen-containing compounds, *J. Biol. Chem.* **237**, 2574–2577 (1962).

40. M. S. Walker and J. B. Walker, Repression of transamidinase activity during embryonic development, *J. Biol. Chem.* **237**, 473–476 (1962).

41. G. B. Gerber, G. Gerber, T. R. Koszalka and L. L. Miller, The rate of creatine synthesis in the isolated, perfused rat liver, *J. Biol. Chem.* **237**, 2246–2250 (1962).

42. H. Fisher, R. C. Salander and M. W. Taylor, Growth and creatine biosynthesis in the chick as affected by the amino acid deficiencies of casein, *J. Nutrition* **58**, 459–470 (1956).

43. D. N. Paton, Creatine excretion in the bird and its significance, *J. Physiol.* **39**, 485–504 (1909–1910).

44. B. L. O'Dell, O. A. Laerdal, A. M. Jeffay and J. E. Savage, Arginine metabolism in the growing chick, *Poultry Sci.* **37**, 817–821 (1958).

45. E. Mellanby, Creatin and creatinin, *J. Physiol.* **36**, 447–487 (1907–08).

46. Y. Sendju, The changes in creatine and creatinine during the incubation of the hen's egg, *J. Biochem. (Japan)* **7**, 181–189 (1927).

47. W. E. Knox, The adaptive control of enzyme activity in animals, in *Molecular and Cellular Structure*, Ronald, New York, 1961, pp. 13–33.

48. J. Monod and F. Jacob, General conclusions: teleonomic mechanisms in cellular metabolism, growth, and differentiation, in *Cold Spring Harbor Symposium Quant. Biol.* **26**, 389–401 (1961).

49. H. B. Fell and E. Mellanby, Metaplasia produced in cultures of chick ectoderm by high vitamin A, *J. Physiol.* **119**, 470–488 (1953).

50. C. E. Wilde, Differentiation in response to the biochemical environment, in *Cell, Organism and Milieu*, Ronald, New York, 3–43 (1958).

51. J. W. Lash, F. A. Hommes and F. Zilliken, Induction of cell differentiation. I. *In vitro* induction of vertebral cartilage with a low molecular weight tissue component, *Biochim. Biophys. Acta* **56**, 313–319 (1962).

52. R. Levi-Montalcini and S. Cohen, *In vitro* and *in vivo* effects of a nerve-growth stimulating agent isolated from snake venom, *Proc. Nat. Acad. Sci. U.S.* **42**, 695–699 (1956).

53. R. C. Huang and J. Bonner, Histone, a suppressor of chromosomal RNA synthesis, *Proc. Nat. Acad. Sci. U.S.* **48**, 1216–1222 (1962).

54. H. H. Rauen, H. Kersten and W. Kersten, Mode of action of actinomycin, *Z. Physiol. Chem.* **321**, 139–147 (1960).

55. J. Hurwitz, J. J. Furth, M. Malamy and M. Alexander, The inhibition of the enzymatic synthesis of RNA and DNA by actinomycin D and proflavin, *Proc. Nat. Acad. Sci. U.S.* **48**, 1222–1230 (1962).

56. J. B. Walker, Feedback control of enzyme levels in higher animals, in *The Molecular Basis of Neoplasia*, Univ. of Texas, Press, Austin, 403–419 (1962).

57. P. Weiss, From cell to molecule, in *The Molecular Control of Cellular Activity*, McGraw-Hill, New York, 1–72 (1962).

58. H. J. Almquist, The amino acid requirements of animals, in *Protein and Amino Acid Nutrition*, Academic Press, New York, 349–380 (1959).

59. H. J. Almquist, E. Mecchi and F. H. Kratzer, Creatine formation in the chick, *J. Biol. Chem.* **141**, 365–373 (1941).

60. D. M. Hegsted, G. M. Briggs, C. A. Elvehjem and E. B. Hart, The role of arginine and glycine in chick nutrition, *J. Biol. Chem.* **140**, 191–200 (1941).

61. J. E. Savage and B. L. O'Dell, Arginine requirement of the chick and the arginine-sparing value of related compounds, *J. Nutrition* **70**, 129–134 (1960).

62. H. H. Mitchell, Some species and age differences in amino acid requirements, in *Protein and Amino Acid Nutrition*, Academic Press, 11–73 (1959).

63. A. Hunter, Physiology of creatine and creatinine, *Physiol. Rev.* **2**, 586–626 (1922).

64. W. C. Rose, The metabolism of creatine and creatinine, *Ann. Rev. Biochem.* **2**, 187–206 (1933).

65. H. H. Beard, The biochemistry of creatine and creatinine, *Ann. Rev. Biochem.* **10**, 245–264 (1941).

66. A. H. Ennor and J. F. Morrison, Biochemistry of the phosphagens and related guanidines, *Physiol. Rev.* **38**, 631–674 (1958).

Synthesis of Experimentally Induced Glutamine Synthetase (Glutamotransferase Activity) in Embryonic Chick Retina *in Vitro*[1]

DAVID L. KIRK

AARON MOSCONA

With the technical assistance of Nilda Saenz.

INTRODUCTION

Detailed studies on mechanisms controlling differentiation in embryonic cells and tissues require, in our opinion, experimental systems in which the appearance and activity of characteristic enzyme patterns can be manipulated

Developmental Biology, **8**, 341–357 (1963). Reprinted with permission.

[1] Supported by grants from the National Science Foundation (G-23852), National Cancer Institute (C-4272), and the Dr. Wallace C. and Clara A. Abbott Fund of the University of Chicago.

and effectively modified. A particularly desirable situation would be one in which it would be possible to cause a precocious appearance in a tissue of an enzyme system that is normally associated with the onset of functional differentiation at a later stage of development. It has been recently found (Moscona and Hubby, 1963) that when the neural retina of the early chick embryo is isolated and cultivated *in vitro* there is a precocious appearance and a very rapid increase of glutamotransferase activity in this tissue. The data suggested that this striking increase in enzyme activity, days in advance of normal ontogeny, was not a nonspecific response to tissue transplantation, but that it represented a modification or acceleration of an aspect of the developmental pattern typical to the retina. The possibilities of a precocious induction, derepression, or stimulation of the enzyme-forming system at the level of geonomic or cytoplasmic controls were raised, but the information available did not suffice for further consideration of the mechanisms that might be involved. Since this experimental system appeared highly suitable (both as a specific case and possibly as a model of more general significance) for detailed investigation of mechanisms involved in controlling tissue-specific enzymatic patterns, it has been further studied with particular reference to: (1) functional identity of the enzyme, (2) whether the experimentally induced increase in its activity represented new synthesis or an activation of preexisting enzyme, independent of biosynthetic processes, and (3) factors affecting level of enzyme activity in cultured tissue. It will be noted that the enzyme assay method outlined here is a modification of previous ones; detailed discussion of these modifications will be made elsewhere together with a report of some further improvements which have subsequently been made (Kirk, 1963).

Some of the advantages of chick neural retina for studies on the molecular aspects of differentiation were listed previously (Moscona and Hubby, 1963). It can be isolated readily and cleanly in relatively large quantities from embryos of different ages and lends itself well to studies *in vitro* at both tissue and cellular levels. In the embryo, active cell proliferation in this tissue is greatly reduced past the tenth day of incubation (Coulombre, 1961), and thus the phenomena that accompany further growth and differentiation are not as complicated by extensive cell replication as in some other embryonic systems. In addition to its homogeneous developmental origin, the retina appears also to be relatively homogeneous with respect to presence of glutamotransferase in its different layers (Rudnick, 1963); thus for purposes of studying this enzymatic activity it can be treated, tentatively, as a uniform cell population.

A more satisfactory definition of the actual functional identity of the retinal enzyme detectable by its glutamotransferase activity was sought, and the evidence suggests that it is a glutamine synthetase. Although the precise metabolic role of retinal glutamotransferase (or glutamine synthetase) is uncertain, its relevance to retinal function can be inferred from the following lines of information. The *in vivo* appearance and accumulation of retinal glutamotransferase in the last few days of embryonic life is temporally correlated with functional maturation of the retina as indicated by appearance of both visual pigments and the electroretinogram (Rudnick and Waelsch, 1955; Wald and Zussman, 1938). Secondly, neural tissues in general are characterized by high levels of glutamine synthetase (Meister, 1962; Wu, 1963) and by highly active metabolic pools of glutamate, glutamine, and associated metabolites (Garfinkel, 1962); neural retina is no exception to this pattern (Pirie, 1956). Last, it appears that the retina depends upon synthesis of glutamine for maintenance of electrolyte balance, a phenomenon as yet incompletely explained (Pirie, 1956). All these facts contributed to our interest in this system and stimulated a series of improvements in both the culture and assay procedures previously used (Moscona and Hubby, 1963) resulting in increased precision of the system and, thus, increased usefulness as a model for studying this sort of enzymatic differentiation.

The previous report (Moscona and Hubby, 1963) discussed only the appearance of enzymatic *activity* and offered no information concerning synthesis of enzyme molecules. This communication deals more directly with this problem. Since no quantitative technique for isolation of this enzyme yet exists (Meister, 1962; Pamiljans *et al.*, 1962), direct evidence of *de novo* synthesis was not feasible and less direct methods were used: a systematic search for enzyme activators or inhibitors at various developmental stages and a determination of the sensitivity of the appearance of activity *in vitro* to the inhibitor of protein synthesis, puromycin. Furthermore, the recent demonstration (Davidson *et al.*, 1963) that continued synthesis of a product characteristic of a differentiated cell line was dependent upon an actinomycin D-sensitive process (presumably DNA-primed synthesis of messenger RNA) raised the question to what extent appearance and maintenance of retinal glutamotransferase activity was under control of an actinomycin-sensitive mechanism.

Finally, investigation was also made of the influence of the substrate and end product of the enzyme (i.e., glutamate and glutamine), glucose, other ocular tissues and extracts of young embryos upon the *in vitro* appearance of glutamotransferase activity.

MATERIAL AND METHODS

Retinal Cultures

Organ cultures of embryonic chick neural retina were established as previously described (Moscona and Hubby, 1963). Two retinas, each cut in two pieces, were suspended in 24 ml of culture medium in a 125-ml Erlenmeyer flask; the flasks were then gassed with a mixture of 5% CO_2 in air, sealed and placed on a gyratory shaker rotating at 85 rpm (diameter of rotation $3/4$ inch) at 38°C for 12, 24, or 48 hours. Random variability was minimized by distributing pieces of tissue from each pair of retinas through control and experimental flasks. Thus, while each culture contained the equivalent of two retinas, in no case was all the tissue in one culture flask derived from a single embryo. Unless otherwise mentioned all studies were performed on retinas from embryos of 10 days' incubation. A minimal maintenance medium was routinely used; it consisted of 100 parts Tyrode's solution, 10 parts horse serum, and 1 part of a penicillin-streptomycin mixture (Microbiological Associates). Additions to the medium were made in sterile, neutral, Tyrode's-based solutions at the expense of the basal Tyrode's solution. Whenever experimental protocol called for a change of medium, part of the control cultures were simultaneously changed to fresh medium. A thorough investigation of the effect of light upon retinal cultures indicated a slightly higher rate of enzymatic growth in the dark, so that in the routine procedure retinas were isolated under normal illumination but cultured in a darkened incubation room.

At the conclusion of the culture period, tissues were sampled for routine histological examination, harvested, washed quickly three times in cold Tyrode's solution by decantation, collected by mild centrifugation, and lyophilized immediately in the plastic centrifuge tubes. Just prior to analysis, tissues were suspended in 2.5 ml of cold phosphate buffer (0.01 M, pH 7.1), packed in ice, and submitted to about three 5-second bursts of ultrasound (20 Kcps) from the probe of a Branson model 75 sonifer tuned to maximum output. Such ultrasonic treatment yielded a lightly opalescent, homogeneous suspension and released significantly more activity than Potter-Elvejhem glass grinding.

Enzyme Assays

Glutamotransferase was determined by the following modification (Kirk, 1963) of standard procedures (Moscona and Hubby, 1963; Rudnick and Waelsch, 1955). To 0.35 ml of cold sonicate (diluted with phosphate buffer when necessary) was added 0.50 ml of a fresh pH 5.4 solution containing: L-glutamine, 120 μmoles; acetate buffer, 50 μmoles; NaH_2PO_4, 5 μmoles; ATP, 0.05 μmole. This mixture was preincubated 10 minutes at 38°C, where-

TABLE 1. Properties of embryonic retinal glutamotransferase (20-day embryos)

Assay Conditions	Relative Activity	pH Optimum
Standard (see text)	100	5.4
Decreased Mn^{++}		
2.5 μmoles	92	6.3
1 μmole	87	6.8
0	<1	?
Hydroxylysine added		
5 μmoles	39	—
50 μmoles	11	—
Methionine sulfoximine added		
2.5 μmoles	31	—
5 μmoles	18	—
5 μmoles plus 10 μmoles methionine	13	—
Synthetase (by the method of Levintow *et al.*, 1955)	20–35	—

upon 0.15 ml of a solution (pH 5.4) containing 30 μmoles hydroxylamine and 5 μmoles $MnCl_2$ was added to start the reaction. Each assay was run in triplicate, one tube receiving all but the hydroxylamine and serving as the blank. The reaction was stopped with the standard ferric chloride reagent (Moscona and Hubby, 1963) after an incubation time estimated to produce approximately 0.3–0.6 μmole of product. Absorbance was determined on a Zeiss PMQII spectrophotometer at 500 mμ and related to a succinohydroxamate standard and a biologic standard (see Kirk, 1963). Glutamine synthetase was determined by the method of Levintow *et al.* (1955). Protein was determined by the method of Lowry *et al.* (1951), and specific activity was defined as micromoles of glutamohydroxamate formed per hour per milligram of protein.

Materials

Puromycin, adenine nucleotides, and all amino acids employed (except hydroxylysine and methionine sulfoximine) were obtained from Nutritional Biochemicals Corporation. DL-*allo*-δ-hydroxylysine was obtained from Sigma Chemical Company. DL-methionine-*dl*-sulfoximine was obtained from California Biochemical Corporation. Actinomycin D was generously supplied by Merck, Sharp, & Dohme Inc.

RESULTS

Properties of Retinal Glutamotransferase

At least two discrete enzymes with glutamotransferase activity are known: glutamine synthetase and glutaminase (Meister, 1962). The enzyme most studied in neural tissue is glutamine synthetase. Among its characteristic properties are an absolute divalent cation requirement (Mn^{++} effective at lower levels than Mg^{++}), an inverse shift in pH optimum with Mn^{++} concentration (for the transferase reaction at least), a ratio of transferase to synthetase between 2 and 15 depending on tissue source and preparative methods (cf. Meister, 1962; Pamiljans *et al.*, 1962), a noncompetitive inhibition by DL-*allo*-δ-hydroxylysine (Wu, 1963), and methionine-insensitive inhibition by methionine sulfoximine (Tower, 1960).

By using these properties, preparations of retinal tissue from 20-day embryos and/or retinal cultures were tested to determine whether embryonic retinal glutamotransferase activity is due to a glutamine synthetase (Table 1). It was found that in all cases there was indeed an absolute requirement for a divalent cation: in the absence of added Mn^{++} ion the transferase activity was less than 1% that obtained in the presence of 5 μmoles/ml. Furthermore, as the Mn^{++} level was lowered from 5 to 2.5 to 1 μmole/ml, the

TABLE 2. Production of glutamohydroxamate (GHA) from glutamine by retinas of different ages, assayed separately and combined

Age[a]	Volume[b]	Retinal Equivalent[c]	μmoles GHA/hr	Predicted Value
7	0.35	1.7	0.061	—
10	0.35	1.1	0.280	—
18	0.20	0.16	0.276	—
7	0.25	1.2 ⎱	0.184	0.182
18	0.10	0.08 ⎰		
10	0.25	0.79 ⎱	0.340	0.338
18	0.10	0.08 ⎰		

[a] Days of incubation of donor embryo.
[b] Ml of sonicate used per assay.
[c] Number of retinas represented by the volume of sonicate used.

pH optimum of the transferase reaction catalyzed by embryonic retina shifted from 5.4 to 6.3 to 6.8. Preliminary assays of synthetase activity of crude sonicates yielded transferase:synthetase ratios between 3:1 and 5:1. DL-*allo*-δ-hydroxylysine added to the assay mixture at the level of 5 μmoles/ml inhibited the transferase activity of 20-day retina by 61%; at 50 μmoles the degree of inhibition was about 90%. DL-methionine-*dl*-sulfoximine also was a definite inhibitor of the reaction: 2.5 μmoles/ml gave 70% inhibition, 5.0 μmoles/ml resulted in 80% inhibition. The effect of the sulfoximine could not be reversed by methionine. It is particularly important that by no test yet performed has it been possible to differentiate (qualitatively) between the properties of the enzyme which develops in the retina of late embryos and that which can be caused experimentally to develop several days precociously in the retina in culture. On the basis of these data and in the absence of any data to the contrary, it must be assumed (1) that the enzyme being investigated here is a *glutamine synthetase;* (2) that it is identical in retina in the embryo and in culture; (3) that its precocious appearance under the experimental conditions described represents, indeed, an acceleration of a developmental trait characteristic of retinal differentiation.

Evidence for Synthesis of Enzyme

1. Absence of Detectable Inhibitors or Activators. As noted above, the previous report discussed only changes in specific activity of the retina and made no attempt to answer the question of *de novo* synthesis versus activation of preexisting molecules or removal of a specific enzyme inhibitor (Moscona and Hubby, 1963). According to preliminary data (Hubby, Moscona, and Saenz, unpublished) the activities of retinas from early and late embryos were additive, suggesting the absence of any change in concentration of either a competitive inhibitor or a hitherto-unidentified activator. Such mixed assays have been repeated and some representative data are given in Table 2. The precisely additive nature of these results indicates the absence of detectable change in concentration of any activators or competitive inhibitors during this period (from 7 to 18 days of incubation) when retina is undergoing marked escalation of glutamotransferase activity. Similar additive data have been obtained in mixed assays of cultured and freshly isolated retinas. The second classical approach to this problem—varying dilution and incubation time inversely—has been applied to many stages of *in ovo* and *in vitro* retinal development. In all cases there is a slight departure (10–15%) from first-order kinetics with respect to enzyme (cf. Kirk, 1963). This appears, however, to be a result of inherent instability of the enzyme at prolonged incubation times, since it is more dependent upon time of incubation than upon degree of dilution. In any case, no significant difference has yet been observed in this departure from linearity with age or history of the retina.

2. Inhibition by Puromycin of the Normal Glutamine Synthetase Increase. While the above studies preclude a major participation

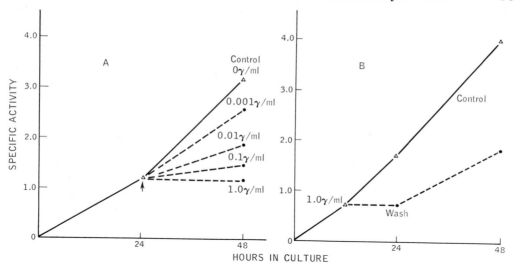

Fig. 1. The effect of puromycin upon the glutamine synthetase (glutamotransferase activity) of 10-day chick neural retinal cultures. Specific activity is defined as micromoles of glutamohydroxamic acid produced per hour per milligram of protein. (A) Concentration-dependent effect of puromycin. Puromycin was supplied to retinas precultured for 24 hours in control medium, and the cultures were maintained for an additional 24 hours. (B) Partial reversibility of the puromycin effect. Puromycin was added to 12-hour cultures and left in 12 hours. The cultures were then washed and transferred to fresh puromycin-free medium for the remainder of the cultivation period.

of variation in competitive inhibitors or activators in the apparent enzymatic growth of the retina, they do not exclude the possibility that removal of *noncompetitive* inhibitors or modification of inactive but preexisting enzyme molecules is involved. In an attempt to answer this question, puromycin, an inhibitor of protein synthesis, was used. It was applied in varying concentrations to 10-day retinas, either at the time of explantation into the medium or after a precultivation period of 12 or 24 hours (by which time the tissues had developed readily detectable levels of enzymatic activity). As can be seen from Fig. 1A, there is a definite dose-dependent depression exerted by puromycin on the normal rate of increase in glutamotransferase activity. Puromycin at a level of 1.0 μg per milliliter of culture medium prevented, consistently and completely, any increase in specific activity of the cultures for as long as it was present, whether added after zero, 12, or 24 hours of culture. Levels as high as 10 μg/ml caused no statistically significant decrease in enzymatic activity from the values existing prior to treatment (at least during

the following 24 hours). That the retinal cells had not been irreversibly damaged by such puromycin treatment is demonstrated by the reversibility data plotted in Fig. 1B. The cultures from which the data in Fig. 1B were obtained were washed three times in Tyrode's solution, cultured 20 minutes in puromycin-free medium, and then transferred to fresh medium, where they remained for the rest of the cultivation period. The degree of reversibility was very variable—sometimes nil—but with vigorous washing, after exposure to puromycin, reversibility could be demonstrated. Histologic examination of puromycin-treated retinas confirmed the opinion that levels of puromycin which completely blocked enzymatic growth were not grossly cytotoxic. From these data it can be concluded that at least one step in the appearance of glutamotransferase activity *in vitro* is puromycin sensitive; in the absence of any contrary data, this can be taken as strong presumptive evidence for *de novo* synthesis of the enzyme under culture conditions.

3. Inhibition by Actinomycin of the Normal Glutamine Synthetase Increase. Since

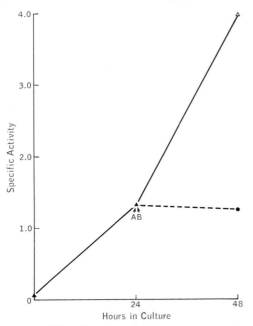

Fig. 2. The effect of a brief exposure to actinomycin D on the glutamine synthetase (glutamotransferase activity) of organ cultures of neural
retinas of 10-day chick embryos. Actinomycin D
(1 µg/ml) was added to the cultures at *A*; at *B* (20
minutes) the cultures were washed and transferred
to fresh medium for the remainder of the cultivation
period.

the experimentally induced appearance of
glutamine synthetase involves protein synthesis, it is of interest to determine to what
extent this synthetic process is under continuous nuclear control. As an initial approach
to this problem retinal cultures were briefly
exposed to low concentrations of actinomycin
D, an inhibitor of DNA-dependent RNA synthesis (Hurwitz *et al.*, 1962). As seen in Fig.
2, a 20-minute exposure to 1.0 µg of this anti-
biotic per milliliter was sufficient to block
completely and irreversibly further increase
in the enzyme in cultures previously undergoing a high rate of enzymatic growth. This
finding, coupled with the puromycin effect,
indicates that the increase in the appearance
of glutamine synthetase in cultured retina
depends upon biosynthetic activities which
appear to be under rather direct and continuous control by DNA. Furthermore, attention
is drawn to the fact that both puromycin and
actinomycin at the appropriate levels com-

pletely blocked further increase in enzymatic
activity, without ever causing any significant
reduction from preexisting enzymatic levels
even when administered at tenfold blocking
concentrations; this clearly suggests that the
enzyme itself is relatively stable, but that the
RNA involved in its production is, under the
conditions of these experiments, of low stability. Proof of such suppositions rests, of
course, upon demonstration that these metabolic inhibitors are exerting their generally
accepted effects upon the retina; hence,
studies of the synthetic and turnover rates of
retinal proteins and nucleic acids (via labeled
precursors) have been commenced at this
writing.

Absence of Detectable Control Factors in Ocular Tissues and Embryo Extracts

Since the enhancement in rate of enzyme
production commences practically immediately upon isolation of the retina from the
embryo, the possible role of systemic sup-
pressors in controlling the level of enzyme in
the retina *in situ* must be considered. The possibility was tested by culturing 10-day neural
retina in the presence of pigmented epithelium
(tapetum) or vitreous humor from the same
embryos, and by culturing retina in medium
supplemented with saline extracts of 7- or
10-day whole chick embryos. In none of these
cultures was there any significant effect upon
the rate of enzyme synthesis in the explanted
retinas. While these results do not preclude
the existence of such systemic control factors,
they indicate that if such occur their demonstration will require a more subtle approach.
Such work is in progress.

The Partial Suppressing Effect of Glutamine and Glutamate

After having tentatively established the occurrence of *de novo* synthesis of glutamine
synthetase in the explanted retina, a prime
consideration is the mechanism whereby this
synthesis is normally repressed for several additional days in the embryo and derepressed
or stimulated in culture. In the light of current theories of control over gene expression
(Jacob and Monod, 1961), the reports that

in HeLa cells (DeMars, 1958) and L cells (Paul and Fottrell, 1963) glutamotransferase activity is depressed when glutamine is added to the culture medium were of particular interest. In this context it was postulated that perhaps isolation to culture effected rapid enzymatic growth by exposing the retina to subrepressing levels of glutamine or inducing levels of glutamate. Earlier data demonstrating a partial repressing effect of glutamine in culture (Hubby, Moscona, and Saenz, unpublished) had supported this possibility. Thus it was of obvious interest to determine whether, and to exactly what extent, the glutamine synthetase level of explanted retinas could be controlled by varying the concentrations of glutamine or glutamate in the culture medium.

Retinas from 10-day embryos were isolated and grown for 48 hours in the standard Tyrode's-horse serum culture medium supplemented with glutamine or glutamate at various concentrations. The results are presented

$$\frac{\text{control activity-experimental activity}}{\text{control activity}} \times 100$$

graphically in Fig. 3. It can be seen that *both* glutamine and glutamate were effective in partially depressing enzymatic growth in the explanted retina. Whether this partial repressing effect of glutamate represents a significant difference between the response of this tissue and that of HeLa (DeMars, 1958) and L cells (Paul and Fottrell, 1963) is as yet unknown, since the effect of glutamate was not tested with either of those cell lines. However, it is quite clear that under our experimental conditions, neither glutamate nor glutamine depressed enzymatic growth completely: the glutamate curve plateaus at less than 20% repression and the glutamine curve appears to be plateauing at something less than 70% repression. In an attempt to further examine the specificity and significance of these inhibitory effects, analogous studies were made employing γ-aminobutyric acid, glutathione (both oxidized and reduced), asparagine, and aspartic acid. These substances were chosen for their known metabolic and chemical similarity to glutamate and glutamine.

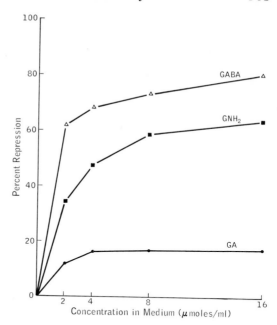

Fig. 3. The effect of glutamate, glutamine, and γ-aminobutyrate on glutamine synthetase (glutamotransferase activity) of 10-day chick neural retina in culture for 48 hours. GA, glutamic acid; GNH_2, glutamine; GABA, γ-aminobutyric acid.

Although γ-aminobutyric acid proved to be more effective than either glutamine or glutamate (Fig. 3), even this curve, if extrapolated at constant slope, would not reach 100% repression until the concentration reached approximately 100 μmoles/ml—a grossly unphysiologic level. Even the cultures which were grown in the presence of 16 μmoles of γ-aminobutyric acid per milliliter and which demonstrated 80% repression relative to control cultures were synthesizing new enzyme at ten times the rate of retinas of similar chronologic age *in situ*. Neither glutathione (reduced or oxidized), asparagine, nor aspartate had any detectable effect upon the enzymatic growth. These data suggest that glutamate, glutamine, and γ-aminobutyrate may have a rather specific role in quantitatively modifying the amount of glutamine synthetase produced by this tissue; however, this is far from the qualitative sort of control expected of a Jacob-Monod type of repressor substance, and it is inadequate to explain the difference in response to *in ovo* and *in vitro* conditions. While this in no way detracts from the possible applicability of the Jacob-Monod model to this aspect of retinal differentiation, it does indicate that the mechanism controlling glutamine synthetase synthesis in the differentiating retina is not by simple and reversible end product inhibition or substrate stimulation. Whether the three amino acids which partially suppress formation of glutamine synthetase in retinal cultures function strictly by a simple negative-feedback control on the already derepressed enzyme-forming system or whether they are converted very slowly and at different rates to a common metabolite which functions as a repressor substance is as yet undetermined.

The Absence of an Effect of Elevated Glucose

The results obtained with γ-aminobutyrate prompted an examination of the effect of glucose content of the medium, since the role of this amino acid in energy metabolism of neural tissue is well established (Albers, 1960; Tower, 1960). It was postulated that the effect of explanation upon glutamotransferase activity of the retina might be part of a general compensatory stimulation of glutamate metabolism resulting from an energy deficiency of the Tyrode's-horse serum medium. If this were true, not only would the observed effects of glutamate, glutamine, and γ-aminobutyrate be expected, but glucose enrichment of the medium should markedly repress formation of the enzyme. Experimental enrichment of the medium up to eight times the control level, however, yielded no statistically significant effect upon glutamine synthetase production.

DISCUSSION

The findings presented in this paper raise a number of points for discussion; however, the somewhat exploratory and novel nature of some of the findings reported calls for postponement of detailed consideration and discussion of their implications. The present results justify further interest in embryonic retinal glutamine synthetase as a system for studying mechanisms that control the appearance and activity of tissue-characteristic enzymatic patterns. The demonstration that the glutamotransferase activity of the retina both in the embryo and in culture is attributable to a glutamine synthetase places the phenomenon in a more meaningful physiologic context. By all available indications, *de novo* synthesis of the enzyme appears to be involved in both the normal development and the precocious development in culture; the evidence appears to exclude the possibility that the precocious increase in enzyme activity of the cultured retina is due to purely trivial causes such as dilution of an enzyme inhibitor.

The suggestion, from studies with actinomycin, that genomic control is exerted directly and continuously over the synthesis of the enzyme during its early ontogenesis broadens the relevance of the problem since it may ultimately provide insight into the nature of differential gene expressions in differentiating vertebrate cells. It should be restated here that in this system an actinomycin-sensitive process (presumably nuclear synthesis of RNA) appears essential to new synthesis of the enzyme, but not to maintenance of preexisting activity. This suggests that the enzyme protein is relatively stable, but that its synthesis is dependent on a relatively labile RNA messenger. If tracer studies substantiate this impression, the immediacy of nuclear control over retinal glutamine synthetase will be demonstrated to be intermediate to that proposed by Davidson *et al.* (1963) for control of polysaccharide (AMPS) synthesis in cultured fibroblasts and that demonstrated by Reich *et al.* (1962) for control of hemoglobin synthesis. In the former case an actinomycin-sensitive process appears to be essential for maintenance of preexisting levels of enzyme activity (suggesting lability of both the enzyme and the enzyme-forming system); in the latter case *de novo* synthesis of the tissue-specific protein proceeds uninterrupted in the presence of actinomycin (demonstrating the stability of the corresponding messenger). It is conceivable that an entire spectrum of such relationships will occur, wherein the apparent immediacy of nuclear control over differentiated processes will be predicated by the stability of the characteristic protein and the corresponding RNA.

Summary

The phenomenon of precocious appearance and rapid enhancement of glutamotransferase activity of embryonic chick neural retina in response to explanation *in vitro* has been subjected to more detailed scrutiny. On the basis of cofactor requirements, pH optima, response to specific inhibitors, and ratio of transferase to synthetase activity, the enzyme undergoing change was classified as a glutamine synthetase.

Tests for the presence of enzyme activators and/or inhibitors undergoing change during increase in enzyme activity were negative, suggesting that increase in activity was due to synthesis of new enzyme.

This was substantiated by the finding that low levels of puromycin blocked completely and reversibly increases in enzyme activity under culture conditions; and that actinomycin D similarly blocked such increases irreversibly. Preexisting levels of activity appeared stable in the presence of either inhibitor. These data were interpreted to mean than enhancement of glutamotransferase activity which occurs in culture is due to synthesis of new enzyme; it also suggested a lability of the RNA involved and consequently a rather direct genomic control over the rate of synthesis of the enzyme in early ontogenesis.

Pigmented epithelium of embryonic eye, vitreous humor, and embryo extract showed no effect on the increase in glutamine synthetase activity in the explanted retina; this was interpreted as diminishing but not excluding the possibility that a stable, diffusible systemic factor is responsible for control of early ontogenesis of this enzyme in the embryo.

Glutamine, glutamate, and γ-aminobutyrate were found to lower synthesis of the enzyme in culture when added to the medium, but none of these amino acids appeared capable of total repression at concentrations approaching physiological values. Glutathione (oxidized and reduced), asparagine, aspartate, and glucose all had no demonstrable affect upon the growth of the enzyme in culture.

References

Albers, R. W. (1960). Gamma-amino butyric acid. In *The Neurochemistry of Nucleotides and Amino Acids* (R. O. Brady and D. B. Tower, eds.), pp. 146–158. Wiley, New York.

Coulombre, A. J. (1961). Cytology of the developing eye. *Intern. Rev. Cytol.* **11**, 161–194.

Davidson, E. H., V. G. Allfrey, and A. E. Mirsky. (1963). Gene expression in differentiated cells. *Proc. Natl. Acad. Sci. U.S.* **49**, 53–60.

DeMars, R. (1958). The inhibition by glutamine of glutamyl transferase formation in cultures of human cells. *Biochim. Biophys. Acta* **27**, 435–436.

Garfinkel, D. (1962). Computer simulation of steady state glutamate metabolism in rat brain. *J. Theoret. Biol.* **3**, 412–422.

Hurwitz, J., J. J. Furth, M. Malany, and M. Alexander. (1962). The role of deoxyribonucleic acid in ribonucleic acid synthesis. III. The inhibition of the enzymatic synthesis of ribonucleic acid and deoxyribonucleic acid by actinomycin D and proflavin. *Proc. Natl. Acad. Sci. U.S.* **48**, 1222–1229.

Jacob, F., and J. Monod. (1961). Genetic regulatory mechanisms in the synthesis of proteins. *J. Mol. Biol.* **3**, 318–356.

Kirk, D. L. (1963). In preparation.

Levintow, L., A. Meister, E. Kuff, and G. H. Hogeboom. (1955). Studies on the relationship between the enzymatic synthesis of glutamine and the glutamyl transfer reaction. *J. Am. Chem. Soc.* **77**, 5304–5308.

Lowry, O. H., N. J. Rosebrough, A. L. Farr, and R. J. Randall. (1951). Protein measurement with the Folin phenol reagent. *J. Biol. Chem.* **193**, 265–275.

Meister, A. (1962). Glutamine synthesis. In *The Enzymes* (P. D. Boyer, H. Lardy, and K. Myrbäck, eds.), Vol. 6, pp. 443–468. Academic Press, New York.

Moscona, A. A., and J. L. Hubby. (1963). Experimentally induced changes in glutamotransferase activity in embryonic tissue. *Developtl. Biol.* **7**, 192–206.

Pamiljans, V., P. R. Krishnaswamy, G. D. Dumville, and A. Meister. (1962). Studies on the mechanism of glutamine synthesis; isolation and properties of the enzyme from sheep brain. *Biochemistry* **1**, 153–158.

Paul, J., and P. F. Fottrell. (1963). Mechanism of D-glutamyl transferase repression in mammalian cells. *Biochim. Biophys. Acta* **67**, 334–336.

Pirie, A. (1956). *Biochemistry of the Eye*, pp. 205–231. Blackwell, Oxford.

Reich, E., R. M. Franklin, A. J. Shatkin, and E. L. Tatum. (1962). Action of actinomycin D on animal cells and viruses. *Proc. Natl Acad. Sci. U.S.* **48**, 1238–1244.

Rudnick, D. (1963). Distribution of glutamotransferase activity in the chick retina. *Develop. Biol.* **7**, 94–102.

Rudnick, D., and H. Waelsch. (1955). Development of glutamotransferase and glutamine synthetase in the nervous system of the chick. *J. Exptl. Zool.* **129**, 309–326.

Tower, D. B. (1960). The neurochemistry of asparagine and glutamine. In *The Neurochemistry of Nucleotides and Amino Acids* (R. O. Brady and D. B. Tower, eds.), pp. 173–204. Wiley, New York.

Wald, G., and H. Zussman. (1938). Carotenoids of the chicken retina. *J. Biol. Chem.* **122**, 449–460.

Wu, C. (1963). Glutamine synthetase. I. A comparative study of its distribution in animals and its inhibition by DL-*allo*-δ-hydroxylysine. *Comp. Biochem. Physiol.* **8**, 335–351.

Molecular Facets of Mitotic Regulation: Synthesis of Thymidine Kinase[*]

YASUO HOTTA

HERBERT STERN

This report, although concerned with a specific enzyme, is aimed at revealing a pattern of behavior which may generally underlie the component events of the mitotic cycle. The experiments have been performed on a specialized group of cells which are antecedents of pollen—the microspores of *Lilium longiflorum* (var. Croft). During the life of the microspore, which extends for several weeks, thymidine kinase activity (and other biochemical activities) appears at a precisely defined time and endures for no more than 24 hr.[1,2] The periodicity is demonstrable in both intact cells and their extracts. The question raised as a result of this observation concerned the mechanism by which a cell whose interphase spanned several weeks could regulate the appearance and disappearance of a specific enzyme activity in the course of 24 hr. The results which follow provide a partial answer to this question.

Proceedings of the National Academy of Sciences, **49**, 648–654 (1963). Reprinted with permission.

* This work was supported by grants from the National Science Foundation (G15947) and U.S. Public Health Service (GM07897).

METHODS

Lily anthers were cultured by the technique recently described for those of a related genus, *Trillium*.[3] Each group of six anthers was placed in a tube containing 0.2 ml of "Hoagland's medium." The medium is adequate for anthers only at the stages of development studied; earlier stages, or longer growth periods, require a far more complex medium. All cultures were maintained at 15°C by keeping the tubes in a waterbath.

Thymidine kinase was assayed as previously described.[2] Fractionation of microspore proteins for electrophoresis was carried out in the following way: the microspores were homogenized in 0.33 M sucrose-0.004 M $MgCl_2$—0.05 M Tris buffer, pH 7.0 ("SMT" solution) with a Teflon pestle. After checking microscopically for the absence of the whole cells, the suspension was centrifuged at 1,500 × g for 8 min. The pellet was washed once with SMT and the combined supernatant solutions centrifuged at 32,000 × g for 20 min. Analyses of the fractions thus sedimented are not considered here. The supernatant solution was spun at 36,000 rpm for three hr in a Spinco preparative centrifuge using an SW-39 rotor. The soluble fraction was 90% saturated with ammonium sulfate at 0°C and allowed to stand for 20 min, and the precipitated proteins were collected by centrifugation. The clarified solution was lyophilized and checked for enzyme activity. The precipitate was washed once with saturated ammonium sulfate solution, dissolved in 0.05 M phosphate buffer (pH 7.6), and dialyzed against $M/200$ of the same buffer 4–5 hr with continuous stirring and 4 changes of outer solution. The dialyzed solution of protein was lyophilized and dissolved in $1/10$ the original volume of water. It was used as such for electrophoretic resolution. Protein was determined with either the Nessler or Folin reagent.

RESULTS

Predictability of Periodicity in Cultured Anthers

The sequence and timing of those events studied in cultured anthers are shown in Fig. 1. Two features of this sequence deserve emphasis. First, the pattern of periodicity is much the same as that which has been observed on the intact plant; regulation is therefore independent of the parent plant. Second, the sequence and timing are reproducible. The experiments conducted would have been impossible without the predictability of thymidine kinase appearance within 1 day. For any group of six anthers removed from the plant, the expected time of appearance was computed from the bud length and the regression line (Fig. 1). Since each analysis required the removal of a single anther, intervals between the six possible analyses varied from 12 to 24 hours. Consistent removal of one set of microspores at the point of maximum kinase activity was therefore unlikely. It will be seen that the absolute magnitude of individual peaks varies, although only one peak is present in each group of anthers.

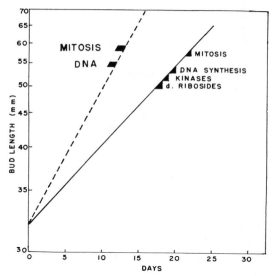

Fig. 1. Timing of mitotic events in lily anthers cultured at 15°C. The dotted line included for comparison represents the relationships between flower bud length, time of growth, DNA synthesis, and mitosis in the intact plant; it is based on the data of Taylor and McMaster.[7] The times of events indicated on the solid line were experimentally determined: d. ribosides (production of deoxyribosidic compounds); kinases (the appearance of thymidine and thymidylic kinase), DNA synthesis, and mitosis. The usefulness of the slope was made evident by the fact that the occurrence of each of the events could be predicted within ±1 day for anthers removed from buds ranging from 35–48 mm in length.

Penetration of Reagents

Unlike the behavior of other plant tissues, anthers show a marked resistance to diffusion of externally added substances into the microspores. This resistance is partly overcome by the technique of culture; pertinent data are given elsewhere.[3] Using isotopic compounds as markers, it has been found that relatively little accumulation occurs during the first 60 hr. Within five days, however, much of the label is removed from the medium, and at such time the fraction of the total label present in the microspores equals or exceeds the ratio of microsporal tissue to that of the anther as a whole. The accelerated accumulation of added reagents following two days of exposure to the medium is characteristic of the amino acids and nitrogenous bases tested.

There is, moreover, no close parallel between the extent to which these substances are utilized in syntheses and their rates of accumulation. For the purposes of comparison, three days were arbitrarily set as the time required for added reagents to reach the microspores in effective concentrations. The arbitrariness is unavoidable but is not a serious bar to the interpretation of results.

Effects of Inhibitors of RNA or Protein Synthesis

The first objective was to determine whether the short-lived appearance of enzyme activity during microspore interphase represented a *de novo* synthesis of enzyme. Paucity of material precluded its isolation and the direct measurement of absolute amounts. Instead, an indirect aproach was followed, based upon established evidence of the inhibitory effects of various reagents on protein synthesis. 8-Azaguanine (and later, 5 fluorouracil) were used to distort the synthesis of RNA.[4,5] DNA would be unaffected since it is not synthesized during the interval stated. Chloramphenicol was used to interrupt the presumed translation of RNA information.[6] 5-Methyl tryptophane and ethionine were introduced to block or distort the pattern of amino acid incorporation into protein. The results of these tests were single and uniform (Fig. 2*A*): all the reagents, if added prior to the normal appearance of enzyme activity, virtually abolished such activity. As might be expected, none of the succeeding steps in the mitotic cycle followed. 32 P-phosphate was not incorporated into DNA even 5 days later than the normally occurring interval of synthesis, nor were any nuclear divisions observed, although the cells were viable. In this set of experiments all reagents were added 8–10 days before the expected appearance of the enzyme. Allowing 3 days for accumulation in the microspores, it may be estimated that the inhibitors were present for at least 5 days prior to the time at which enzyme activity normally appears. If such appearance is due to a synthesis of protein by the commonly accepted sequence of molecular events, then an interval of greater or lesser duration should exist immediately prior to, or coincident with, the appearance of enzyme activity when the reagents are no longer effective. It is possible to specify intervals within an error of ± 1 day, and this is sufficient for our present purpose. It may be seen from Fig. 2*B* that if azaguanine is added $4\frac{1}{2}$ days before the appearance of the enzyme, it is no longer an effective inhibitor. It would therefore appear that azaguanine must be present in the microspores at least 1–2 days prior to the normal spurt in enzyme activity. Similar remarks apply to chloramphenicol except for the indication that the latter is still effective at a time when azaguanine no longer inhibits. This relationship is so gratifyingly compatible with current interpretations of the molecular sequence in protein synthesis, but so close to the margin of error in our experimental timing, that it is best to consider the result as a fortuitous association rather than as an established demonstration.

The fact that azaguanine had much the same effect, whether added 10 or 4 days prior to the expected appearance of enzyme, made it probable that the process inhibited was of limited duration and occurred no earlier than 2–3 days before the enzyme appeared. If so, then addition of guanine before that interval should reverse the effect of azaguanine irrespective of the time at which the latter was administered. It was first established that guanine itself had no effect on the periodicity of the enzyme and that azaguanine was ineffective if added simultaneously with guanine. The results of adding either guanine or a mixture of guanine-azaguanine at various times after administration of azaguanine alone are shown in Fig. 3. The observed behavior thus bears out the interpretation. A secondary effect of the reversal may, however, be noted. Frequently, though not always, the peak of enzyme activity following reversal is broader than the normal. It appears as though the combination has not only restored the ability of the microspores to form enzyme but has somewhat interfered with its regulated removal. This point will be discussed elsewhere.

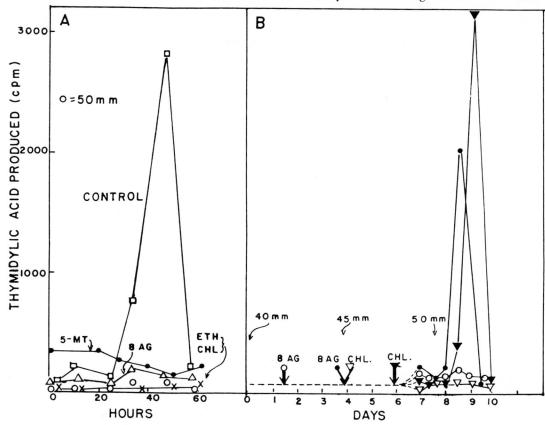

Fig. 2. Inhibition of appearance of thymidine kinase by various reagents. Anthers were cultured in 0.2 ml of standard medium except for the addition of indicated reagents: 5-methyl tryptophane (5-MT) 0.4 mg; ethionine (eth.), 0.4 mg; chloramphenicol (chl.), 0.04 mg; 8-azaguanine (8-ag), 0.02 mg. Assay conditions described in text. (*A*) Inhibitors added at beginning of culture period. Anthers taken from buds ranging from 36–42 mm in length. The curves drawn are random selections and are typical for the eight or more series run with each inhibitor; in no case did treated microspores show activities above 370 cpm; in most cases the highest value for any set was considerably lower. (*B*) Inhibitors added at times indicated. To interpret these results allowance must be made for the lag in uptake of reagents by microspores which is of the order of 2–3 days. The ineffectiveness of azaguanine and chloramphenicol when added beyond a certain bud length is patent. Ethionine and 5-methyl tryptophane were not tested in this way. Activities are expressed as total counts per microspore from ½ anther.

Incorporation of Labeled Amino Acids in Relation to Enzyme Appearance

Taken together, the first sets of experiments are most simply interpreted as demonstrating that the appearance of thymidine kinase in the microspores is dependent upon a synthesis of RNA and protein. If labeled amino acids are added to the culture medium 8–10 days before the expected appearance of enzyme, and the soluble proteins of the microspores analyzed a few days before and during the interval of enzyme appearance, the ratio of their respective activities is 840:4,250. Differences related to other protein fractions are also evident but they are incidental to the present problem. Chloramphenicol or azaguanine which inhibit the appearance of thymidine kinase also suppress the labeling of the soluble proteins. Results from experiments with labeled amino acids are thus consistent with the conclusion drawn from the first set of studies.

The general correspondence between pro-

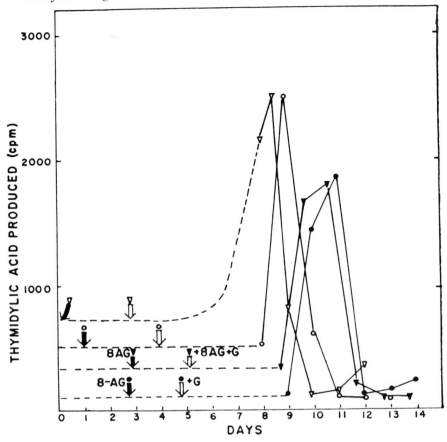

Fig. 3. Reversal by guanine of inhibitory action of 8-azaguanine. Solid arrows indicate time at which 0.02 mg of azaguanine (8-ag) was added. Circles represent experiments in which anthers were transferred (open arrows) to standard medium saturated with guanine (g); triangles represent those in which anthers were transferred to a mixture of azaguanine and guanine. Guanine alone had no effect. First measurements of activity were made at the beginning of the solid lines. A broadening of the peak may be noted in some of the plots; the effect was frequent.

tein synthesis and thymidine kinase activity falls short as a demonstration that the enzyme, or part of it, is one of the protein components synthesized. To clarify this point the soluble proteins were fractionated electrophoretically. A large number of anther groups was cultured in the presence of labeled amino acid, and microspores were isolated before, during, and after the expected time of enzyme appearance. The results of this experiment are shown in Fig. 4. The most pertinent feature of the graphs is that only during the interval of enzyme appearance do the soluble proteins of the microspores show a labeled component coincident with the position of

enzyme activity. For practical reasons it was impossible to determine the specific activity of the protein in the enzyme region. The cellulose acetate strips, when stained with nigrosin, showed a characteristic pattern of bands which, on the whole, changed little during the intervals tested. The positions of the bands provided a convenient way of identifying the location of enzyme, but stain at the locus of the enzyme was undetectable. It may be surmised that protein at the region of enzyme had a comparatively high specific activity, but no quantitative measure of such activity is available. The difference in over-all levels of radioactivity between the curves in Fig. 4*A* and 4*B*

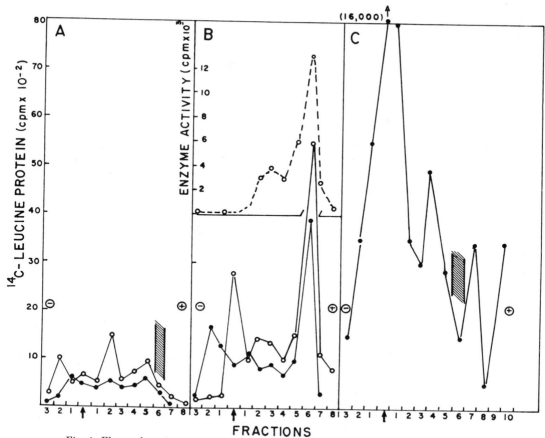

Fig. 4. Electrophoretic separation of soluble proteins from microspores before (*A*), during (*B*), and after (*C*) appearance of thymidine kinase activity. In order to obtain sufficient material for analysis, microspores from 36 or 48 anthers were pooled for each run. Culture conditions were standard except for the addition of 1 microcurie of ^{14}C-leucine (S.A. = 4 μc/mg) per tube containing 0.15 ml of Hoagland's solution. Buds of approximately 39–42 mm were used in these experiments and the labeled amino acid added at the start. Selection of microspores at desired intervals from each set of anthers was made on the basis of the curve in Fig. 1. Preparation of soluble fraction is described under "Methods." Negligible amounts of enzyme activity were present in (*A*) and (*C*); shaded bars indicate position of enzyme when present. Cellulose acetate strips (2 cm width) were used in these tests. The position of origin is indicated by a solid arrow. Runs were at 2°C for 6 hr with 1.4 m-amps of current and at a pH of 7.4 (0.05 *M* phosphate). Values recorded are total for each pool of microspores. In (*A*) and (*B*) two separate experiments were run, one with 36 anthers, the other with 48.

reflects the fact (noted above) that there is a greater incorporation of label in soluble proteins during the interval of enzyme appearance. The difference in patterns between Fig. 4*B* and 4*C* indicates a pronounced synthesis of some other type (or types) of protein following the appearance of enzyme. Since the amount of enzyme activity in *A* or *C* was much too small for detection, the distances

from origin and band pattern were used to approximate the position of the enzyme. It is to be noted that microspores isolated for Fig. 4*C* were exposed to label during the formation of enzyme activity. The experiment was intended to determine whether disappearance of enzyme was paralleled by a disappearance of label in the enzyme region. In this respect the results can hardly be considered decisive.

The open circle curve in Fig. 4B is comparable with that in 4C since they represent extracts from the same number of microspores. Thus, to the extent that the level of activity is lower in the region of the enzyme and that the pattern of label distribution has shifted, the results bear out the conclusion that the original enzyme protein has been removed.

In a different set of experiments using ^{14}C-alanine it was noted that incorporation of label into soluble proteins over an 8-day period was only partly suppressed if either azaguanine or chloramphenicol were added at the same time as the amino acid. The effect was far more pronounced with chloramphenicol, but, since the two reagents appeared to be equally effective in inhibiting the appearance of thymidine kinase, it seemed reasonable to expect in the case of treated cells that virtually no radioactivity would be present on the electrophoretic strip in the region of enzyme if that region contained principally enzyme protein. The curves in Fig. 5 make it plain that suppression of enzyme appearance is matched by an absence of label in the enzyme region. Taken together, all the experi-

ments thus far reported point in one direction: a synthesis of either a part or the whole of the enzyme, thymidine kinase. Thus, the likeliest explanation of the initial phase of the phenomenon under examination—the regulated appearance of enzyme activity at a fixed point of interphase—is that the process being observed is an induction of enzyme synthesis.

DISCUSSION

The target of these studies has been to disclose some of the mechanisms which a cell may utilize to regulate its cyclical behavior. Such studies have been possible because the miscrospores in lily are synchronized in development and because the sequential events in their life cycle are sufficiently separated in time to permit individual study. It is now apparent that a shift in metabolic processes at a characteristic phase of the cycle has all the earmarks of induced enzyme synthesis. We do not know the nature of the inducer nor its locus of origin. The parent plant plays no immediate role since the microspores undergo a normal cycle of development in anthers which have been put in culture weeks before the occurrence of mitosis. Since no attempt was made to culture the microspores in isolation, it is idle to speculate on whether the stimulus to induction is of exogenous or endogenous origin. What appears to be the most significant aspect of these studies is the evidence that a cell may use identical mechanisms for regulating internal cycles of development and for adapting to novel nutritional conditions. It seems reasonable to suppose that the periodicity in other biochemical activities of the microspores may be regulated by mechanisms similar to that governing thymidine kinase. If so, then, in the ultimate sense at least, the problem of mitosis is a problem of regulated gene action.

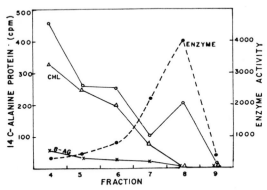

Fig. 5. Effect of chloramphenicol and azaguanine on incorporation of ^{14}C-alanine into soluble proteins at time when appearance of thymidine kinase is inhibited. Conditions of culture and electrophores are similar to that under Fig. 4, 1 μcurie of ^{14}C-alanine replacing that of ^{14}C-leucine. Microspores of 48 anthers were pooled for each of these experiments. The total soluble protein in each pool was 350 micrograms. In all cases mcrospores were removed for analysis at the time when enzyme appearance was expected. $\frac{1}{10}$ of each fraction eluted from acetate strip used for enzyme assay, and values recorded are total counts of thymidylic acid produced.

SUMMARY

The brief appearance of thymidine kinase activity prior to DNA synthesis in microspores of *Lilium* is due to a *de novo* synthesis of protein. The chain of events leading to such synthesis begins with the formation of RNA; any of the steps in the sequence may be blocked by an appropriate inhibitor.

[1] Erickson, R. O., *Amer. J. Bot.*, **35**, 729 (1948).

[2] Hotta, Y., and H. Stern, *J. Biophys. Biochem. Cytol.*, **11**, 311 (1961).

[3] *Ibid.*, *J. Cell Biol.*, **16**, 259 (1963).

[4] Abbreviations: RNA, ribonucleic acid; DNA, deoxyribonucleic acid.

[5] Hotta, Y., S. Osawa, and T. Sakaki, *Devel. Biol.*, **1**, 65 (1959).

[6] Aronson, A. J., and S. Spiegelman, *Biochim. Biophys. Acta*, **53**, 84 (1961).

[7] Taylor, J. H., and R. D. McMaster, *Chromosoma*, **64**, 189 (1957).

9

RNA Synthesis

ONE OF THE CONSEQUENCES of fertilization is the initiation of protein synthesis. How the egg prepares itself for this event is a subject of central concern and one about which little is known. Attention has not yet been directed to the time of synthesis, or to the sources and modes of storage of ribosomal, transfer, and messenger RNA (m-RNA) in the developing oocyte. Of particular interest is the storage of m-RNA.

Recent work has made clear that sea-urchin eggs are fully equipped at maturity with the three kinds of RNA required for protein synthesis. Addition of polyribonucleotides to a cell-free extract of unfertilized eggs promotes the incorporation of amino acids into protein. (Wilt and Hultin 1962; Nemer and Bard 1963; and Tyler 1963). It therefore appears that at least ribosomes and transfer RNA are present in the unfertilized egg and are prepared to function when a template is provided. m-RNA is also present since unfertilized eggs, in which new RNA synthesis is inhibited with actinomycin D, can make protein upon fertilization. (Gross and Cousineau 1963; Gross, Malkin, and Moyer 1964).

How the quiescent state of the mature unfertilized egg is maintained is not understood if all components are present. It seems clear that m-RNA, present in the egg, does not serve as a template for protein synthesis before fertilization. It must be in a "repressed" state. Belitsina *et al.* (1964) have suggested that m-RNA leaves the nucleus in a protein shell. Perhaps it remains protected until fertilization, by a basic, histone-like polypeptide. Conceivably, following the cortical reaction, lysosomes break down and release enzymes which free the protein-bound m-RNAs.

If a generalization from developing feathers is valid, the m-RNA may be in nonfunctional polysomes which relatively late in development are activated to start protein synthesis (*Humphreys, Penman, and Bell 1964*).* Some evidence has been interpreted to show that polysomes form after (Hultin 1964) and are not present before sea urchin fertilization (Monroy and Tyler 1963; Stafford, Sofer, and Iverson 1964); but the experimental procedures used might have missed them in the unfertilized egg.

The synthesis of RNA, including m-RNA, is temporarily halted after the egg reaches maturity. Whether this is accomplished by gene repression, by control of RNA polymerase, or by some other mechanism is unknown. At fertilization, synthesis of m-RNA begins anew (*Nemer 1964*) and in the sea urchin is required for development past blastula.

Transfer RNA "synthesis" after fertilization and during cleavage (*Nemer 1964*) may consist only in addition or turnover of the pCpCpA terminal group of transfer RNA (Glisin and Glisin 1964).

* Italicized references indicate articles which appear in this book.

314

In most forms studied, ribosomal RNA synthesis does not begin until after gastrulation is completed (*Nemer 1964; Brown and Gurdon 1964*). This work provides evidence that the nucleolus is the source of ribosomal RNA. In some tissues of the mutant, nucleoli appear during development; and in these, some cytoplasmic RNA has been observed (Esper and Barr 1964).

In chick embryos no qualitative change occurs in the synthesis of ribosomal RNA between 7 hours and 7 days of incubation (*Lerner, Bell, and Darnell 1963*). In cells of the chick embryo (*Lerner, Bell, and Darnell 1963*) as in other cells (Scherrer and Darnell 1962) labeled with P^{32} orthophosphate or uridine-2-C^{14}, radioactivity appears in a high molecular weight precursor (40S) before it appears in ribosomal RNA. This high molecular weight fraction appears to be largely but not entirely ribosomal RNA precursor.

During development different tissues appear to have different functional m-RNAs. Skin and feathers have a unique distribution of m-RNA sizes as measured by polysome size (Bell 1964, *Humphreys, Penman, and Bell 1964*, Chapter 10). Each tissue probably has a unique "polysome profile" but only some can be clearly distinguished as unique (*Scott and Bell, 1964* and 1965). Using the technique of hybridization of RNA with DNA entrapped in agar, McCarthy and Hoyer (1964) have shown that there are substantial differences among rapidly labeled RNAs isolated from different tissues.

In the lens a shift in functional m-RNA at 11 days of development is signaled by the appearance of a new polyribosomal peak consisting of aggregates of eight to ten ribosomes (Scott and Bell, 1965). It is not known whether the message associated with the ribosomes in the new peak is synthesized at 11 days or is made earlier and put into use at that time. By 14 days of lens development, at least two classes of message of different half lives are present. One has a half life of 3–4 hours and the other a half life of 30 hours or more.

The question can be asked: "What kinds of proteins are synthesized during development on m-RNA which has a long half life?" It was recognized early that hemoglobin must be one of them since it is synthesized in an enucleate reticulocyte (Bishop *et al.* 1961). Proteins, probably involved in spindle formation, are made on long-lived m-RNA in the sea urchin (Gross and Cousineau 1963). Embryonic feather and lens proteins (Bell 1964; *Humphreys, Penman, and Bell 1964; Scott and Bell 1964*) are also synthesized on templates of long half life. Cells of the feather, lens, and reticulocyte have in common an early "nuclear death" and produce large quantities of cell-specific proteins probably before and after nuclear function ceases. Of the large number of tissues examined in the developing chick long-lived messages were detected in only a few (*Scott and Bell 1964*).

Regulation of protein synthesis at the level of m-RNA function appears to occur in yet another way. Nonfunctional polysomes are made in the feather before keratinization and are activated at about the time keratinization begins (*Humphreys, Penman, and Bell 1964*, Chapter 10). This may be a useful device for synthesizing rapidly a few kinds of proteins such as keratins in the feather or spindle proteins in the cleaving egg. If these ideas are correct, control of protein synthesis at several levels must be exercised: one at the level of DNA read off where messages are transcribed from genes, since in each tissue each moment of development may be characterized by a unique pattern of m-RNA synthesis; another at the level of the polysome where the latter is either inactive or active; and a third in stabilization of some m-RNAs to give them a long functional life span.

REFERENCES

1. Belitsina, N. V., M. A. Ajtkhozhin, L. P. Cavrilova, and A. S. Spirin (1964). Informational ribonucleic acids of differentiating animal cells. *Bikhimiia* **29**:362–374.
2. Bell, E. (1964). Protein synthesis in differentiating chick skin. In W. J. Rutter (ed.), *Metabolic Control Mechanisms in Animal Cells*, Natl. Cancer Inst. Mon. **13**, pp. 1–12, Government Printing Office, Washington, D.C.
3. Bishop, J., *et al.* (1961). Control of specificity in hemoglobin synthesis. *Nature* **191**:1365–1368.
4. Esper, H., and H. J. Barr (1964). A study of the developmental cytology of a mutation affecting nucleoli in Xenopus embryos. *Develop. Biol.* **10**:105–121.
5. Glisin, V. R., and M. Glisin (1964). Ribonucleic acid metabolism following fertilization in sea urchin eggs. *Proc. Natl. Acad. Sci.* **52**:1548–1553.
6. Gross, P. R., and G. H. Cousineau (1963). Effects of actinomycin D on macromolecular synthesis and early development in sea urchin eggs in response to fertilization. *Exptl. Cell Res.* **25**:405–417.
7. Hultin, T. (1964). On the mechanisms of ribosomal activation in newly fertilized sea urchin eggs. *Develop. Biol.* **10**:305–328.
8. McCarthy, B. J., and B. H. Hoyer (1964). Identity of DNA and diversity of messenger RNA molecules in normal mouse tissues. *Proc. Natl. Acad. Sci.* **52**:915–922.
9. Monroy, A., and A. Tyler (1963). Formation of active ribosomal aggregates (polysomes) upon fertilization and development of the sea urchin. *Arch. Biochem. Biophys.* **103**:431–435.
10. Nemer, M., and S. G. Bard (1963). Polypeptide synthesis in sea urchin embryogenesis: an examination with synthetic polyribonucleotides. *Science* **140**:664–666.
11. Scherrer, K., and J. E. Darnell (1962). Sedimentation characteristics of rapidly labelled RNA from HeLa cells. *Biochem. Biophys. Res. Comm.* **7**:486–490.
12. Stafford, D. W., W. H. Sofer, and R. M. Iverson (1964). Demonstration of polyribosomes after fertilization of the sea urchin egg. *Proc. Natl. Acad. Sci.* **52**:313–323.
13. Tyler, A. (1963). The manipulations of macromolecular substances during fertilization and early development of animal eggs. *Am. Zool.* **3**:109–126.
14. Wilt, F. H., and T. Hultin (1962). Stimulation of phenylalanine incorporation by polyuridylic acid in homogenates of sea urchin eggs. *Biochem. Biophys. Res. Comm.* **9**:313–317.

Templates for the First Proteins of Embryonic Development*

PAUL R. GROSS
LEONARD I. MALKIN†
WAYNE A. MOYER‡

The gathering strength of the messenger hypothesis,[1] and accumulating evidence in favor of polyribosomes as the sites of protein synthesis,[2] are exerting strong influence on

Proceedings of the National Academy of Sciences, **51**, 407–413 (1964). Reprinted with permission.

We are grateful to Drs. Albert Tyler, Alberto Monroy, Cyrus Levinthal, and David A. Shemin for discussions of various problems associated with this work and for the opportunity to examine unpublished data. Drs. Arya K. Bal, Gilles H. Cousineau, and Miss Meredith Stevens have been of material assistance.

* Supported by grants from the National Science Foundation (GB-156) and the American Cancer Society.

current research in chemical embryology. The scheme now generally accepted for microorganisms and certain mammalian cells[1,2] provides a number of specific mechanisms by which cellular differentiation could be initiated and controlled. Their essential feature is a direct genomic regulation of the spectrum

† National Institutes of Health postdoctoral fellow.

‡ Some of the data reported are taken from a thesis submitted by W. A. Moyer to the Graduate School of Brown University in partial fulfillment of the requirements for the degree of Master of Science.

of proteins made in different cells of the developing organism.

Sea urchin eggs, with a long history of use in experimental embryology,[3] are a particularly favorable material, because they can be obtained in quantity, develop with excellent synchrony, and are reasonably permeable to labeled precursors. During the past two years, a conflict has arisen from experiments on macromolecule synthesis during early development in these forms. Some of the data were available earlier, but the conflict itself stems from the requirements of the current scheme of protein synthesis, according to which the sequence information is carried by more-or-less unstable messenger RNA's. Protein synthesis is either greatly stimulated or actually switched on at fertilization. RNA synthesis is negligible or absent before fertilization, and even after fertilization, is either very slow[4-6] or absent.[7] Brachet *et al.*[7] and Gross and Cousineau[8] have expressed doubt that the postfertilization synthesis of messenger RNA could be sufficient to account for the observed stimulation of protein synthesis. Nemer[5] and Wilt,[6] among others, consider that postfertilization RNA synthesis does supply missing templates, and that this gives competence to previously inactive ribosomes and may therefore switch on protein synthesis. The inactivity of ribosome preparations from unfertilized eggs, their activation upon fertilization, and their responsiveness to poly-U[9, 10, 12, 24] have been used in support of the second hypothesis. Consideration of the behavior of parthenogenetic merogones and experiments with actinomycin D[4, 11] have, however, led Gross and Cousineau[8] to support the idea that templates for the early proteins may pre-exist in the unfertilized egg. Tyler[12] has reported experiments on egg fragments and homogenates thereof whose results are consistent with such an idea.

The experiments reported here do not prove that templates pre-exist in the unfertilized egg; but if templates are a requirement for all protein synthesis, they make such a conclusion reasonable. They suggest strongly that the early acceleration of protein synthesis following fertilization cannot depend upon new messenger RNA.

The strategy is based upon the following considerations. Failure to label RNA with exogenous precursors after fertilization is necessary but *not* sufficient evidence that no RNA is being synthesized. For various reasons, the pools of immediate precursors might be inaccessible to exogenous label. More useful would be a system in which messenger RNA synthesis *is* demonstrated, or in which some heavy, nonribosomal RNA can be labeled. If the synthesis of these RNA's were then turned off without an accompanying depression of protein synthesis, and if the block to RNA synthesis were imposed at fertilization, then it could be concluded that some, at least, of the first proteins made in development are assembled independently of genomic readout (cf. Gross *et al.*[13]).

MATERIALS AND METHODS

Two species of sea urchins were used. *Arbacia punctulata* was obtained at Woods Hole, and *Lytechinus pictus* was supplied from the California coast through the kindness of Professor Albert Tyler. The gametes were obtained by routine methods for each species: excision of ovaries and testes for Arbacia, and isotonic KCl injection for Lytechinus. In all experiments, the eggs were used only if they gave 90% or better fertilization *after* any pretreatment.

Protein Synthesis

Eggs were suspended at a density of about 10^4 ml^{-1} in MBL artificial sea water.[14] They were fertilized by the addition of 1 ml of 1% sperm suspension per 100 ml of egg suspension. At various intervals thereafter, 1-ml aliquots were removed to test tubes containing: 0.05 ml C^{14}-L-valine, 10 μc/ml and 5.8 μg/ml (from New England Nuclear Corp.); 0.025 ml unlabeled valine (200 μg/ml); and 0.075 ml double-strength artificial sea water.[14] The embryos were agitated in this medium by very gentle bubbling with air; after 20 min, incorporation was stopped by adding trichloroacetic acid (TCA) to a final concentration of 5%, plus 0.5 mg/ml unlabeled valine. After centrifugation, the pellets were resuspended in cold TCA and stored in the cold.

They were then brought to 90°C in 5% TCA and held there for 20 min, washed again in cold TCA, and dissolved in N NaOH. Proteins were reprecipitated with acid and then washed with water, ethanol-ether-chloroform (2:2:1), and ether, and finally air-dried. The dry protein was dissolved in 1 ml of N hyamine hydroxide in methanol,[15] and mixed for liquid scintillation counting with Bray's solution.[16] Triplicate samples of the embryo suspensions were collected and treated as described, except that the final precipitate was dissolved in 0.5 N NaOH and analyzed for protein by the method of Lowry *et al.*[17]

RNA Extraction

RNA was extracted from embryos (which had been centrifuged and frozen at $-40°C$) by the hot phenol method, essentially as employed by Scherrer and Darnell.[18] Pellets were resuspended in 3 ml of homogenization medium (sodium acetate buffer, 0.01 M pH 5; NaCl, 0.1 M; MgCl$_2$, 10^{-3} M; sodium dodecyl sulfate, 0.5%, bentonite, 1 mg/ml; unlabeled uridine, 1 mg/ml). Bentonite was purified according to Fraenkel-Conrat *et al.*[19] The pellets were homogenized by hand for 1 min in a Potter-Elvejhem homogenizer with a Teflon pestle and immediately brought to 60°C and combined with hot water-saturated phenol. Three extractions were performed, and then the aqueous phase was incubated for 15 min with 0.25 mg of 2 × crystallized DNAase (Nutritional Biochemicals Corp.), followed by a fourth phenol extraction. The RNA was precipitated from the final chilled aqueous layer with addition of two volumes of cold ethanol. Phenol was removed by washing the precipitate with ether. The RNA was stored as a precipitate under 75% ethanol; for sedimentation analysis it was dissolved in sodium acetate buffer (0.01 M), pH 5, containing NaCl (0.1 M) and MgCl$_2$ (10^{-3} M).

Sedimentation Analysis

0.2 ml of the RNA solution were layered atop 4.5 ml of a sucrose gradient (5–20% w/w, linear, in acetate-NaCl-MgCl$_2$). The sucrose had been stirred overnight in the cold with 1 mg/ml bentonite, then cleared by high-speed centrifugation. Gradients were centrifuged for the times indicated in the figure legends at 37,000 rpm in a Spinco Model L centrifuge, swinging-bucket head/type SW-39L. Fractions were collected dropwise from the tubes. These were diluted to 1 ml for measurement of the optical density at 260 mμ and for scintillation counting in Bray's solution. Sample gradients were checked for linearity in a sugar refractometer. *E. coli* 4S RNA and hemoglobin were used as sedimentation velocity markers. H^3- and C^{14}-uridine were used to label RNA in these experiments and were obtained from the New England Nuclear Corporation or Schwarz BioResearch, Inc. Activity data are given in the appropriate figure legends.

Actinomycin D was generously supplied by Dr. H. B. Woodruff of Merck, Sharp and Dohme.

RESULTS

1. Rates of Protein Synthesis During Continued Exposure to Actinomycin

It has been established that actinomycin, in concentrations at 20 μg/ml or above, depresses RNA turnover to a small fraction of the normal rates after the first 4 hr of development, and that the rate of protein synthesis continues as high as that in controls for considerably longer.[8] To eliminate possible ambiguities in the design of the earlier experiments, and to obtain better estimates of the actual rates, a pulse experiment was done with C^{14}-valine, during the first 26 hr of development (i.e., to the gastrula stage).

Results are shown in Fig. 1. In controls, protein synthesis began at fertilization, and the rate rose steadily for about 3 hr. It remained high and constant until 8 hr postfertilization, then rose rapidly again for the next 7 hr, attaining a level twice that of the initial plateau. From the fifteenth to the twenty-sixth hour, there was no change. In embryos which had been exposed to 20μg/ml of actinomycin D for 3 hr before fertilization, the postfertilization release of protein synthesis took place just as in the controls. By 5 hr, the rate was somewhat higher than in the controls.

This condition persisted until the controls began to enter the second acceleration. Actinomycin-treated embryos showed no sign of this second rate increase; the rate of protein synthesis now began a slow decline. At the end of the experiment, actinomycin embryos were still incorporating labeled amino acid at about the same rate as had been attained 2 hr after fertilization.

2. Effect of Actinomycin on the Synthesis of Heavy RNA

a. Arbacia. Eggs were suspended in MBL artificial sea water alone or with 20 μg/ml actinomycin D at a density of 2×10^4 cells (0.58 mg protein) per ml. Following a 3-hr preincubation at 23°C, the eggs were fertilized and placed in contact with tritiated uridine. Further details are given in the legend to Figs. 2 and 3. The time of exposure to labeled precursor was 20 min. Fig. 2 shows the sedimentation behavior of the control RNA, and Fig. 3 that of the RNA from actinomycin-treated embryos. Centrifugation was suf-

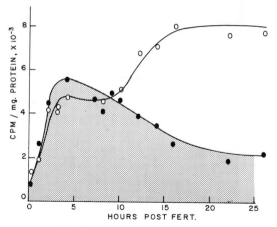

Fig. 1. Rates of incorporation of C^{14}-L-valine into fertilized eggs of Arbacia, with and without actinomycin D (20 μg/ml). Filled circles: 20-min pulse incorporations for embryos in actinomycin, pretreated with actinomycin for 3 hr before fertilization. Open circles: controls in normal artificial sea water. Activity and preparation data in the text.

ficiently prolonged to spread the 18–4S region over the gradient, since it was anticipated, on the basis of Wilt's[6] observations and others,

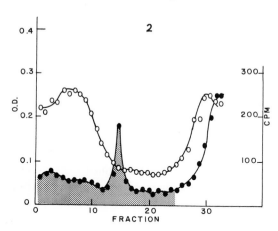

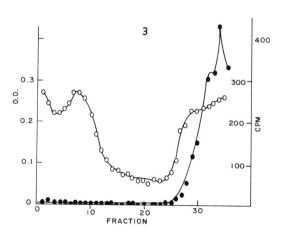

Figs. 2 and 3. Distribution of radioactivity in RNA of Arbacia eggs. Fig. 2, controls; Fig. 3, eggs pretreated for 3 hr with actinomycin D (20 μg/ml) and remaining in the presence of the drug during the pulse incubation. Eggs were fertilized and then placed in contact with H^3-uridine, 0.2 mc, and 20 μg/ml. After 20 min, eggs were sedimented and frozen at -40°C. RNA was extracted with hot phenol-SLS-bentonite, as described in the text. 0.2 ml of the RNA dissolved in buffer (acetate, 0.01 M, NaCl 0.1 M, MgCl$_2$ 10^{-3}M pH 5) was layered onto 4.5 ml of a sucrose gradient (5–20%, linear) in the same buffer, and the gradients were spun in a Spinco SW-39L rotor at 37,000 rpm for 8 hr. Two-drop fractions were collected for measurement of O.D. at 260 mμ and for liquid scintillation counting with Bray's solution. A minimum of 1,000 counts were recorded for each point. Open circles: optical density. Filled circles: counts/min. On the basis of previous experience and marker location, we assign sedimentation constants (approximate) of 18S and 4S to the first and second O.D. peaks, respectively. The small red pellet in each tube had negligible radioactivity. The shaded area in Fig. 2 represents non-4S RNA labeled in the controls.

that much of the label would be found there. Labeled RNA in controls was found, however, throughout the gradient, significant amounts of it heavier than 18S. The O.D. readings represent ribosomal and transfer RNA. There was a large incorporation into the 4S region as well. The nature of the peak of radioactivity in the 10S region is unknown, but it is not due to DNA.

Figure 3, which represents the actinomycin-RNA, explains why the drug does not reduce RNA synthesis to zero in these cells: incorporation of label into species sedimenting at 4S and less is very rapid. Much of it may reflect end-labeling of the terminal CCA sequence of transfer RNA, via conversion of the uridine to cytidine. The important point, however, is that there is no detectable incorporation of label into heavier species of RNA. On the assumption that messenger RNA's coding for polypeptides of normal length, would sediment at rates faster than 4S,[23] we may conclude that actinomycin had at least severely depressed messenger RNA synthesis.

b. Lytechinus RNA and Protein Synthesis. This result seemed worth confirming in another species. Eggs of *Lytechinus pictus* were accordingly preincubated with or without actinomycin (20 μg/ml) for 200 min. The suspensions were each then divided; an aliquot was placed in contact with C^{14}-valine (0.20 μc and 5 μg/ml) for measurement of amino acid incorporation into protein, and another was given C^{14}-uridine to label the RNA. All suspensions were then fertilized simultaneously, and incubated at 17°C for 1 hr. This interval is equivalent to the 20-min pulse given Arbacia eggs at 23°; at the end of it, all eggs, both controls and actinomycin-treated, were in metaphase of the first division.

At the end of the hour, the suspensions were quickly chilled and centrifuged; the RNA-labeled eggs were frozen and processed for sucrose-gradient analysis; protein-labeled eggs were fixed with 5 per cent TCA.

The actinomycin-treated embryos incorporated somewhat more amino acid into protein than did the controls: the rates were

0.032 μg valine incorporated/mg cell protein for the actinomycin-treated eggs and 0.025 μg/mg for the controls. Sedimentation data are plotted in Figs. 4 and 5, with pertinent experimental details given in the legend. The result of this experiment duplicates that obtained with Arbacia: there was a small but significant synthesis of heavy RNA in the controls, RNA whose sedimentation is non-coincident with that of the ribosomal RNA represented by the first two optical density peaks (at 28S and 18S, approximately[5]), as well as a relatively heavy incorporation into material sedimenting at 4S and less. In the presence of actinomycin, the 4S material is labeled as in the control, but there is no measurable incorporation into heavy molecules.

3. Developmental Effects

While we are not here primarily concerned with developmental implications, it is worth documenting the characteristic effects of actinomycin on mitosis and differentiation for the same experiment in which both early protein and early RNA synthesis data are available. Aliquots of the two suspensions of Lytechinus eggs used in the sedimentation analysis were permitted to remain in the waterbath. After 18 hr, controls were rapidly swimming mesenchyme-blastulae, as exemplified by Fig. 6a. The embryos in actinomycin had divided at about the same rate as the controls, and had produced a blastocoel, but none had altered beyond an early blastula morphology, except that continued cell division had caused numbers of cells to loosen from the blastula wall. Half of the embryos had formed cilia and were rotating sluggishly; the others had not. One third had hatched. Figure 6b shows one of the actinomycin embryos at this time, with its fertilization membrane still intact. Figure 6c is a phase-contrast surface view of the actinomycin embryo, provided to show that mitotic division, and not fragmentation, was taking place: the phase contrast optics reveal normal cell contact planes and the fact that every cell has a nucleus. One of the cells in the optical plane is at metaphase.

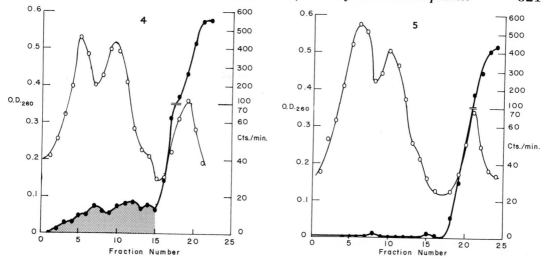

Figs. 4 and 5. *Lytechinus pictus.* Same experimental design as in Figs. 2 and 3. Preincubation with actinomycin for 200 min. Pulse duration: 0–60 min postfertilization. RNA label: C^{14}-uridine, 0.5 μc and 4.0 $\mu g/ml$, in artificial sea water. For protein synthesis and development data, see text. Centrifugation time at 37,000 rpm: 5 hr. Fig. 4, controls; Fig. 5, actinomycin-treated eggs. O.D. peaks (open circles) correspond, on the basis of previous experience, to (approx.) 28S, 18S, and 4S, with sedimentation toward lower fraction numbers. The filled circles give counts/min of each fraction in 15-ml Bray's solution. At least 3,000 counts were accumulated per sample. Shaded area in Fig. 4 represents newly synthesized non-4S RNA. Each fraction comprised 3 drops from a 4.7-ml gradient.

DISCUSSION AND CONCLUSIONS

Biological and chemical implications of a complete but inhibited system of protein synthesis (including templates) in the unfertilized egg are discussed at length elsewhere.[8] It is, however, worthwhile to state what is, in our opinion, demonstrated by these experiments. First, we find (in agreement with Nemer[5] and Wilt[6]) that synthesis of non-ribosomal, non-4S RNA begins very soon after fertilization. To what extent the heavy, new RNA is messenger and to what extent it is a ribosomal precursor or other RNA is not certain, but in view of the enormous supply of ribosomes packaged into the egg, and in view of Nemer's pulse-chase results,[5] it seems likely that an important fraction of the new RNA is messenger.

Actinomycin, at 20 $\mu g/ml$, inhibits the synthesis of RNA heavier than *ca.* 25,000 mol wt. The failure to suppress incorporation *in toto*, as is accomplished with suitable concentrations of this drug in bacteria,[22] results from

the rapid synthesis of 4S material, or possibly from rapid end-labeling of the CCA sequence of transfer RNA, or both. Perhaps there are long GC-free regions of sea urchin DNA, which are used as templates by the RNA polymerase even in the presence of actinomycin: the specificity of actinomycin for dGMP residues in DNA has been well established.[21] Possibly the low molecular weight RNA is made in an RNA-dependent system.

The effect on RNA synthesis contrasts with the protein synthesis rates, which are equal to or higher than in the controls. The condition persists for many hours; the very slow decay of protein synthesis in actinomycin-treated embryos suggests that the templates for the early proteins are very stable in this system.

Failure of the second rise in protein synthesis rate suggests that an important class of new messenger RNA's has not been elaborated; the timing of this rise in controls suggests a relation to the differentiation of primary mesenchyme, skeleton formation, and gastrulation.

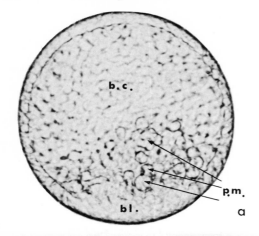

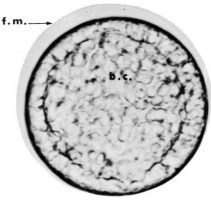

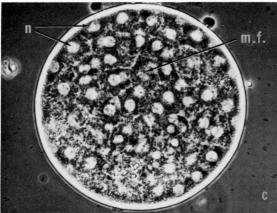

Fig. 6. Development of Lytechinus embryos from RNA-labeling experiment described in text and in Figs. 4 and 5. (*a*) Mesenchyme blastula from control suspension, showing thin body wall, blastocoel (b.c.), primary mesenchyme cells (p.m.) migrating away from presumptive region of gastrula invagination (bl.). These embryos were swimming vigorously. (*b*) Embryo from actinomycin-suspension, with blastocoel, body wall 1–3 cells thick, and fertilization membrane (f.m.), showing that hatching had not occurred in this specimen. The actinomycin-treated embryos died in this condition. (*c*) Phase-contrast surface view of an actinomycin-treated embryo, showing cell contact planes in the body wall, and a nucleus (n) in each cell. One cell in the optical plane is in metaphase (m.f.). This provides evidence that division continued in actinomycin, but that no differentiation occurred beyond a stage resembling the early blastula.

We conclude that the release of protein synthesis from whatever inhibits it in the unfertilized egg does not require messenger RNA synthesis. Since defective ribosomes,[10] absence of transfer RNA,[24] and deficiency in amino acid-activating enzymes[25] have been eliminated as possible causes of the inhibition, its nature remains a problem.

The low molecular weight RNA that does become labeled in the presence of actinomycin D might represent incomplete messenger fragments, capable of stimulating the synthesis of some abnormal polypeptides. It is known, however, that the sea urchin egg must make some proteins for each division,[26] and presumably serious changes in the character of proteins made after fertilization would lead to inhibition of mitosis. But the actinomycin-treated embryos divide at normal or near-normal rates, indicating that some of the proteins being assembled are also normal.

We now consider it, therefore, a good working hypothesis that the first proteins are made by the embryo independently of direct genomic control; that their templates (if all protein synthesis requires templates) are present in the unfertilized egg. It is perhaps of interest that many or all of these templates bear information about the proteins needed for cell division,[27] but not about differentiation beyond the early blastula.

Summary

In the presence of actinomycin D, two species of sea urchin egg fail to incorporate isotopically labeled uridine into RNA of high molecular weight, while controls do so. Both actinomycin-treated and control eggs do begin to synthesize new proteins immediately after fertilization. It is concluded that the release of protein synthesis from its prefertilization inhibition is not a result of the synthesis of new messenger RNA. Such synthesis is required for normal development beyond the early blastula.

[1] Monod, J., and F. Jacob, in *Cellular Regulatory Mechanisms*, Cold Spring Harbor Symposia on Quantitative Biology, vol. 26 (1961), p. 389.

[2] Goodman, H. M., and A. Rich, *Nature*, **199**, 318 (1963).

[3] Harvey, E. B., *The American Arbacia and Other Sea Urchins* (Princeton University Press, 1956).

[4] Gross, P. R., and G. H. Cousineau, *Biochem. Biophys. Res. Commun.*, **10**, 321 (1963).

[5] Nemer, M., *Proc. N.A.S.*, **50**, 230 (1963).

[6] Wilt, F. H., *Biochem. Biophys. Res. Commun.*, **11**, 447 (1963).

[7] Brachet, J., *et al.*, *Biochim. Biophys. Acta*, **72**, 662 (1963).

[8] Gross, P. R., and G. H. Cousineau, *Exptl. Cell Res.*, **33**, 368 (1964).

[9] Hultin, T., *Exptl. Cell Res.*, **25**, 405 (1961).

[10] Wilt, F. H., and T. Hultin, *Biochem. Biophys. Res. Commun.*, **9**, 313 (1962).

[11] Melton, C. R., *Genetics*, **48**, 901 (1963).

[12] Tyler, A., *Am. Zoologist*, **3**, 109 (1963).

[13] Gross, P. R., W. Spindel, and G. H. Cousineau, *Biochem. Biophys. Res. Commun.*, **13**, 405 (1963).

[14] Cavanaugh, G., ed., *Formulae and Methods of the Marine Biological Laboratory, IV* (Woods Hole, 1956).

[15] Herberg, R., *Science*, **128**, 199 (1958).

[16] Bray, G., *Anal. Biochem.*, **1**, 279 (1960).

[17] Lowry, O., *et al.*, *J. Biol. Chem.*, **193**, 265 (1951).

[18] Scherrer, K., and J. Darnell, *Biochem. Biophys. Res. Commun.*, **7**, 486 (1962).

[19] Fraenkel-Conrat, H., B. Singer, and A. Tsugita, *Virology*, **14**, 54 (1961).

[20] Hurwitz, J., *et. al.*, *Proc. N.A.S.*, **48**, 1222 (1962).

[21] Reich, E., I. H. Goldberg, and M. Rabinowitz, *Nature*, **196**, 743 (1962).

[22] Levinthal, C., A. Keynan, and A. Higa, *Proc. N.A.S.*, **48**, 1631 (1962).

[23] Monier, R., *et al.*, *J. Mol. Biol.*, **5**, 311 (1962).

[24] Nemer, M., and S. G. Bard, *Science*, **140**, 664 (1963).

[25] Maggio, R., and C. Catalano, in preparation.

[26] Hultin, T., *Experientia*, **7**, 410 (1961).

[27] Gross, P. R., and G. H. Cousineau, *J. Cell Biol.*, **19**, 260 (1963).

Regulation of Protein Synthesis in the Embryogenesis of the Sea Urchin*

MARTIN NEMER

A rapid increase in protein synthesis occurs after fertilization of the sea urchin egg.[1] To determine the reason for this change and to understand the mechanisms for the regulation of protein synthesis through embryonic development, the enzymic and nucleic acid components involved were studied by two distinct approaches: (1) Cell-free ribosomal preparations from eggs and embryos were examined for their ability to execute the two sequential sets of reactions necessary for protein synthesis; namely, the production of specific amino acyl soluble RNAs[2] and the assemblage of the amino acids into polypeptide chains specified by messenger RNA. (2) The major components of RNA of the sea urchin egg were characterized by sedimentation analysis and their fate in the course of development was examined together with the nature of the RNA newly synthesized at various embryonic stages.

Symposium: Metabolic Control Mechanisms. National Cancer Institute Monograph, No. 13, 141–154, 1963. Government Printing Office, Washington, D.C.

* Presented at the Symposium on Metabolic Control Mechanisms in Animal Cells, Boston, Mass., May 27–30, 1963.

Supported by grant CA-05936 from the National Cancer Institute, National Institutes of Health, Public Health Service.

Abbreviations used: polyU, polyuridylic acid; polyUG, polyuridylic-guanylic acid; PEP, phosphoenolpyruvate; GTP, guanosine triphosphate; RNA_p, pulse RNA; RNA_c, chase RNA.

METHODS AND MATERIALS

Eggs and Embryos. For studies on polypeptide synthesis, the species *Arbacia punctulata* and *Lytechinus pictus* were used. For RNA synthesis *Strongylocentrotus purpuratus* was studied. Eggs were fertilized and allowed to develop[3] in artificial sea water at 20° C in the presence of penicillin and streptomycin (30 and 50 mg/ml, respectively).

Assay of Polypeptide Synthesis. Polypeptide synthesis was measured after incorporation of labeled amino acids (either phenylalanine or leucine) by a homogenate fraction, prepared as follows: At various developmental stages eggs were packed by light centrifugation in homogenizing vessels, and an equal volume of homogenization medium,[1] containing 0.006 M mercaptoethanol was added. After gentle homogenization at 0 to 5° C, the homogenate was centrifuged for 10 minutes at 12,000 × g. The supernatant fluid (approximately 1 ml) was passed through a column (1.2 × 10 cm) of Sephadex-25 equilibrated with incubation medium, which was the same as the homogenization medium except that sucrose was omitted. The front of the effluent solution, which had been effectively dialyzed against incubation medium, was called the S-12 fraction, and was adjusted to contain 0.50 mg per ml RNA and approximately 5 mg per ml protein.[4, 5]

Incubations were performed with 0.2 ml of S-12 fraction at 30° C for 45 or 60 minutes. The rate of incorporation of phenylalanine was constant up to 1 hour. The reactions were stopped with addition of trichloroacetic acid (to 5%). Samples were heated at 90° C for 20 minutes, and the precipitates were washed and plated on glass-fiber discs. Radioactivity was measured in a gas-flow counter with a Micromil window and a counting efficiency of approximately 30 percent. Samples were counted at infinite thinness. All assays were in duplicate.

Incorporation in RNA. At various developmental stages, 1 cc of eggs or embryos was settled by light centrifugation and suspended to 5 cc with sea water for 10 or 20 minutes, during which time they were exposed to a concentration of either 3.5 or 7 μM H^3-uridine (2.77 mc/μmole; New England Nuclear Corportation). At the end of this pulse period the eggs were suspended in sea water containing unlabeled uridine (5 mM). Half of this suspension was centrifuged quickly. The embryos in the pellet were frozen immediately to −80° C and stored. The other half of the suspension was centrifuged lightly, then resuspended in 100 ml sea water containing 0.5 mM uridine. These continued developing for 4 hours. After this chase period the embryos were centrifuged and their pellet was frozen and stored as described.

Extraction of RNA. For further processing the eggs or embryos were thawed and homogenized in a solution of 0.5 percent dodecyl sulfate, 0.01 M $MgCl_2$, 0.1 M NaCl, and 0.01 M acetate buffer, pH 6.0. Samples were immediately submitted to phenol extraction at 60° C.[6, 7]

Sedimentation Analysis. Purified RNA in a solution containing 0.01 M $MgCl_2$, 0.1 M NaCl, and 0.01 M acetate buffer, pH 6.0, was applied to a 5 to 20 percent linear sucrose gradient[8] in the same solution, containing 100 μg per ml bentonite. Samples were centrifuged for 11 hours at 25,000 rpm in the Spinco head SW25.1. Equal fractions were collected. Optical densities at 260 mμ were determined and the radioactivities of aliquots of the fractions in scintillation fluid[9] were measured in a scintillation counter. At least duplicate pulse-chase experiments with different batches of eggs were performed for every embryonic stage represented. All pertinent figures have been normalized to contain a total of 10 optical density$_{260}$ units of RNA per gradient.

The sedimentation constants of the various RNA peaks were estimated by addition to the sucrose gradients of a trace of P^{32}-labeled RNA, prepared from strain L cell fibroblasts (gift of R. Perry), containing components of known sedimentation constants.[10] With the 18S component of the P^{32}-marker RNA as a standard, the approximate S values of the peaks were derived by the method of Martin and Ames.[11]

Results and Conclusions

Polypeptide Synthesis

The apparent check on protein synthesis in the unfertilized egg may result from limitations on the concentrations of enzymatic components responsible either for the production of specific amino acyl sRNA's or the assemblage of polypeptides. Although the endogenous protein synthesis measured by phenylalanine incorporation with the S-12 fraction of unfertilized eggs is very low, a 200-fold increase in the incorporation of phenylalanine in polypeptide can be obtained by the addition of polyU to the system (Fig. 1 and Table 1). When polyUG is used as template RNA,

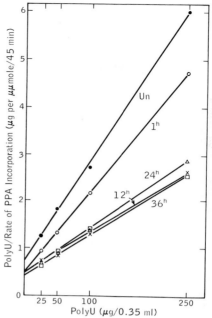

Fig. 2. Effect of concentration of polyU on polyphenylalanine synthesis by the S-12 fraction of *Lytechinus pictus* at various stages of development: • unfertilized egg; ○ 1-hour zygote; × 12-hour blastula; △ 24-hour gastrula; □ 36-hour gastrula. The reaction mixture was the same as that of Fig. 1, except the concentration of yeast sRNA was 0.7 mg per ml, and polyU was varied as indicated on the abscissa. The ratio of polyU concentration to rate of PPA incorporation is given on the ordinate. The volume of the reaction mixture of 0.35 ml contained 1 mg protein. L-phenylalanine-C14 was 3.5 μM.

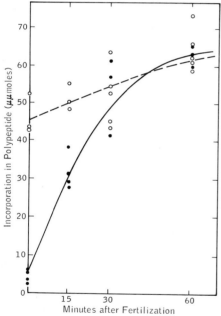

Fig. 1. Polyphenylalanine and protein synthesis by S-12 fraction of *Arbacia punctulata* before and after fertilization. Incorporation in protein is •; in polyphenylalanine is ○. The reaction mixture contained the following in μmoles per ml: 50 Tris buffer pH 7.8; 10 $MgCl_2$; 240 KCL; 6 mercaptoethanol; 1 ATP; 5 PEP; 0.06 GTP; and 7 mμmole per ml L-phenylalanine-C14 (150,000 counts/min). The total volume of 0.85 ml also contained 20 μg PEP kinase; 3 mg S-12 protein; 0.5 mg polyU or a mixture of 20 L-amino acids minus phenylalanine each 22 μmole per ml. Incubations were at 30°C for 60 minutes. Incorporation of phenylalanine in protein (in absence of polyU) has been multiplied by 20.

an 11-fold stimulation of leucine incorporation is seen (see Table 3).

The rate of protein synthesis in the S-12 fractions of *A. punctulata* increased 14-fold during the first 60 minutes after fertilization; at the same time polyphenylalanine synthesis increased less than 1.5-fold (Fig. 1).

The maximal velocities (Vmax) of polyphenylalanine synthesis were determined in the presence of excess yeast sRNA in S-12 fractions of *L. pictus* prepared at different embryonic stages. Figure 2 shows the ratio of polyU concentration to polyphenylalanine concentration plotted against polyU concentration, in accordance with the Lineweaver-Burk modification of the Michaelis-Menten relation.[12] The calculated Vmax increased from 50 μμmoles of phenylalanine incorpo-

TABLE 1. Incorporation in polypeptide by S-12 fractions of various embryonic stages of *Lytechinus pictus**

Polypeptide	Incorporation in Polypeptide ($\mu\mu$moles/100 μg S-12 RNA)			
	Unfertilized	Cleavage	Blastula	Gastrula
	Batch Number 1			
Protein	5	24	50	
PPA	51	65	75	
	Batch Number 2			
Protein	5	16	63	58
PPA	49	59	106	96
	Batch Number 3			
Protein	2	9		40
PPA	21	51		82
Average ratio PPA/protein	10	3.6	1.6	1.8

* S-12 fractions from 3 batches of eggs were assayed for PPA (polyphenylalanine) synthesis according to conditions in Fig. 2; except the yeast sRNA concentration and the polyU were each 0.5 mg per ml. For protein synthesis a mixture of 20 L-amino acids minus the labeled amino acids was present at 0.22 μmole per ml. Protein synthesis for batch 2 was measured by incorporation of L-leucine-C14, 1 mμmole per ml. Phenylalanine incorporation in protein was multiplied by 20, and leucine incorporation by 8.

rated in 45 minutes in the unfertilized egg to 60 in the 1-hour zygote, to approximately 100 in the 12-hour blastula, where it remained constant through the 24- and 36-hour gastrula stages. Thus the capacity of the system for polyphenylalanine synthesis increased with development to a value twice that of the unfertilized egg.

In the development of *L. pictus* to blastulae the rate of protein synthesis increased considerably, but further development to gastrulae took place with much less increase (Table 1). In this second phase the ratios of polyphenylalanine to protein synthesis were essentially constant (Table 1); that is, they changed at the same rate.

Protein synthesis and the synthesis of polypeptide directed by synthetic messenger polyribonucleotides were studied in the presence of an excess[3] of yeast sRNA or in the absence of added yeast sRNA in the S-12 fractions derived at various stages of development. In the presence of an excess of polyU, the concentration of endogenous sRNA in the S-12 fraction of unfertilized eggs of *L. pictus* could support only 9 percent of the polyphenylalanine synthesis that could be achieved in the presence of an excess of yeast sRNA (Table 2). In the course of development (Table 2) there was a substantial

increase in this synthetic capacity determined by the concentration of endogenous sRNA. In the presence of polyUG, the S-12 fraction from eggs of *A. punctulata* allowed 59 percent of the incorporation of leucine in polypeptide attained with added yeast sRNA (Table 3). At the blastula stage, the endogenous concentration of sRNA was completely adequate to support the requirements of leucine incorporation in the presence of polyUG. PolyUG presents much less demand on the supply of leucyl sRNA than polyU on the supply of phenylalanyl sRNA. In both cases the supply of endogenous sRNA appears to increase with development.

In both species the addition of yeast sRNA had little effect on the incorporation of leucine or phenylalanine in protein. Unless yeast sRNA is lacking in transfer RNA's specific for the sea urchin, endogenous levels of sRNA are adequate at all stages for the needs of protein synthesis.

RNA, Old and New

Chemical measurements indicate that there is practically no change in the amount of RNA present through early development.[13, 14] Nevertheless, incorporation of various radioactive precursors into the RNA of the sea urchin embryo has been detected.[15-18] If this in-

TABLE 2. Dependency on added yeast sRNA for protein and polyphenylalanine synthesis at different stages of development in *Lytechinus pictus**

Stage	Leucine Incorporation in Protein ($\mu\mu$moles/100 μg S-12 RNA)			Phenylalanine Incorporation in Polyphenylalanine ($\mu\mu$moles/100 μg S-12 RNA)		
	−sRNA	+sRNA	Percent Capacity	−sRNA	+sRNA	Percent Capacity
Unfertilized	0.56	0.64	87	3.9	42	9
1-hour zygote	1.83	2.07	88	4.3	53	8
12-hour blastula	5.48	7.85	70	14.7	96	15
24-hour gastrula	6.74	7.25	93	22.2	90	25

* Conditions were the same as those for Table 1. A mixture of 20 L-amino acids minus leucine, 0.22 μmoles per ml; L-leucine-C^{14}, 1 mμmole per ml; polyU, 0.7 mg per ml in incubations with L-phenylalanine-C^{14}. Yeast sRNA, 0.7 mg per ml.

TABLE 3. Dependency on added yeast sRNA for incorporation of leucine in polypeptide in presence and absence of polyUG in *Arbacia punctulata**

Stage	Leucine Incorporation in Polypeptide ($\mu\mu$moles/100 μg S-12 RNA)					
	−PolyUG			+PolyUG		
	−sRNA	+sRNA	Percent Capacity	−sRNA	+sRNA	Percent Capacity
Unfertilized	0.41	0.46	91	2.93	5.00	59
1-hour zygote	2.43	2.58	94	4.28	6.58	65
12-hour blastula, late	3.93	3.85	102	6.18	6.28	98

* Conditions were the same as those of Table 2. PolyUG (5 : 1), 0.6 mg per ml.

corporation does not entail a net increase, a substantial net synthesis of any one RNA compartment would have to come at the expense of another. An increase with development in the concentration of one such compartment, that of transfer RNA, as deduced, will be corroborated by the following data. This study was undertaken to examine more closely the role of RNA, that which is stored in the egg as well as that which is synthesized allowing the issuance of new genetic information.

Pulse and Chase RNA

The sedimentation pattern of incorporation following a short exposure (pulse) to radioactive precursor has been compared to that at the end of a subsequent incubation in the presence of unlabeled precursor (chase). The portion of radioactive RNA of the pulse destined for stable components will be found associated with them following the chase. On the other hand, any rapidly degraded RNA will only be detectable after a pulse and not at the end of a chase. The course of

embryogenesis of the sea urchin, it will be demonstrated, is marked by striking changes in the character of pulse and chase RNA (RNA$_p$ and RNA$_c$, respectively).

Unfertilized Eggs. Nucleosides are utilized to a lesser degree before than after fertilization;[19] nevertheless, their incorporation into the RNA of the unfertilized egg is detectable. The characteristics of this incorporation were studied by sedimentation analysis of RNA from eggs that had been incubated with H^3-uridine for a 20-minute pulse and those that had been incubated in unlabeled uridine for a 4-hour chase, following the 20-minute pulse. After the pulse, radioactivity was distributed through the gradient into peaks of approximately 4, 17, and 22S (Fig. 3A). Following the chase, the same distribution persisted, but with a slight increase in specific activity. In both cases the 4S RNA was the only major component labeled. The 17 and 22S components appeared relatively stable.

Just-Fertilized Egg. Exposure of eggs 5 minutes after fertilization to a 20-minute

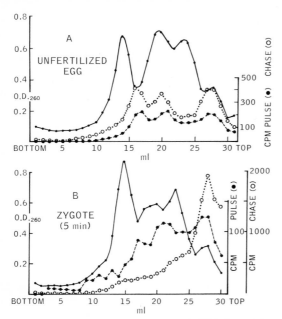

Fig. 3. Sedimentation diagrams of RNA from (A) unfertilized and (B) just-fertilized eggs. Eggs were pulsed for 20 minutes with H^3-uridine (7 μM) and chased for 4 hours in the presence of 0.5 mM unlabeled uridine. *Solid curve* represents absorbancy at 260 mμ. *Dotted lines* represent radioactivities of pulse (•) and chase (○).

pulse of H^3-uridine resulted in a pattern of incorporation similar to that of the unfertilized egg (Fig. 3B). Any expected difference between the unfertilized and fertilized egg is manifested only quantitatively, since the latter has an appreciably greater specific activity. In contrast to the behavior of the unfertilized egg, a 4-hour chase results in the incorporation into all the major RNA components, predominantly into the 4S RNA (Fig. 3B). The increase in specific activity during the chase is too great to decide whether the pulse RNA peaks at 17 and 22S have disappeared or have been obscured by the pattern of the chase.

Pregastrula Stages. Embryos at various stages were exposed to H^3-uridine for a pulse of 10 minutes. Half of these were further incubated in the presence of unlabeled uridine for a chase of 4 hours. At the 8- to 16-cell cleavage stage, the pulse radioactivity of the extracted RNA was spread throughout the sucrose density gradient but with a peak displayed at approximately 10S (Fig. 4B). In-

corporation during the chase was mainly into the 4S RNA, with appreciable labeling of the 13S RNA and smaller activity in the 28 and 18S regions. The same pattern was displayed up to the 24-hour mesenchyme blastula stage (Fig. 4C). During development to this stage, the pulse-labeled peak at 10S became progressively broadened toward the heavy region of the gradient and the degree of utilization of labeled uridine increased. Figure 4A represents an incubation following the first division (1½ hours). The character of the RNA_p is intermediate between that of the just-fertilized egg and those in the cleavage and blastula stages; that is, it is apparently a composite containing the 17 and 22S peak as well as the 10S peak.

Postgastrula Stages. A pronounced change in the characteristics of the pulse RNA occurred after gastrulation. In the pulse of the 45-hour gastrula (Fig. 4D) the 10S region no longer predominated in amount of incorporation. Instead, the radioactivity was dispersed throughout the gradient with substantial amounts present in regions of greater than 30S. The corresponding chase RNA was also different. A large amount of incorporation was found for the first time in the 28 and 18S RNAs. The optical absorbancy of the 13S RNA described only a shoulder instead of a large peak, and little activity was associated with it. In the prism (60 hours) and in the 72-hour pluteus (Fig. 4E) the pattern of incorporation of pulse RNA was similar to that seen in the gastrula. After chasing, a large amount of activity was found in the major RNA components.

Approximately 6 percent of the total RNA of the egg is 4S. This value rises by a factor of 2 and 3 when the blastula and gastrula stages, respectively, are reached (Fig. 4). This increase agrees with that seen for transfer RNA in the two other species studied.

Relative Amounts of Synthesis of Various RNA's During Development

The 4S and non-4S RNA can be viewed separately by graphically subtracting the activity (the product of the specific activity and total optical density units) of the 4S RNA from that of the total RNA. The resultant non-4S RNAs of the pulses of various stages are represented on a single scale in Fig. 5 against the optical density pattern of the gastrula stage. Clearly, with development the degree of labeling increases as markedly as the pattern of sedimentation behavior changes. The shift to the heavier region of the gradient is coincident with the pronounced rise in incorporation in ribosomal RNA at gastrulation.

The rapidly synthesized non-4S RNA consists of a component (m) that is rapidly degraded, concordant with its function as messenger, and a component (pr) that is precursor to stable or ribosomal RNA (s).[7] The fraction, $pr/(m + pr)$, of the rapidly synthesized RNA $(m + pr)$ converted to s can be estimated for an interval which is long enough for essentially all of pr to be converted to s. An adequate chase represents such an interval. Thus, if the first RNA products $(4S\ RNA + m + pr)$ in a given interval are derived from the same precursor pool, P, then

1. $P_c/P_p = (m + pr)_c/(m + pr)_p = 4S\ RNA_c/4S\ RNA_p$ or $(m + pr)_c = (m + pr)_p\ (4S\ RNA_c/4S\ RNA_p)$.

2. If $s = pr$, then
$pr/(m + pr)_c = s/(m + pr)_p\ (4S\ RNA_c/4S\ RNA_p) = $ non-4S $RNA_c/($non-4S $RNA_p)\ (4S\ RNA_c/4S\ RNA_p)$.

Calculations of the fraction of the total radioactivity (cpm) of the rapidly synthesized non-4S RNA, as represented in Fig. 5, converted to stable non-4S RNA yield the values given in Table 4. In the pregastrula stages this fraction was approximately 0.33. But only half of this was represented by the known ribosomal 28 and 18S RNAs; the other half was 13S RNA. The postgastrula stages retained much more of the rapidly synthesized RNA in the ribosomal constituents, about 0.52 in the 45-

Fig. 4. Sedimentation diagrams of RNA from embryos at various stages: Embryos were pulsed for 10 minutes with H³-uridine (3.5 μM) and chased 4 hours in the presence of 0.5 mM unlabeled uridine. Representations are the same as for Fig. 3: pulse (•) and chase (○).

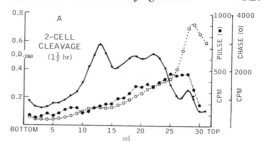

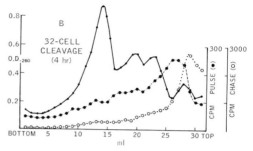

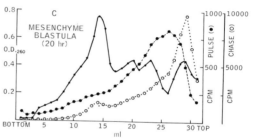

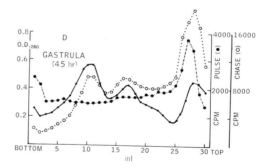

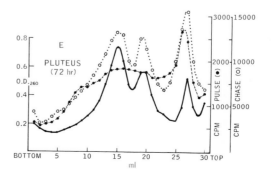

TABLE 4. Interrelationships involving 4S and non-4S RNA of *Strongylocentrotus purpuratus*

Stage	Hour	Ratio of Incorporation (Range)	
		$s/(m+pr)$*	$s/4S$ RNA$_c$
Cleavage	1–10	0.31 (0.30–0.33)	0.54 (0.53–0.56)
Blastula	20–28	0.34 (0.32–0.38)	0.87 (0.65–1.10)
Gastrula	45–49	0.52	1.14
Pluteus	72–76	0.59 (0.55–0.62)	2.20 (1.9–2.50)

* Fraction of rapidly synthesized non-4S RNA $(m+pr)$ converted to stable or ribosomal RNA $(s = $ non-4S RNA$_c)$.

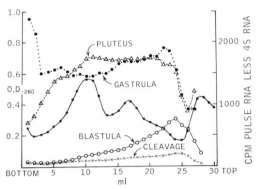

Fig. 5. A comparison of the sedimentation characteristics of non-4S pulse RNA at various embryonic stages obtained by graphically subtracting the radioactivity of 4S RNA from the pulse RNA of Fig. 4.

hour gastrula and 0.59 in the 72-hour pluteus.

While the ratios $s/(m+pr)$ and thus s/m apparently increase in the course of development, the ratio $s/4S$ RNA$_c$ also increases (Table 4). This ratio rises from a value of 0.5 in the early cleavage stages (again including 13S RNA) to 2.2 in the 72-hour pluteus. Therefore, during development the synthesis of ribosomal RNA increases relative to both messenger and transfer RNA.

DISCUSSION

Before and After Fertilization. The incorporation of phenylalanine or leucine into polypeptide is stimulated greatly by the addition of synthetic messenger polyribonucleotides. Since this incorporation is coupled to the formation of phenylalanyl or leucyl sRNA[20] through activating and transfer enzymes, the activities of these enzymes apparently considerably exceed the needs of protein synthesis in the egg.

The number of amino acid residues incorporated into protein and into polypeptide, induced by synthetic RNA template, can be compared: Phenylalanine is 5 percent and leucine is 12 percent of the amino acids incorporated in this protein.[3] The values for their incorporation can be multiplied by 20 and 8, respectively, to represent the amount of incorporated amino acid residues. Less than 10 percent of the polypeptide synthesized on polyUG (5:1) template is leucine.[20] The unfertilized egg can then incorporate tenfold more amino acid residues into polyphenylalanine than into protein, and can synthesize tenfold more polypeptide, directed by polyUG, than protein. If activities tested with synthetic messenger polyribonucleotides are comparable to endogenous protein synthesis, then the polypeptide synthetic capacity of the enzymes and ribosomes of the unfertilized egg exceeds the observed amount of protein synthesis, and cannot be a limiting factor.

Thus the unfertilized egg contains a large reservoir of ribosomes, whose ability to synthesize protein may be limited by a lack of mRNA. The ribosomal capacity for protein synthesis increases after fertilization, apparently because mRNA becomes newly available. A messenger component, if there is any, ought to be demonstrable in rapidly synthesized RNA, since its function as template has been shown to involve a rapid metabolic turnover.[21] Before and after fertilization in the species *S. purpuratus*, the RNA$_p$ contained two peaks of approximately 17 and 22S. These sedimentation values are also characteristic of bacterial RNA. The extremely high concentration of radioactivity could have served to detect a minute amount of bacterial contamination and yet could have failed to reveal RNA synthesis attributable to the egg itself. If there is synthesis of mRNA following fertilization, it is not apparent from these results.

Developmental Patterns of RNA Synthesis. During the early cleavage stages, the nature of the RNA_p experiences a transition (Fig. 4A) from the pattern of the unfertilized egg to a pattern with a predominant peak of approximately 10S (Fig. 4B). This may be a transition between the synthesis of messengers patterned by the maternal genome for use before and immediately after fertilization and that of messengers to be involved in the developmental process. This pattern of rapidly synthesized RNA, appearing in all of the pregastrula stages, exhibits a progressive developmental change, whereby the peak broadens toward the heavier region of the gradient. This peak may be a group of mRNAs whose average size increases during this period of development.

The final form taken by RNA_p in this progression occurs in all the postgastrula stages. Its sedimentation pattern is polydisperse with a large proportion of radioactivity of greater than 30S. It is a pattern that has been demonstrated in highly developed growing cells.[7, 22] The sharp rise in ribosomal RNA synthesis, seen in chase experiments with gastrulae, coupled with the appearance of substantial radioactivity in RNA_p greater than 30S, agrees with the hypothesis of Scherrer, Latham, and Darnell[22] that this part of the RNA_p is precursor to ribosomal RNA. The calculated proportion of the rapidly synthesized RNA converted to 28 and 18S RNA rises from less than 20 percent in the early cleavage stages to 60 percent in the late pluteus (Table 4).

Old and New RNA in the Regulation of Protein Synthesis. The reservoir of functional ribosomes in the unfertilized egg may largely serve the needs of the embryo in the early stages. A great difference in the increases in the ability of embryonic extracts to synthesize polypeptide where the messenger is in excess (polyphenylalanine synthesis) as compared to where the messenger is apparently limiting (endogenous protein synthesis) is evident in the stages of *L. pictus* before the blastula

(Table 1). During that period, a greater emphasis may have been placed on the synthesis of mRNA to program the functional ribosomes already present than to construct new ribosomes. Thus endogenous protein synthesis increased more rapidly than polyphenylalanine synthesis. However, a comparison of the blastula and gastrula revealed that further increases were approximately the same for polypeptide synthesis limited and not limited by messenger. Apparently in a second phase of development the emphasis on messenger synthesis was reduced. This succession of periods of relatively high and low proportions of messenger synthesis was demonstrated in the pattern of RNA synthesis of *S. purpuratus*. The ratio of synthesis of labile non-4S RNA to that of stable non-4S RNA (messenger to ribosomal) was greater in the pregastrula than in the postgastrula stages (Table 4). Such a demarcation in the nature of the synthesis of RNA may be expected to influence the kinds of regulation of protein synthesis during embryogenesis.

Summary

Control of protein synthesis in the embryogenesis of the sea urchin was studied through examination of (1) the activities of the components of cell-free ribosomal systems, prepared from *Arbacia punctulata* and *Lytechinus pictus* and (2) the cellular synthesis of RNA by eggs and embryos of *Strongylocentrotus purpuratus*.

The stimulation of polypeptide synthesis by polyribonucleotides (polyU and polyUG) was used to evaluate the rate-limiting factors involved in the increases in protein synthesis observed after fertilization and in subsequent development. In the early stages of development, the increase in the rate of protein synthesis far exceeded the increase in rate of polypeptide synthesis elicited by synthetic messenger polyribonucleotides. Either these two classes of synthesis represent differentially activated classes of ribosomes present in the egg or the more striking increase in endogenous protein synthesis is attributable to messenger RNA made available after fertilization and through early development.

Distinctly different sedimentation patterns were displayed by the rapidly synthesized RNA of three phases of development of *S. purpuratus:* The unfertilized-egg and just-fertilized-egg patterns have characteristically two peaks (approximately 17 and 22S); a peak at approximately 10S dominates in the pregastrula embryo; and the postgastrula pattern is polydisperse. The last is coincident with a markedly enhanced synthesis of ribosomal RNA, as detected by incorporation in chase experiments.

From two lines of evidence, it is proposed that in an early phase of development, after fertilization, the reservoir of ribosomes originating in the unfertilized egg largely serves the needs of the embryo for protein synthesis. Rather than the construction of new ribosomes during this period, the production of labile or mRNA predominates, presumably to program the functional ribosomes already present. A similar emphasis on transfer RNA production occurs over this interval. In a later embryonic phase, the synthesis of ribosomal RNA increases relative to the other RNA components.

REFERENCES

1. Hultin, T.: Activation of ribosomes in sea urchin eggs in response to fertilization. *Exp Cell Res* 25: 405–417, 1961.
2. Stulberg, M. P., and G. D. Novelli: Amino acid activation. In *The Enzymes* (Boyer, P. D., Lardy, H., and Myrbäck, K., eds.). New York, Academic Press Inc., vol. 6, 1962, p. 401.
3. Nemer, M., and S. G. Bard: Polypeptide synthesis in sea urchin embryogenesis: An examination with synthetic polyribonucleotides. *Science* 140: 664, 1963.
4. Ogur, M., and G. Rosen: The nucleic acids of plant tissue. I. The extraction and estimation of desoxypentose nucleic acid and pentose nucleic acid. *Arch Biochem Biophys* 25: 262, 1950.
5. Lowry, O. H., N. J. Rosebrough, A. L. Farr, and R. J. Randall: Protein measurement with the folin phenol reagent. *J Biol Chem* 193: 265, 1951.
6. Scherrer, K., and J. E. Darnell: Sedimentation characteristics of rapidly labeled RNA from HeLa cells. *Biochem Biophys Res Commun* 7: 486–490, 1962.
7. Perry, R.: The cellular sites of synthesis of ribosomal and 4S RNA. *Proc Nat Acad Sci USA* 48: 2179, 1962.
8. Britten, R. J., and R. B. Roberts: High-resolution density gradient sedimentation analysis. *Science* 131: 32, 1960.
9. Bray, G. A.: A simple efficient liquid scintillator for counting aqueous solutions in a liquid scintillation counter. *Anal Biochem* 1: 279–285, 1960.
10. Homma, M., and A. S. Graham: Synthesis of mengoviral ribonucleic acid in L-cells. *Biochim Biophys Acta* 61: 642, 1962.
11. Martin, R. G., and B. N. Ames: A method for determining the sedimentation behavior of enzymes: application to protein mixtures. *J Biol Chem* 236: 1372–1379, 1961.
12. Lineweaver, H., and D. Burk: The determination of enzyme dissociation constants. *J Amer Chem Soc* 56: 658, 1934.
13. Schmidt, G., L. Hecht, and S. J. Thannhauser: The behavior of the nucleic acids during the early development of the sea urchin egg (Arbacia). *J Gen Physiol* 31: 203, 1948.
14. Elson, D., T. Gustafson, and E. Chargaff: The nucleic acids of the sea urchin during embryonic development. *J Biol Chem* 209: 285, 1954.
15. Villee, C. A., M. Lowens, M. Gordon, E. Leonard, and A. Rich: The incorporation of P^{32} into the nucleoproteins and phosphoproteins of the developing sea urchin embryo. *J Cell Comp Physiol* 33: 93, 1949.
16. Abrams, R.: Synthesis of nucleic acid purines in the sea urchin embryo. *Exp Cell Res* 2: 235, 1951.
17. Scarano, E., and H. M. Kalckar: Nucleic acid synthesis in developing sea urchin embryos. *Publ Staz Zool (Napoli)* 24: 188, 1953.
18. Nemer, M.: Characteristics of the utilization of nucleosides by embryos of *Paracentrotus lividus*. *J Biol Chem* 237: 143–149, 1962.
19. Nirenberg, M. W., J. H. Matthaei, and O. W. Jones: An intermediate in the biosynthesis of polyphenylalanine directed by synthetic template RNA. *Proc Nat Acad Sci USA* 48: 104–109, 1962.
20. Speyer, J. F., P. Lengyel, C. Basilio, and S. Ochoa: Synthetic polynucleotides and the amino acid code, IV. *Proc Nat Acad Sci USA* 48: 441–449, 1962.
21. Naono, S., and F. Gros: Synthèse par *E. coli* d'une phosphatase modifiée en présence d'un analogue pyrimidique. *C R Acad Sci (Paris)* 250: 3889–3891, 1960.
22. Scherrer, K., H. Latham, and J. E. Darnell: Demonstration of an unstable RNA and of a precursor to ribosomal RNA in HeLa Cells. *Proc Nat Acad Sci USA* 49: 240, 1963.

Absence of Ribosomal RNA Synthesis in the Anucleolate Mutant of *Xenopus Laevis*

DONALD D. BROWN

J. B. GURDON

Few new ribosomes appear in the cytoplasm of embryos of *Rana pipiens* or *Xenopus laevis* (the South African "clawed toad") before the tail bud stage.[1] At this time the amount of cytoplasmic ribosomes begins to increase; this rise is correlated with an increase of protein in the high speed supernatant fraction as well as with the first appearance or increase of many enzymes. Soon after these events, the embryos develop a requirement for magnesium ions in the medium. Magnesium-starved embryos characteristically stop growing in length and die at early swimming stages (Shumway[2] stages 21–23 for *Rana pipiens*,[1] or Nieuwkoop-Faber[3] stage 40 for *Xenopus laevis*[4]). The magnesium requirement coincides with the onset of intense ribosome synthesis and presumably is based on the important role of magnesium ions in maintaining the integrity of the functional ribosome particle.

The study of ribosome synthesis during amphibian development has been extended utilizing the lethal anucleolate mutant of *Xenopus laevis* first described by Elsdale *et al.*[5] These workers discovered a heterozygote mutant with only one nucleolus (1-*nu*) in each cell, whereas wild-type *Xenopus laevis* have two nucleoli (2-*nu*) in the majority of their diploid cells. The progeny resulting from the mating of two heterozygotes (1-*nu*) fall into three groups having two, one, or zero nucleoli per cell. The ratio of these genotypes is 1 : 2 : 1, respectively,[5, 6] as expected of a typical Mendelian factor. The heterozygotes (1-*nu*) lack a secondary constriction ("nucleolar organizer") on one of two homologous

chromosomes in diploid cells;[7] the two comparable chromosomes of the anucleolate homozygous mutants (0-*nu*) both lack this secondary constriction. The anucleolate mutant (0-*nu*) has numerous small nucleolar "blobs" instead of typical nucleoli, and both nuclear and cytoplasmic RNA have been shown histochemically to be lower in 0-*nu* embryos after hatching than in controls (1-*nu* and 2-*nu*).[8]

Development of 0-*nu* embryos is first retarded shortly after hatching.[5, 9] The mutant embryos become microcephalic and oedematous and die as swimming tadpoles before feeding. It was apparent that magnesium-starved embryos were to some extent phenocopies of the homozygous mutants (0-*nu*) since retardation of embryogenesis and growth occurred in both groups of embryos at about the same developmental stage (Fig. 1). The above data, as well as recent studies relating nucleolar function to ribosome synthesis, suggested that the anucleolate mutant might be incapable of synthesizing ribosomes and ribosomal RNA.

MATERIAL AND METHODS

Radioactivity was introduced into developing embryos by incubation with $C^{14}O_2$ at pH 6.0.[10] The methods for measuring ribosome and DNA contents have been described previously.[1] Total RNA was isolated from frozen embryos after homogenization in 0.1 M sodium acetate pH 5.0 containing 4µg/ml polyvinyl sulfate (a ribonuclease inhibitor prepared synthetically by the method of Bernfeld *et al.*)[11] and 0.5% sodium lauryl sulfate (Mann Research Co.). The homogenate was shaken for 5–10 min at 0°C with an equal vol of phenol. Nucleic acids were precipitated

Proceedings of the National Academy of Sciences, **51**, 139–146 (1964). Reprinted with permission.
The authors are indebted to Miss Elizabeth Littna for her expert technical assistance and to Dr. Igor Dawid for his critical reading of the manuscript.

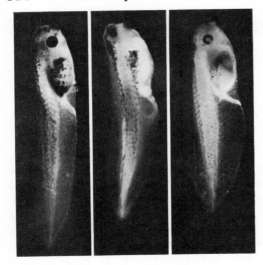

Fig. 1. Comparison of control (left), anucleolate (middle), and magnesium-deficient (right) embryos of *Xenopus laevis*. These embryos are siblings that have developed for the same length of time. Initial symptoms characterizing the anucleolate mutant and magnesium deficiency syndrome are apparent.

RESULTS AND DISCUSSION

Absence of Ribosomal RNA Synthesis in the Anucleolate Mutant

Values for the RNA and DNA contents of anucleolate and control embryos are presented in Table 1. The most pronounced difference between the anucleolate *Xenopus* (0-*nu*) and the control mixture of 1-*nu* and 2-*nu* embryos is the reduced quantity of RNA and in particular the small amount of ribosomes in the 0-*nu* mutants.

The relatively small numbers of ribosomes

TABLE 1. Comparison of RNA and DNA contents of anucleolate and control *Xenopus laevis* embryos

	μg/Embryo	
	Homozygous Mutant	Control*
DNA†	0.88	0.97
Total RNA†	5.1	11.8
RNA contents of isolated ribosomes‡	3.2	5.4

* Analyses performed on a mixture of heterozygous (1-*nu*) and wild-type (2-*nu*) embryos.
† Control and mutant sibling embryos were at stages 40–41.[3]
‡ Control and mutant sibling embryos were at stages 38–40.[3]

from the aqueous phase with 2 vol of ethanol and 0.1 vol of M sodium chloride, and the precipitate was dissolved in 0.01 M sodium acetate pH 5.0 containing 1 μg/ml polyvinyl sulfate. DNAase I (5 μg/ml) and 10^{-3} M $MgCl_2$ were added and the solutions incubated for 10 min at 20°C. The RNA was further purified by two subsequent precipitations with NaCl-ethanol and the final precipitate drained of alcohol and dissolved in 1 ml of the 0.01 M sodium acetate-polyvinyl sulfate solution. Zonal sucrose gradient centrifugation[12] was performed in the SW-25 rotor of the Spinco Model L centrifuge for 14½ hr at 24,000 rpm. The nucleic acid solutions were layered over linear gradients of sucrose which varied from 20% to 5% and which contained 10^{-4} M versene and 0.01 M sodium acetate pH 5.0. Following centrifugation, the tubes were punctured and fractions collected for optical density measurement at 260 mμ and radioactivity determinations. Nucleic acids precipitated from each fraction by adding trichloroacetic acid to a concentration of 5% were caught on Millipore filters (HA) and dried. After phosphor was added, the filters were counted in a liquid scintillation counter.

present in the 0-*nu* embryos might have been synthesized entirely during oögenesis before meiotic reduction when the growing oöcytes were heterozygous for nucleolus formation. Alternatively some ribosome synthesis might have occurred during embryogenesis. To distinguish between these possibilities, radioactive precursor was presented to the developing embryos during neurulation, when ribosomal RNA synthesis is known to have already begun in wild-type embryos;[4, 13] at this stage the 0-*nu* mutants are still developing normally and are morphologically similar to the control embryos. RNA was isolated 48 hr after termination of the radioactive incubation period so that ample time was allowed for complete utilization of the precursor and its incorporation into RNA. The density gradient centrifugation patterns of the total RNA isolated from 90 anucleolate (0-*nu*) mutants and

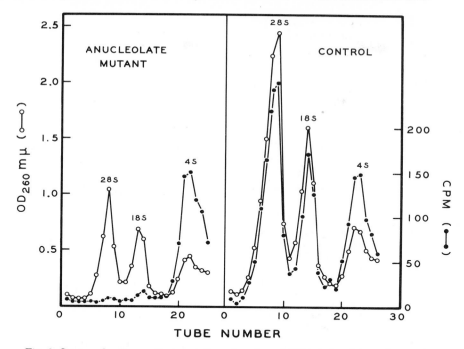

Fig. 2. Sucrose density gradient centrifugation of total RNA isolated from 0-*nu* and control embryos. Two heterozygote (1-*nu*) adults were mated and the embryos allowed to develop to neurulation (Nieuwkoop-Faber[3] stages 14–18). At this time the embryos were incubated in a closed serum bottle at pH 6.0 with about 0.2 μc $C^{14}O_2$ for 20 hr at 18°C with mild shaking. By the end of this incubation period, development had proceeded to stages 26–28 (muscular response), and the mutant embryos were still indistinguishable grossly from the control embryos. The medium was changed, and the embryos continued development in nonradioactive tap water for 48 hr at 20°C (stages 40–41). The anucleolate mutants were recognized by examination of their tail tips with a phase contrast microscope and separated from the two control genotypes (1-*nu* and 2-*nu*). Both groups were then washed with distilled water and frozen at −20°C. The frozen embryos were packed in dry ice and flown from Oxford to Baltimore for chemical analysis. The bulk of the RNA (o——o) is represented by optical density measurements at 260 mμ. The RNA synthesized between neurula and muscular response stage is represented by the radioactive measurements (•——•).

90 controls (a mixture of 1-*nu* and 2-*nu* embryos) are shown in Fig. 2. The mutants contain about one half as much total RNA as the controls. This quantity (5 μg/embryo) is about the same as that found in the unfertilized egg of *Xenopus laevis*.[4] The control *Xenopus* embryos have synthesized radioactive 28S and 18S ribosomal RNA as well as 4S RNA. However, the 0-*nu* mutants have synthesized less than 5 per cent as much radioactive ribosomal RNA but about the same amount of 4S material as the control embryos. The radioactivity in the 4S region was eluted from the Millipore filters with dilute NH_4OH, made 0.3 N with KOH and incubated overnight at

37°C. About 80% of the radioactivity in both mutant and control samples was presumably RNA since it was rendered acid-soluble by this treatment. The remaining alkali-resistant radioactivity was solubilized by hot TCA and probably was partially degraded radioactive DNA.

In these 0-*nu* mutants the ribosomal RNA made during oögenesis has persisted, and the embryos are incapable of synthesizing new ribosomal RNA. Since these embryos develop normally to early swimming stages, it can be concluded that *Xenopus* embryos do not *need* new ribosomal RNA until after this stage of development.

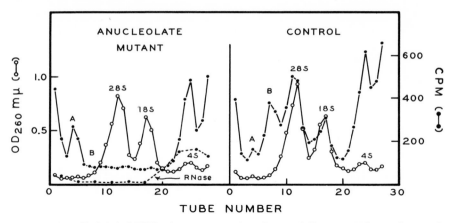

Fig. 3. Rapidly labeled RNA of mutant (*0-nu*) and control *Xenopus* embryos. Previously separated *0-nu* mutants and control (*1-nu* and *2-nu*) embryos (32 embryos each) at stage 27–28 were placed in 2 ml vial with 1 ml of preboiled Holtfreter-M++ medium[1] containing 0.3 *M* sodium phosphate pH 6. After gently blowing CO_2-free air over the medium for 5 min, the vials were sealed with rubber injection caps, and 25 *μc* of $Na_2C^{14}O^3$ dissolved in 0.01 *M* NaOH was injected into each bottle. The vials were gently shaken for 2 hr at 21°C, then cooled, and the embryos washed with cold distilled H_2O. Nonradioactive RNA (0.8 mg) isolated from *Xenopus* oöcytes was added to each group of embryos and the total RNA purified. The purified RNA was dissolved in 1.5 ml, and 1.0 ml (equivalent to RNA from 20 embryos) was centrifuged. The remaining 0.5 ml of the mutant RNA preparation was made 0.1 *M* with tris buffer pH 7.2 and incubated in a total volume of 1 ml with 20 *μg* of pancreatic RNAase for 10 min at 20°C. Values for the RNAase-treated preparation have been corrected for volume and tube number so that they are directly comparable with the untreated RNA.

Synthesis of Rapidly Labeled RNA by the Anucleolate Mutant

To define the classes of rapidly labeled RNA synthesized by the mutant, RNA was isolated immediately after a 2-hr incubation with labeled precursor (Fig. 3). Because of the small number of embryos used in this experiment, purified carrier RNA (unlabeled) was added at the beginning of the isolation procedure, so that the optical density peaks of the carrier RNA serve as reference markers for the three classes of bulk RNA, i.e., 28S, 18S, and 4S RNA.

Experiments by Scherrer *et al.*[14] and Perry[15] indicate that the 28S and 18S ribosomal RNA molecules are both derived from larger precursor molecules. Radioactive label appears first in these rapidly sedimenting precursors and only later in 28S and 18S RNA. The results plotted in Fig. 3 demonstrate that 2 hr after addition of radioactivity the control already has synthesized 28S and 18S RNA as well as at least two distinct peaks

of heavier RNA (labeled *A* and *B*). In contrast, the mutant embryos not only failed to synthesize typical 28S and 18S ribosomal RNA but also lack the heavy precursor RNA that sediments in region *B* of Fig. 3 (about 35S). Yet heavier classes of RNA (type A and even more rapidly sedimenting molecules) have been synthesized by the mutant, as well as heterogeneous RNA that sediments throughout the gradient solution. This latter observation is more evident when the sedimentation pattern of rapidly labeled mutant RNA is compared before and after ribonuclease digestion (Fig. 3).

The rapidly labeled RNA synthesized by the mutant is most probably "messenger" RNA. This conclusion is based on the fact that in the mutant all the radioactive RNA sedimenting more rapidly than 4S can be recovered associated with the purified ribosomes of the mutant. When isolated by this technique, the rapidly labeled RNA is degraded to molecules having sedimentation constants between 4 and 18S. The base com-

TABLE 2. Nucleotide composition of 28S and 18S ribosomal RNA and 4S RNA purified from *Xenopus laevis* eggs and embryos

Approximate S Value	Unfertilized Eggs			Stage 45 Embryos		
	28	18	4	28	18	4
AMP	17	22	20	18	22	21
GMP	37	31	28	37	31	31
CMP	30	29	32	28	29	30
UMP	16	18	20	17	18	18
% GC	67	60	60	65	60	61

Following density gradient centrifugation, the RNA was precipitated from the sucrose solutions with cold TCA, washed with ethanol, and hydrolyzed in NHCl at 100°C for 1 hr. Base composition was determined following chromatography in the isopropanol: HCl solvent described by Wyatt.[22]

position of this heterogeneous RNA labeled with P[32], which has been isolated in association with purified ribosomes of normal *Xenopus* embryos, is invariably DNA-like.[4]

The Nucleolus as the Site of Ribosomal RNA Synthesis

In control *Xenopus* embryos, although other classes of RNA are synthesized at earlier stages, new *ribosomal* RNA synthesis is not detectable until gastrulation,[4] the same stage that definitive nucleoli first become visible cytologically. (The many small "blobs" seen in blastula nuclei do not seem to be equivalent to "definitive" nucleoli.) Although synthesis of ribosomal RNA begins at gastrulation, the quantity of this newly synthesized RNA remains small when compared to the RNA already present in the unfertilized egg. It is only after hatching that the total RNA content of wild-type *Xenopus* embryos begins to increase significantly.[4] The absence of typical nucleoli at very early stages of development has been reported for other amphibia[16] as well as other developing organisms.[17] Furthermore, Beermann[18] has described developmental arrest in anucleolate recombinants resulting from the mating of two different species of the dipteran, *Chironomus*. The relationship between nucleolar function and ribosome synthesis has been suggested by several observations including electron microscopy,[19, 20] base composition analyses,[20] and radioautographic studies.[15] The close correlation of the time of ribosomal RNA synthesis with the appearance of definitive nucleoli in

Xenopus and particularly the simultaneous absence of both ribosomal RNA synthesis and normal nucleoli in the 0-*nu* mutant support this relationship.

Difference in Nucleotide Composition between 28S and 18S RNA

This single mutation prevents the formation of both 28S and 18S RNA molecules (Fig. 2); however, evidence has been presented suggesting that the structure of these two molecules is determined by different gene loci. Yankofsky and Spiegelman[21] have shown that 23S and 16S ribosomal RNA of bacteria hybridize independently with homologous bacterial DNA. Thus, the two molecules must have different nucleotide sequences each complementary to a distinct region of the bacterial DNA. In *Xenopus*, the 28S and 18S ribosomal RNA have different base compositions. Table 2 contains analyses for 28S, 18S, and 4S RNA's separated by density gradient centrifugation from RNA purified from ovarian eggs and embryos of *Xenopus laevis*. The 28S RNA has a significantly higher G-C content than the 18S RNA. There is also a difference in base composition between the 23S and 16S ribosomal RNAs of different bacteria[23] as well as the 28S and 18S ribosomal RNAs of chick embryos.[24]

Quantitative Regulation of Ribosomal RNA Gene Activity

The rates of ribosomal RNA synthesis in 1-*nu* and 2-*nu* embryos were compared. The results shown in Table 3 demonstrate that all three classes of RNA molecules are synthesized at comparable rates by the heterozygote and homozygous wild-type embryos. Furthermore, the synthesis of 28S and 18S RNA is coordinate since their specific activities are the same. Thus, the haploid complement of ribo-

TABLE 3. RNA synthesis by 1-*nu* and 2-*nu* *Xenopus laevis* embryos

	1-*nu*	2-*nu*
Total RNA μg/Embryo	9.1	10.8
	CPM/μg RNA	
28S	0.45	0.38
18S	0.39	0.37
4S	0.95	0.89

The same protocol that is described in the legend to Fig. 2 was followed. Thus, sibling embryos were made radioactive at the same stage and under the same conditions. The radioactive 1-*nu* and 2-*nu* embryos were separated, and the specific activity of 28S, 18S, and 4S RNA was calculated following density gradient centrifugation of the purified RNA.

somal RNA genes in the heterozygote must produce twice as much ribosomal RNA as do the same genes in the wild-type homozygote. It is of interest to note that the combined volume of the 2 nucleoli in 2-*nu* embryos is the same as that of the single nucleolus in 1-*nu* heterozygotes.[6, 25]

Genetic Basis of the Anucleolate Condition

The mutation affecting nucleolar number behaves as a single Mendelian factor and results in a cytologically visible alteration on one chromosome, i.e., in "the nucleolar organizer" region.[7] The defect when homozygous does not alter nucleic acid metabolism generally, but specifically prevents the synthesis of both molecular species of ribosomal RNA. Thus DNA (Table 1), 4S RNA (Fig. 2), and rapidly labeled high molecular weight heterogeneous RNA (Fig. 3) are all synthesized by the mutant 0-*nu* embryos. Furthermore, the relative synthesis of both 28S and 18S RNA is the same (Table 3), even at different developmental stages when ribosomal RNA is formed at widely different rates.[4]

Spiegelman[26] and Scherrer *et al.*[14] have reasoned that closely linked genes (perhaps whole operons[27]) might be transcribed as single large RNA molecules ("polycistronic" RNA[28]) which are subsequently degraded specifically to smaller and, in the case of ribosomal RNA, stable subunits. If adjacent 28S and 18S genes were transcribed together as a single molecule, such a large precursor would be expected to have a molecular weight of about $2-3 \times 10^6$ with a sedimentation constant of approximately 35S. This is about the sedimentation constant of the ribosomal RNA precursor (Region *B*, Fig. 3). This hypothesis accounts for the fact that large precursor molecules give rise to smaller ones as well as providing a molecular basis for coordinate expression of the several genes of an operon. Since the 28S and 18S ribosomal RNA molecules function together as components of a single structure, the ribosome, it is reasonable that their synthesis should be controlled together.

Two general mechanisms adequately account for the characteristics of the anucleolate mutant. The anucleolate condition might be considered as a primary defect of nucleolus formation which secondarily results in the absence of ribosomal RNA synthesis. The alternative hypothesis would have the primary defect of preventing ribosomal RNA synthesis. This latter idea suggests that the nucleolus marks the location of ribosomal RNA and ribosome synthesis in the nucleus, and the presence of the nucleolus is secondary to these synthetic processes. The comments to follow do not distinguish between these two general possibilities but serve to analyze pertinent genetic mechanisms in the light of the data presented in this report.

The consequences of the anucleolate mutation cannot be explained by the alteration of a "repressor or activator" substance[27] that might circulate in the nucleoplasm and inhibit or activate the structural genes for ribosomal RNA. If a substance exists in the nucleoplasm which regulates expression of the ribosomal RNA genes, it would be expected to act equally on *both* nucleolar organizers of a diploid cell (unless it only acts in the immediate vicinity of its own synthesis). Thus an altered repressor such as a "super-repressor"[29] would be *dominant* resulting in an *anucleolate heterozygote* since the altered repressor would inhibit expression of both nucleolar organizers in diploid cells. If, on the other hand, expression of nucleolar organizers required the constant presence of an "activator" substance of endogenous origin, the nonproduction of such a substance would have a *recessive* effect, i.e., the heterozygote embryos (1-*nu*) would contain two nucleoli in each cell just as the control embryos. *In fact, the anucleolate mutation has resulted in nonfunctional gene loci which remain nonfunctional even in the presence of their normal alleles.*

It is highly probable that many genes are involved in the synthesis of ribosomal RNA. Both in bacteria[21] and in mice[30] the ribosomal RNA is complementary to 0.3% of the DNA (0.6% of the nucleotide pairs). It seems likely that a similar proportion will be present in the *Xenopus laevis* genome since ribosomal RNA can constitute such a large fraction of the gene product. If so, there must be thousands of separate gene loci for each class of ribosomal RNA.

If the DNA for ribosomal RNA is distributed among many chromosomes, it is difficult to imagine how its products can be concentrated into one nucleolus, while still accounting for the biochemical and cytological properties of the 0-*nu* and 1-*nu* embryos. On the other hand, the entire complement of DNA for ribosomal RNA may be adjacent on a single chromosome. Since there are 18 haploid chromosomes in *Xenopus* the ribosomal region would occupy roughly 10% of one of them, presumably the one containing the nucleolar organizer.

A single deletion would account for the results but would require the loss of an extremely large piece of DNA. Alternatively, an operator mutation[27] would account for the features of the anucleolate mutation. However, this would imply that a single operator locus could control the expression of thousands of genes.

Any mechanism invoked to explain ribosomal RNA synthesis must account for the fact that the activity of the entire complement of genes determining ribosomal RNA structure can be restricted by a single mutation.

SUMMARY

A mutation in *Xenopus laevis* that prevents the formation of a normal nucleolus at the same time prevents the synthesis of 28S and 18S ribosomal RNA as well as high molecular weight ribosomal RNA precursor molecules. DNA, 4S RNA, and rapidly labeled heterogeneous RNA are synthesized by the anucleolate mutant. Anucleolate mutants survive until the swimming tadpole stage and show normal differentiation of all the main cell types despite their inability to synthesize new ribosomal RNA. Homozygous mutants (0-*nu*) and control embryos conserve the ribosomes made during oögenesis and associate rapidly synthesized RNA with these old ribosomes.

The 28S and 18S ribosomal RNAs differ in base composition and are probably products of different genes; yet their synthesis is coordinate. In the heterozygous (1-*nu*) embryos, the wild-type genes regulate to produce twice as much 28S and 18S ribosomal RNA as do the same genes when present in homozygous wild-type individuals. Since the activity of the entire complement of genes determining ribosomal RNA structure can be curtailed by a single mutation, it is suggested that these genes are under common control and located at the "nucleolar organizer" site of a single chromosome.

[1] Brown, D. D., and J. D. Caston, *Develop. Biol.* **5**, 412 (1962).

[2] Shumway, W., *Anat. Record*, **78**, 139 (1940).

[3] Nieuwkoop, P. D., and J. Faber, *Normal Table of Xenopus laevis (Daudin)* (Amsterdam: North-Holland Publishing Company, 1956).

[4] Brown, D. D., manuscript in preparation.

[5] Elsdale, T. R., M. Fischberg, and S. Smith, *Exptl. Cell Res.* **14**, 642 (1958).

[6] Fischberg, M., and H. Wallace, in *The Cell Nucleus* (London: Butterworth, 1960), p. 30.

[7] Kahn, J., *Quart. J. Microscop. Sci.*, **103**, 407 (1962).

[8] Wallace, H., *Quart. J. Microscop. Sci.*, **103**, 25 (1962).

[9] Wallace, H., *J. Embryol. Exptl. Morphol.*, **8**, 405 (1960).

[10] Cohen, S., *J. Biol. Chem.*, **211**, 337 (1954).

[11] Bernfeld, P., J. Nisselbaum, B. Berkeley, and R. Hanson, *J. Biol. Chem.*, **235**, 2852 (1960).

[12] Britten, R. J., and R. B. Roberts, *Science*, **131**, 32 (1960).

[13] Brown, D. D., and J. D. Caston, *Develop. Biol.*, **5**, 435 (1962).

[14] Scherrer, K., H. Latham, and J. E. Darnell, *Proc. N.A.S.* **49**, 240 (1963).

[15] Perry, R. P., *Proc. N.A.S.* **48**, 2179 (1962).

[16] Karasaki, S., *Embryologia*, **4**, 273 (1959).

[17] Cowden, R. R., and C. L. Markert, *Acta Embryol. Morphol. Exptl.*, **4**, 142 (1961).

[18] Beermann, W., *Chromosoma*, **11**, 263 (1960).

[19] Birnstiel, M. L., and B. B. Hyde, *J. Cell Biol.*, **18**, 41 (1963). Dr. Elizabeth Hay has found the same particulate structure resembling ribosomes in nucleoli of *Xenopus laevis* embryos (personal communication).

[20] Gall, J. G., in *Cytodifferentiation and Macromolecular Synthesis* (New York: Academic Press, 1963), p. 119.

[21] Yankofsky, S. A., and S. Spiegelman, *Proc. N.A.S.* **49**, 538 (1963).

[22] Wyatt, G. R., *Biochem. J.*, **48**, 584 (1951).

[23] Midgley, J. E. M., *Biochim. Biophys. Acta*, **61**, 513 (1962).

[24] Lerner, A. M., E. Bell, and J. E. Darnell, Jr., *Science*, **141**, 1187 (1963).

[25] Barr, H. J., and H. Esper, *Exptl. Cell Res.*, **31**, 211 (1963).

[26] Spiegelman, S., in *Informational Macromolecules* (New York: Academic Press, 1963), p. 27.

[27] Jacob, F., and J. Monod, in *Cellular Regulatory Mechanisms*, Cold Spring Harbor Symposia in Quantitative Biology, vol. 26 (1961), p. 193.

[28] Ohtaka, Y., and S. Spiegelman, *Science*, **142**, 493 (1963).

[29] Willson, C., D. Perrin, F. Jacob, and J. Monod, unpublished observations cited in ref. 27.

[30] Hoyer, B. H., personal communication.

Ribosomal RNA in the Developing Chick Embryo

A. MARTIN LERNER
EUGENE BELL
JAMES E. DARNELL, JR.

Abstract. *Developing chick embryos from the stage of primitive-streak formation make ribosomal (28S and 16S) RNA. The size and composition of the RNA appears to be constant throughout the first 7 days of development.*

Recent advances in molecular genetics and biochemistry have outlined the major steps in the transcription of genetic information into specific protein molecules (*1*). The active unit of protein synthesis in many different types of cells is the ribonucleoprotein particle, the ribosome, or as has recently been described, groups of ribosomes called polyribosomes (*2*). The RNA molecule (messenger RNA) which serves the function of information transport is attached to the ribosomes, but is distinguishable from ribosomal RNA on the basis of size and base composition (*1, 3*).

It can be anticipated that these new ideas and techniques dealing with the control of protein synthesis will be useful to the embryologist, since differentiation is accompanied by changing patterns of protein synthesis in cells all of which presumably contain the same genetic potential.

As a preliminary to the study of messenger RNA in the developing chick embryo, an examination of ribosomal RNA from embryos of different ages was carried out. The size and overall composition of ribosomal RNA is constant during embryogenesis and ribosomal RNA is synthesized from the earliest embryonic stages.

Newly synthesized RNA of embryonic cells was labeled with radioisotope by two different procedures. (i) The embryo was removed

Reprinted from *Science*, **141**, No. 3586, 1187–1188 (September 20, 1963.) Copyright © 1963 by the American Association for the Advancement of Science.

from the egg and pressed through a wire screen (80 mesh). The resulting single cells and cell aggregates were collected in warmed (37°C) Eagle's medium (4) containing 5 percent calf serum (5 ml/embryo), and were kept in suspension by a rotating magnetic stirring bar. Radioisotope (P^{32} carrier-free orthophosphate or uridine-2-C^{14}) was either in the medium at the time of disaggregation of the embryo, or was added shortly afterward. In experiments with P^{32}, Eagle's medium containing dialyzed serum was used, and the radioactive phosphate was substituted for the usual phosphate. At the conclusion of the labeling period, the cells were centrifuged (5 min at 600g), and washed twice in Earle's saline solution. (ii) Radioisotope was placed directly in the upper portion of the yolk sac. The embryo was subsequently removed from the egg and disaggregated and the cells were washed as described above.

The RNA was extracted either immediately after labeling or after storage of the cells at −70°C (5). The base ratios of RNA represent distribution of P^{32}-labeled nucleotide in alkaline hydrolysates (5). The DNA was isolated as described by Marmur (6), and base ratios were determined after acid hydrolysis (7).

Sucrose-gradient analysis (8) of the RNA from the chick embryo revealed two larger components (28S and 16S), and a smaller (4S) component (see OD$_{260}$ in Fig. 1). This size distribution of RNA has been observed in many different kinds of cells, and the larger components have been shown to be derived from ribosomes. These will, therefore, be referred to as ribosomal RNA. The apparent large amount of 4S RNA in Fig. 1 was not always observed, and the ratio of optical densities at 260 to 280 mμ indicated contamination with non-nucleic acid material in this region of the gradient.

Figure 1 shows that relatively long periods of exposure to isotope (P^{32} for 4 to 18 hours) result in incorporation of radioactivity into ribosomal RNA of similar size in embryos of from 4 hours to 7 days of age. This represents a striking difference in embryogenesis between the chick embryo and the frog em-

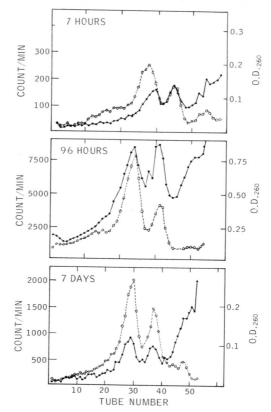

Fig. 1. Formation of ribosomal RNA during embryogenesis of the chick embryo. 200 μc P^{32} were placed into the yolk sac and RNA was extracted (4) from several embryos at each age along with extract from two 7-day chick embryos which served as the reference for the OD measurements. The 7-hour sample was derived from about ten embryos, 3-hours old labeled for 4 hours; the other samples were labeled for the 16 hours concluding at 96 hours and 7 days.

bryo. Brown and Caston (9) have recently shown that only one type of ribosomal RNA is formed during the first 96 hours of development in the frog egg. Presumably one of the factors underlying this difference is that during early differentiation in the chick embryo the cell mass is increasing, while in the frog egg, individual cells are being formed within an already existing mass.

In addition to similarity in size from day 1 to 7, ribosomal RNA was similar in composition when 3- and 7-day chick material was studied (Table 1). The 28S RNA from material obtained at both 3 and 7 days had identical base ratios, as did also the 16S RNA.

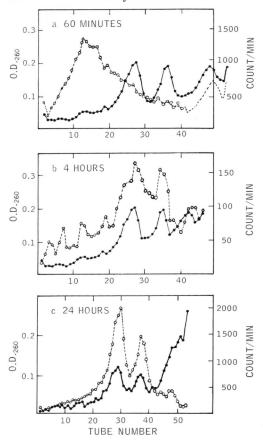

Fig. 2. Sedimentation analysis of labeled RNA from a suspension of 7-day chick-embryo cells. A suspension of cells from three 7-day embryos prepared as described were incubated with 6 μc C14-uridine (33 μc/μmole) in 30 ml Eagle's medium in (*a*) 1 hour, (*b*) 4 hours, and (*c*) 24 hours. RNA was then extracted and analyzed on sucrose gradients (*5*). Solid lines •——•, optical density; broken lines o——o, count/min.

TABLE 1. Base composition of chick embryo RNA and DNA. C, cytosine; A, adenine; G, guanine; U, uracil; and T, thymine

Mol. Size (S)	Age of Embryo (Days)	Base				
		C	A	G	U(T)	G+C
		(% of Total Base)				
		RNA				
28	7	28	19	34	18	62
	3	24	18	36	22	60
16	7	25	24	29	22	54
	3	25	24	30	21	55
40	7	25	23	28	25	53
		DNA				
	7	22	28	22	28	44

There was a distinct difference, however, between the base composition of 28S and 16S molecules at both times. This agrees with the recent finding (*10*) that the two ribosomal RNA molecules in *Escherichia coli* are derived from separate loci on the DNA template.

When animal cells in culture are exposed to P^{32} orthophosphate or uridine-2-C^{14}, radioactivity accumulates in a precursor of high molecular weight (35S and 45S) before it appears in ribosomal RNA. Actinomycin D, which stops further RNA synthesis (*11*), has been used to follow the change of precursors from 45S and 35S to 28S and 16S RNA in the absence of further RNA synthesis (*5*).

With labeling periods of 30 to 60 minutes, material of large molecular weight (40S) is preferentially labeled also in the chick embryo (Fig. 2). The guanine-cytosine (G-C) content of the 40S material (Table 1) was similar to that of 16S ribosomal RNA and intermediate between that of 28S ribosomal RNA and DNA. Attempts to use actinomycin D to follow the fate of the 40S RNA in chick-embryo cells in suspension, as was done with HeLa cells, have been unsuccessful owing to the disintegration of the cells within 4 hours in medium containing actinomycin. Thus, although it is quite likely that some of the 40S material is ribosomal precursor RNA, the fraction remains uncertain.

The results of these experiments indicate a similarity of ribosomal RNA throughout embryogenesis. Although subtle changes in ribosomes during development could not be detected by our techniques, it seems reasonable to search for different messenger RNA molecules as the basis for the formation of different proteins which appear as development proceeds (*12*).

REFERENCES AND NOTES

1. *Cold Spring Harbor Symp. Quant. Biol.* 26 (1961).
2. J. R. Warner, P. Knopf, A. Rich, *Proc. Natl. Acad. Sci. U.S.* 49, 122 (1963).
3. S. Penman, K. Scherrer, Y. Becker, J. E. Darnell, *ibid.* 49, 654 (1963).
4. H. Eagle, *Science* 130, 432 (1959).
5. K. Scherrer and J. E. Darnell, *Biochem. Biophys. Research Commun.* 7, 486 (1962).

K. Scherrer, H. Latham, J. E. Darnell, *Proc. Natl. Acad. Sci. U.S.* 49, 240 (1963).
6. J. Marmur, *J. Mol. Biol.* 3, 208 (1961).
7. A. Marshak and H. J. Vogel, *J. Biol. Chem.* 189, 597 (1951).
8. R. J. Britten and R. B. Roberts, *Science* 131, 32 (1960).
9. D. D. Brown and J. D. Caston, *Develop. Biol.* 5, 412 (1962).

10. S. A. Yankofsky and S. Spiegelman, *Proc. Natl. Acad. Sci. U.S.* 49, 538 (1963).
11. E. Reich, R. M. Franklin, A. J. Shatkin, E. F. Tatum, *ibid.* 48, 1238 (1962).
12. Supported by the U.S. Public Health Service and the National Science Foundation. We thank Mrs. M. Heeter and Mrs. P. Goodwin for technical assistance.

Protein Synthesis during Development: Control through Messenger RNA*

ROBERT B. SCOTT

EUGENE BELL

Abstract. *Utilization of long-lived messenger RNA appears to be the exception rather than the rule in cells which are differentiating and synthesizing large amounts of specialized product at the same time. The fact that polyribosomes synthesize protein after RNA synthesis is turned off by actinomycin D is used to demonstrate messenger RNA of long half-life. The data suggest that most tissues examined have short-lived messenger RNAs, but the ocular lens can synthesize protein after an incubation of 24 hours in 40 μg of actinomycin D per milliliter. A common basis for the presence of long-lived messenger RNA in the cells of the lens, the feather, and in reticulocytes is discussed.*

A mark of the differentiated cell is its capacity to synthesize structural or enzymatic cell specific proteins. Some cells, such as skin, liver, muscle, connective tissue, reticulocyte, pancreas and thyroid, produce large amounts of one or a few kinds of protein. We have asked whether all or only some differentiating cells synthesize their specialized product on messenger RNA which has a long half-life.

Science, 145, 711–713, August 14, 1964. Copyright © 1964 by the American Association for the Advancement of Science.

* This work was supported by a grant from the National Science Foundation, No. GB-614. Robert B. Scott was aided by a postdoctoral research scholarship of the American Cancer Society.

It has already been shown that hemoglobin (1) and feather proteins (2, 3) are synthesized on messenger RNA which has a long life span. In bacteria the half-life of messenger RNA is about 2 minutes (4), while in HeLa cells the half-life of messenger RNA is about 3 hours (5). In some if not all cells of the down feather some messenger RNAs have a half-life which is longer than 24 hours (3).

Polyribosomal protein synthesis can be demonstrated as early as the first day of incubation (6) in the chick embryo, although apart from blood cells the earliest actual demonstration of messenger RNA of long half-life has been in the 9-day skin. The earliest chick blood cells in which hemoglobin can be detected have been shown to contain messenger RNA of long half-life (7). In sea urchin embryos it has been shown that immediately after fertilization proteins can be synthesized without production of new RNA (8). This condition appears to persist throughout cleavage and implies that stable messenger is present in the ovum and is put to use for a limited time after fertilization. Similar data on chick embryos of comparable age are not available.

There are at least two ways by which differentiating cells can make large amounts of one or a few characteristic proteins. The first

14 DAYS LENS

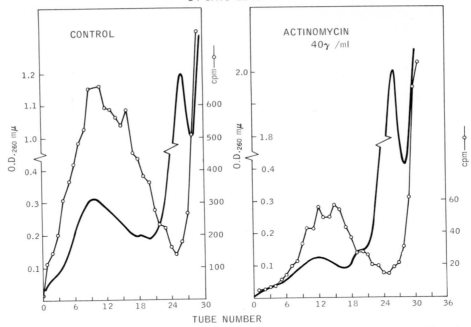

Fig. 1. Fourteen-day embryonic lenses. Two groups of lenses (approximately 12 dozen) were removed aseptically, cut and incubated 23 hours with agitation at 37°C in 25 ml Charity Waymouth medium (15) with 4 mg penicillin, 2.5 mg streptomycin, and phenol red indicator. The experimental flask also contained 40 μg of actinomycin D per milliliter (16). The medium was then removed and tissues were labeled for 3 minutes at 37°C in buffered saline with 20 μc of C14-labeled algal hydrolysate per milliliter but no actinomycin. The reaction was stopped with ice cold saline and the tissues were washed three times before suspending in four volumes of cold hypotonic buffer (0.01M tris, pH 7.4; 0.0015M Mg++; 0.01M KCL) for 30 minutes. Samples were homogenized gently with three to six strokes of a tightly fitting Dounce homogenizer. Nuclei were sedimented at 600 g for 10 minutes and sodium deoxycholate was added to the supernatant to give a concentration of 0.5 percent prior to layering on a linear 25 ml sucrose gradient (15 to 30 percent W/W) in the same buffer. Gradients were centrifuged at 24,000 rev/min in an SW-25 rotor of a Spinco Model L centrifuge for 2 hours at the 15°F setting. Twenty (drop) fractions were collected and the optical density at 260 mμ was recorded continuously on a Gilford spectrophotometer. To each fraction 0.5 ml of 2N NaOH was added. Protein was precipitated with trichloracetic acid at a final concentration of 5 percent and collected on Millipore filters. The radioactivity was counted on aluminum planchets in a low background gas flow counter.

is through the repeated use of limited amounts of long-lived specific messenger RNAs. The second is to make the specific protein through the continued synthesis of short-lived messenger RNAs. To determine which of these alternatives can best describe the use of messenger RNA in different cell types, a variety of embryonic and adult chicken tissues have been examined for long-lived polyribosomes. Long-lived polyribosomes are defined as those which will function to produce new protein for long periods after RNA synthesis has been reduced to less than 2 percent of controls by treating tissues (*in vitro*) with

actinomycin D for varying periods. It is assumed that polyribosomes which function under the foregoing conditions provide a measure of the stability of messenger RNA.

Protein synthesis on polyribosomes in ocular lenses from embryos 13, 14, 15, or 20 days old was not abolished after tissues were incubated for 21 to 24 hours in 40 μg of actinomycin D per milliliter (Fig. 1). Treatment of the labeled homogenate with ribonuclease at 4°C for 10 minutes moves all of the counts in the polysome region to the 74S peak. The incorporation of uridine-2-C14 into 14-day lenses during a 2-hour period of labeling was

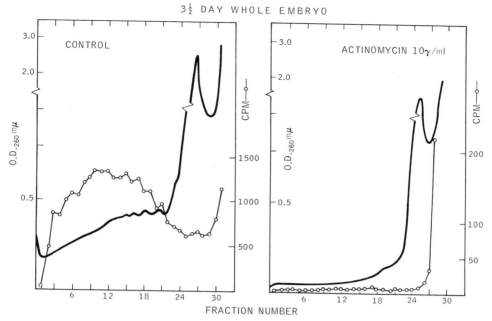

Fig. 2. Optical density profile of polyribosomes of whole 3½-day chick embryo showing radioactivity of nascent protein in the control and the effect of actinomycin D. The peak at fraction 25 represents single ribosomes.

1.5 percent of controls after 22 hours in 40 μg of actinomycin D per milliliter as judged by radioactivity of RNA extracted by a hot-phenol procedure (Table 1). Incorporation of amino acid into protein on polyribosomes in lenses treated with actinomycin D ranged from 4 percent to 16 percent of controls. It is clear from these data that there are some

messenger RNAs in the ocular lens which have a life span comparable to the long lived messenger RNA in feather cells (2, 3).

In contrast to the foregoing results, in studying the sedimentation in a sucrose density gradient of the polyribosomes from 3½-day old chick embryos it is seen that no labeled amino acids were incorporated into

TABLE 1. Results of 2-hour labeling period with uridine-2-C14 after 23 hours incubation of 14-day-old embryonic lenses (72 lenses in each sample) in 25 ml of Charity Waymouth medium

Treatment	RNA OD 260 mu Units	Counts/Min.	Counts/Min./OD
Control 1 (nutrient media only)	0.395	548	1387
Control 2 (nutrient media only)	0.598	809	1352
Experimental 1 (media plus actinomycin)	0.627	8.6	13.7
Experimental 2 (media plus actinomycin)	0.560	15.8	28.2

$$\frac{\text{Experimental average cpm/OD}}{\text{Control average cpm/OD}} \times 100 = 1.55\%$$

Experimentals contained 40 μg of actinomycin D per milliliter and each contained penicillin and streptomycin. After dividing each group into two parts, RNA was extracted according to the method of Scherrer and Darnell (14).

proteins on polyribosomes after tissues were incubated for 21 hours with actinomycin D (10 μg per milliliter). In fact by 6 hours in 6-day-old whole embryos treated with actinomycin D, protein synthesis on polyribosomes is already less than 10 percent of that on polyribosomes of untreated controls. Examination of 3-, 4-, 5-, or 6-day-old embryos shows the same absence of long-lived messenger RNA after actinomycin treatment.

After 5 days of incubation many organs of the embryo are morphologically well differentiated; these include liver, brain, skeletal, and smooth muscle. However, the skin is poorly developed and feather primordia have not yet appeared. It should be pointed out that there is essentially no contribution to the polyribosome profile from circulating blood cells, because the tissues are washed free of blood during preparation.

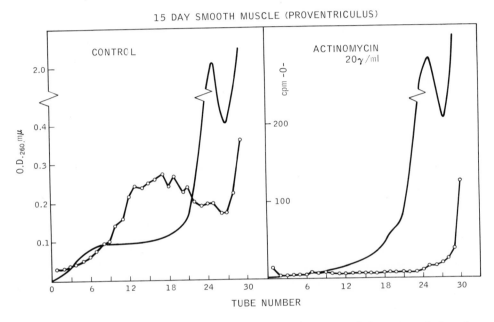

Fig. 3. Polyribosomal protein synthesis in the smooth muscle of the proventriculus of 15-day chick embryos and the effect of actinomycin.

Some older embryonic tissues were similarly treated with actinomycin and homogenates were studied for persistence of polyribosomes (Figs. 3 and 4). Protein synthesis on polyribosomes in 15-day liver and smooth muscle (proventriculus), 14- and 16-day skeletal muscle, and 9-day brain was completely inhibited by treatment with 20 μg of actinomycin per milliliter.

In order to obtain adequate samples of adrenal, pancreas, and spleen, pullet tissues were used, and the ovary was studied in adult hens. Only that portion of the ovary containing the relatively immature ova was selected for incubation. Satisfactory polysome profiles were difficult to obtain in some of these older

tissues, but in homogenates not treated with deoxycholate, radioactivity incorporated into the membrane-bound ribosomes (9) could be compared with and without actinomycin treatment. Long-lived messenger was found in none of these tissues. It is possible that some tissues are more adversely affected by actinomycin D than others, and that our failure to demonstrate long-lived messenger RNAs in some reflects this. However, in tissues such as the pancreas or adrenal, protein synthesis (greater than 10 percent of control levels) can still be measured after incubation of 17 or 15 hours respectively in actinomycin D. By 24 hours protein synthesis in both is brought to a halt.

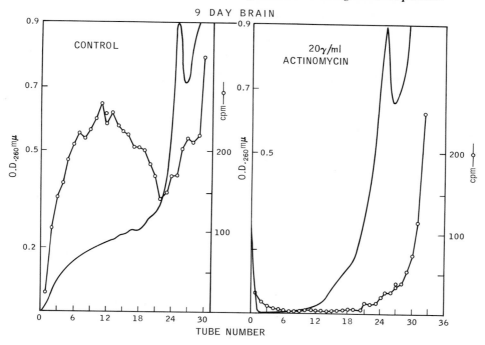

Fig. 4. Polyribosomal protein synthesis in the brain of 9-day chick embryos showing inhibition by actinomycin.

From our data and previous data it is now evident that large fractions of relatively stabilized protein-forming complexes (messenger RNA and ribosomes) can be demonstrated in some but not all highly specialized cells which produce large amounts of a limited variety of specific protein. It has been reported that lamb thyroid (10) and adult rat liver (11, 12) continue to synthesize protein after treatment with actinomycin D. Cells which clearly have long-lived messenger RNA, namely lens, down feather, and reticulocyte, share a number of features. Each type makes large quantities of a limited number of proteins (crystallins, keratins, and hemoglobin, respectively), and in each case long-lived messenger RNA is found during periods of intense protein synthesis and cell differentiation. Also common to these cell types, which convert virtually their entire substance into a single product, is early cell death or loss of the nucleus shortly after a spurt of intense protein synthesis which occurs at least in part through the repeated use of long-lived messenger molecules. In the differentiation of mammalian erythrocytes, the nucleus is lost and the cytoplasm then functions independently for a limited period. The fate of nuclei in the feather cells and in cells of the lens is not clear, although it has been shown that in the central, more differentiated, portions of the lens no DNA can be detected (13). In feather cells, however, the nucleus along with the cytoplasm seems to "keratinize." We have no information on the fate of the DNA. In all three cell types the nucleus is effectively "turned off" as differentiation of the cell progresses towards its terminal state. By the time this occurs differentiation of these cell types is a one way street paved with messenger RNA molecules which have a long half-life.

REFERENCES AND NOTES

1. E. Reich, R. M. Franklin, A. J. Shatkin and E. L. Tatum, *Proc. Natl. Acad. Sci. U.S.* 48, 1238 (1962).
2. E. Bell, in *Symposium on Metabolic Control Mechanisms in Animal Cells*, W. Rudder, Ed., National Cancer Institute Monograph No. 13. (U.S. Government Printing Office, Washington, 1964), p. 1.

3. T. Humphreys, S. Penman and E. Bell, *Biochem. Biophys. Res. Comm.* **17**, 618 (1964).

4. C. Levinthal, A. Keynan and A. Higa, *Proc. Natl. Acad. Sci. U.S.* **48**, 1631 (1962).

5. S. Penman, K. Scherrer, Y. Becker and J. E. Darnell, *Proc. Natl. Acad. Sci. U.S.* **49**, 654 (1963).

6. R. B. Scott and E. Bell, unpublished observations.

7. F. Wilt, personal communication.

8. P. R. Gross, L. A. Malkin and W. A. Moyer, *Proc. Natl. Acad. Sci. U.S.* **51**, 407 (1964).

9. E. C. Henshaw and H. H. Hiatt, *J. Mol. Biol.* **7**, 122 (1963).

10. R. W. Seed and I. Goldberg, *Proc. Natl. Acad. Sci. U.S.* **50**, 275 (1963).

11. G. Giudice and G. D. Novelli, *Biochem. Biophys. Res. Commun.* **12**, 383 (1963).

12. M. Revel and H. H. Hiatt, *Proc. Natl. Acad. Sci. U.S.* **51**, 810 (1964).

13. P. Mandel and M. L. Schmitt, *Compt. Rend. Soc. Biol. Paris* **151**, 368 (1957).

14. K. Scherrer and J. E. Darnell, *Biochem. Biophys. Res. Commun.* **7**, 486 (1962).

15. J. Paul, *Cell and Tissue Culture* (E. and S. Livingstone Ltd., Edinburgh, 1959), pp. 78–79.

16. Actinomycin D was a gift from Merck, Sharpe, and Dohme, Inc., Rahway, N.J.

☼ 10 ☼

Synthesis of Cell Specific Products

ONE MARK of the differentiated cell is its principle product, be it antibody, growth factor, enzyme, characteristic structural or functional protein, mucopolysaccharide, secretion product, or chloroplast. Whatever the product, the cell can be characterized by it.

How genes for the product are activated is a mystery. For example, what change antigens bring about in antibody-producing cells to program the sequential synthesis of two proteins, 19s and 7s antibodies (*Nossal Szenberg, Ada, and Austin 1963*),* is still unknown. It is clear, however, that both antibodies can be made by the same cell. Related is the observation of Attardi, Cohn, Horibata, and Lennox (1964) who show that the same cell is capable of producing antibody to more than one antigen.

That tissue interactions, hormones, or growth substances may result in gene activation is discussed in other chapters. The dramatic events of development such as cleavage, gastrulation, neurulation, and cell migration changing as they do the relation of cells to their immediate environments may bring about changes of gene expression. It is probable also that many still unidentified less spectacular events activate genes which function during differentiation and in the specialized cell.

When do genes for a specialized product begin to function? The answer may require that a distinction be made among very low or barely perceptible levels of gene activity, high levels of gene function and complete repression. It is possible to detect certain proteins, for which there are good assays, very early in development. Among these are xanthine uricase, pancreatic amylase, the sulfating enzymes for chondrogenesis, and hemoglobin. High concentrations of these proteins are associated with later stages of development. For example, before induction of the epithelial rudiment of the pancrease (*Rutter, Wessells, and Grobstein 1964*), pancreatic amylase is present in the embryo at the level of about 5 molecules per cell. After induction it increases to from 10^5 to 10^6 molecules per cell. Are there then two kinds of repressors? One which shuts off m-RNA synthesis completely, and one which does so almost completely? Perhaps during early development genes are never completely repressed but, because of our inadequate methods of detection, their products go unnoticed. The "debut" of a protein may mean only an enhanced rate of m-RNA production and not necessarily *de novo* synthesis.

Whether development generally proceeds by a sequence of gene repressions or gene activations or both is still an open question. Do more cistrons function in cells of a blastula than in cells of a somite? It is conceivable that during early dif-

* Italicized references indicate articles which appear in this book.

ferentiation most genes are active but at low levels and that synthesis of specialized products results from *complete* repression of a large number of irrelevant genes as well as accelerated transcription of relevant ones. The following observations suggest that DNA transcription may be less restricted in younger than in older embryonic cells. In the maturing amphibian oocyte from 10,000 to 20,000 loops of the lampbrush chromosome are making RNA, at least an RNA precursor is incorporated into them (Gall and Callan 1962). This can be contrasted with the 277 bands which have been shown to be active in adult salivary gland chromosomes of Chironomus. During development of the chick, synthesis of cardiac myosin is at first widespread and then gradually restricted to heart-forming cells (*Ebert 1953*). Globin-like components of hemoglobin can be detected very early, in fact in the unincubated blastoderm (*Wilt 1962*). It will be of interest to determine whether they occur in all cells or in presumptive blood cells only. The thesis that cells which eventually specialize might make a large variety of specific products in small amounts early in development will require careful scrutiny.

Not all products of specialized cells are made within the cell. A recent illustration of this is provided by *Roth and Porter (1964)* who show that yolk protein is transported from an extraovarian source to the developing oocytes. Their evidence is morphological but the transfer of yolk protein to the egg has been shown immunochemically by Telfer (1954, 1961) in other insects. *Roth and Porter (1964)* reject the oocyte nurse cells and follicular epithelium as sources of yolk protein on the grounds that none at the right time have the organelles usually associated with synthesis of protein for secretion or storage (Palade and Siekevitz, 1956).

Herrmann (1963) has shown that the protein-forming machinery of cells undergoes change during development. In studies on developing chick muscle, he found evidence for enlargement of the endoplasmic reticulum at a time when synthesis of actomyosin begins to exceed the synthesis of other proteins.

It seems probable that specialized control mechanisms and structural modifications are employed by cells which synthesize specific products. These would be dictated by the ultimate function which the cell or tissue performs. Cells of the skin, lens, and blood which are destined for early death have unique problems; they all synthesize large amounts of protein and do so while "dying." These cells most likely have devices for controlling protein synthesis at the level of m-RNA (translation) as well as at the level of DNA (transcription) (*Scott and Bell, 1964*, Chapter 10; Scott and Bell 1965; *Humphreys, Penman, and Bell, 1964*). The use of long-lived m-RNA by cells engaged in specialized synthesis is not universal in the embryo, but seems more widespread in the adult (Henshaw and Hiatt 1963).

The routes from the undifferentiated state to the specialized cell may be many and may involve a variety of molecular controls, each set tailored to the needs of the final outcome: the differentiated cell.

REFERENCES

1. Attardi, G., M. Cohn, K. Horibata, and E. Lennox (1964). Antibody formation by rabbit lymph node cells. I. single cell responses to several antigens. *J. Immun.* **92**:335–345.

2. Gall, J. G., and H. G. Callan (1962). H³-uridine incorporation in lampbrush chromosomes. *Proc. Natl. Acad. Sci.* **48**:562–570.

3. Henshaw, E. C., T. B. Bojarski, and H. H. Hiatt (1963). Protein synthesis by free bound rat liver ribosomes *in vivo* and *in vitro*. *J. Mol. Biol.* **7**:122–129.

4. Herrmann, H. (1963). Quantitative studies of protein synthesis in some embryonic tissues. In M. Locke (ed.), *Cytodifferentiation and Macromolecular Synthesis*, Academic Press, New York, pp. 85–118.

5. Palade, G. E., and P. Siekevitz (1956). Liver microsomes. An integrated morphological and biochemical study. *J. Biophys. Biochem. Cytology* **2**:171–200.

6. Scott, R. B., and E. Bell (1965). Messenger RNA utilization during chick lens development. *Science* **147**:405–407.

7. Telfer, W. H. (1954). Immunological studies

of insect metamorphosis. II. The role of a sex-limited blood protein in egg formation by the Cecropia silkworm. *J. Gen. Physiol.* **37**:539–558.

8. Telfer, W. H. (1961). The route of entry and localization of blood proteins in the oocytes of saturniid moths. *J. Biophys. Biochem. Cytology* **9**:747–759.

An Analysis of the Synthesis and Distribution of the Contractile Protein, Myosin, in the Development of the Heart

J A M E S D . E B E R T

The development of the heart presents a series of problems in morphogenesis and differentiation which afford an unexcelled opportunity for the analysis of the interrelationships of specific structural and functional properties during ontogeny. As the heart is formed, so it begins to beat. In the chick embryo of 7 somites the paired primordia of the heart have already begun to fuse; local contractions have been recorded in the heart of the 9-somite embryo.[1,2] The onset of contractility has been correlated with the time at which significant histogenic changes have been recorded, e.g., the first appearance of cross-striations at the 10-somite stage[3] and the first detectable glycogen in the embryo of "about 28 hours."[4] The early contractions have been described as of a fundamental myogenic nature since they occur well in advance of the time at which the first nerve fibers approach the heart.

The early morphogenesis and onset of contractility of the heart are foreshadowed by a precocious restriction of the heart-forming cells to relatively well-defined areas of the blastoderm. Willier and Rawles[5] and Rawles[6] have described two large bilaterally situated areas of the head-process blastoderm endowed with heart-forming potency. No critical information has been presented concerning the location of the heart-forming areas earlier

Proceedings of the National Academy of Sciences, **39**, 333–344 (1953). Reprinted with permission.

than the head-fold stage. Rudnick[7] has concluded from a review of the pertinent data that the heart mesoderm must be very early in a highly organized state, and is early invaginated to migrate laterally to its definitive position. A similar conclusion was reached by Bacon[8] in his analysis of the development of the heart in *Amblystoma*.

In contrast to the fund of information from the field of experimental morphogenesis, information concerning the chemistry and cellular physiology of the development of the heart is almost completely lacking. The void may be due, at least in part, to the difficulties encountered in studying the contractile proteins in minute quantities, as illustrated by the experiences of Herrmann and his coworkers,[9, 10] who have not been able to make determinations of actomyosin in skeletal muscle of the chick embryo prior to the ninth day of incubation, although fibrillations and cross-striations have been observed in the 7-day embryo, a time at which muscular response to mechanical stimulation and histological differentiation of motor centers in the central nervous system also have been described. In the present investigation the difficulty in detecting minute quantities of cardiac contractile proteins is largely overcome through the application of the precise techniques of immunochemistry.

In earlier reports[11, 12] it was shown, by absorption and precipitin tests, that antisera produced in rabbits against extracts of adult chicken heart will react with extracts of the early chick embryo prior to the morphogenesis of the heart. The early blastoderm must therefore contain antigens identical, or closely related, to those of adult heart. This conclusion is supported by the finding that when early blastoderms are cultured in media containing antiheart sera, the development of the heart is differentially suppressed.

It becomes of interest to determine next the relationship of the specific antigenic components of cardiac muscle present in the early blastoderm to the contractile proteins, actin and myosin. We ask the following questions:

(1) Do actin and myosin develop simultaneously? Is the development of each protein an independent event or does the development of one precede that of the second and have a causal role in its synthesis?

(2) Are there differences in the contractile proteins of cardiac and skeletal muscle which play a significant role in the precocious restriction of cardiac contractile proteins to the heart-forming areas of the blastoderm, and in the early onset of contractility? Only after the facts relative to the time of synthesis and distribution of the cardiac contractile proteins are available will it be possible to attack the basic problem of the factors controlling their synthesis. The specific objective of this report is to present findings relative to the time of synthesis and progressive localization of cardiac myosin in the early chick embryo.

Methods and Results

1. Preparation of Myosin. Cardiac and skeletal myosins were extracted from heart and hind limb muscle, respectively, of adult New Hampshire Red chickens of both sexes, following the method described by Mommaerts and Parrish,[13] in which myosin and actomyosin are simultaneously precipitated from the muscle extract by dialysis, most of the actomyosin being irreversibly insoluble. The remaining actomyosin is precipitated from the redissolved myosin by adjusting the ionic strength and pH. Actin-free myosin is

then crystallized by dilution with glass-distilled water. Twelve to 36 fresh adult chicken hearts were used in each extraction (100 to 350 g. of fresh cardiac muscle). Two minor deviations from the technique described by Mommaerts and Parrish should be noted: (1) following dialysis for 18 hours, the ionic concentration of the muscle extracts is frequently not reduced sufficiently to permit maximal precipitation; therefore, 200 ml. of glass-distilled water per 100 g. of muscle is added directly to the extract following dialysis. (2) Mommaerts and Parrish describe an average yield of 1.2 g. of myosin from 100 g. of muscle. Our yields have been consistently lower: from chicken cardiac muscle, 750 mg. of myosin per 100 g., and from chicken skeletal muscle, 410 mg. of myosin per 100 g. of muscle extracted.

It must be emphasized at the outset of the discussion that although the extraction technique employed yields actin-free myosin which approaches purity, the final product is not monodisperse. Mommaerts and Parrish state that the purity of their preparations is of the order of 85–90 per cent. Preliminary studies of cardiac myosin indicate that the degree of purity of the preparation is only slightly lower than that described by Mommaerts and Parrish.

2. Production of Antisera. Despite the brief positive report by Kesztyus, Nikodemusz, and Szilagyi[14] that myosin is antigenic, our early attempts to produce potent antisera in rabbits against cardiac myosin from adult chickens were unrewarding.[12] Hence it seems advisable to record here, briefly, the more important details of the immunization procedure which has proved to be reliable in our laboratory during the past year. First, it is essential that the myosin used for injections be either freshly prepared or stored for less than one week at $-20°C$. In the latter case, it should be thawed only once. The use of freshly extracted myosin for each injection is prohibitively expensive of both time and materials, hence we have made extractions weekly. The myosin should be a bluish-translucent gel; no shreds are desired. The myosin is stored and injected in the phosphate-KCl solution described by Mommaerts and Parrish, at pH 6.8, ionic strength 0.5.

Individual rabbits vary greatly in their antibody response to injected myosin. To date, of 22 rabbits injected with cardiac myosin, only 12 have produced antisera of sufficient potency to be of value. In general, the immunization schedules are so arranged that each adult male rabbit receives a series of intravenous injections on alternate days over a two-week period, totaling 18–20 mg. of protein, is rested for 4–6 days and bled. After 20–25 days further rest, a second series of injections is started, in which a first injection of 4–6 mg. of protein is given intraperitoneally, followed by a total of 48–60 mg., intravenously, on alternate days over a two-week period. Once again the rabbits are bled following 4–6 days rest. Our rabbits have consistently built up circulating antibodies against myosin rapidly, and lost them rapidly. Hence the rabbits are bled 4–6 days rather than the more general 7–10 days after the last injection of a series. Sera are sterilized by passage through a Seitz filter and stored at −20°C. No preservative is added.

3. Specificity of Antisera. The titer and specificity of each serum was determined by the precipitin technique, employing homologous or heterologous antigen. A preliminary titration was made with a constant volume of full-strength serum and progressively decreasing quantities of homologous antigen. The end-point of the antigen dilution series was then titrated with serial dilutions of serum. In this manner, inhibition due to excess antigen is avoided, the serum end-point being greatest with the last active dilution of antigen.[15–17] A total of 54 antisera from 22 rabbits has been assayed. Appropriate controls have been carried out with sera of uninjected rabbits. The effective serum dilution titers of the antisera tested ranged from 1:64 to 1:8192. Only those sera with titers of at least 1:512 with homologous antigen were retained (31 antisera). Potent sera were then tested for reactivity with heterologous antigen (skeletal myosin). The results clearly show

that the antisera against cardiac myosin are highly tissue-specific, i.e., that cardiac and skeletal myosins differ markedly in antigenic constitution. The highest titer obtained in tests of 27 antisera against cardiac myosin with nine separate fresh preparations of the heterologous antigen, skeletal myosin, is 1:256. There is a consistent difference of 4–5 tubes in the reactivity of each serum with homologous and heterologous antigen. In further tests, antisera were first completely absorbed with adult skeletal myosin, and then tested with homologous antigen. Much of the specific reactivity of the sera was retained. The reduction in reactivity due to elimination of antibodies to reactive groups in the heterologous antigen ranged from 1 to 4 tubes. Therefore, due to the marked difference in antigenic constitution of cardiac and skeletal myosins, it is possible to prepare, by absorption procedures, antisera highly specific for adult cardiac myosin. In the sections to follow, all references to antisera against adult cardiac myosin refer to these highly specific, absorbed antisera.

4. Myosin in the Developing Heart. It will be of interest to examine next the evidence pertaining to the antigenic specificity of cardiac myosin during development, as determined by an analysis of the reactivity of antisera against adult cardiac myosin with cardiac extracts from embryos of 36 hours to 18 days incubation. All embryos used in these experiments were of the New Hampshire Red breed, from eggs incubated at 37.5°C. After removing the embryos from the eggs as quickly as possible, the hearts were removed (in an iced Petri dish), freed from excess blood with filter paper, weighed rapidly on a micro-torsion balance and minced finely with scissors on chilled waxed paper. The mince was homogenized in a Ten Brock glass tissue grinder in buffered KCl solution. At 18 days, 60 hearts, and at 13 days, 144 hearts were extracted by the technique described for adult cardiac muscle, with a workable yield of purified myosin. At the earlier stages, however, it was necessary to employ a crude extract of cardiac muscle (containing both myosin and

TABLE 1.   Cardiac myosin in the early embryo

Hamburger and Hamilton Stage	Total Number of Embryos Extracted	Number of Fresh Extracts Tested	Number of Antisera Used with Each Extract	Total Number of Test Series	Number of Positive Reactions	Highest Titer
1	264	5	3	15	0	—
2	248	5	3 or 4	18	1	4
3	236	5	3	15	15	256
4	381	7	2 or 3	17	17	256
5	140	3	2 or 3	8	8	512

actomyosin), since a measurable yield of puri-fied myosin could not be obtained from the small quantities of material available. Hearts of embryos of from 36 hours to 12 days in-cubation were homogenized in the buffered KCl solution. The homogenate was clarified by filtration through cheesecloth followed by centrifugation at 3600 r.p.m. for 30 minutes at 1°C. Both the purified cardiac myosin from older embryos and the clarified cardiac extract from younger embryos were tested for reactivity with antisera against adult cardiac myosin employing several modifications of the precipitin technique, including (1) the ring test, (2) the Hanks technique,[15, 18] and (3) the micro (capillary) method of Ten Cate and Van Doorenmaalen,[19] kindly demon-strated to me by the authors in their labora-tory. All preparations from cardiac muscle, both the purified myosin and the clarified ex-tract from younger embryos, reacted posi-tively with all antisera tested. Cardiac extracts and purified cardiac myosin from embryos at the following stages have been tested: 36, 48, and 72 hours, 5, 7, 9, 12, 13, 15, and 18 days. At least three separate fresh extracts have been tested at each stage, each extract being reacted with at least three potent anticardiac myosin sera. Further, by the absorption tech-nique, employing repeated absorptions with embryonic cardiac antigens of any of the stages tested, it has been clearly demonstrated that all activity of the antisera for adult car-diac myosin can be removed. It is concluded, therefore, that the embryonic heart, from 36 hours through 18 days incubation, contains antigens or reactive groups identical, or closely related to those found in adult cardiac myosin.

5. *Cardiac Myosin in the Embryo Prior to Morphogenesis of the Heart.* The question next arises as to the time at which the reactive groups of cardiac myosin first can be detected in the early embryo. In this series of experi-ments, embryos in stages 1 to 5 of the Ham-burger-Hamilton series (pre-streak through head-process stages) were extracted following the method described for the extraction of cardiac tissue of embryos from 36 hours to 12 days incubation. Three dozen or more embryos at each stage were rapidly removed from the yolk, trimmed and washed to remove adhering yolk, and homogenized in ice-cold KCl-phosphate solution in the Ten Brock grinder. The homogenate was allowed to stand for 1 hour at 2°C., with constant stirring, and then clarified by filtration through cheese-cloth, followed by centrifugation. The resul-tant clear extract was used as the test antigen in precipitin tests with antisera against adult cardiac myosin, chiefly by the Hanks and capillary methods. The results, which are sum-marized in Table 1, are based on 73 separate serum dilution series of reactions, for which a total of 1269 embryos has been extracted. It is clear that reactive groups identical with or closely related to cardiac myosin first can be detected in the embryo by the methods em-ployed at stage 3, the mid-streak blastoderm. All tests of pre-streak, and 17 out of 18 tests of initial streak embryos were negative. At the latter stage one exception was noted—a trace reaction in the first 2 tubes of 1 series. The experiment was repeated with 3 addi-tional fresh extracts of embryos at the same stage; all were completely negative with the same antiserum; therefore the trace reaction is not regarded as significant, likely being due

TABLE 2. Anterio-posterior distribution of cardiac myosin

Hamburger and Hamilton Stage	Total Number of Embryos Extracted	Number of Fresh Extracts Tested	Number of Antisera Used with Each Extract	Total Number of Test Series	Section of Embryo Tested	Number of Positive Reactions	Highest Titer
4	601	11	2–4	29	Ant.	29	64
					Mid (node)	29	256
					Post.	29	256
5	664	12	2–4	31	Ant.	0	—
					Mid (node)	31	256
					Post.	2	4

to an error in staging one or more embryos in the extract in question.

6. Distribution of Cardiac Myosin in the Early Embryo. Rawles[6] has mapped rather precisely the shape, average dimensions and position of the heart-forming areas in the chick blastoderm at the head-process stage. Her cogent analysis has provided the experimental target for the present investigation. Attention was directed first to a study of the distribution of cardiac myosin in the anterio-posterior axis of the embryo at stages 4 and 5. The blastoderm at stage 4 or 5 was divided into 3 segments, designated anterior, mid (containing the node), and posterior, by 2 transverse cuts made with glass or freshly sharpened steel needles across the blastoderm at the levels defined by Rawles as the anterior and posterior limits of the heart-forming areas, 0.6 mm. in front of, and 0.45 mm. behind, the node, respectively. Anterior, mid, and posterior segments, respectively, were pooled in cold buffered KCl solution and extracted following the procedure described for whole embryos. The clarified extracts were tested for the presence of reactive groups of cardiac myosin by the capillary method. The results are summarized in Table 2. It is clear that in the embryo at stage 4, cardiac myosin is found in all 3 sections of the embryo in the anterio-posterior axis. The data further suggest, but do not prove, that the amount of cardiac myosin in the mid and posterior segments is greater than in the anteriormost region of the stage 4 embryo. In order to establish the observed difference

as a significant one it will be necessary to so modify the present micro-techniques that strictly quantitative data can be obtained. Efforts in this direction are being continued. In the embryo at stage 5, cardiac myosin is confined to the mid segment in the anterio-posterior axis, being absent from the anterior and posterior segments. Cardiac myosin is limited in its distribution in the anterio-posterior axis, therefore, to a region slightly over one millimeter in length. The possible mechanism of the progressive localization of cardiac myosin will be discussed in a later section, but it should be emphasized at this point that the demonstrated localization is of a specific contractile protein and not merely of prospective cardiac cells destined for the synthesis of that protein.

Next let us consider the distribution of cardiac myosin in the medio-lateral axis. Again the data of Rawles provide the morphological basis for our experiments. Groups of embryos at stages 4 and 5 were transected as previously described, 0.6 mm. before, and 0.45 mm. behind, the node. The mid-piece, however, was further subdivided into 3 sections, by 2 cuts perpendicular to its cut surfaces, 0.2 mm. on either side of (and roughly parallel to) the node. The resultant sections, designated left lateral, median, and right lateral, respectively, were pooled and extracted, and tested for the presence of the reactive groups of cardiac myosin as previously described. The data are summarized in Table 3.

In the embryo at stage 4, cardiac myosin is approximately equally distributed in the 3

TABLE 3.   Medio-lateral distribution of cardiac myosin

Hamburger and Hamilton Stage	Total Number of Embryos Extracted	Number of Fresh Extracts Tested	Number of Antisera Used with Each Extract	Total Number of Test Series	Section of Embryo Tested	Number of Positive Reactions	Highest Titer
4	271	6	2 or 3	13	Left lat.	13	64
					Median (streak)	13	64
					Right lat.	13	64
5	339	7	2 or 3	16	Left lat.	16	64
					Median (streak)	14	8
					Right lat.	16	64
6–7	273	5	2 or 3	11	Left lat.	11	128
					Median (streak)	0	—
					Right lat.	11	128

sections tested in the medio-lateral axis, and has not been localized to the heart-forming areas. In the embryo at stage 5, although cardiac myosin is largely localized in the lateral areas, traces of the reactive groups are found in the median section (0.4 mm. wide) containing the streak. Thus the data are not in complete agreement with the finding by Rawles that the median area does not produce heart when grafted to the chorioallantoic membrane. Although the reaction is weak, it is consistently found and is believed to be significant. It appeared likely that cardiac cells are being invaginated even as the streak regressed. In order to determine whether the localization of cardiac myosin to the prospective heart-forming areas is complete at a later stage, the experiments were extended to include stages 6–7 (stage 6 is the transitional head-fold stage, difficult to "schedule"; hence stages 6 and 7 are pooled). The results, shown in Table 3, demonstrate that in the embryo at stages 6–7 the median (streak) region does not contain cardiac myosin detectable by the immunochemical methods employed.

DISCUSSION

The labile protein which has been characterized from the physicochemical point of view (at least within reasonable limits), and designated "myosin" by most workers in the field of muscle chemistry has been the myosin extracted from rabbit skeletal muscle. The further questions as to whether myosin is species- and organ-specific have received little attention. A recent study[20] of skeletal myosins prepared from tissues of the rabbit, rat, and mouse has led to the conclusion that the myosins from these species are practically indistinguishable on the basis of a comparison of electrophoretic properties, sedimentation rates, yields, viscosities, and specific refractive increments. On the other hand, the very fact that myosins have been shown to be antigenic argues for species differences of sufficient magnitude to account for their observed ability to stimulate antibody production. Kesztyus, Nikodemusz, and Szilagyi[14] report that rabbit skeletal myosin is antigenic in dogs, but that it is not isoantigenic. Our own findings show that chicken cardiac myosin is antigenic in the rabbit.

With respect to the problem of the organ-specificity of myosin, Snellman and Gelotte[21] have reported that cardiac and skeletal myosins of the rabbit show several differences, e.g., in solubility and in the sedimentation constant, and in the firmness with which actin and myosin are bound (less in cardiac than in skeletal actomyosin). The results of the present study clearly show that cardiac and skeletal myosins are markedly different in antigenic constitution, a difference which has been of importance in establishing the specificity of the antisera employed in detecting cardiac myosin in the early embryo. The question remains unanswered, however, as to whether antigenic differences reflect important physical differences in the proteins, and is currently the objective of a comparative physical study in this laboratory.

Next let us consider the question as to whether embryonic cardiac myosin is qualitatively the same as that in the adult. On the basis of differences in behavior of actomyosins from newborn and adult animals (guinea pigs, rats, mice) upon the addition of adenosinetriphosphate, Ivanov and Kasinova[22] concluded that actomyosin in the newborn animal differs qualitatively from that in the adult. Csapo and Herrmann[10] do not support this conclusion, arguing that, at least in their comparison of chick embryonic and adult actomyosins, only quantitative changes occur. Our findings support the latter view, inasmuch as the reactive groups of cardiac myosin capable of combining with specific antisera to adult cardiac myosin do not change qualitatively from the embryo of 36 hours to the embryo of 18 days or, in fact, to the adult fowl.

It will be of interest to consider next the questions of the time of synthesis and localization of cardiac myosin in the early embryo, with particular reference to the concept of organ-forming areas. It is necessary to recognize at the outset of the discussion that while the data clearly demonstrate that a major synthesis of cardiac myosin is initiated only after the prospective mesodermal cells of the epiblast have invaginated, the evidence does not permit a discussion of the problem of mechanism of synthesis. It is clearly possible that "traces" of cardiac myosin may be present in the earlier embryo quantities which cannot be detected even by the highly sensitive methods employed. The present findings do present a sound chemical basis for further experiments designed to test the related hypotheses of the regulation of the growth and differentiation of an organ by its own products[15,23] and of pattern formation involving the specific suppression of embryonic differentiation by metabolites of differentiated tissues.[24] We ask, for example, whether the reported failure of cardiac tissues to differentiate in the presence of extracts or products of fully differentiated heart muscle[23,24] results from a suppression of the synthetic activities of the tissue (e.g., in the synthesis of contractile proteins), or from a failure in morphogenesis of synthesized products.

Tests of developmental potencies of small pieces of the chick blastoderm through transplantation to the chorio-allantoic membrane clearly show that each of the isolated pieces possesses a relatively restricted developmental capacity. Particular structures develop only from rather definite areas of the blastoderm; in short, the organ-forming areas are localized to a remarkable extent. Recently, the nature and significance of the concept of the organ-forming areas has been the object of sharp criticism.[25] Yet most of the investigators who have employed this approach have been acutely aware of its major limitation, namely that each of the isolated pieces is triploblastic, and have, in fact, emphasized the importance of tissue interactions. Moreover, it has been recognized that the degree of specificity of localization of the several organ-forming areas differs. In fact, on the basis of his recent investigation of the localization of prospective neural plate in the early chick blastoderm, in which the results obtained by transplantation and explantation are shown to be in close agreement with those obtained by marking methods, Spratt[26] has concluded that both types of methods reveal primarily the prospective fates of different regions of the blastoderm. In the case of the heart-forming areas, however, as Rudnick has emphasized,[7] the areas are amazingly large, exceeding in size the actual myocardial anlagen. Thus it appears that the heart-forming areas are areas of prospective potency and not of prospective fate.

Implicit in our definition of an organ-forming area, e.g., the heart-forming area, has been the assumption that the cells of that area of the embryo are destined to become specialized for the synthesis of the specific proteins characteristic of the definitive organ, and that the progressive localization of the heart-forming area is a localization of pro-spective myosin (and other cardiac protein) synthesizing cells. Yet the present findings demonstrate the progressive localization of the specific reactive groups of cardiac myosin, and not merely of prospective cardiac cells. Cardiac myosin is synthesized in the early embryo and can be detected in stage 3; in the embryo at stage 4, the protein is detected in all sections of the embryo analyzed (pre-sumably in the mesoderm, although the pres-ent experiments do not prove this), being more concentrated in the mid and posterior, than in the anteriormost, regions. This finding is not in complete agreement with the results of explantation experiments. Spratt[27] studied the development of pulsating heart masses from anterior and posterior pieces of early blastoderms cultivated *in vitro*, and con-cluded that although heart-forming potency is wide-spread in pre-streak embryos (see also ref. 28), it later becomes localized in the median portion of the posterior half of the streak at stage 4. Rudnick[29, 30] likewise found that prior to its definitive localization at stage 5, the center of the heart-forming region lies posterior in the streak. The present findings do suggest that the synthesis of myosin is greater in the posterior than in the anterior part of the blastoderm; nevertheless some cardiac myosin is synthesized in the anterior part of the embryo. It is interesting to note that both Spratt and Rudnick used the classi-cal plasma-embryo extract medium in their explantation studies, a medium which accord-ing to the reports cited above[23, 24] might suppress cardiac differentiation, since in the absence of a statement to the contrary, the em-bryo extract is assumed to be an extract of the whole embryo, including the heart.

In the embryo at stage 5, and even more clearly at stages 6–7, the localization of cardiac myosin is in good agreement with the data of Rawles. Cardiac myosin is pro-gressively restricted in distribution; at stage 5 the protein is limited at least to the region bounded by the anterior and posterior borders of the heart-forming areas defined by Rawles, *viz.*, 0.6 mm. forward of, and 0.45 mm. be-hind, the node. The localization of cardiac myosin in the medio-lateral axis is not com-pleted until stages 6–7, although the protein is largely confined to the lateral heart-forming areas at stage 5.

It is probable that the bulk synthesis of cardiac myosin is initiated only following the invagination of the prospective cardiac cells through the patent streak. The first con-dition being fulfilled, myosin is synthesized in all areas of the embryo tested.

Emphasis has already been placed on the fact that it is those cells already actively syn-thesizing cardiac myosin, as defined by its combining groups which are localized, and not merely those cells destined to synthesize the protein. Obviously the present findings do not fall readily into any category with respect to current theories of differentiation. In fact, no single interpretation is offered here. If it is postulated either that myosin synthesis is a self-limiting reaction or that other factors are limiting (e.g., availability of substrate, to cite one of the arguments frequently ad-vanced), it then becomes necessary to explain the disappearance of myosin from the non-cardiac areas of the blastoderm. At first thought it appears unlikely that the specificity of the protein might be altered and the protein redirected into other channels. Yet Daly and Mirsky[31] have offered evidence of the synthe-sis of a protein "pool" in the exocrine pan-creas, a pool from which highly specific pro-teins are rapidly synthesized as the secretory activity of the gland demands that the supply of specific enzymes be replenished. The degree of change of specificity in these transforma-tions is not known. It is possible that the lo-calization of the protein is merely a sorting-out or segregation phenomenon, the result of cellular movements within the mesoderm. Our present knowledge of morphogenetic move-ments within the mesoderm does not permit a critical evaluation of this possibility.

The question is posed as to whether it will be possible to characterize other organ-form-ing areas by immunochemical or biochemical methods. Obviously an organ or tissue must fulfill two criteria for successful experimentation in this direction, both of which are admirably fulfilled in the heart-forming areas: it must be an organ which attains early morphological or functional status and for which a sound chemical basis of function has been established. Several of the organ-forming areas which fulfill the second criterion, e.g., the thyroid-forming area, fail when the first criterion is considered. In our laboratory at present one possibility is being investigated (in addition to the analysis of the synthesis of cardiac actin as related to the present study), *viz.*, an immunochemical study of the "pigment-forming area" of the blastoderm. Further discussion and interpretation of the findings and their bearing on the significance of the concept of "organ-forming areas" is reserved pending the outcome of these experiments.

Contribution number 521 from Indiana University Zoological Laboratories. The investigation is supported by grants from the National Science Foundation (NSF-G15) and Indiana University, and by an Indiana University Graduate School Research Fellowship. I wish to acknowledge the intellectual and material aid of the staff of the Department of Biology, Massachusetts Institute of Technology, where the investigation was initiated, and the technical assistance of Alton M. Mun and Louise A. Ross.

[1] Hamburger, V., and Hamilton, H. L., *J. Morph.*, **88**, 49–92 (1951).

[2] Patten, B. M., and Kramer, T. C., *Am. J. Anat.*, **53**, 349–375 (1933).

[3] Lewis, M. R., *Johns Hopkins Hosp. Bull.*, **30**, 176–181 (1919).

[4] Allen, H. J., *Biol. Bull.*, **36**, 63–70 (1919).

[5] Willier, B. H., and Rawles, M. E., *Proc. Soc. Exptl. Biol. Med.*, **32**, 1293–1296 (1935).

[6] Rawles, M. E., *Physiol. Zool.*, **16**, 22–42 (1943).

[7] Rudnick, D., *Quart. Rev. Biol.*, **19**, 187–212 (1944).

[8] Bacon, R. L., *J. Exptl. Zool.*, **98**, 87–125 (1945).

[9] Herrmann, H., *Ann. N. Y. Acad. Sci.*, **55**, 99–108 (1952).

[10] Csapo, A., and Herrmann, H., *Am. J. Physiol.*, **165**, 701–710 (1951).

[11] Ebert, J. D., *J. Exptl. Zool.*, **115**, 351–377 (1950).

[12] Ebert, J. D., *Ann. N. Y. Acad. Sci.*, **55**, 67–84 (1952).

[13] Mommaerts, W. F. H. M., and Parrish, R. G., *J. Biol. Chem.*, **188**, 545–552 (1951).

[14] Kesztyus, L., Nikodemusz, S., and Szilagyi, T., *Nature*, **163**, 136 (1949).

[15] Ebert, J. D., *Physiol. Zool.*, **24**, 20–41 (1951).

[16] Martin, D. S., *J. Lab. Clin. Med.*, **28**, 1477–1482 (1943).

[17] Kabat, E., and Mayer, M., *Experimental Immunochemistry*, Charles C Thomas, Springfield, Ill., 1948.

[18] Hanks, J. H., *J. Immunol.*, **28**, 95–104 (1935).

[19] Ten Cate, G., and Van Doorenmaalen, W. J., *Koninkl. Ned. Akad. Wetenschap., Proc.*, **53**, 3–18 (1950).

[20] Miller, G., Golder, R. H., Eitelman, E., and Miller, E., *Arch. Biochem. and Biophys.*, **41**, 125–137 (1952).

[21] Snellman, O., and Gelotte, B., *Exp. Cell Res.*, **1**, 234–252 (1950).

[22] Ivanov, I. I., and Kasinova, B. S., *Doklady Akad. Nauk. S. S. R.*, **60**, 417 (1948).

[23] Weiss, P., *Science*, **115**, 487–488 (1952).

[24] Rose, S. M., *Anat. Rec.*, **113**, 527 (suppl.) (1952).

[25] Waddington, C. H., *The Epigenetics of Birds*, Cambridge University Press, 1952.

[26] Spratt, N. T., Jr., *J. Exptl. Zool.*, **120**, 109–130 (1952).

[27] Spratt, N. T., Jr., *ibid.*, **89**, 69–101 (1942).

[28] Olivo, O. M., *Compt. rend. assoc. anat.*, **23**, 357 (1928).

[29] Rudnick, D., *Anat. Rec.*, **70**, 351–368 (1938).

[30] Rudnick, D., *J. Exptl. Zool.*, **79**, 399–427 (1938).

[31] Daly, M. M., and Mirsky, A. E., *J. Gen. Physiol.*, **36**, 243–255 (1952).

Single Cell Studies on 19S Antibody Production*

G. J. V. NOSSAL

A. SZENBERG

G. L. ADA

CAROLINE M. AUSTIN

In many model systems of antibody production, a single injection of an antigen leads to the formation first of 19S macroglobulin antibody and later of 7S gamma globulin antibody (1–7). The cellular mechanisms and biological purpose of this characteristic sequence are still obscure. A number of studies in humans (8–12) have shown that β-2 macroglobulins are contained in, and presumably produced by, plasma cells of varying degrees of maturity. Moreover, lymphoid germinal center blast cells may contain macroglobulin (12). However, the specific cells responsible for the transient 19S antibody synthesis of a normal primary immune response have not been identified. In previous studies, we have used an *in vitro* system to investigate antibody production by single cells (13). In the present report, modifications of these techniques are described which have allowed us to determine the cellular basis of 19S antibody production to *Salmonella* flagellar antigens in rats.

MATERIALS AND METHODS

Animals

Wistar albino rats of both sexes, bred at the Hall Institute by random mating, were used. Rats were 12 weeks old at the first immunization, and weighed 180 to 220 gm. They were fed on "Barastoc" dog cubes, cabbage, and tap water.

Immunization

The antigen used throughout was purified flagella from *Salmonella adelaide* bacteria,

(strain SW 1338, H antigen fg; O antigen 35). These were prepared by a modification of Koffler's technique, previously described (14). For primary immunization, rats received 50 μg of antigen into each hindfootpad. For secondary immunization, rats received a similar pair of injections 6 to 8 weeks after the primary immunization.

Antibody Titrations

The anti-H antibody titer of serum samples or of fractions from density gradient ultracentrifugation runs was determined by the method of bacterial immobilization (14). Serial twofold dilutions of the samples were prepared in 0.9 per cent NaCl supplemented with 1 per cent (v/v) fetal calf serum. To each dilution, an equal volume (0.25 ml) of a fresh, diluted, highly motile bacterial culture of standard optical density was added. The bacteria used were *Salmonella derby* (strain SW 721, H antigen fg; O antigen 1, 4, 12), which share the H but not the O antigen with the immunizing strain. Final concentration of bacteria was *ca.* 10^6 per ml. After 30 minutes at room temperature, small droplets from each dilution were placed on slides under paraffin oil and examined for bacterial motility at 125-fold magnification, darkground. A standard degree of partial (*ca.* 80 per cent) immobilization was taken as the end-point of the titration. All samples were coded and read by a single observer to minimize subjective error. Under these conditions, the method was reproducible to $\pm$ 0.5 $\log_2$. The reciprocal of the dilution giving an end-point was termed the titer of the sample.

2-Mercaptoethanol Treatment of Samples

Samples of serum diluted 1:5 in 0.9 per cent NaCl, or of fractions from ultracentrifuge runs, were brought to a final concentra-

Reprinted by permission of The Rockefeller Institute Press, from *Journal of Experimental Medicine*, 1963, **119**, 485–503.

* Supported by Research Grant AI-0-3958 from the National Institute for Allergy and Infectious Diseases, Bethesda, and by a grant from the National Health and Medical Research Council, Canberra, Australia.

tion of 0.1 M 2-mercaptoethanol (ME), and incubated at 37°C for 60 minutes. It has been shown by Deutsch and Morton (15), and since repeatedly, that such treatment destroys the antibody activity of macroglobulins, while leaving that of 7S gamma globulin unaffected. As no effect of this concentration of ME on the bacteria used in immobilization titrations was evident, antibody content of ME-treated samples was determined without prior dialysis.

Zone Centrifugation of Serum Samples

Zone centrifugation (16) was carried out in a Spinco model L centrifuge fitted with an SW39 rotor. Sucrose solutions (22.5 and 32.5 per cent in 0.5 M phosphate buffer, pH 7.5) were mixed to form a linear gradient (volume 4.5 ml). Samples (0.1 ml) of serum were diluted with 0.2 ml of water, and this solution was layered over the sucrose solution. The rotor was centrifuged for 16 hours at 100,000 g, 2°C, and allowed to decelerate with the brake off. Fractions (0.2 to 0.25 ml) were collected in a fraction collector, following slow upward displacement of the tube contents by a 50 per cent sucrose solution. Each fraction was diluted with 3 ml of 0.9 per cent NaCl, the optical density (1 cm cuvette, 280 mμ) determined, and anti-H antibody titer estimated both before and after ME treatment.

In some experiments, marker proteins of known sedimentation constants were added in trace amounts to the serum layer. These proteins were bovine serum albumin (Armour Pharmaceutical Company, Kankakee, Illinois, fraction 5), normal rat 7S globulin (prepared as described below), and edestin (kindly supplied by Dr. P. A. Charlwood). Each protein was trace labeled with iodine-131 by a method similar to that described by Hunter and Greenwood (17).

Preparation of Popliteal Lymph Node Cell Suspensions

Single cell suspensions in a modified Eisen's medium were prepared from immunized popliteal lymph nodes as previously described (18).

Single Cell Techniques

a. Selection of Cells for Study. As considerable interest was attached to the early stages of the primary response, and as antibody-producing cells are then infrequent (19) it was decided to preselect antibody-producing cells by the method of bacterial adherence (18) before detailed single cell study. In a de Fonbrune oil chamber (20) a drop containing some thousands of washed popliteal lymph node cells was mixed with a drop containing a fresh, highly motile culture of *S. adelaide.* After some minutes, certain cells became surrounded by a corona of bacteria adhering specifically to the cell surface. Previous study has shown that this test is a good index of a cell's antibody-forming capacity (21, 22). Adherence-positive cells were identified (200-fold magnification, phase contrast) and transferred to a fresh droplet for washing.

b. Preparation of Single Cell Microdroplets. As adherent bacteria would have interfered with subsequent antibody assay, it was necessary to remove them from the surface of the cell before preparing single cell droplets. This was achieved by repeatedly drawing in and expelling the cell through a micropipette orifice just wider than the cell (*ca.* 8 to 10μ). The resultant shearing stresses eventually removed the adherent bacteria. Three technical considerations led us to base this study on single cell antibody *content* rather than *production.* Firstly, we feared that the attachment and subsequent forcible removal of adherent bacteria might impair cell viability, though in fact the cells looked normal after these treatments. Secondly, if the cell does not need to metabolize during incubation, one can use droplets of 10^{-7} to 10^{-8} ml, 10 to 100 times smaller than those used for the study of single cell antibody production. Thus antibody can be obtained in concentrated form, a distinct advantage for quantitative work. Thirdly, in order to obtain good phase contrast visualization of the cells for purposes of cytological classification, it was necessary to flatten them artificially against the coverslip of the oil chamber. We feared that this essential step might also damage protein synthetic capacity.

Accordingly, adherence-positive cells, now without adherent bacteria, were manipulated singly into clean droplets of nutrient broth for two further washes to ensure complete removal of serum or lymph antibody. Then they were deposited on the under surface of the coverslip of the oil chamber, with a minimal amount of fluid. Almost immediately, the majority of the surrounding fluid was sucked back, and the cell was thus forced against the glass and artificially flattened. Under high-power ($\times$ 787) phase contrast, a considerable amount of structural detail could then be seen. Nuclear and nucleolar outline, pallor in the Golgi region, mitochondria, and cytoplasmic granules or vesicles were readily visualized. This allowed us to classify positive cells as blasts, immature plasma cells, and mature plasma cells as previously described (18, 19, 21, 22). Two positive cells were classified as lymphokinecytes (23), or atypical small lymphocytes with a distinct rim of cytoplasm. These various cell types are illustrated in Figs. 1 to 6.

c. Estimation of Antibody Content of Single Cell Droplets. After the histological diagnosis had been recorded, the cell was broken by one or more sharp blows with the edge of the micropipette, resulting in lysis and release of intracellular antibody. The near empty droplet was then refilled with a standard volume of nutrient broth. Volume was standardized by measuring the length of fluid columns in the micropipette with an eyepiece vernier. It was now necessary to measure the content of total (19S + 7S) and of ME-resistant (7S) antibody of the droplet. Thus each droplet was divided into two equal parts, one to be treated with an equal volume of broth, and the other with an equal volume of 0.2 M ME in broth. Preliminary experiments failed to show destruction of immobilizing activity in droplets of 19S antibody-containing serum. This was due to the diffusion of ME from the droplet into the liquid paraffin during incubation. Preequilibration of the paraffin with 0.1 M ME at 37°C eliminated this difficulty. Thus it was necessary to transfer the half droplet for measurement of ME-resistant anti-body to a second oil chamber which contained preequilibrated paraffin. ME-treated half droplets were incubated at 37°C for 1 hour. Then serial twofold dilutions of each half droplet were made in nutrient broth, and 5 motile *S. adelaide* bacteria added to each dilution. After 10 minutes, the immobilization endpoint was read, just as in a routine serum titration, and with care, the same order of repeatability was achieved. Single cell titers were expressed as $\log_2$ of the reciprocal of the dilution of the original droplet giving an immobilization end-point. Cells in which the antibody content was wholly destroyed by ME treatment were classified as 19S cells; those in which the antibody content was not affected or reduced by only 1 $\log_2$ were classified as 7S cells; and those in which reduction was greater than 1 $\log_2$, and thus regarded as definite, but in which readily detectable antibody remained after ME treatment, were regarded as double producers. Detailed justification of this classification follows below.

Preparation of Antiserum against Rat 7S Gamma Globulin

A pooled serum from rats killed late in the secondary response was dialyzed against 0.0175 M phosphate buffer, pH 6.3, and chromatographed on a DEAE cellulose column (24). The first sharp protein peak eluted from the column with the same buffer was found to contain 80 per cent of the initial (ME-resistant) immobilizing activity. This fraction gave a single peak in the Beckman model E analytical ultracentrifuge, with a sedimentation constant of approximately 7S. Rabbits were immunized repeatedly with 2 to 4 mg of this 7S globulin in Freund's complete adjuvant, and were bled frequently throughout their immunization course. At a stage when immunoelectrophoretic analysis of the serum samples showed there to be a single line of precipitation against the 7S γ-globulin fraction of normal rat serum, the rabbit sera were tested for their ability specifically to neutralize rat antibodies. For this purpose, two rat antisera against *S. adelaide* were chosen. The first, taken on the 5th day of the primary response, contained solely ME-sensitive antibody. On gradient density centrifugation, it gave a sedimenting peak of activity, presumed to be 19S. The second, taken on the 8th day of the secondary response, contained solely ME-resistant antibody, and gave a slowly sedimenting peak. This was presumed to be 7S antibody. Undiluted rabbit "anti-rat 7S globulin" serum added in equal quantities to rat 7S or 19S anti-*Salmonella* sera reduced the titers in both instances, though the effect on the 7S antibody was more marked. However, when the rabbit anti-7S serum was first diluted 1:10, and then added to equal volumes of rat 7S or 19S antisera, the 19S serum showed no reduction in titer, but the 7S serum was markedly reduced. In this way, dilutions of the 7S serum giving titers of 50 or less were rendered totally inactive. Dilutions giving higher titers were reduced in activity, but some antibody remained. Thus, for single cell studies, the rabbit serum showing the greatest power to discriminate between 7S and 19S was used at a final dilution of 1:20, and single cell droplets were diluted so as to give titers in the vicinity of 50 (5 to 6 logs$_2$) or less.

Single Cell Techniques

Alternative Method of Identifying Double Producers. The above serum was used in a further series of single cell experiments designed to obtain additional information about cells containing both 7S and 19S antibody. Single cell droplets were prepared exactly as in the first series of experiments. Then a small sample of each drop was removed, and tested by the instillation of 5 to 10 motile bacteria. The speed of immobilization and degree of agglutination enabled one to estimate approximately the strength of the whole droplet. Droplets believed to be very strong (in the titer range 7 to 9 logs$_2$) were diluted 7- to 10-fold with broth; progressively weaker appearing droplets were diluted 2- to 7-fold; and obviously very weak or negative droplets were discarded. This procedure was adopted so that no diluted droplets would have titers much above 6 logs$_2$ or below 1 log$_2$. Then, each

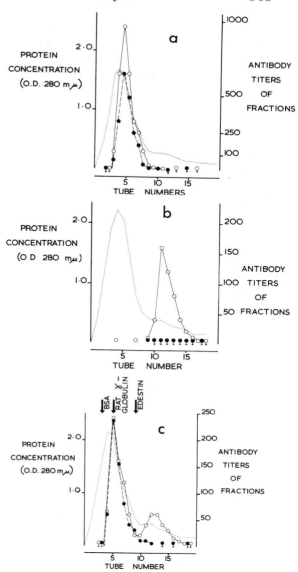

Figs. 1 *a* to 1 *c*. Zone centrifugation of sera from rats immunized with *Salmonella* flagella. ······, protein concentration; o——o, antibody titer before treatment with mercaptoethanol (ME); •-----•, antibody titer after treatment with mercaptoethanol. The results are consistent with ME-insensitive antibody being 7S and suggest that ME-sensitive antibody is about 19S. Fig. 1 *a*. Serum from rat containing ME-insensitive antibody. Fig. 1 *b*. Serum from rat containing ME-sensitive antibody. Fig. 1 *c*. Artificial mixture of sera containing ME-insensitive and ME-sensitive antibody. The arrows indicate localization of the peak tubes when bovine serum albumin (4.4S), rat γ-globulin (7S) from normal serum, or edestin (14S) are centrifuged under the same conditions.

diluted droplet was divided into four equal parts. One acted as a control; the second was treated with an equal quantity of 1:10 rabbit anti-rat 7S globulin serum (room temperature, 30 minutes); the third was treated with ME (0.1 M, 37°C, 60 minutes), and the fourth sequentially received both treatments. Next, 5 to 10 motile bacteria were instilled into each quarter droplet, and immobilization assessed after 10 minutes. The untreated and doubly treated droplets acted as, respectively, positive and negative controls. Some cells yielded droplets reduced by ME but not by the anti-7S serum. These were classified as 19S producers. Others gave droplets reduced by the anti-7S serum yet unaffected by ME. These were the 7S producers. A substantial number of droplets showed the presence of antibody in both the ME-treated and anti-7S treated quarters (though often the speed of immobilization showed the antibody titer to have been reduced in one or both), but no residual antibody in the doubly treated droplet. Such cells were classified as double producers.

RESULTS

Zone Centrifugation of Sera

First it had to be established that rats made 19S and 7S antibodies to *Salmonella* flagella, and that these were, respectively, ME-sensitive and ME-resistant. Figures 1 *a* to 1 *c* show the results of zone centrifugation and subsequent ME-treatment of fractions obtained from sera containing predominantly 7S antibody (Fig. 1 *a*), 19S antibody (Fig. 1 *b*), or an artificial mixture of the two (Fig. 1 *c*). The serum containing 7S antibody was obtained on the 8th day of a secondary response and gave a titer of 12,000. For purposes of illustration, it seemed desirable to have a serum containing 19S antibody in equally high titer, and this was prepared by injecting a rat with 100 pg of flagella (insufficient to give detectable antibody production) and 6 weeks later, with 100 ng of flagella. Four days later, the rat's serum contained antibody to a titer of 9600, which was completely ME-sensitive. The results of zone centrifugation of this serum are shown in Fig. 1 *b* (19S serum alone) and in Fig.

1 *c* (19S serum and 7S serum mixed in equal parts). Clearly, there are two peaks of antibody activity. The first, which moves down the gradient at a rate exactly equal to that of purified 7S gamma globulin, is resistant to ME, though occasionally reductions of 0.5 to 1 $\log_2$ are obtained. The second, which sediments somewhat faster than edestin (mol wt 300,000; sedimentation constant 14S), is completely sensitive to ME. A similar pattern is observed when the 7S serum is diluted 1:10 and mixed with a 19S serum taken on the 5th day of a typical primary response, although of course the two peaks are much lower. We have observed that recovery of 19S antibody from the gradient is less efficient than that of 7S antibody, an observation consistent with the known instability of 19S antibody activity (2). We have attempted to achieve separation of the two main fractions of antibody in sera taken on the 3rd or 4th day of a secondary immune response to 100 μg of flagella. Although single cell studies (*vide infra*) have shown that 19S antibody-containing cells are common at these times, we have not identified a 19S peak in such sera. We believe that this may be due to the great excess of 7S antibody remaining from the primary response, and to the instability of 19S antibody. As our results show that rat antibodies against *Salmonella* H antigens can be *ca.* 19S or 7S, and that the former is ME-sensitive while the latter is ME-resistant, we will now regard "19S" and "ME-sensitive" as synonymous in the context of our single cell studies.

Serum Antibody Titers in Rats Immunized with 100 μg of Flagella

To determine accurately the sequence and kinetics of formation of 19S and 7S antibody, 6 rats were given 100 μg of flagella and bled at 4, 5, 6, 7, 11, 14, 28, and 42 days thereafter. An aliquot of each sample was treated with ME. The results of the mean titers of total antibody and ME-resistant antibody are given in Fig. 2. In the early primary response, the antibody is predominantly ME-sensitive, but after day 5 progressively increasing quantities of ME-resistant antibody appear. The antibody found in the late primary response is

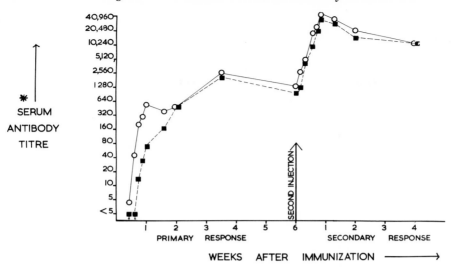

Fig. 2. Serum antibody titers of rats immunized with *Salmonella* flagella. ○———○, total antibody titer; ■———■, titer of antibody remaining after ME treatment.
    * The titer refers to the reciprocal of the dilution of serum giving an end-point of bacterial immobilization.

predominantly 7S, as judged both by ME resistance and gradient density centrifugation. In the secondary response, there is a statistically significant difference $(0.05 > p > 0.02)$ on days 2 and 3 between the total antibody titer and the titer of ME-resistant antibody. After day 3, there is no significant difference between the total antibody and ME-resistant antibody content of the sera.

Antibody Content of Single Cells

Quantitative results on the 19S and/or 7S antibody content of 92 single cells are given in Table I and Figs. 3 to 6. Table I shows that cells on the 4th day of the primary response, while giving a positive bacterial adherence test, do not contain sufficient antibody to be detected by the immobilization test. On the 5th

TABLE I. The nature of the antibody content of single cell microdroplets at various stages of the primary and secondary responses to *S. adelaide* flagella

Day of Immune Response	Number of Cells Examined	Number of Cells Containing Detectable Antibody	Number of 19S Cells	Number of 7S Cells	Number of "Double"* Cells	Titer Range†
Primary						
4	13	0	0	0	0	<1
5	5	3	3	0	0	<1–1½
6	13	13	12	1	0	1–7
7	12	12	4	7	1	1–5½
14	5	4	0	4	0	<1–9
Secondary						
2	7	3	2	1	0	<1–3
3	20	19	7	9	3	<1–8
4	12	12	1	8	3	1–9½
5	5	5	0	5	0	2½–10½
Total	92	71	29	35	7	<1–10½

    * "Double" cells are cells containing antibody the titer of which is significantly diminished $(> 1 \log_2)$ but not abolished by ME-treatment.
    † Titers of single cell droplets are expressed as the $\log_2$ of the reciprocal of the dilution of the original droplet giving an end-point of immobilization.

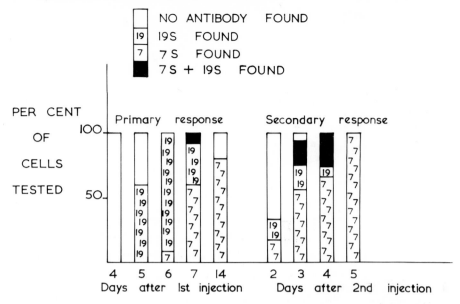

Fig. 3. Proportion of single cells containing 19S, 7S, or both types of antibody. The percentage refers to cells tested on a particular day.

day, some positive cells were encountered and these all contained 19S antibody. On day 6 and thereafter, nearly all cells studied contained readily detectable antibody, sometimes in surprisingly large amounts. On day 6, nearly all the cells contained 19S antibody but by day 7, 7S producers had appeared in considerable numbers. On day 14, only 7S producers could be found. In the secondary response, some cells positive for antibody content could be found already on the 2nd day, and by day 3 nearly all the cell droplets studied gave high antibody titers. Both 19S and 7S cells were seen, as were 3 cells apparently containing both types of antibody. By the 4th day of the secondary response, pure 19S-containing cells were rare, and again a substantial proportion of the cells appeared to contain both types of antibody. By the 5th day, only 7S-containing cells could be found. This changing pattern is shown in Fig. 3. Figure 4 shows the correlation between cell morphology and antibody type produced. Two lymphokinecytes (one containing 19S and one 7S antibody) and 2 unidentified cells are omitted. ME-sensitive antibody was found in all 3 cell types (blasts, immature plasma

cells, and mature plasma cells; see Plate 58, Figs. 1 to 6), as was ME-resistant antibody. Thus, morphological appearance provided no guide as to the type of antibody a cell was likely to contain. In the primary response, blasts produced only 19S antibody, and no 7S-producing blasts were found. However, in the secondary response, morphologically indistinguishable plasmablasts contained 7S antibody already on the 2nd and 3rd days. On the 5th day of the primary response, fully mature plasma cells always contained 19S antibody, while on the same day of the secondary response, cells of indistinguishable appearance always contained 7S antibody.

Figure 5 shows the mean titers of the single cell droplets, omitting double producers, and counting cells giving a titer of < 1 as containing no antibody. In both primary and secondary response, there was a tendency for cells to become stronger with time, though there is no evidence to indicate whether this represented an increase in the quantity of antibody per cell, or simply in the avidity or quality. In the secondary response, cells seemed to gain full synthetic capacity much more quickly, as both 7S and 19S blasts with

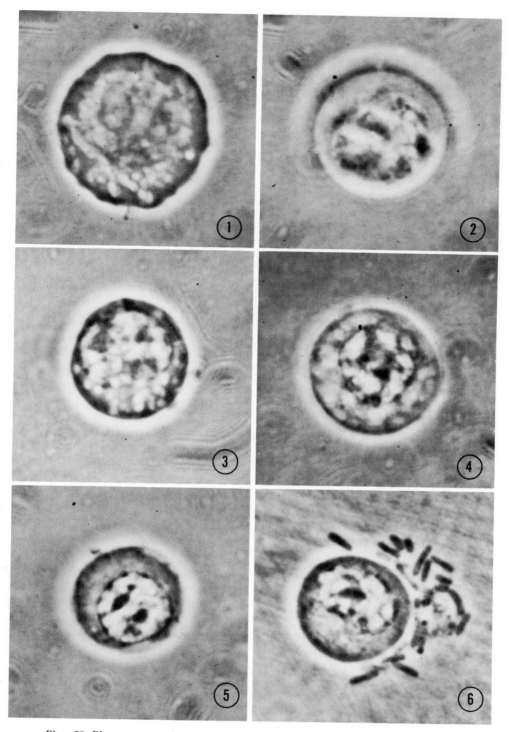

Plate 58. Phase contrast photomicrographs of antibody-producing cells in microdroplets. × 630. Fig. 1. Blast cell. Figs. 2 and 3. Immature plasma cells. Figs. 4 and 5. Mature plasma cells. Fig. 6. Mature plasma cell showing bacterial adherence.

TABLE II. Studies on the effect of anti-7S serum, ME, or both on the antibody content of single cell droplets

Day of Immune Response	Number of Cells Examined*	Number of 19S Cells†	Number of 7S Cells‡	Number of "Double" Cells§
Primary				
5	7	7	0	0
6	8	3	2	3
7	10	0	7	3
Secondary				
3	7	3	2	2
4	13	0	11	2
5	7	0	7	0
Total	52	13	29	10

* The morphological pattern of adherence-positive cells was similar to that shown in Fig. 4, except that 1 7S-containing blast was found on the 6th day of the primary response.

† 19S cells gave droplets in which antibody was destroyed by ME but not by anti-7S serum.

‡ 7S cells gave droplets in which antibody was destroyed by anti-7S serum but not by ME.

§ "Double" cells gave droplets in which antibody was destroyed only when both treatments were used.

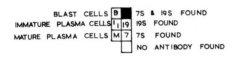

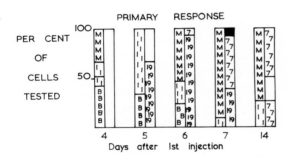

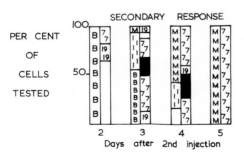

Fig. 4. Proportion of blasts, immature plasma cells, and mature plasma cells containing 19S, 7S, or both types of antibody. For the left-hand histograms, the percentage indicates what proportion of the cells belonged to each category on each day. For the right-hand histograms, the percentage indicates what proportion of cells of each day was forming 7S, 19S, or both types of antibody.

high titers were found already on day 3. Maximal titers achieved by cells in the secondary response were only slightly higher than those of mature plasma cells found later in the primary response. Moreover, the most active 19S cells had only slightly lower titers than the best 7S cells. In Fig. 6, the same data are expressed in a different way, this time to include the 7 double producers. The sum of the titers of, respectively, 19S and 7S antibody of all the droplets was obtained, and divided by the total number of cells (19S, 7S, doubles, and negative cells) tested on that day. It can be seen that the antibody content of the popliteal lymph node cell population expressed in this way mirrors reasonably closely the proportions of antibody present in the serum at the various times. Moreover, it is shown that cells appearing to contain both antibodies occurred only at times when the switch-over from 19S to 7S antibody production was in progress.

Further Study of Double Producers

While only 7 of the 92 cells studied quantitatively were classified as double producers, the true number of such cells was probably larger. In the above studies, cells containing a substantial amount of 7S antibody and a smaller amount of 19S would have been reduced to only a slight, and probably undetectable extent by ME treatment. Accordingly, a further series

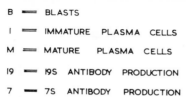

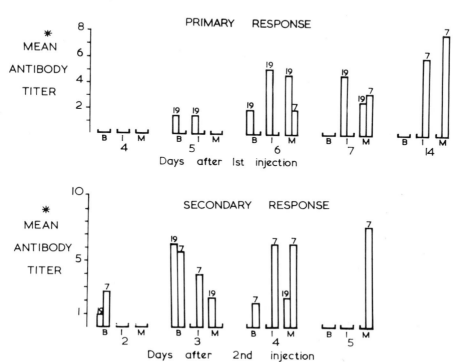

Fig. 5. Mean antibody titer of single cell microdroplets containing 19S or 7S antibody. *B*, blast cells; *I*, immature plasma cells; *M*, mature plasma cells; 7 indicates 7S producers; *19* indicates 19S producers.

  * The titer is the $\log_2$ of the reciprocal of the dilution of the original single cell droplet giving an end-point of bacterial immobilization.

of non-quantitative experiments was performed using the rabbit "anti-rat 7S globulin" serum described above. Single cell droplets were divided into quarters and treated as described under Single Cell Techniques, Alternative method. Double producers were cells yielding droplets the antibody of which was reduced only partially by either ME or anti-rat 7S globulin but wholly by a combination of the two. The results of this study are given in Table II. Ten double producers were found amongst 52 cells, a somewhat larger proportion than in the quantitative studies. Often, we formed the impression that the degree of reduction achieved with anti-7S serum in these

droplets was greater than that achieved by ME, suggesting that such cells would indeed have been classified as 7S producers by the technique used in the previous set of experiments. Again, 19S-containing cells included blasts, immature plasma cells, and mature plasma cells, as did 7S cells. Of the 10 double producers, 6 were immature plasma cells and 4 were mature plasma cells.

Cellular Basis of Anti-O Antibody Production

From both studies, six cells were encountered which contained only anti-O antibody, presumably directed against contaminating

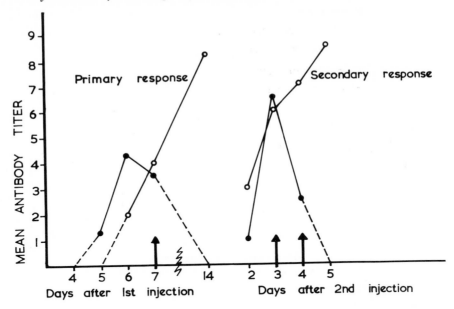

Fig. 6. Mean antibody titers of all single cell drops. The means include "double" cells as well as 19S and 7S cells. The arrows indicate times at which double cells were encountered. •——•, 19S antibody content; ○——○, 7S antibody content; –––––, an extrapolation to zero, no active cells of the category concerned having been found on that day.

traces of O antigen in the flagellar preparation. All of these droplets were completely neutralized by ME treatment.

DISCUSSION

These experiments show that both 19S and 7S antibodies are formed by cells of the plasma cell family. Of 144 adherence-positive cells examined, 123 contained detectable antibody. Of these, 26 were blast cells, presumably plasmablasts; 38 were immature plasma cells, 57 were mature plasma cells, 1 was a lymphokinecyte, and 1 was unidentified. No morphological differences were observed between 19S- and 7S-containing cells.

Following primary injection of the flagella antigen, 19S antibody formation clearly preceded the 7S response. In the first 5 days, all antibody-containing cells found were 19S producers, and consisted of blasts and immature plasma cells. Late in the primary response, only 7S-containing cells were found, and these consisted mainly of mature plasma cells with a few immature forms. On days 6 and 7, 7 cells were found containing both types of antibody. This corresponded to the time when substantial amounts of 7S antibody were first found in the serum. Following secondary injection of the antigen, there was no clear sequence in the appearance of 19S and 7S antibody. Blast cells, containing either 7S or 19S antibody, were found already by day 2. By day 5, only 7S-containing cells could be found, all of which were mature plasma cells. On days 3 and 4, a considerable proportion of cells containing both types of antibody were found. Thus, double producers occurred only at times when the switch from 19S to 7S antibody production was occurring (Fig. 5). Presumably such cells were undergoing a process of intracellular switchover when the animal was killed.

We favor the following simple hypothesis to explain these data. When the antigen is injected the first time, all cells capable of responding embark on 19S antibody production. Some of these mature, produce their quota of 19S antibody, and disappear. After some 19S antibody has been formed, a proportion of the proliferating cells switch to the production of 7S antibody. There is a short period during which the two functions overlap, and cells examined at that stage contain both types of antibody. Soon the change is completed, and plasma cells found late in the primary response produce only 7S antibody. In the secondary response, some blast cells go through a similar transition, but more rapidly. Others, perhaps the progeny of cells which have gone through the transition during the primary response, may form 7S antibody *ab initio*. This course of events applies only to the model system here described. Some antigens, such as *Salmonella* somatic (O) antigen, cause 19S antibody production only (2, 7). Others, for example monomeric flagellin (25), appear to initiate 7S antibody production without the prior formation of 19S antibody as determined by the ME sensitivity of sera. Moreover, the antigen used in the present experiment, when injected in minute doses, results in the production of 7S antibody without detectable precedent 19S antibody formation (25). It would thus be unwise to attempt to formulate a general hypothesis at this stage.

Mellors and Korngold (12), studying the cellular origin of human immunoglobulins by fluorescent antibody techniques, found that while most plasma cells contained either 7S or 19S globulin, an occasional cell contained both. This finding is consistent with our results, and such cells may have represented normal human cells going through the transition as discussed above.

Immunoglobulins consist of L (light) chains and H (heavy) chains (26, 28), and H chains from macroglobulins differ in a number of respects from those of 7S γ-globulins (26, 27). Our cells which switch from 19S to 7S production apparently continue to produce only 1 type of antibody-combining site per cell (13). Presumably this is due to changes in the synthesis and/or assembly of the subunits, but until uniformity of opinion on the location of the combining site has been achieved (26–28), it would be premature to attempt an interpretation of our results in terms of current concepts of globulin structure.

Uhr *et al.* (4) have shown that there is no long-term memory for 19S antibody production in guinea pigs injected with phage antigens. In our system, this is not the case. Three days after a secondary injection of 100 μg of flagella, many cells containing only 19S antibody can be found, whereas this is not possible until the 5th day of the primary response. Confirmatory evidence of 19S memory by zone ultracentrifugation of serum has not been obtained using 100 μg of flagella, possibly due to the technical difficulties mentioned above. However, when a very small primary dose of flagella (insufficient to cause detectable antibody formation) was injected, followed by a larger dose 6 weeks later, a secondary 19S response could be clearly shown by ME treatment and zone centrifugation studies of sera. This work will be reported in detail in a later communication.

It has been suggested (2) that 19S antibody formation in adult mammals is a vestigial response in which the animal briefly recapitulates phases of its phylogeny and ontogeny. While the 7S system plays the major role in adult animals, the 19S system may still be of great importance in immature animals (7, 29) and in lower species (3, 30). Our present findings are not directly relevant to this question, but the concept does provide a rational biological basis for an otherwise somewhat puzzling series of events.

Finally, two qualifying comments should be made. We have argued as if the type of antibody a cell contains is a true reflection of the type of antibody it is currently producing. In view of previous studies (21, 22), we feel this to be a reasonable assumption, but it is not proven in the present context. Secondly, because of the complex quantitative micromanipulations involved, we have been able to study only 144 cells, representing a smaller sample than in most of our previous work.

SUMMARY

Rats were immunized with *Salmonella adelaide* flagella. By zone centrifugation of serum samples in sucrose gradients, it was shown that, as in many other systems of antibody formation, the first response was the formation of 19S, mercaptoethanol (ME)-sensitive antibody. This was quickly replaced by 7S, ME-insensitive antibody. Popliteal lymph node cell suspensions were prepared, and cells with antibody on their surface were identified by the method of bacterial adherence. By micromanipulation such cells were washed, placed into microdroplets, examined under high-power phase contrast and broken to release intracellular antibody. These droplets were then studied in either of two ways. In the first method, each droplet was halved and one half treated with ME. Then both halves were titrated for immobilizing antibody through serial twofold dilution of the half microdroplets. Droplets showing destruction of antibody by ME were classified as 19S; those showing no reduction in titer as 7S; and those showing significant ($> 1 \log_2$) reduction as double producers; i.e., cells containing both 7S and 19S antibodies. In the second method, droplets were divided into 4 equal quarters, for testing after treatment with either ME, or a specific rabbit anti-rat 7S globulin serum, or both. In these experiments, cells showing some remaining antibody after treatment with either reagent, but not after treatment with both reagents, were classified as double producers.

Of 144 cells tested, 123 contained readily detectable amounts of antibody. These comprised 42 19S cells, 64 7S cells, and 17 double producers. The double producers were frequent at times when the switchover from 19S to 7S antibody production was occurring. All except 4 of the cells in the study could clearly be identified as members of the plasma cell series. Though 7S cells became more frequent as the cell population matured, no clear-cut correlation between cell immaturity and 19S production could be obtained. In the primary response many fully mature plasma cells contained only 19S antibody; conversely, in the secondary response many blasts contained 7S antibody. No morphological difference between 19S and 7S cells could be found.

The results suggested that many cells or cell clones go through a sequence whereby each forms first 19S and later 7S antibody with identical combining sites.

We wish to thank Sir Macfarlane Burnet for his interest in this work, Mr. John Pye for help in the preparation of purified rat 7S γ-globulin, and Mr. K. Clarke and Miss J. Milner for excellent technical assistance.

BIBLIOGRAPHY

1. Bauer, D. C., and Stavitsky, A. B., On the different molecular forms of antibody synthesized by rabbits during the early response to a single injection of protein and cellular antigens, *Proc. Nat. Acad. Sc.*, 1961, **47**, 1667.

2. Bauer, D. C., Mathies, M. J., and Stavitsky, A. B., Sequences of synthesis of γ-1 macroglobulin and γ-2 globulin antibodies during primary and secondary responses to proteins, *Salmonella* antigens, and phage, *J. Exp. Med.*, 1963, **117**, 889.

3. Uhr, J. W., Finkelstein, M. S., and Franklin, E. C., Antibody response to bacteriophage φX 174 in non-mammalian vertebrates, *Proc. Soc. Exp. Biol. and Med.*, 1962, **111**, 13.

4. Uhr, J. W., and Finkelstein, M. S., Antibody formation. IV. Formation of rapidly and slowly sedimenting antibodies and immunological memory to bacteriophage φX 174, *J. Exp. Med.*, 1963, **117**, 457.

5. Stelos, P., and Taliaferro, W. H., Comparative study of rabbit hemolysins to various antigens. II. Hemolysins to the Forssman antigen of guinea pig kidney, human type A red cells, and sheep red cells, *J. Infect. Dis.*, 1959, **104**, 105.

6. Lo Spalluto, J., Miller, W., Jr., Dorward, B., and Fink, C. W., The formation of macroglobulin antibodies. I. Studies on adult humans, *J. Clin. Inv.*, 1962, **41**, 1415.

7. Bellanti, J. A., Eitzman, D. W., Robbins, J. B., and Smith, R. T., The development of the immune response. Studies on the agglutinin response to *Salmonella* flagellar antigens in the newborn rabbit, *J. Exp. Med.*, 1963, **117**, 479.

8. Curtain, C. C., and O'Dea, J. F., Possible sites of macroglobulin synthesis: A study made with fluorescent antibody, *Australasian Ann. Med.*, 1959, **8**, 143.

9. Mellors, R. C., Nowoslawsi, A., and Korngold, L., Rheumatoid arthritis and the cellular origin of rheumatoid factors, *Am. J. Path.*, 1961, **39**, 533.

10. Cruchaud, A., Rosen, F. S., Craig, J. M., Janeway, C. A., and Gitlin, D., The site of synthesis of the 19S γ-globulins in dysgammaglobulinemia, *J. Exp. Med.*, 1962, **115**, 1141.

11. Solomon, A., Fahey, J. L., and Malmgren, R. A., Immunohistologic localization of

gamma-1-macroglobulins, beta-2A-myeloma proteins, 6.6 S gamma-myeloma proteins and Bence Jones proteins, *Blood*, 1963, **21**, 4.

12. Mellors, R. C., and Korngold, L., The cellular origin of human immunoglobulins, *J. Exp. Med.*, 1963, **118**, 387.

13. Nossal, G. J. V. and Mäkelä, O., Elaboration of antibodies by single cells, *Ann. Rev. Microbiol.*, 1962, **16**, 53.

14. Nossal, G. J. V., Studies on the transfer of antibody-producing capacity. I. The transfer of antibody-producing cells to young animals, *Immunology*, 1959, **2**, 137.

15. Deutsch, H. F., and Morton, J. K., Dissociation of human serum macroglobulins, *Science*, 1957, **125**, 600.

16. Kunkel, H. G., Macroglobulins and high molecular weight antibodies, *Plasma Proteins*, 1960, **1**, 279.

17. Hunter, W. M., and Greenwood, F. C., Preparation of iodine-131 labelled human growth hormone of high specific activity, *Nature*, 1962, **194**, 495.

18. Mäkelä, O., and Nossal, G. J. V., Bacterial Adherence. A method for detecting antibody production by single cells, *J. Immunol.*, 1961, **87**, 447.

19. Nossal, G. J. V., Mitchell, J., and McDonald, W., Autoradiographic studies of the immune response. IV. Single cell studies on the primary response, *Australian J. Exp. Biol. and Med. Sc.*, 1963, **41**, 423.

20. de Fonbrune, P., *Technique de Micromanipulation*, Paris, Masson et Cie., 1949.

21. Mäkelä, O., and Nossal, G. J. V., Study of antibody-producing capacity of single cells by bacterial adherence and immobilization, *J. Immunol.*, 1961, **87**, 457.

22. Mäkelä, O., and Nossal, G. J. V., Autoradiographic studies on the immune response. II. DNA synthesis amongst single antibody-producing cells, *J. Exp. Med.*, 1962, **115**, 231.

23. Vasquez, J. J., Antibody- or gamma globulin-forming cells, as observed by the fluorescent antibody technic, *Lab. Inv.*, 1961, **10**, 1110.

24. Peterson, E. A., and Sober, H. A., Chromatography of proteins. I. Cellulose ion exchange adsorbents, *J. Am. Chem. Soc.*, 1956, **78**, 751.

25. Ada, G. L., Nossal, G. J. V., Pye, J., and Abbot, A. The behaviour of active bacterial antigens during the induction of the immune response. Part A: The properties of flagellar antigens from Salmonella, *Nature*, 1963, **199**, 1257.

26. Edelman, G. M., Benacerraf, B., Ovary, Z., and Poulik, M. D., Structural differences among antibodies of different specificities, *Proc. Nat. Acad. Sc.*, 1961, **47**, 1751.

27. Edelman, G. M., Benacerraf, B., and Ovary, Z., Structure and specificity of guinea-pig 7S antibodies, *J. Exp. Med.*, 1963, **118**, 229.

28. Fleishman, J. B., Porter, R. R., and Press, E. M., The arrangement of the peptide chains in gamma globulin, *Biochem. J.*, 1963, **88**, 220.

29. Fink, C. W., Miller, W. E., Dorward, B., and Lo Spalluto, J., The formation of macroglobulin antibodies. II. Studies on neonatal infants and older children, *J. Clin. Inv.*, 1962, **41**, 1422.

30. Silverstein, A. M., Uhr, J. W., Kraner, K. L., and Lukes, R. J., Fetal response to antigenic stimulus. II. Antibody production by the fetal lamb, *J. Exp. Med.*, 1963, **117**, 799.

The Ontogeny of Chick Embryo Hemoglobin*

FRED H. WILT†

A fundamental issue in cellular differentiation is the mechanism by which a portion of the genome is selectively expressed. Differential gene activity in embryogenesis may be

Proceedings of the National Academy of Sciences, **48**, 1582–1590 (1962). Reprinted with permission.

* This research has been supported by grants from the National Science Foundation and the National Institutes of Health.

† Author's address: Department of Biology, Purdue University, Lafayette, Indiana.

indirectly approached by a study of the origin of protein synthesizing machinery. Hemoglobin is a suitable protein to use as an index of activity of a particular protein synthesizing system. Its structure, function, genetic regulation, physiological role, and mode of synthesis are better understood than those of any other protein of the metazoa. The present investigation is a description of the time and place of origin of globin, heme, and hemoglobin in the developing chick embryo. The results serve as a foundation from which to launch investigations on the mode of control of synthesis of hemoglobin. Furthermore, the present analysis presents some interesting features of the ontogeny of proteins. First, as other investigators have shown,[1] a protein population characteristic of a particular tissue differentiation may appear long before visible morphological differentiation occurs; second, the relative proportions of classes of proteins in a population may differ at different developmental ages; third, the relative rates of synthesis of an apoprotein and its prosthetic group may change during differentiation.

METHODS

1. *Preparation of hemoglobin* (Hb). Hemoglobin was prepared from adult white Leghorn chicken blood by a procedure similar to Drabkin's.[2] After collection of citrated whole blood the erythrocytes were washed 7 times in saline, hemolyzed in saline containing 0.1% saponin, and stroma and ghosts removed by centrifugation. A crude Hb was obtained by precipitation with 2.8 M potassium phosphate buffer (pH 6.8), and further purified by three cycles of ammonium sulfate fractionation, the 60–70% saturated fraction containing Hb. The Hb was finally crystallized by dialysis against 2.8 M potassium phosphate buffer (pH 6.8). The extent of purification was estimated by spectrophotometric determination of heme to protein ratios,[3] DNA contamination,[4] and zone electrophoresis.[5] No further purification was obtained by ethanol precipitation, alumina gel cream adsorption, protamine sulfate precipitation, or DNAase digestion. Protein was determined by the method of Lowry *et al.*[6]

2. *Hb antisera.* Antisera to Hb were prepared in 8 rabbits. After a primary injection of 40 mg of Hb in Freund's adjuvant, followed by a 10-day rest, 20 mg of alum precipitated Hb was injected into the marginal ear vein on alternate days for 10 injections. After a 7-day rest, another 7 injections of alum precipitated Hb were made, and the rabbits were bled 5–12 days after the last injection.

γ-globulin was prepared from antisera by 5 cycles of precipitation with 50% saturated ammonium sulfate. The final precipitate was dissolved in a volume of 0.9% saline equivalent to one-half the original volume of serum and dialyzed against 0.9% saline. γ-globulin preparations were exhaustively absorbed with lipid free egg yolk powder (Schechtman and Hoffman[7]). Interfacial ring tests were carried out according to Boyd.[8] Double diffusion Ouchterlony analyses were carried out in washed agar containing 0.9% NaCl, 0.01% merthiolate, and 0.01 M tris hydroxyl methyl amino methane buffer (pH 7.2).[9]

3. Electrophoresis and immunoelectrophoresis on agar were carried out on microscope slides according to the method of Wieme.[10] Starch block electrophoresis was performed as recommended by Kunkel,[5] and starch gel electrophoresis carried out by the procedure of Smithies.[11]

4. Culture of chick blastoderms in watch glass cultures was carried out by Spratt's technique.[12] All media contained 100 mg % glucose, 0.65% agar, Howard's chick saline, and either potassium phosphate–sodium bicarbonate buffer or diluted egg white (final pH 7.9). All embryos were from a single flock of white Leghorn chickens. Extracts of embryos were prepared by washing the blastoderm, or pieces of it, in 3 changes of saline, freezing and thawing of the embryos after macerating in a small volume of distilled water, and centrifugation for 30 min at 30,000 $\times$ gravity. The supernatant was carefully aspirated leaving the pad of lipid in the centrifuge tube.

5. Double labeling studies were carried out by culturing blastoderms for 5 hr on Spratt's albumen medium containing H^3 leucine and $Fe^{59}Cl_3$. Extracts of blastoderms were reacted with control and immune globulins. After incubation for 1 hr at 37°C and 23 hr at 4°C, the antigen-antibody precipitates were isolated by centrifugation at 30,000 $\times$ gravity, and the precipitates washed 3 times with 0.9% saline buffered at pH 7.0 with 0.1 M potassium phosphate. The precipitates were dissolved by heating at 80° for 30 min in 0.05 ml of 1 N KOH and transferred to low K^{40}

glass scintillation counting vials. Liquid scintillation counting procedures were based on the procedure of Brown and Badman.[13] The vials contained the antigen-antibody precipitate dissolved in 1 *N* KOH, 1.5 ml of 1 *M* Hyamine‡ hydroxide in methanol, 0.05 ml of 2 *N* HCl, and 8 ml of redistilled toluene containing 4 gm of 2,5-diphenyloxazole and 50 mg of 1,4-bis-2(5-phenyloxazolyl)-benzene per liter. Counting was carried out on a split channel Packard Tri-Carb scintillation counter at a photomultiplier voltage of 880 volts. The lower pulse height discriminator registered pulses between 5 and 45 volts, giving an efficiency of 3.77% for H^3 and 36.3% for Fe^{59} with a background of 29.4 cpm. The upper pulse height discriminator collected pulses from 45–100 volts, counting H^3 with an efficiency of 0% and Fe^{59} with an efficiency of 16.7%, the background being 6 cpm. All vials were subsequently re-examined for quenching after counting by the addition of H^3 toluene and Fe^{59} standards.

Fe^{59} counts were corrected for decay from the time of culture using a half-life of 45.1 days.

Other methodological details are described in the text.

THE ADULT HEMOGLOBIN

An important detail in the preparation of avian hemoglobin is to avoid rupture of the erythrocyte nuclei with subsequent release of large amounts of DNA. The use of saponin for hemolysis satisfies this requirement. The final product had an absorption spectrum similar to adult human Hb. The oxyhemoglobin, methemoglobin, cyanomethemoglobin, carbonmonoxyhemoglobin, and reduced hemoglobin derivatives were prepared. They all showed absorption spectra characteristics similar to the same derivatives of human hemoglobin.[14] The preparation contained no detectable DNA (< 0.001%). Analytical ultracentrifugation in the Spinco Model E centrifuge disclosed only one homogeneous component. Quantitative precipitation profiles

‡ Purchased from Packard Instrument Corp., Chicago, Illinois.

determined by ammonium sulfate and potassium phosphate precipitation demonstrated apparent homogeneity.[15] No nonheme proteins (evaluated by comparing amido-black and benzidine staining) were present in zone electrophoretic analyses.

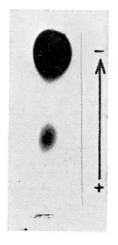

Fig. 1. Adult chicken Hb was subjected to agar gel electrophoresis according to the procedure of Wieme.[10] (0.05 *M* veronal buffer, pH 8.6.)

Moving boundary electrophoresis disclosed an initial sharp peak which, after prolonged electrophoresis, gave rise to two components of similar mobilities. Agar gel electrophoresis at pH values from 5.6–8.6 in potassium phosphate, sodium citrate, sodium barbituate, and boric acid buffers revealed only two components (Fig. 1). Methemoglobin, cyanomethemoglobin, and carbonmonoxyhemoglobin derivatives also displayed two components after agar gel electrophoresis. The mobilities of the methemoglobin derivatives were slightly lower than those of the components of oxyhemoglobin. Both of the components evident after zone electrophoresis contained heme. Starch gel electrophoresis and starch block electrophoresis in borate and barbital buffers at pH 8.6 revealed two components, although the separation was not as distinct as with agar gel electrophoresis. Huisman[16] has also reported two Hb fractions of adult chicken hemoglobin after chromatography on amberlite IRC-50, and Saha *et al.*[17] and Fraser[18] have described two components after paper electrophoresis.

The immunological response of rabbits to Hb was qualitatively similar in all 8 of the rabbits. Precipitating antibodies were present

Fig. 2. Gamma globulin from immune serum was placed in the central well in this double diffusion test of the specificity of the antibody. Chicken hemoglobin (hb), bovine serum albumen (sa), an aqueous extract of egg yolk (y), rat hemoglobin (rh), and frog hemoglobin (fh) were deposited in the peripheral wells.

in substantial amounts in 6 of the 8 rabbits. The antisera and γ-globulins prepared from them showed no precipitin reaction in agar gel diffusion tests with bovine serum albumin, frog hemoglobin, rat hemoglobin, rabbit hemoglobin, or aqueous extracts of fresh egg yolk (Fig. 2). Interfacial ring tests with undiluted antisera showed clearly visible reac-

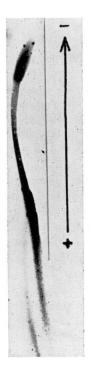

Fig. 3. A typical microimmuno-electrophoretic pattern displayed by adult chicken hemoglobin was obtained after electrophoresis at 16 V/cm for 45′ in 1.5% agar containing 0.05 M veronal buffer (pH 8.5). Enlarged three times.

tions with 0.001 per cent Hb, and reactions in agar gel diffusion tests using γ-globulin showed clear reactions with 0.1 μg of Hb. Agar gel double diffusion tests carried out over a wide range of antigen dilutions revealed two precipitation lines, one line being much more dense than the other. The same two lines appeared when purified globin was used as the antigen (prepared by the method of Anson and Mirsky[19]), and Bjorklund inhibition tests[20] showed heme did not participate in the precipitin reaction. It is concluded that the use of these antisera results in the detection of two avian specific globins. There was never any reaction with control sera or γ-globin fractions prepared from them.

Immunoelectrophoresis of the adult Hb disclosed that the major electrophoretic component gives rise to the dense precipitation line with antibody, and the minor component reacts to give a fainter and distinct line. There is, however, an invariable "tailing" of the heavy precipitation line into the region opposite the minor electrophoretic component, as shown in Fig. 3. This is probably the result of incomplete electrophoretic resolution of the two components after agar gel electrophoresis.

In summary, the hemoglobin of the adult chicken is apparently a mixture of two similar globin populations, which differ slightly in electrophoretic mobility and immunological reactivity.

EMBRYONIC GLOBIN

The time of appearance and type of globin present in the developing embryo were investigated by immunological methods employing the agar gel diffusion test. Extracts of 10–20 embryos in a volume of 0.3 ml were sufficient for an analysis. The extracts contained 0.5–1.5 mg protein per ml. Blastoderms of unincubated eggs contained two immunologically distinct reactants. The same two components, or precipitation lines, were present until 36–48 hours of development. One of the two precipitation lines gave reactions of identity with the minor adult immunological component; the other was distinct from both adult components. Forty-eight-hour and 72-hour blastoderms contained two components immunologically identical to the adult globins (Figs. 4–6). The interpretation is that the early chick blastoderm contains one component immunologically identical to the minor adult globin. A second distinct component which cross-reacts with the antibodies only persists until 48 hours of development. Furthermore, the evidence suggests that as this early component disappears a component immunologically identical to the major adult globin appears. All three of these globin-like molecules in embryo extracts precipitate between 60–70 per cent saturation with ammonium sulfate. Immunoelectrophoretic patterns from two- and three-day embryos are qualitatively identical to those of the adult. Embryos less than 36 hours old show a pattern quite similar after immunoelectrophoresis to adult patterns. However, with such small amounts of antigen it is necessary to deposit excessive amounts of protein in the agar gel, the conditions for resolution are not optimal, and the only prudent conclusion is that the patterns are similar. This does help strengthen the conclusion, however, that these immunological reactants are globins.

It was thought possible, with the use of these same methods, to map the distribution of globin in different areas of the blastoderm. However, the quantitative precision of agar gel diffusion analysis leaves much to be desired; only 5- to 10-fold differences in concentration can be detected by watching the time of appearance of precipitation lines. Anterior and posterior halves of entire early primitive streak and of 12- to 14-somite blastoderms were compared, as were the pellucid and opaque portions of the blastoderms of the same two groups. There was no apparent difference between anterior and posterior halves of the blastoderm, but the precipitation lines appeared earlier from extracts of area opaca than of area pellucida. This was true at both stages examined. The antigen is apparently widely distributed, but is present in higher amounts in the area opaca. These crude localization methods should be fol-

lowed up by the use of fluorescent antibody staining, an area of research now under investigation.

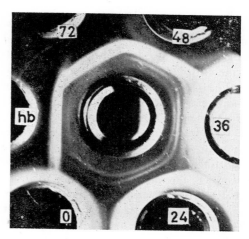

Fig. 4. This agar gel diffusion plate summarizes the minimal number of hemoglobin antigens present in blastoderms of various stages of development. Immune γ-globulin was placed in the central wells. Hb is adult chicken hemoglobin; the numbers designate the number of hours of incubation of the eggs before preparation of the extracts of the blastoderm. Blastoderms from head process to the 2-sonite stage were selected for the 24-hr extract; 8- to 11-somite blastoderms were selected for the 36-hr extract.

Fig. 5. This agar gel diffusion plate shows the relation of the hemoglobin antigens of the unincubated blastoderm to adult hemoglobin.

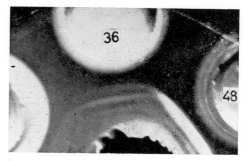

Fig. 6. This agar gel diffusion plate shows the relation of the hemoglobin antigens of 36-hr and 48-hr blastoderms.

The Formation of Hemoglobin

Even though globin-like molecules are present in very early blastoderms, immunological methods do not distinguish globin from hemoglobin. O'Brien[21] has applied the very sensitive dimethoxy benzidine stain for hemoglobin to developing chick embryos. The reaction is dependent upon heme for the pseudoperoxidase activity of hemoglobin. The reaction is first positive in the cells of the prospective blood islands in the area opaca at 7 somites, the nuclei staining more intensely than the cytoplasm. In a few hours the intensity of cytoplasmic staining increases and becomes more widely distributed through the area opaca. It has been possible to confirm the results of O'Brien except that the appearance of staining is first detected in 8- and 9-somite blastoderms. The results suggest that globin is present before heme incorporation into globin takes place. The finding by O'Brien that 8-azaguanine, applied prior to 7 to 9 somites of development, inhibits the appearance of benzidine staining seemed to provide a useful

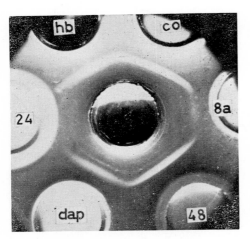

Fig. 7. This agar gel diffusion plate shows the effect of 8-azaguanine on the development of the major adult hemoglobin antigen. (8A, embryos cultured in the presence of 8-azaguanine; co, embryos cultured on Spratt's albumen medium; dap, embryos cultured in the presence of 2,6-diamino purine; 48, uncultured 48-hr embryos; 24, uncultured 24-hr embryos; hb, adult chicken hemoglobin.) All the wells with embryo extracts contained about 1.5 mg of protein.

tool. Although 12 different nucleoside analogs were tested for their ability to inhibit hemoglobin development *in vitro* (5-bromodeoxyuridine, 5-bromodeoxycytidine, 5-fluorouracil, and thiouracil were effective inhibitors at definitive primitive streak stages), 8-azaguanine was selected for further study because of O'Brien's earlier findings. Embryos were explanted at 3 stages (definitive primitive streak, 6 to 7 somites, or 15 to 16 somites) on Spratt's minimal medium containing 10 mg per 100 ml of 8-azaguanine, and cultured for 20 hours. Selected living embryos were stained for hemoglobin[21] and subsequently fixed, the remainder being used to make extracts for immunological analysis. 8-Azaguanine completely abolished Hb formation at definitive primitive streak and 7-somite stages, and slightly reduced it at the 15-somite stage. Precipitation patterns of extracts from embryos cultured on 5-bromodeoxyuridine, 5-bromodeoxycytidine, 5-fluorouracil, and 2,6-diamino purine were identical to the controls. Extracts of embryos cultured on 8-azaguanine showed a definitive reaction for the major adult globin even though no benzidine staining material could be detected (Fig. 7). This suggested a differential action of 8-azaguanine, i.e., heme and globin synthesis might be dissociable.

The hypothesis that there are differing rates of apoprotein synthesis and prosthetic group attachment at different developmental stages was put to the following critical test. Embryos at definitive primitive streak to 2-somite stage, 7- to 8-somite stage, and 15- to 18-somite stage were cultivated on Spratt's albumin-saline-agar medium containing mixtures of $Fe^{59}Cl_3$ and H^3 leucine. After 5 hours of development *in vitro*, the ratio of H^3/Fe^{59} into antibody precipitable protein was determined. Preliminary experiments on over 1,800 blastoderms using widely varying leucine to iron ratios were carried out. Precipitates were collected by filtration through Millipore filters or by centrifugation, the latter proving to be more reliable because the Millipore filters exhibited nonspecific adsorption of leucine. These experiments showed that almost no iron was incorporated into antibody precipitable

TABLE 1. Incorporation of Fe^{59} and H^3 leucine into embryonic hemoglobin

Experiment	Stage	H^3 Leucine/Embryo (cpm)	H^3/Fe^{59}
1	0– 2 somites	38	22.2
1	7– 8 somites	196	13.1
1	15–18 somites	164	8.0
2	0– 2 somites	30	19.2
2	7– 8 somites	194	11.7
2	15–18 somites	175	9.17

Embryos were cultured for 5 hr on media containing 10^7 cpm of H^3 leucine and 3.6×10^5 cpm of $Fe^{59}Cl_3$ per ml at the previously stated counting efficiencies. It was necessary to culture 45 embryos of the 0–2 somite stage, 30 embryos having 7–8 somites, and 15 embryos having 15–18 somites for each experiment at this isotope level. 100 µg of adult carrier hemoglobin was added to each extract. Counts recorded are the differences between precipitates from extracts to which was added excess immune and nonimmune γ-globulin. No visible precipitate was present in control tubes and counts did not deviate by more than 5% from background in control tubes. The maximum standard deviation in counting was 3%.

material prior to the 7- to 8-somite stage, although some leucine was incorporated at this early stage. Table 1 presents the results of a duplicate pair of experiments using the final procedures outlined in the *Methods* section. The H^3/Fe^{59} ratio changes as a function of developmental age. Even though almost no iron is incorporated at the definitive primitive streak stage, leucine incorporation is definitely present. Between this stage and the 8-somite stage incorporation of leucine into globin on a per embryo basis rises at least 5-fold. Incorporation of iron rises even faster and consequently the H^3/Fe^{59} ratio decreases. If this same experiment is carried out in the presence of 8-azaguanine, the results are identical except the incorporation into antibody precipitable material is reduced about 3-fold in 7- to 8-somite embryos. There is no depression of incorporation at the 2-somite or 16-somite stage. The H^3/Fe^{59} ratios do not differ from those of control embryos cultured in the absence of 8-azaguanine. The previous suggestion that heme and globin synthesis are dissociable by 8-azaguanine is apparently not correct. But the hypothesis that at early stages globin synthesis occurs without substantial heme incorporation is supported.

DISCUSSION

The finding that adult hemoglobin contains two distinct components is in agreement with several other studies. D'Amelio and Salvo[22]

have, however, stated that a third hemoglobin component is present in chickens. This component is electrophoretically distinct from, but immunologically identical to, the major component. Differences in our findings could be due to differences in hemoglobin purification or strain differences in the birds. This component has not been observed in this laboratory using the methods of D'Amelio and Salvo. As D'Amelio has previously demonstrated, there are two adult components which are immunologically distinct.

Beard[23] has reported the definite presence of hemoglobin antigens at the 8-somite stage, and the possibility of globin antigens even earlier. The present studies demonstrate that a molecule whose immunological characteristics, behavior to ammonium sulfate, and electrophoretic mobility on agar are similar to the minor adult component is present in unincubated blastoderms. Furthermore, a cross-reacting component is present until at least 48 hours of development. Although this transient component behaves electrophoretically like the major adult component, it is immunologically distinguishable. D'Amelio and Salvo[22] have studied chick embryo hemoglobin from 47 hours until 11 days of incubation. They find the presence of two components at 48 hours of development which are similar to the two adult components; the embryonic components have a greater electrophoretic mobility than the adult components.

The mobility differences are not great, however, and could be due to mobility differences between purified and unpurified hemoglobins. In this laboratory the electrophoretic mobilities on agar gel of the two components from 48-hour embryos (after partial purification by ammonium sulfate) are indistinguishable from the mobilities of the adult components. Fraser[18] has shown the presence of the two adult Hb components, although in different relative concentrations, from 5 to 21 days of incubation.

O'Brien's and Beard's work shows, as do the present isotopic studies, that hemoglobin synthesis assumes a rapid rate at about the 8-somite stage, and that this occurs primarily in the blood islands. Some globin synthesis goes on prior to this time, although little heme iron is incorporated. 8-Azaguanine depresses but does not eliminate the increase in rate of synthesis at the 8-somite stage. Evidently the 8-azaguanine depression is substantial enough to reduce the eventual hemoglobin concentration below the threshold for benzidine staining.

A number of unanswered questions raised by this study may now be attacked experimentally. The identity of embryonic and adult globin is being determined by isotope dilution studies and fingerprinting. The precise distribution of heme and globin in the blastoderm is being analyzed by fluorescent antibody and autoradiographic studies. It is also feasible to begin experimentation on the nature of the control mechanisms in hemoglobin biosynthesis. The interrelations between the transient "embryonic" globin and the adult molecule, the possible interdependence of heme and globin synthesis, and the nature of the abrupt increase in synthesis at about 8 somites of development are issues which may be subjected to experimental analysis.

SUMMARY

An investigation of chick embryo hemoglobin synthesis using immunological and electrophoretic methods revealed 2 globin-like components in the unincubated blastoderm. One component is apparently identical to the minor adult globin component, the other is immunologically distinguishable from both adult components. This distinctive component disappears at approximately 36–48 hours of incubation concomitant with the appearance of the major adult component. Heme and globin synthesis proceed rapidly after the embryo has acquired 7 to 8 somites. Prior to this stage some globin synthesis occurs, but practically no heme iron is incorporated into hemoglobin.

I am grateful for the technical assistance of Martha Clouser, Daphne Dunn, and Devi Mulchandani.

[1] Ebert, J. D., in *The Cell*, ed. A. E. Mirsky and J. Brachet (New York: Academic Press, 1959), vol. 1, p. 619.

[2] Drabkin, D. L., *Arch. Biochem. Biophys.*, **21**, 224 (1949).

[3] Drabkin, D. L., and J. H. Austin, *J. Biol. Chem.*, **98**, 721 (1932); Drabkin, D. L. and J. H. Austin, *J. Biol. Chem.*, **112**, 51 (1935–36).

[4] Ceriotti, G., *J. Biol. Chem.*, **198**, 297 (1952).

[5] Kunkel, H. G., in *Methods of Biochemical Analysis*, ed. D. Glick (New York: Interscience, 1954), p. 141.

[6] Lowry, O. H., N. J. Roseborough, A. C. Farr, and R. J. Randall, *J. Biol. Chem.*, **193**, 265 (1951).

[7] Schechtman, A. M., and H. Hoffman, *J. Exp. Zool.*, **120**, 375 (1952).

[8] Boyd, W. C., *Fundamentals of Immunology* (New York: Interscience, 1956).

[9] Ouchterlony, O., *Prog. Allergy*, **5**, 1 (1958).

[10] Wieme, R. J., *Clin. Chim. Acta*, **4**, 317 (1959).

[11] Smithies, O., *Biochem. J.*, **61**, 629 (1955).

[12] Spratt, N. T., *J. Exp. Zool.*, **106**, 345 (1947).

[13] Brown, W. O., and H. G. Badman, *Biochem. J.*, **78**, 571 (1961).

[14] Hunter, F. T., *The Quantitation of Mixtures of Hemoglobin Derivatives by Photoelectric Spectrophotometry* (Springfield, Ill.: Charles C Thomas, 1951). Klein, D. E., J. L. Hall, and A. A. King, *J. Biol. Chem.*, **105**, 753 (1934).

[15] Roche, J., Y. Derrien, and M. Montte, *Bull. Soc. Chim. Biol. Tr. Mem.*, **23**, 1114 (1941).

[16] van der Helm, H. J., and T. H. J. Huisman, *Science*, **127**, 762 (1958).

[17] Saha, A., R. Dutta, and J. Ghosh, *Science*, **125**, 447 (1957).

[18] Fraser, R. C., *Exp. Cell Res.*, **25**, 419 (1961).

[19] Anson, M. L., and A. E. Mirsky, *J. Gen. Physiol.*, **13**, 469 (1930).

[20] Bjorklund, B., *Proc. Soc. Exp. Biol. Med.*, **79**, 319 (1952).

[21] O'Brien, B. R. A., *Exp. Cell Res.*, **21**, 226 (1960); O'Brien, B. R. A., *J. Embryol. Exp. Morphol.*, **8**, 202 (1961).

[22] D'Amelio, V. and A. M. Salvo, *Acta Embryol. Morphol. Exper.*, **2**, 118 (1959); D'Amelio, V. and A. M. Salvo, *Zeit. f. Natur-forsch.*, **14**, 455 (1959); D'Amelio, V. and A. M. Salvo, *Exp. Cell Res.*, **18**, 364 (1959); D'Amelio, V. and A. M. Salvo, *Acta Embryol. Morphol. Exper.*, **4**, 250 (1961).

[23] Beard, R. G., in *Annual Report of Carnegie Institution of Washington, Dept. of Embryology*, No. **57** (1958), p. 336, Ebert, J. D., *ibid.*, No. **57** (1958), p. 337; Beard, R. G., *ibid.*, No. **58** (1959), p. 389.

Control of Specific Synthesis in the Developing Pancreas[1]

WILLIAM J. RUTTER[2]

NORMAN K. WESSELLS

CLIFFORD GROBSTEIN

Embryonic differentiation includes the selective control of cell proliferation and the expression of diversified morphology and physiological function. The chemical mechanisms of regulation of such complicated processes may be exceedingly varied but, at least at present, they all share the common feature of being unknown. Many basic principles of development at the cell and tissue level, however, have been defined; for example, there is considerable evidence to suggest that distinctive cell types frequently develop from an interaction between dissimilar precursor tissues. As summarized in Table 1, a number of organ systems arise from an association of mesenchyme, a tissue composed primarily of fibroblast-like cells that characteristically produce an extracellular matrix of collagen and other materials, and epithelium, a highly ordered, closely packed system of cells with little extracellular material. The results of experiments *in vivo* and *in vitro* have supported the concept of an epithelium-mesenchymal interaction. Experiments *in vivo*, involving removal or transposition of the interacting elements or the interposition of a suitable barrier between them, have been intrinsically informative, but the major experimental evidence defining the interaction has been derived from experiments *in vitro* involving separation and recombination of the tissue elements. The morphological features of differentiation are produced only in the presence of both tissue components. The demonstration of morphogenesis of organ rudiments *in vitro* is especially significant from an experimental point of view, since it implies that at least some phases of cytodifferentiation can be obtained *in vitro* and, thus, are generally susceptible to more searching kinds of analyses. The further demonstration of an interaction of the tissues across a filter membrane under conditions *in vitro* (6, 7, 14, 21), for example, indicated that direct cell contact among the tissues was not necessary but that diffusible or at least mobile substances were causally involved.

Of the various possibilities for an analysis at the molecular level of tissue interactions leading to cytodifferentiation, the pancreas system was chosen because, in addition to distinctive morphological changes, differentiation in this tissue leads to the production of

Symposium: Metabolic Control Mechanisms. National Cancer Institute Monograph, No. 13: 51–65, 1964. Government Printing Office, Washington, D.C.

[1] Presented at the Symposium on Metabolic Control Mechanisms in Animal Cells, Boston, Mass., May 27–30, 1963.

[2] John Simon Guggenheim Memorial Fellow, 1963–64.

TABLE 1. Epithelium-mesenchyme interactions in embryonic development

Organ	*In Vivo* Removal, Transposition, or Interference	In Vitro Separation and Direct Recombination	Separation and Recombination Transfilter
Kidney	+ (1)	+	+ (2–4)
Salivary		+	+ (5, 6)
Thymus		+	+ (7)
Pancreas		+	+ (8)
Thyroid		+	(9)
Pituitary		+	(10)
Mammary		+	(11)
Lung		+	(12)
Skin	+ (13)	+	+ (15, 16)
Feather	+ (17)	+	− (18, 19)
Limb bud	+ (20–23)		

a number of chemically well-characterized enzymes and hormones. The appearance of these substances, therefore, could be used to quantitatively assess the differentiation process.

Golosow and Grobstein (8) have already defined some pertinent developmental features of this system: 1) Morphogenesis of pancreatic epithelium occurs *in vitro* if mesenchymal tissue is present; 2) the tissue interaction can occur across a filter membrane; and 3) a variety of mesenchymal tissues are effective in supporting the morphogenesis (in contrast to some systems in which there is apparently a more specific requirement for a particular mesenchymal tissue). The experimental system of Golosow and Grobstein (8), employed in the present study, is schematically presented in Plate-fig. 1. The pancreatic rudiment was dissected from an 11-day mouse and separated into mesenchyme and epithelial portions by appropriate incubation in trypsin solution and subsequent mechanical agitation with a micropipette. The epithelial rudiment was then quartered into sections, each containing approximately 1,500 cells (22), and each section placed on a separate filter assembly by means of a plasma clot. The mesenchyme was dissected from another pancreatic rudiment, or more usually from the salivary rudiment, of a 13-day mouse embryo and placed on top of the filter. The assembly was then put in the well of a suitable culture dish containing the basal medium and incubated at 38°C. The appearance of typical cultures during incubation is shown at the bottom of Plate-fig. 1. Fell (22), in this laboratory, showed that the cell number increased about 30 times during a 5-day culture period, but proliferation was most rapid during the 2d and 3d day. During this period the cells organized into acinar clusters that could be recognized visually in living epithelia as small doughnut-like structures. At the end of the 4th day or beginning of the 5th, the cultures became optically opaque, presumably due to the intracellular accumulation of the specific pancreatic products. In the system without mesenchyme, the epithelium spreads, usually without developing a perceptible morphological pattern and certainly without the formation of optically dense regions. The rate of cell proliferation was also significantly lower in the absence of mesenchyme (24, 25). This system, therefore, involves the regulation of cell duplication as well as specific morphological and presumably metabolic events.

The present work primarily concerns the process of development of specific metabolic function in this system. The aim has been, first, to characterize the kinetics of appearance of a specific pancreatic product, the enzyme amylase, and second, to employ amylase activity measurements as a quantitative indication of functional differentiation to define some characteristics of the epithelium-mesenchymal interaction.

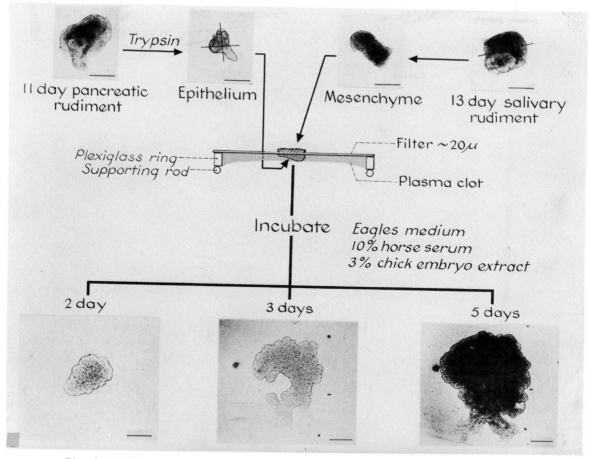

Plate-fig. 1. Schematic representation of experimental procedure for pancreatic morphogenesis *in vitro*. The experimental procedure involves (1) dissection and separation of embryonic tissues (*first line* of photographs); (2) appropriate placement of tissues on filter assembly: pieces of pancreatic epithelium on underside of the filter in a plasma clot, the mesenchyme stranded on upper side of the filter; and (3) incubation of filter assemblies under defined nutritional conditions, at 38°C, 5 percent CO_2 and air.

Solid line below each tissue indicates 150 μ. Internal diameter of the filter assembly is 3.3 mm. The relative size on filter assembly of the mesenchyme and epithelium is overemphasized by approximately twofold and tenfold, respectively. The appearance of typical pancreatic epithelia after various periods of culture is indicated by photographs at *bottom* of figure. The camera was focused on the underside of the filter directly on the epithelial tissue. The mesenchyme spread diffusely on the upper filter membrane contributes to the background.

Amylase Activity during Development of the Pancreatic Epithelium in Vivo and in Vitro

The enzyme amylase was chosen for the present studies because it is a prominent product of the pancreas and can be assayed conveniently. The classical amylase assay, involving the disappearance of the starch-iodine chromophore, was readily modified (*23*) to an appropriate degree of sensitivity (approximately 10^6 enzyme molecules, assuming the turnover number of the mouse and hog pancreas enzymes is the same). Protein was measured by a microadaptation (*23*) of the Folin-Lowry method (*26*), sensitive to about 0.2 μg protein. All the experimental results are expressed in terms of specific activity; thus,

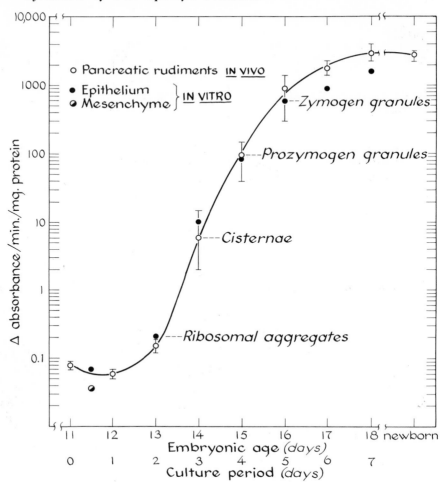

Text-fig. 1. Amylase activity in the developing pancreas and correlation with intracellular structures. *Open circles* represent the specific activity of intact pancreatic rudiments (epithelium + mesenchyme) dissected from embryos. *Points* represent averages of approximately 40 rudiments in early periods and steadily decrease to about 20 at later embryonic stages. *Solid bars* indicate the range of values in the experimental sample. *Closed circles* present the average specific amylase activity of *in vitro* pancreatic epithelia cultures at various intervals. At the early times more than 75 cultures were included in these analyses. At later culture periods this number decreased to 30. The dispersion about the average value was similar to that found in the intact rudiment. *Half-closed circles* represent amylase specific activity of salivary mesenchyme used in the experiments (24 mesenchymal tissues). Kallman's observations (27) of the approximate time of the appearance of intracellular structures, robosomal aggregates, cisternae, prozymogen granules, and zymogen granules are indicated by *dotted lines*.

differences reflect changes in the proportion of this enzyme activity relative to other proteins in the system.

Text-fig. 1 shows the specific activity of amylase in pancreatic rudiments isolated from mice embryos at various ages and also of the pancreatic epithelia at various periods of culture. Eleven- and 12-day rudiments exhibited a low level of activity (less than 10 molecules of amylase/cell, again assuming the turnover number of the mouse pancreas enzyme is the same as the hog pancreas enzyme). In rudiments from 13-day embryos there was a significant increase in specific amylase activity and in subsequent days it increased to about 50,000-fold over the basal level. The specific activity of amylase in cultures followed closely that of the directly isolated rudiments, at least during the first 5 days in culture. After longer periods there was greater variability in the activity of individual cultures and some central necrosis was often observed, perhaps as a result of the release and "activation" of hydrolytic enzymes. A major source of variation in analyses *in vivo* and *in vitro* was the uncertainty of the age of the embryos ($\pm$ 12 hours), but the generally satisfactory correlation in the development of amylase activity in the two systems with respect to both time course and quantitative amylase accumulation suggested that the *in vitro* system is an adequate reflection of the *in vivo* phenomenon.

The specific amylase activity in mesenchyme tissue does not change appreciably during the culture period, but, if environmental influences are causally related to the changes observed in the pancreatic epithelium, they are without effect on mesenchyme cells.

The data presented here complement other studies on the developing pancreas. Kallman (27), with the electron microscope, observed the fine structure of cells during the process of pancreatic morphogenesis, especially in the *in vitro* culture system. Abundant ribosomal aggregates were seen throughout the initial 2 days of culture. In view of the recent studies in reticulocytes, these might be the functional units of protein synthesis (28, 29). At approximately the time of initial rise in amylase activity, presumably indicating an increase in amylase synthesis, isolated rough membranes (cisternae) were detected in a few cells. The number and size of the cisternae increased in a more or less parallel fashion with the increase in specific activity of amylase during continued cultivation. In the later periods of culture, prozymogen granules containing relatively little material were observed, and grandually the heavily packed zymogen granules accumulated. The zymogen granules, no doubt, are largely responsible for the opacity of differentiated epithelial cultures. These combined studies suggest a smoothly coordinated sequence of cytological events in which synthesis of amylase, and probably other pancreatic enzymes, is correlated with the formation of intracellular structures that are probably involved in their synthesis storage and secretion.

Wessells (30) has shown by a combination of autoradiographic and cytological methods that the cell proliferation occurring throughout the culture period is primarily localized in the outer regions of the tissue; differentiation, on the other hand, proceeds in the internal areas where there are few, if any, mitoses and little DNA turnover. The kinetics of amylase increase shown in Text-fig. 1, therefore, is not a reflection of the synchronous differentiation of a homogeneous population of cells, but represents the integrated activities of cells in different stages of differentiation. Rather than the time scale on the figure, therefore, as little as 2 days may be required from the initiation of specific synthesis in a particular cell until it is packed with zymogen granules. If the increase in amylase activity is a result of synthesis of new enzyme molecules, and if the turnover number of a single protein synthesizing unit is approximately one protein molecule per minute (24, 25), then the number of enzyme molecules produced per cell (employing the turnover number of the hog pancreas enzyme) during the period of amylase accumulation (3–5 days of culture) would require about 20 to 40 amylase synthesizing units per cell. Because only a limited population of the cells is involved in zymogen granule formation (30) and because the time of synthesis of amylase may be several minutes, the number of amylase synthesizing units may be higher by as much as an order of magnitude in the cells involved in the synthesis of this protein.

REPLACEMENT OF MESENCHYME REQUIREMENT FOR PANCREATIC EPITHELIUM DIFFERENTIATION BY EMBRYO PARTICLE FRACTION

In subsequent experiments the level of specific amylase activity was used as a quantitative indication of differentiation. These

TABLE 2. Mesenchymal competence for supporting pancreatic epithelial differentiation

Organ	Morphogenesis*	Amylase Specific Activity (Δ Absorbance/ Min/mg Protein)
Salivary	+	800
Pancreas	+	240
Kidney	+	—
Lung	+	—
Stomach	+	—
Spleen	+	300
General mesenchyme	+	—

* In part from Golosow and Grobstein (8).

measurements were also correlated with visual observations of optically dense areas, which presumably reflect the presence of zymogen granules and are represented by positive (+) morphogenesis.

Attempts to simplify the differentiative system were in part based on the finding, illustrated by the data in Table 2, that a variety of mesenchymal tissues are competent to support morphogenesis of pancreatic epithelium. The embryo, it was reasoned, was so sufficiently enriched with mesenchymal tissues that an extract of the whole embryo might be effective in replacing intact mesenchyme in this system. The results of an experiment designed to test the action of a crude extract of embryo in this system are reported in Table 3. In the absence of embryo extract, no differentiation was observed. In confirmation of previous studies, the presence of 3 percent

embryo extract supported differentiation in the presence, but not in the absence, of mesenchyme. Higher levels of embryo extract did not apparently affect the system in the presence of mesenchyme, but supported cytodifferentiation in the absence of added mesenchyme. With high levels of embryo extract, the cultures resembled those obtained with added mesenchyme, both in general size and amylase specific activity. Hence the embryo extract replaced the significant features of the mesenchyme effect in these cultures.

The results of assays for the factor or factors supporting pancreatic development in fractions from embryo extract are shown in Table 4. The activity was broadly distributed within the sedimentable fractions and was virtually absent from the "soluble" fractions. Various methods of extraction in both balanced-salt (Tyrode's solution) and sucrose

TABLE 3. Requirements for *in vitro* differentiation of pancreatic epithelium

Experiment	Culture Conditions		Morphogenesis†	Analysis 5-Day Cultures	
	Mesenchyme	Chicken Embryo* Extract (%)		Amylase Specific Activity (Δ Absorbance/Min/mg Protein)	
				Mesenchyme	Epithelium
1	+	0	—	None detected ($<$ 0.2)	4
2	+	3	+ +		250
3	+	20	+ +		220
4	—	3	—		None detected ($<$ 0.5)
5	—	10	+ +		165
6	—	20	+ +		240

* Concentration based on volumes of crude embryo extract [embryos extracted with an equal volume of Tyrode's solution under defined conditions (23)].
† Microscopic evidence of zymogen granules in cultures.

TABLE 4.   Differentiative activity of embryo extract fractions

Experi-ment	Fraction Tested at 20 Percent Level*	Analysis 5-Day Cultures	
		Morphogenesis	Amylase Specific Activity (Δ Absorbance/ Min/mg Protein)
1	Initial extract	+ +	370
2	1000 $\times$ g Sediment	+ +	300
3	1000–10,000 $\times$ g Sediment	+ +	235
4	10,000–100,000 $\times$ g Sediment	+ +	330
5	100,000 $\times$ g Supernatant	−	2
6	Ultrafiltrate	−	< 0.5
7	10,000–100,000 $\times$ g Sediment + 100,000 $\times$ g Supernatant	+	130

* Based on volume of fractions (sedimentable, suspended in 0.3 initial extract volume).

media have all given fractions in which the biological activity is broadly distributed. The "differentiative activity" in the fractions, based on protein or mass, was higher in the fraction sedimenting between 10,000 and 100,000 $\times$ g, but this may be misleading since there is some evidence suggesting that the observed activity is influenced by the state of aggregation of the material; we have thus hesitated to express the "differentiative activity" in terms of specific activity.

As shown in Table 5, adult liver microsomal and mitochondria fractions prepared by standard procedures, as well as DNA and RNA, were all inactive when tested over a wide range of concentrations. In addition, collagen, which is produced more or less specifically by mesenchymal tissues, was also inactive over a wide range of concentrations.

Results of studies on the effect of some hydrolytic enzymes on the activity of the active fractions are shown in Table 6. Ribonuclease- and deoxyribonuclease-treated particle fractions still retained their biological activity under conditions in which the respective substrates were hydrolyzed rapidly. These experiments appear to rule out soluble nucleic acids as the dominant factors in this system, but, of course, do not rule out forms of nucleic acids unavailable to the enzymes. Treat-

TABLE 5.   Effect of cell fractions and specific macromolecules on differentiation of pancreatic epithelium

Experi-ment	Additions to:	Concentration*	Analysis 5-Day Cultures	
			Morpho-genesis	Amylase Specific Activity (Δ Ab-sorbance/Min/mg Protein)
1	Adult liver microsomal fraction	0.4–20%*†	−	None detected
2	Adult liver mitochondrial fraction	1–20%*†	−	(< 0.5)
3	DNA (salmon sperm)	10–1000 μg/ml*	−	(< 0.5)
4	RNA (yeast)	10–1000 μg/ml*	−	(< 0.5)
5	Collagen (calf skin)	20–4000 μg/ml*	−	(< 0.5)
6	Embryonic 100,000 $\times$ g sediment	20%‡	+ +	540

* At high concentrations cultures became necrotic.
† Based on volumes of cell fractions obtained from a 1 : 10 homogenate according to conventional procedures.
‡ Based on volumes of 10–100,000 $\times$ g sediment suspended in 0.3 volume original extract of embryo extract.

TABLE 6.   Effect of hydrolytic enzymes on differentiative activity of embryo particle fraction

Experiment	Treatment of 100,000 × g Particle Fraction (Min)*	Analysis 5-Day Cultures	
		Morphogenesis	Amylase Specific Activity (Δ Absorbance/Min/mg Protein)
1	None	++	480
2	Ribonuclease, 60	++	500
3	Deoxyribonuclease, 60	++	480
4	Trypsin, 15	+	40
5	Trypsin, 60	−	0.5
6	Trypsin + trypsin inhibitor, 60	++	100
7	Trypsin inhibitor, 60	++	560

* All incubations were carried out at 38° C.

ment with trypsin, on the other hand, destroys the activity in the fractions. The partial loss of activity in fractions treated with trypsin and the trypsin inhibitor suggests that the trypsin inhibitor does not completely inhibit the enzyme under these conditions, since incubation in the presence of inhibitor alone does not significantly change the activity over controls. These data suggest that protein may play a dominant role in the biological effect, but in this complex system secondary effects cannot be ruled out. The fact that the material is found in embryonic cells, but not in adult tissues so far tested, suggests that the active material is primarily concentrated in embryonic tissues. The general characteristics of the particle fractions suggest the differentiative activity may reside in the intracellular matrix or may be bound to the cell membrane. The questions of: (1) the possible multiplicity of active factors and (2) whether the action of mesenchyme and embryo fractions are mediated by the same molecules may be resolved by isolation and characterization of the active substance(s).

Effect of Actinomycin D on the Differentiation of Pancreatic Epithelium

Some initial experiments on the nature of the differentiative process have centered about the events during the early period of development of pancreatic epithelia *in vitro*. It is considered significant that the system becomes independent of mesenchyme and embryo fractions about the time of the initial rise in amylase activity. This correlation suggests that the action of the particle fraction may be to initiate or support a series of events culminating in the development of an effective synthesizing system for the specific pancreatic enzymes. An approach to the examination of this postulate has employed specific inhibitors. Inhibition of specific protein synthesis by actinomycin D may reflect a requirement for DNA-dependent RNA synthesis (*31, 32*) during the period of observation. Preliminary experiments have shown that treatment of the pancreatic epithelia with 1 μg per ml of actinomycin D, a concentration usually used for inhibition of RNA synthesis, resulted in loss of viability of the cultures. But at a concentration of 0.01 μg per ml inhibition of growth was observed, though the cells appeared healthy and mitotic activity was observed. The results of some of the experiments testing the effect of this low level of actinomycin D on differentiation of pancreatic epithelium in the presence of mesenchyme and embryo particle fractions are summarized in Plate-fig. 2. Cultures were treated with actinomycin D for a 5-hour period at various times of culture. The cultures were then incubated for the remainder of the 5-day period. There is a gradient of sensitivity of the cultures according to the period of treatment, e.g., when cultures are treated from 48 to 53 hours, the tissues grow but produce only a few zymogen granules. The specific activity of amylase is far below that normally found in 5-day cul-

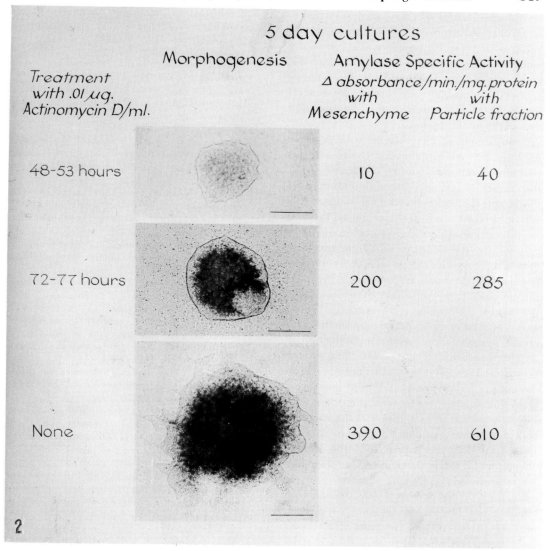

Plate-fig. 2. Effect of actinomycin D on differentiation of pancreatic epithelium. Pancreatic epithelia cultures in the presence of mesenchyme or the 10,000–100,000 × *g* sediment fraction from 9-day chicken embryo extract (suspended in culture medium) were treated with actinomycin D for periods indicated. Afterward cultures were washed 3 times with Tyrode's solution and incubated with standard culture medium (with embryo particle fraction where appropriate) until 120 hours total culture period (media were changed at 24-hour intervals). Morphogenesis is indicated by photographs of typical cultures at 120 hours. *Solid line below* cultures indicates 200 μ. The amylase specific activities are average analysis of approximately 40 cultures (treatment 48–53 hours), of approximately 30 cultures (treatment 72–77 hours), and approximately 30 cultures (no treatment).

tures but is more than in normal 48- to 53-hour cultures; therefore, there is apparently a limited continued synthesis of amylase under these conditions. On the other hand, at 72 hours the system is more refractory to actinomycin D; the subsequent synthesis of amylase and the visual evidence of zymogen granule formation approach that of untreated cultures. Prolonged cultivation of the tissues does not appreciably alter these results. Thus the data are consistent with the postulate that a relatively long-lived messenger RNA, necessary for the synthesis of specific pancreas enzymes, is synthesized from 48 to 72 hours in the cultures of these experiments. The generally similar results in the experiments in which the active particulate fraction from the embryo replaced the mesenchyme confirm the general similarity of the action of this fraction and that of the mesenchyme.

Pretreatment of mesenchyme with as much as 1 μg per ml actinomycin D did not apparently affect the viability of these cells or the ability to support the differentiation of the pancreatic epithelium. This suggests the active product may perhaps be synthesized by the cells routinely and is not produced in response to the addition of epithelium. The data are suggestive of an action by the active particulate fraction and mesenchyme on the genome of the epithelial cell, which makes it available for specific RNA synthesis.

Action of the embryo fraction on the pancreatic system cannot be enzyme induction in its simplest form: There is an effect on the growth and morphogenesis of the cells within the culture before the synthesis of messenger RNA for amylase; moreover, there is a considerable period after addition of the particles before specific synthesis of amylase begins. Indeed, it is not claimed that the mesenchyme or the active particulate fractions confer an essential "pancreatic character" on the epithelium. The pancreatic epithelium obtained from 11-day mouse embryos already may be biased in the direction of pancreas formation. The possibility that these particulate fractions instead may play a more general role in supporting the differentiation of a number of epithelia must be considered. It is thus possible that the discovery of the particulate fractions is of more relevance to the problem of obtaining differentiative behavior under conditions *in vitro* than to one of classical embryonic induction. What is perhaps most significant from all of this is that this experimental system appears to be willing to tell us more.

REFERENCES

1. Gruenwald, P.: Development of the excretory system. *Ann NY Acad Sci* 55: 142–146, 1952.

2. Grobstein, C.: Inductive interaction in the development of the mouse metanephros. *J Exp Zool* 130: 319–340, 1955.

3. ———: Transfilter induction of tubules in mouse metanephrogenic mesenchyme. *Exp Cell Res* 10: 424–440, 1956.

4. Grobstein, C., and A. J. Dalton: Kidney tubule induction in mouse metanephrogenic mesenchyme without cytoplasmic contact. *J Exp Zool* 135: 57–74, 1957.

5. Grobstein, C.: Analysis *in vitro* of the early organization of the rudiment of the mouse submandibular gland. *J Morphol* 93: 19–43, 1953.

6. ———: Morphogenetic interaction between embryonic mouse tissues separated by a membrane filter. *Nature* (London) 172: 869–871, 1953.

7. Auerbach, R.: Morphogenetic interactions in the development of the mouse thymus gland. *Develop Biol* 2: 271–284, 1960.

8. Golosow, N., and C. Grobstein: Epithelio-mesenchymal interaction in pancreatic morphogenesis. *Develop Biol* 4: 242–255, 1962.

9. Hilfer, S. R.: The stability of embryonic chick thyroid cells *in vitro* as judged by morphological and physiological criteria. *Develop Biol* 4: 1–21, 1962.

10. Sobel. H.: The behavior *in vitro* of dissociated embryonic pituitary tissue. *J Embryol Exp Morph* 6: 518–526, 1958.

11. Lasfargues, E. Y.: Cultivation and behavior *in vitro* of the normal mammary epithelium of the adult mouse. II. Observations on the secretory activity. *Exp Cell Res* 13: 553–562, 1957.

12. Dameron, F.: L'influence de divers mesenchymes sur la différenciation de l'epithelium pulmonaire de l'embryon de poulet en culture *in vitro*. *J. Embryol Exp Morph* 9: 628–633, 1961.

13. McLoughlin, C. B.: The importance of mesenchymal factors in the differentiation of chick epidermis. II. Modification of epidermal differentiation by contact with different types of mesenchyme. *J Embryol Exp Morph* 9: 385–409, 1961.

14. Wessells, N. K.: Tissue interactions during skin histodifferentiation. *Develop Biol* 4: 87–107, 1962.

15. Dodson, J. W.: On the nature of tissue interactions in embryonic skin. *Exp Cell Res* 31: 233–235, 1963.

16. Cavins, J. M., and J. W. Saunders: The influence of embryonic mesoderm on the regional specification of epidermal derivatives in the chick. *J Exp Zool* 127: 221–248, 1954.

17. Sengel, P.: La différenciation de la peau et des germes plumaires de l'embryon de poulet en culture *in vitro*. *Ann Biol* 34: 29–52, 1958.

18. Wessells, N. K.: Unpublished data.

19. Zwilling, E.: Interaction between ectoderm and mesoderm in duck-chicken limb bud chimaeras. *J Exp Zool* 142: 521–532, 1959.

20. Bell, E., M. T. Gasseling, J. W. Saunders, Jr., and E. Zwilling: On the role of ectoderm in limb development. *Develop Biol* 4: 177–196, 1962.

21. Saunders, J. W., Jr., and M. T. Gasseling: Trans-filter propagation of apical ectoderm maintenance factor in the chick embryo wing bud. *Develop Biol* 7: 64–78, 1963.

22. Fell, P., and C. Grobstein: Unpublished observations.

23. Rutter, W. J.: Unpublished data.

24. Loftfield, R. B., and E. A. Eigner: The time required for the synthesis of a ferritin molecule in rat liver. *J Biol Chem* 231: 925–943, 1958.

25. Dintzis, H. M.: Assembly of the peptide chains of hemoglobin. *Proc Nat Acad Sci USA* 47: 247–261, 1961.

26. Lowry, O. H., N. J. Roseborough, A. L. Farr, and R. J. Randall: Protein measurement with the Folin phenol reagent. *J Biol Chem* 193: 265–275, 1951.

27. Kallman, P., and C. Grobstein: Fine structure of differentiating mouse pancreatic exocrine cells in culture. *J Cell Biol* 20: 399–413, 1964.

28. Warner, J. R., P. M. Knapf, and A. Rich: A multiple ribosomal structure in protein synthesis. *Proc Nat Acad Sci USA* 49: 122–129, 1963.

29. Gierer, A.: Function of aggregated reticulocyte ribosomes in protein synthesis. *J Molec Biol* 6: 148–157, 1963.

30. Wessells, N. K.: DNA synthesis, mitosis, and differentiation in pancreatic acinar cells *in vitro. J Cell Biol* 20: 415–433, 1964.

31. Reich, E., R. M. Franklin, A. J. Shatkin, and E. L. Tatum: Action of actinomycin D on animal cells and viruses. *Proc Nat Acad Sci USA* 48: 1238–1245, 1962.

32. Hurwitz, J., J. J. Furth, M. Malamy, and M. Alexander: The role of deoxyribonucleic acid in ribonucleic acid synthesis. III. The inhibition of the enzymatic synthesis of ribonucleic acid and deoxyribonucleic acid by actinomycin D and proflavin. *Proc Nat Acad Sci USA* 48: 1222–1230, 1962.

Yolk Protein Uptake in the Oocyte of the Mosquito *Aedes Aegypti* L.

THOMAS F. ROTH

KEITH R. PORTER

Abstract. *Yolk proteins are thought to enter certain eggs by a process akin to micropinocytosis but the detailed mechanism has not been previously depicted. In this study the formation of protein yolk was investigated in the mosquito* Aedes aegypti *L. Ovaries were fixed in phosphate-buffered osmium tetroxide, for electron microscopy, before and at intervals after a meal of blood. The deposition of protein yolk in the oocyte was correlated with a 15-fold increase in 140 mμ pit-like depressions on the oocyte surface. These pits form by invagination of the oocyte cell membrane. They have a 20 mμ bristle coat on their convex cytoplasmic side. They also show a layer of protein on their concave extracellular side which we propose accumulates by selective adsorption from the extraoocyte space. The pits, by pinching off from the cell membrane become bristle-coated vesicles which carry the adsorbed protein into the oocyte. These vesicles lose the coat and then fuse to form small crystalline yolk droplets, which subsequently coalesce to form the large proteid yolk bodies of the mature oocyte. Preliminary radioautographs, and certain morphological features of the fat body, ovary, and midgut, suggest that the midgut is the principal site of yolk protein synthesis in the mosquito.*

In 1932 Jukes and Kay (21) suggested that yolk protein of the egg of the domestic fowl

Reprinted by permission of The Rockefeller Instate Press, from *Journal of Cell Biology*, 1964, 20, 313–332.

is chemically related to the serum proteins of the laying hen. Since then, several investigators (7, 19, 20, 24, 25, 38, 42, 43, 45) have confirmed this finding, and the concept has grown that chicken yolk protein is made in the liver and transported via the circulation to the egg for storage. Similar studies with the frog (14–18) and rat (27) have also shown egg protein to be nearly identical with protein species found in the maternal serum. Of further significance in this regard is the finding that foreign proteins introduced into the circulation appear in the yolk protein substantially unchanged (4, 24).

These observations on oogenesis in the vertebrates as well as Telfer's work with an invertebrate, a saturniid moth (48–50) demonstrate conclusively that, in many instances of egg protein production and deposition, the protein species is made outside of the ovary, probably in the liver or an analogous organ, is secreted into the extracellular spaces, and is then removed from the circulating blood by the developing egg. There are exceptions to this general scheme, one of which is found in the crayfish, which appears to have a highly developed synthetic mechanism in the oocyte cytoplasm for the formation of yolk protein (3).

In the case of the mosquito, which is the object of this study, there are reasons to suppose that yolk deposition in the developing oocyte is accomplished also by removal of the protein from the blood of the insect. In the first place, yolk develops rapidly. In fact, synthesis and storage are essentially completed in as little as 25 hours after a blood meal. Concomitantly, none of the usual structural mechanisms associated with rapid synthesis of protein or lipoprotein, especially for segregation and storage in granules, appear in the fine structure of the follicle cells or the oocyte cytoplasm. Indeed, only one unusual structural feature does appear, which seemingly might be involved in yolk deposition, and that is an elaborate development of pits or wells in the surface of the oocyte. It is the major purpose of this report to describe these pits and to present reasons for interpreting

them as surface differentiations designed specifically for protein uptake and transport into the oocyte.

MATERIALS AND METHODS

The ovary of the adult mosquito *Aedes aegypti* L. was studied. The insects were raised by routine methods (51) at 27°C, and the adult form maintained on raisins until needed. The full development and maturation of oocytes was initiated by feeding 1-week-old adults on the shaved back of a rabbit. Thereafter the mosquitoes were sacrificed at intervals as indicated in the next section. To facilitate handling them, the mosquitoes were chilled to 4°C just prior to fixation.

In preparation for light microscopy, entire mosquitoes sacrificed at various intervals after a blood meal were fixed for 6 hours at 4°C in 10 per cent aqueous acrolein (according to the methods of Feder (12, 13) as modified below). The mosquitoes were then dehydrated in a graded series of 1 : 1 methyl alcohol/1-methoxyethanol, and the abdomens were removed and infiltrated under vacuum for 3 days in six changes of a mixture of 95 per cent glycol methacrylate, 5 per cent Carbowax, and 0.3 per cent α-azodiisobutyronitrile as a catalyst. The final change of the infiltration mixture was allowed to polymerize for 3 days at 60°C before 1.5 μ sections were cut from the blocks. The sections were stained with aqueous 0.5 per cent toluidine blue and 1 per cent acid fuchsin.

For electron microscopic examination, the mosquitoes were fixed with 2 per cent osmium tetroxide, buffered at pH 6.8 and 7.3 according to Millonig (29). Abdomens were removed at predetermined intervals and the cuticles slit to allow rapid penetration of the fixative; fixation was continued for a period of 3 to 4 hours at 4°C. The tissues were thereafter rapidly dehydrated in increasing concentrations of alcohol, with interruption only in 50 per cent alcohol to permit dissection of the ovaries from the abdomen. After dehydration and exposure to two 5-minute changes of propylene oxide, the tissues were infiltrated overnight in a 1 : 1 mixture of propylene oxide and the embeding monomer of Epon. After a fresh change of monomer, the tissues were flat embedded and polymerized at 60°C for 2 days. The embedding monomer was a 1 : 1 mixture of methyl nadic anhydride (MNA)/Epon 812 accelerated with 0.5 per cent 2,4,6-tri(dimethylaminomethyl)phenol (26), which gives very hard blocks.

Sections were cut for the most part on a Cambridge (Huxley) microtome. The "silver" sections were mounted on either carbon stabilized celloidin or uncoated grids. Lead staining according to Millonig (30), or Karnovsky (22) at a dilution of 20:1, gave excellent contrast relatively free of contamination. The sectioned material was examined in an EMU 3 (RCA) or a Philips EM 200.

The mosquitoes that were used for the experiment with labeled leucine were fed on the legs and tail of a 14 gm rat that had been injected intraperitoneally 30 hours previously with 6 mc of L-leucine-H^3 (specific activity 5.0 c/mM) in 0.5 cc water. At intervals of 0.5, 1, 2, 4.5, 16, and 30 hours thereafter, the mosquitoes were sacrificed and embedded for light microscopy. Sections 1.5 μ thick were cut on a Porter-Blum Servall microtome and prepared for autoradiography, following the methods of Caro and van Tubergen (6). Twelve weeks later, the sections were developed, and the number of silver grains compared with the aid of a phase microscope.

OBSERVATIONS

The structure of the mosquito ovary has been described in detail in several light microscope studies (8, 31–33, 36, 41) and is perhaps best summarized in Christophers' monograph (9). It is important to review first this work and current observations on the structure of the ovary at the time when its development in the adult has reached a steady state. This plateau occurs by 3 days after emergence and persists until the adult feeds on blood. This act of feeding initiates a second stage in ovarian development which culminates in the formation of the mature egg.

The Resting Stage

The ovaries of the mosquito lie in the abdomen between the fourth and sixth segments. Each ovary (Fig. 1), consisting of approximately sixty ovarioles, is contained by a muscular mesothelium beneath which lie many tracheae (Fig. 2). Each ovariole in turn is enwrapped by a thin squamous mesothelium of cells showing a kind of striated myofibril (Fig. 3). The ovarioles contain a maturing follicle, a presumptive follicle, and a germarium, and each of the meroistic-polytrophic follicles is comprised of seven nurse cells and one oocyte within a follicular epithelium.

The cells of the follicular epithelium are at this stage cuboidal with large nuclei and little cytoplasm. They are closely applied to each other and joined, neighbor to neighbor, at their apical margins by desmosomes. Their basal surfaces rest on a basement membrane (Fig. 3). At higher magnifications provided by electron microscopy, the nuclei of these cells are seen to have a prominent polymorphic nucleolus enveloped by distinctly granular chromosomal elements superimposed on a lighter nucleoplasm (Fig. 2). The nuclear envelope possesses numerous pores. The cytoplasm, which is relatively sparse in amount, is rich in ribosomes but poor in elements of the endoplasmic reticulum (ER). These flattened cisternae are rough surfaced and occur most especially in the basal halves of the follicle cells. Mitochondria are numerous and possess well ordered, parallel arrays of cristae and several dense granules which in other types of cells are binding sites for divalent cations (37). Occasional Golgi elements and infrequent lysosomes are the other major inclusions.

The single oocyte and seven nurse cells reside beneath the follicular epithelium. The nurse cells, to be described more fully in a subsequent paper, are relatively large (27 μ), the nuclei alone having the width of three follicular epithelial cells. The granular nucleoplasm, with several discrete nucleoli, is limited by a nuclear envelope perforated by

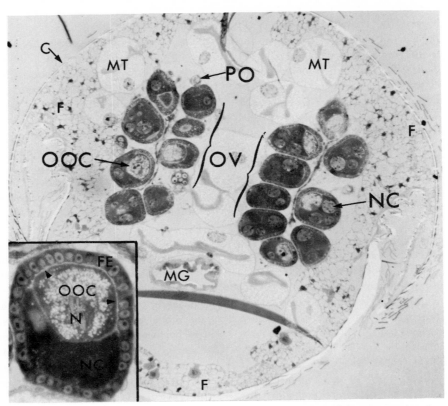

Fig. 1. A light micrograph of a cross-section through a mosquito abdomen at a time just prior to yolk deposition. The section was stained with toluidine blue and acid fuchsin. The ovaries consist of two clusters of ovarioles (*OV*) situated centrally with respect to the spongy fat body (*F*) which encircles the abdomen beneath the cuticle (*C*). A presumptive follicle (*PO*) is joined to each maturing follicle in the region of the nurse cells (NC). The oocyte (*OOC*) is easily identified by the clear, non-staining lipid inclusions in its cytoplasm. In the Malphigian tubules (*MT*) the refractile inclusions, polytene chromosomes, and the lumen are especially evident. An undistended, scalloped midgut (*MG*) is situated in the central portion of the hemocoel just above a fold in the section. × 150. The inset depicts a single follicle at greater magnification. Two nurse cells (*NC*), at the lower half of the follicle, exhibit intense basophilia in the cytoplasm. Numerous refractile lipid droplets surround the nucleus (*N*) of the oocyte (*OOC*). A light region (arrow heads) at the periphery of the oocyte, just within the follicular epithelium (*FE*), is the zone of yolk protein uptake. × 570.

a large number of pores. Immediately outside the nuclear envelope is an accumulation of dense granular material which probably corresponds to the localized thickening of the nuclear envelope reported earlier in *Drosophila* (23). This material at some places extends about 0.5 μ into the "sea" of ribosomes which represents, in part, the matrix of the cytoplasm. The nurse cells also have many rounded mitochondria, occasional lipid droplets, and a few elements of a rough-surfaced

endoplasmic reticulum scattered throughout the cytoplasm. Although the nurse cells are closely applied to each other and to the oocyte and to the follicular epithelium, no evidence exists of cytoplasmic bridges.

The oocyte, as noted above, is readily identified by its uncommon nucleus in which two distinct bodies stand out against the relatively clear nucleoplasm (Fig. 2). One of these, the nucleolus, is a dense, meandering, polymorphic structure which sends long branches out

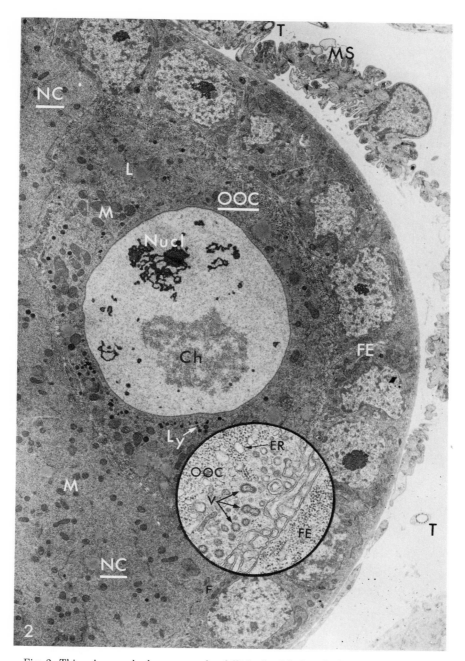

Fig. 2. This micrograph shows part of a follicle fixed before feeding, with a portion of two adjacent nurse cells (NC) and an oocyte (OOC) enclosed by a follicular epithelial layer (FE). A granular, ribosome-filled cytoplasm and scattered mitochondria characterize the nurse cells, while lipid droplets (L), and some denser droplets (LY), clumped chromatin (CH), and complex nucleolus (Nucl) are typical of the oocyte (OOC) at this stage. Great numbers of small, dense vesicles are present in the cortex of the oocyte (see insert). Peripheral to the ovariole is the discontinuous muscular sheath (MS). Tracheoles and trachea (T) lie exterior to this sheath tissue, but within that which surrounds the entire ovary. × 3.700.

The insert depicts at higher magnification a small segment of the vesiculated interface between the oocyte (OOC) and the follicular epithelium (FE). Bristle-coated vesicles (V) and elements of the endoplasmic reticulum (ER) are common in the oocyte cortex immediately beneath the interface. × 20,000.

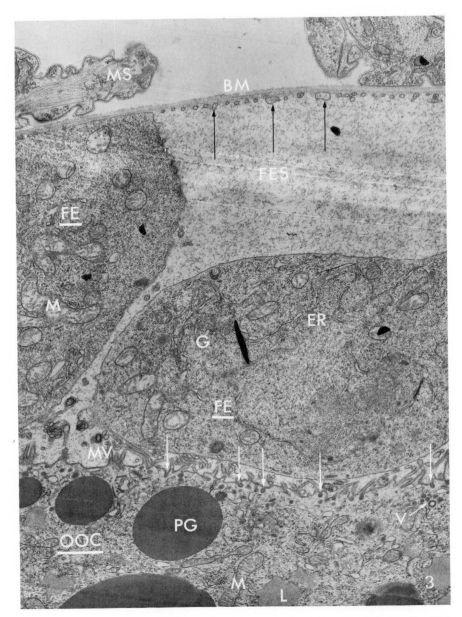

Fig. 3. This micrograph shows parts of two adjacent follicular epithelial cells (*FE*) and an associated oocyte (*OOC*) fixed 7 hours after a blood meal. The follicle cells, separated by large spaces (*FES*), rest upon a typical basement membrane (*BM*). At some points along the basement membrane extremely attenuated extensions of the epithelial cells appear as a row of circular profiles (black arrows). The openings between these provide easy access to the intercellular space for any materials that traverse the basement membrane. The ovariole is covered by a thin reticular sheath of mesothelial cells (*MS*) which contain muscle fibrils. The oocyte at this stage in its development contains large proteid granules (*PG*), lipid droplets (*L*), mitochondria (*M*), and elements of the endoplasmic reticulum in a cytoplasmic matrix rich in ribosomes. The cortical zone, depicted here, possesses other features of special interest. Numerous microvilli (*MV*) extend from the oocyte surface into the intercellular space. Between the microvilli are several small dense pits (white arrows) still continuous with the cell surface. Small pit-derived vesicles (*V*) of the same size, density, and structure as the pits reside in the cortex of the oocyte. A part of a follicle cell in the center shows some profiles of the endoplasmic reticulum (*ER*) and a prominent Golgi component (*G*). × 15,500.

into the nucleoplasm. The other, the chromosomal mass, consists of a unique configuration of synaptic chromosomes which have migrated from their previous peripheral position in the nucleus. This structure will be described in detail elsewhere. The enveloping nuclear membrane, regularly perforated with pores, provides a distinct separation from the rest of the oocyte.

The cytoplasm of the oocyte is characteristically different from that of the surrounding cells (Fig. 2). Mitochondria here are larger with well ordered cristae; dense lysosome-like bodies are more numerous and many multi-lobed lipid droplets are common among the prominent background of free ribosomes. No yolk granules or precursors are evident.

The cortex of the "resting" oocyte is also remarkable in a number of respects. The surface adjacent to the follicular epithelial cells is covered by many unoriented villi. Then, just within this border of microvilli, there are many pit-like invaginations (140 mμ in diameter) of the oocyte membrane and many vesicles with diameters similar to those of the pits (Fig. 2, insert). These structures represent the first manifestation of a cortical differentiation which, as will be described below, appears to prepare the oocyte for the ingestion of large quantities of yolk protein. Although quite numerous even in this early resting stage, before the insect obtains a blood meal, the vesicles and pits are uniformly small and relatively undeveloped as compared with those present later when yolk deposition begins. This uniformity of size and structure is an important point in interpreting subsequent changes in this region. By contrast, that part of the oocyte facing the nurse cells shows relatively few microvilli, pits, and pit-vesicles.

The structure of the "resting" follicle constitutes the base-line on which the substantial alterations that occur in the oocyte of the blood-fed mosquito may be superimposed. A meal of blood or a controlled diet (44) sets in motion a series of changes in cell structure that quickly result in the formation of the mature egg. By 4 hours after the meal, these cytological changes are already in evidence, and after 7 hours they are striking.

Structural Changes Associated with Yolk Formation

A. The Follicular Epithelium. With the onset of yolk deposition after the insect has a blood meal, some striking changes appear in the follicular epithelium. Most obvious are the development of large intercellular spaces (Fig. 3) and a concomitant decrease in desmosomal connections which may be associated with this separation. In some instances, the spaces encountered were large and extended from the basement membrane of the follicle to the oocyte surface. Continuity of the epithelium is, however, not lost and there is a suggestion in the micrograph in Fig. 3 that contact with the basement membrane is retained by a fine reticulation of thin cell extensions. Obviously this behavior of the follicle cells produces open channels between the extrafollicular space and the surface of the oocyte—open, that is, except for the basement membrane.

Some note should be taken of the material that fills these extracellular spaces. It is finely particulate and somewhat flocculent in appearance. Clearly the same material is not present in the interstitial spaces beyond the basement membrane of the ovariole. Throughout the intercellular spaces the distribution of this material is essentially uniform. At the oocyte surface it is continuous with a more condensed layer of similar texture, representing apparently an adsorbed layer of the same material. This tendency to concentrate on this surface is shown only in relation to the oocyte; adjoining surfaces of follicle cells and nurse cells are not so covered (Fig. 4). Even the extremities of the microvilli from the oocyte surface are relatively free.

B. The Oocyte Surface. Thus the surface of the oocyte in the maturing ovariole faces on a greatly expanded space under and between the cells of the follicular epithelium (Figs. 3 and 4). It is especially in this cortical region of the maturing oocyte that a series of important alterations occurs, which are the particular interest of this report. The area of the oocyte facing the follicular epithelium is covered with great numbers of microvilli

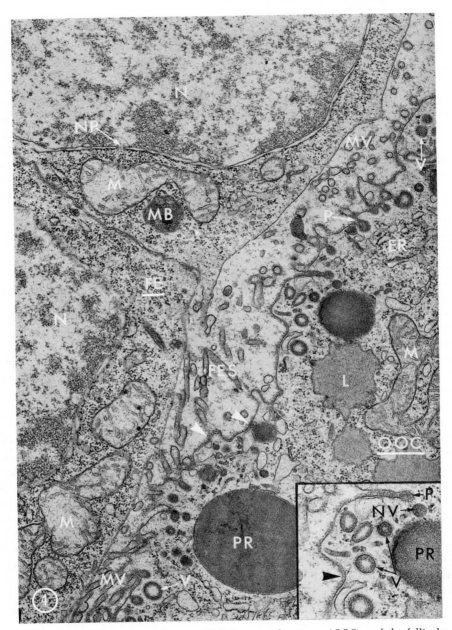

Fig. 4. Micrograph of the interface (*FES*) between the oocyte (*OOC*) and the follicular epithelium (*FE*) 7 hours after a blood meal. A few mitochondria (*M*) and a multivesicular body or lyosome (*MB*) are among the organelles in this region of the follicular epithelial cytoplasm. The nuclei (*N*) show the usual nuclear envelope with pores (*NP*). Between the microvilli (*MV*), which arise from the oocyte surface, are frequent pits (*P*) filled with a dense content. Pit-derived vesicles (*V*), lipid (*L*), mitochondria (*M*), elements of the endoplasmic reticulum (*ER*), and graded stages in proteid droplet (*PR*) formation crowd the oocyte cortex. A uniform layer of dense material (arrows) adheres to the oocyte plasma membrane and is similar in density and texture to that found in the pits, vesicles, and proteid droplets. × 34,500.

The inset at the lower right shows at greater enlargement a portion of the oocyte cortex. The materials contained in the pit (*P*), bristle-coated vesicles (*V*), naked vesicle (*NV*), and proteid droplet (*PR*) all have the same density and granularity as that on the oocyte surface (arrow). Where a vesicle membrane is cut in vertical section, it has the same dimensions as the plasma membrane. × 50,000.

(also somewhat evident in the resting oocyte) which, by 7 hours after the blood meal, push into the extracellular spaces created by the separation of the follicular epithelial cells (Fig. 3). These microvilli vary somewhat in length and are not in any sense regularly disposed like those, for example, of the typical intestinal epithelium. They seem, however, to achieve a uniform diameter (60 mμ) especially in their greatest extension from the surface. One gets the impression from the variation in length and orientation that the population may in life be actively changing, some retracting and others forming.

In between the microvilli, and also disposed irregularly, are numerous dense vesicles which are morphologically similar to the dense vesicles present in the resting oocyte (Figs. 2, 3, and 4). These connect in some instances with the oocyte surface and appear in profiles as small pits or wells (140 mμ in diameter). In other cases they are free and embedded in the cortex up to 0.5 μ from the surface (Fig. 4).

During this period of active yolk deposition there are roughly 300,000 pits on the surface of the oocyte facing the follicle cells. This figure is nearly 15 times the number of pits on the resting oocyte fixed only 7 hours earlier.

The pits and vesicles have structural features in common which help to relate them. It is, for example, characteristic for a cortical vesicle near the surface to be about 140 mμ in over-all diameter and to show, morphologically, 3 distinct layers. Of these, the middle one is most dense and the thinnest (*ca.* 75 A). This layer is obviously equivalent in all its characteristics to the plasma membrane of the oocyte (Fig. 4, insert, and Fig. 5). Internal to this line there is a layer of material 250 to 400 A thick, which by its density and texture can be identified with the layer of material on the external surface of the oocyte cell membrane. External to the middle layer, and continuous with the cytoplasmic matrix, there is a layer or coat about 200 A thick which seems to be made up of small bristles or hairs radiating outward from the dense line. We shall refer to this as the "bristle coat" and to the vesicles as "coated."

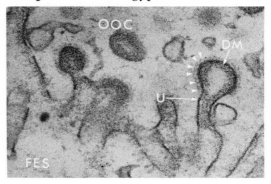

Fig. 5. Several pits are shown in greater detail. A uniform layer of dense material (*DM*) adheres to the 75 A unit membrane (*U*) on the free surface of the pit, while on the cytoplasmic side of the membrane the 200 A bristles (arrows) radiate into the oocyte cortex. The unit membrane has the same thickness and 3-layered structure as that limiting the oocyte. The bristles, in some images, appear joined near their outer ends. *OOC*, oocyte; *FES*, interface between oocyte and follicular epithelium. × 106,000.

It is not difficult to see a close structural relationship between the coated vesicles and the pits. Both show the same 3-layered structure, and it is evident in the pits in Fig. 5 that the middle one of the layers has the thickness and molecular structure of a unit membrane. In the same image, the structure of the inner, adsorbed layer and the outer bristle coat are shown to better advantage than elsewhere.

In other respects the pits seem to represent simply a coated vesicle connected with the surface of the oocyte by a neck. The neck, which is usually about 60 mμ in diameter, varies greatly in length. It may be as long as 150 mμ or essentially nonexistent. In the latter case, the pit is a shallow depression in the oocyte surface, identified, however, as a pit of this type by the characteristic coat on the cytoplasmic side. Apparently these variants represent stages in the development of deep pits from shallow ones and the eventual pinching off of the deepest part of the pit to form a coated vesicle. Ordinarily the bristle coating is not present on the neck of the pit but only over its deepest part, the diameter of which exceeds that of the neck.

The individual cortical vesicles in the cortical zone of a maturing oocyte are no longer of uniform size as they were prior to the blood meal. They display, in fact, a broad spectrum of sizes crowded into the region immediately beneath the membrane and slightly deeper in the cytoplasm (Figs. 3, 4, and 6). Close to the surface the majority are 140 to 150 mμ in diameter and still have the bristle coating. Farther in, there are larger vesicular units with a content of the same density as that of the coated vesicles, but without the characteristic coating. And deeper still, there are vesicles whose content is similar to that of both pits and yolk granules (Fig. 6). Apparently through a fusion of these various units the larger proteid bodies of the mature oocyte gradually develop (Figs. 6, 7, and 8). The yolk material, which first appears as a layer adsorbed onto the oocyte surface, is therefore thought to be taken into the cell via the coated pit and vesicle, possibly changed in character as the vesicles coalesce, and finally incorporated into yolk granules.

It should be noted that profiles of flattened vesicles often appear attached to the limiting membrane of the larger proteid droplets and show open continuity with the content of the droplet (Fig. 6). According to one interpretation, these may represent the remnant of a recently emptied "excoated" vesicle that has fused with a droplet. They might equally well represent small elements of the endoplasmic reticulum or Golgi system possibly contributing some material, maybe in enzyme, to the droplet.

The larger, dense bodies present in the egg cytoplasm, the yolk granules, display a crystalline pattern in their content, and this may exhibit various orientations in a single plane of section (Figs. 6 and 8). This shift in orientation presumably arises from the fusion of several smaller units which had adopted crystalline order before fusion. These large, highly ordered, dense bodies give positive protein and PAS histochemical tests, and thus are considered to be identical with the protein yolk granules observed by the light microscopists (32, 33).

Site of Yolk Synthesis

The implication from the above observations and the literature references on yolk synthesis is that these cortical pits take up material from the extracellular space of the follicle and contribute it to yolk granule formation. The question of immediate interest is where in the insect are the yolk proteins, etc., synthesized. To obtain some clues to this, we made a survey of the cells in the mosquito's abdomen, paying special attention to the occurrence of systems at the fine structure level usually associated with protein synthesis for export.

The cells of the Malpighian tubules, for example, do not possess the ergastoplasmic form of the ER, and show little evidence of an enlarged Golgi component or of secretory granules. Cells of the fat body do show rough ER in substantial amounts, but no secretory granules. From the survey, only the cells of the midgut epithelium emerged as likely candidates for the role of synthesizing yolk protein.

Two types of cells are found in the midgut of the mosquito, one a regenerative and the other an absorptive type (Fig. 9). The apical pole of the latter is covered with closely packed microvilli, each about 140 mμ in diameter and of undetermined length. These have, in turn, upon them a number of tiny microvilli (micromicrovilli) about 200 A in diameter, designed presumably to increase the extent of the cell surface. In the subcortical zone, under the free surface of these cells, numerous mitochondria are crowded into a layer 2 to 4 μ deep which blends into a cytoplasm that is characterized by arrays of rough ER, free ribosomes, and extensive infoldings from the basal and lateral surfaces of the cell. The nucleus, at this postfeeding phase, contains a prominent nucleolus. The prominent development of rough-surfaced ER, and the numerous Golgi profiles with some evidence of secretory granules, encourage the thought that these cells, beside being absorptive, are active in synthesis and secretion. In their fine structure they remind one of vertebrate liver cells.

Autoradiographic Experiments

In an attempt to determine the pathway by which the proteins, formed after a blood meal, enter the different tissues of the abdomen, the mosquitoes were fed on an anesthesized rat

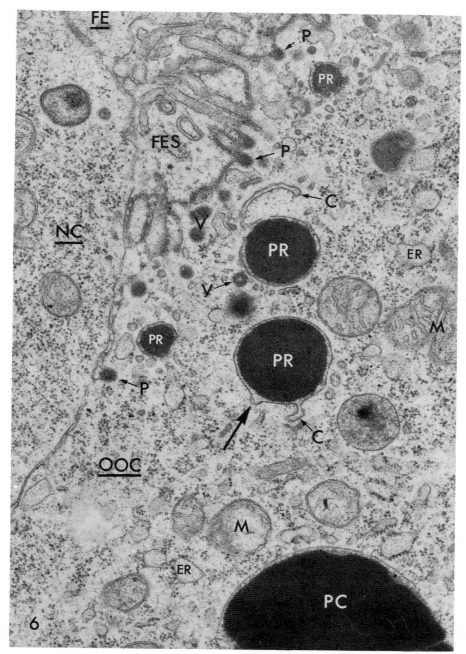

Fig. 6. At the juncture shown here between the follicular epithelium (*FE*), nurse cells (*NC*) and the oocyte (*OOC*), microvilli extend into the widening follicular epithelial space (*FES*) of the maturing ovary. Pits (*P*) along the oocyte cell membrane are filled with a dense material similar to that in the developing proteid droplets (*PR*). In some cases out pocketings appear on the membrane of the droplet (arrow) which are interpreted as vesicles (*V*) that have just emptied their contents into the membrane-limited space (also see Fig. 7). Small cisternae (*C*) are also continuous with the membrane of the droplet. These may represent the membrane remnant of large vesicles that have recently coalesced with the droplet. The content of the yolk protein body assumes a crystalline-like configuration when it matures (*PC*). *ER*, endoplasmic reticulum; *M*, mitochondria. × 41,500.

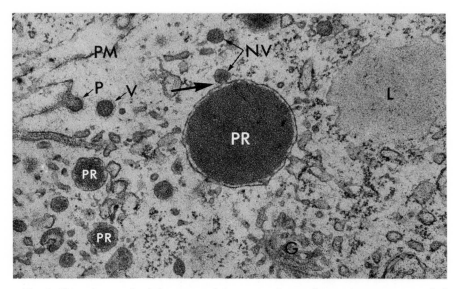

Fig. 7. This micrograph of the cortex of the oocyte shows what we interpret as a naked vesicle (*NV*) in the act of fusing (arrow) with the membrane of the yolk droplet (*PR*). Smaller irregularly shaped droplets (*PR*) and coated vesicles (*V*) are abundant in the area immediately beneath the pit-studded (P) plasma membrane (*PM*). Lipid bodies (*L*) and Golgi components (*G*) are other common inclusions of the egg cytoplasm at this period of yolk formation. × 56,500.

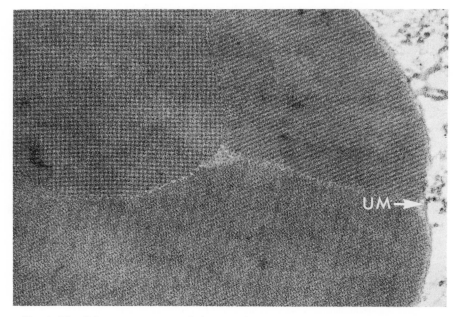

Fig. 8. The different orientation of the crystal lattice planes in the small granules that fuse to form the yolk proteid body is shown in this micrograph. A unit membrane (*UM*) limits the droplets. × 108,000.

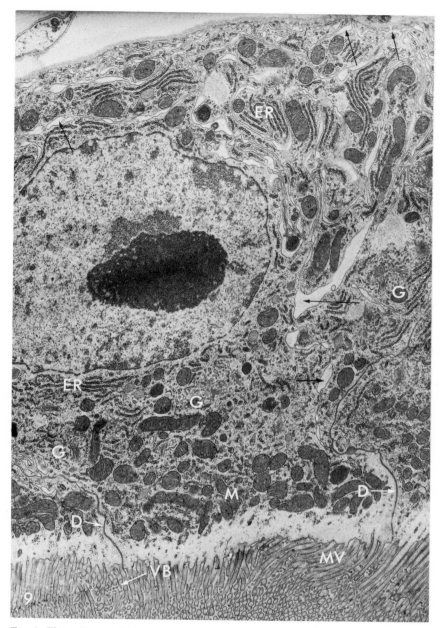

Fig. 9. This micrograph shows the greater part of an epithelial cell from the midgut of the mosquito. The apical pole is covered with microvilli (*MV*) about 140 mμ in diameter, which appear here in both longitudinal and cross-section. Smaller microvilli (*VB*), *ca.* 20 mμ, bud off from the larger ones. In the subapical region, immediately beneath a relatively clear cortex, is a zone densely populated with mitochondria (*M*). At other levels in the cytoplasm, profiles of the endoplasmic reticulum (*ER*) dominate the picture. These profiles describe the system as being constructed in part of large lamellar cisternae, their surfaces heavily encrusted with ribosomes, typical for cells active in protein synthesis. Sections through the Golgi complex (*G*) are scattered about in the supranuclear zone. Prominent also are extensive infoldings of the plasma membrane along the lateral surfaces of the cell, and most especially the basal surface. These infoldings reach in some instances almost to the apical pole of the cell and show irregular dilations (arrows). *D* marks the separation between adjacent cells. × approximately 21,600.

made radioactive by an intraperitoneal injection of DL-leucine-H³. Although the results are quite preliminary, and are now being repeated at the resolution offered by the electron microscope, they give some information of possible significance to this study.

In all samples, silver grains were located in high concentration over the blood meal in the midgut. Above the midgut epithelium, however, the number of silver grains increased from just above background at 0.5 hours after the blood meal to a plateau of about triple background at 4.5 hours, and then were maintained near that level in all samples taken later in yolk formation. In the ovary a similar rise in radioactivity occurred in the nurse cells and oocyte during the early 0.5 to 4.5 hours after a blood meal. Later, in the 16- and 30-hour samples, the number of silver grains increased notably above the protein yolk bodies.

The abdominal fat body does not appear to show a significant increase above background labeling until the 16- and 30-hour samples. The Malphighian tubules exhibit a pattern of labeling similar to that observed above the midgut cells.

DISCUSSION

The proteid droplets in *Aedes aegypti* constitute the major form of yolk protein in the egg (31, 32). By studying the formation of these bodies, we have sought to shed some light on the site of synthesis, transport, and method of uptake of yolk protein by the oocyte.

Sites of Yolk Synthesis

The possible sites of synthesis of yolk protein in the mosquito ovary can be considered, on morphological grounds, to be restricted to three. One could be the follicular epithelial cells; their proximity to the oocyte, for example, suggests a possible involvement in the synthesis of material for oocyte growth and differentiation (Fig. 3). However, these cells contain almost none of the machinery usually associated with intracellular synthesis of protein for secretion (35). They have little of

the rough form of the endoplasmic reticulum, infrequent Golgi bodies, and, at this stage, no evidence of secretory granules or other secretory activity at the cell surface. Only after yolk deposition is essentially completed do the cells of this epithelium show any proliferation of the ER and Golgi complex. When this occurs, these cells are engaged in producing the chorion of the egg (31, 33) and most yolk deposition has already been completed.

The nurse cells and the oocyte itself are the other two possible sites of synthesis, but here, as in the follicular epithelium, the machinery (cytoplasmic inclusions and secretory granules) usually present for such purposes is absent during the short period of yolk deposition. The presence of great numbers of free ribosomes in the cytoplasm of both cells suggests active protein synthesis. This is, however, the pattern found in rapidly growing undifferentiated cells in which the components of the cytoplasmic matrix are being formed, and there is no associated mechanism for the transport and assembling of the protein into yolk droplets.

Therefore, unlike the crayfish oocyte in which the ER is clearly involved in the synthesis of yolk protein (3), or the frog oocyte (52) where the mitochondria are associated with yolk deposition, or the snail oocyte where Favard and Carasso (11) implicate both mitochondria and ER in yolk formation, the mosquito oocyte shows no obvious involvement in the manufacture of its own yolk.

This conclusion is in no way surprising. The uptake and deposition in the oocyte of yolk proteins from extraovarian sources appears to be the common pattern among the vertebrates. And even more pertinent here are the findings of Telfer that the same pattern is true for the insects he has studied. Particularly significant for the interpretation of our observations is Telfer's demonstration, by immunohistochemical studies on the saturniid moth, that certain foreign proteins are taken into the oocyte. He also demonstrated that naturally occurring proteins in the hemolymph are preferentially concentrated in the ovary, and that no yolk protein could be detected in the follicular epithelial cells, the nurse cells, or in the cytoplasm of the oocyte apart from the yolk droplets. He concludes justifiably that yolk proteins are synthesized at some extraovarian point in the insect and transported to the ovary for deposition. Though no similar studies have been made on the mosquito, it seems reasonable to expect that the same mechanisms would be operative in this form.

If the cells of the ovary are not involved, where does yolk synthesis take place? Thus far, as reported here, our studies of the tissues of the mosquito abdomen have identified only certain cells of the midgut as having the structural equipment needed for this function. This consists of ribosome-studded cisternae in parallel arrays and other elements of fine structure usually associated with secretion. These cells at their apical pole are in contact with the contents of the intestine following a blood meal, and on their other side are in a favorable position to secrete into the hemocoel. Furthermore, the autoradiographs in the experiments which included tritiated leucine in the blood, while preliminary, showed definite accumulation and concentration of label over these cells. It seems highly probable, therefore, that these units of the midgut are at least one site of yolk synthesis.

The only other candidates for this role are the cells of the fat body which likewise show rich developments of the rough ER. Here, however, the accumulation of label following the feeding of tritiated leucine is delayed until late in yolk deposition.

The suggestion that the midgut is the principal site of protein synthesis for yolk formation is at variance with a long standing bias among insect physiologists toward the fat body for this role. It is well established that most insects contain protein stored in droplets in the fat body, and as proteins or amino acids are needed this source is mobilized. Our autoradiographic results may be due to the absence of protein in the fat bodies of the 1-week-old mosquitoes we used, and the resultant absence of this potential protein source during oogenesis.

The mechanisms of yolk transport to and uptake by the ovariole, and subsequent concentration in the oocyte, have been considered only briefly by previous investigators except Telfer. In a studious examination of the question, he implicates the oocyte surface and the basement membrane in the selective uptake. The surface of the oocyte, he speculates, might possess a mechanism for selective absorption akin to that demonstrated for the surface of the ameba (5). Uptake and transport might be achieved by a process similar to pinocytosis.

The observations derived from the present study bear mostly on these questions and, in general, support Telfer's speculations.

The spaces between the follicular epithelial cells begin to widen by 4 hours after a blood meal, and by 7 hours have opened sufficiently to allow unobstructed communication from the basement layer to the oocyte surface by this intercellular route (Fig. 3). Before yolk proteins can enter this newly formed space they must pass through the basement layer enclosing the ovariole. Although not all investigators agree that a basement layer is permeable to whole proteins, there is good evidence that certain foreign and maternal proteins present in the blood can penetrate this layer in certain tissues (10, 24, 28, 47, 49).

Again, with respect to the present study, Telfer's findings are especially significant, for they demonstrate that proteins in the hemocoel do traverse the basement layer and are present in the interfollicular space just within. Some device probably exists capable of holding the yolk proteins inside the basement membrane and continuing their inward diffusion. The micrographic evidence bearing on this question describes a coarsely granular material on the inside of the basement membrane, and no resolvable material outside. Furthermore, it suggests that once inside, the protein is complexed into relatively large aggregates which are too large to diffuse out through the membrane. Thus the conditions required for the continuing inward diffusion of the smaller molecular species are maintained with the basement membrane functioning as part of a diffusion pump. What serves to aggregate the proteins into larger complexes is not known, but a factor or factors synthesized in either the follicular epithelial cells or the oocyte could be secreted into the extracellular space to perform the task.

An equally valid possibility is that the serum proteins coprecipitate in the interfollicular space and thus fulfill the same requirement for inward diffusion. In this connection, it is worth noting that Schjeide and Urist (43) have shown that two serum and yolk proteins of the chicken are very similar and that the two components of each, the X_1 phosphoprotein and the X_2 "glycolipoprotein," coprecipitate at a lowered pH and/or lowered ionic strength with the release of protein-bound calcium. If either or both of these conditions were to be met *in vivo*, coprecipitation would explain the aggregates encountered in the interfollicular space.

The same inward migration of yolk protein is doubtlessly influenced as well by the condensation of material on the oocyte surface and its incorporation into the egg. Just what it is, in or on the oocyte surface, that encourages the development of such a layer is likewise not known. That it represents yolk protein is indicated by the observation that this oocyte-associated material in the *Cecropia* moth, for example, is immunologically similar to the yolk protein within the oocyte and the serum proteins in the hemocoel (50).

The Uptake Mechanism

It has been shown here that, in the region of the oocyte surface adjoining the follicular epithelial cells, numerous small depressions or pits extend into the egg cortex. Similar differentiations have been noted by Wartenberg (53) in the oocyte of several amphibians, but without attention to their characteristic fine structure. He interpreted these as engaged in pinocytosis associated with the uptake of materials for yolk formation. We find that the cortical pits number approximately 300,000 in the stage of oocyte development achieved 7 hours after feeding. This represents a 15-fold increase over the number of pits found in the resting stage preceding feeding. Their structure is uniform. Each pit contains a quantity of dense material having the same texture

as that adsorbed on the oocyte surface at other points, which in turn seems related to the flocculent material in the follicular spaces. On their inner convex surfaces facing the cytoplasm, the pits are covered with a border of fine bristles about 200 A long.

Several significant reasons are apparent for associating these pits with yolk protein uptake and the formation of proteid droplets and granules of the maturing egg. The first one is the fact that uptake is in progress when the pit development reaches its most prominent expression. One could argue further that other mechanisms of uptake are not evident and that simple diffusion of yolk through the plasma membrane is highly improbable. Then, it is obvious that vesicles deeper in the cortex are related to the pits and are derivatives of them. These vesicles possess the same content and the same border of bristles.

To this point the animation of this uptake mechanism is not hard to picture and is essentially that which characterizes pinocytosis. When the process of yolk absorption is at its peak, the formation of pits and their derivatives is probably quite rapid. The subsequent fate of the pit-vesicles is somewhat less clear. They apparently lose the bristle border, fuse to form larger vesicles, pick up other satellite vesicles, and progressively grow into "proteid droplets" several times greater in diameter than the pit-vesicles. This interpretation is depicted in Fig. 10.

The content of these larger dense yolk bodies also changes. From a beginning of homogenous density, there gradually emerges evidence of order in the arrangement of the particles, a crystallinity of structure common to yolk granules. This could depend on a process of selective hydrolysis within the vesicle, resulting finally in a high degree of purity in the residual yolk. Therefore, even though the pits and the oocyte surface may be selective, to a degree, in what they adsorb from the periooocyte lymph, subsequent purification is not unlikely.

The role of the bristle border in all of this is hard to imagine. It may have a mechanical function, giving, by virtue of a natural repulsion of the outer ends of the bristles, the spherical form to the base of the pit and

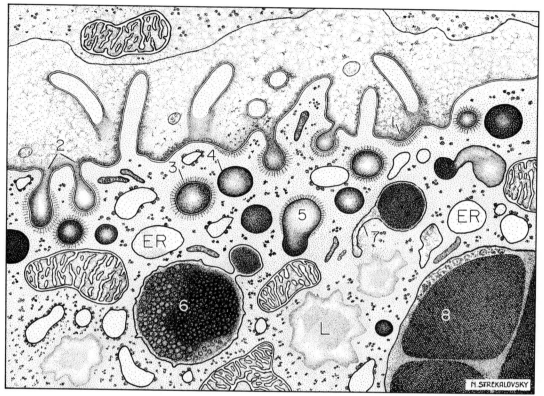

Fig. 10. This schematic drawing interprets the micrographs examined in this study. It depicts changes and events involving the cortical pits and coated vesicles of the mosquito oocyte. At (1) is shown the first stage of invagination into the oocyte of the protein-coated plasma membrane from the intercellular space. The fully developed pit (2), by pinching off, forms the coated vesicle (3). These vesicles lose their bristles to form dense spheres of similar size (4) which then fuse with other dense spheres (5). Often a flattened empty sac is attached to the droplet (7). This sac may be the membrane remnant of a vesicle or perhaps some element of the Golgi complex that has recently fused with the droplet. The larger droplets (6) coalesce to form the large crystalline proteid yolk bodies (8) of the oocyte. Other conspicuous and characteristic inclusions and organelles of the oocyte cytoplasm are mitochondria, vesicles of the rough surfaced endoplasmic reticulum (ER), lipid (L) and ribosomes. At the top of the drawing, microvilli project into the intercellular space fronting on the follicular epithelium. Note the absence of adhering material on the membranes of the follicular epithelial cells (also see Fig. 4). × approximately 60,000.

the pit-vesicles. It is obvious from other observations, however, that cortical pits of this general character form and apparently separate from the surface without this apparatus (34). Perhaps this proposal has less merit than that which associates the specificity of materials adsorbed with characteristics of the bristle border. It is not possible at the moment to be other than vague in these suggestions.

Pits of similar structure have been reported in many cell types (1, 2, 39, 40, 46). Their occurrence is indeed widespread, as will be reported in a subsequent paper. They are not to be confused with the simpler pits found especially in smooth muscle cells and blood vascular endothelial cells (34, 53). The latter have simple, clean limiting membranes and a smaller diameter. At this time we present the working hypothesis that pits of the type found here in the mosquito are, in general, involved in selective uptake of materials (proteins and perhaps non-proteins) from the cell's environment. Since the mechanism evinces some selectivity (39), it is reasonable to propose that different cell types may manifest different specificities, with some cells, such as those of the reticuloendothelial system, showing a broader spectrum of interests than others.

This investigation was supported in part by a Public Health Service Training Grant 2G-707 from The National Institutes of Health, United States Public Health Service.

BIBLIOGRAPHY

1. Anderson, E., The ovary of *Periplaneta americana*, Abstracts of the 2nd Annual Meeting of the American Society for Cell Biology, San Francisco, 1962, 2.
2. Ashford, T., K. R. Porter, and S. Badenhausen, Modulations in the fine structure of rat liver cells under conditions of organ isolation and perfusion, 1964, in press.
3. Beams, H. W., and R. G. Kessel, Endoplasmic reticulum and yolk formation in crayfish, Abstracts of the 2nd Annual Meeting of the American Society for Cell Biology, San Francisco, 1962, 13.
4. Brambell, F. W. R., and W. A. Hemmings, Active transport through embryonic membranes, *Symp. Soc. Exp. Biol.*, 1954, **8**, 476.
5. Brandt, P. W., A study of the mechanism of pinocytosis, *Exp. Cell Research*, 1958, **15**, 300.
6. Caro, L. G., and R. P. van Tubergen, High-resolution autoradiography. I. Methods, *J. Cell Biol.*, 1962, **15**, 173.
7. Chargaff, E., The formation of the phosphorus compounds in egg yolk, *J. Biol. Chem.*, 1942, **142**, 505.
8. Christophers, S. R., The development of the egg follicle in *Anophelines*, *Paludism*, 1911, **2**, 73.
9. Christophers, S. R., *Aedes aegypti* L. *Its Life-history, Bionomics and Structure*, London, Cambridge University Press, 1961, 676.
10. Farquhar, M. G., and G. E. Palade, Glomerular capillary wall in nephritic rats, *J. Exp. Med.*, 1961, **114**, 699.
11. Favard, P., and N. Carasso, Origine et ultrastructure des plaquettes vitellines de la Planorbe, *Arch. Anat. Micro. et Morph. Exp.*, 1958, **47**, 211.
12. Feder, N., Some modifications in conventional techniques of tissue preparation, *J. Histochem. and Cytochem.*, 1960, **8**, 309.
13. Feder, N., personal communication.
14. Flickinger, R. A., Formation, biochemical composition and utilization of amphibian egg yolk, in *Symposium on Germ Cells and Development*, Institut Internationale d'Embryologie and Fondazione A. Baselli, Pavia, Italy, Premiata Tipografia Successore Fratelli Fusi, 1960, 29.
15. Flickinger, R. A., and D. E. Rounds, The maternal synthesis of egg yolk proteins as demonstrated by isotopic and serological means, *Biochim. et Biophysic. Acta*, 1956, **22**, 38.
16. Flickinger, R. A., and O. A. Schjeide, The localization of phosphorus and the site of calcium binding in the yolk proteins of the frog's egg, *Exp. Cell Research*, 1957, **13**, 312.
17. Glass, L. E., Immuno-histological localization of serum-like molecules in frog oocytes, *J. Exp. Zool.*, 1959, **141**, 257.
18. Grant, P., Phosphate metabolism during oogenesis in *Rana temporaria*, *J. Exp. Zool.*, 1953, **124**, 513.
19. Hahn, L., and G. Hevesy, Origin of yolk lecithin, *Nature*, 1937, **140**, 1059.
20. Hosoda, T., T. Kaneko, K. Mogi, and T. Abe, Serological Studies on Egg Production in the Fowl. I. On the locus of serum vitellin production, *Poultry Sc.*, 1955, **34**, 9.
21. Jukes, T. H., and H. D. Kay, Egg yolk protein, *J. Nutrition*, 1932, **5**, 81.
22. Karnovsky, M. J., Simple methods for "staining with lead" at high pH in electron microscopy, *J. Biophysic. and Biochem. Cytol.*, 1961, **11**, 729.

23. King, R. C., Oogenesis in adult *Drosophila melanogaster*. IX. Studies on the cytochemistry and ultrastructure of developing oocytes, *Growth*, 1960, **24**, 265.

24. Knight, P. F., and A. M. Schechtman, The passage of heterologous serum proteins from the circulation into the ovum of the fowl, *J. Exp. Zool.*, 1954, **127**, 271.

25. Laskowski, M., Darstellungsmethode des Serumvitelline, *Biochem. Z.*, 1935, **278**, 345.

26. Ledbetter, M. C., unpublished observations.

27. Mancini, R. E., O. Vilar, J. J. Heinrich, O. W. Davidson, and B. Alvarez, Transference of circulating labeled serum proteins to the follicle of the rat ovary, *J. Histochem. and Cytochem.*, 1963, **11**, 80.

28. Miller, F., Hemoglobin absorption by the cells of the proximal convoluted tubule in mouse kidney, *J. Biophysic. and Biochem. Cytol.*, 1960, **8**, 689.

29. Millonig, G., Advantages of a phosphate buffer for OsO_4 solutions in fixation, *J. Appl. Physics*, 1961, **32**, 1637.

30. Millonig, G., A modified procedure for lead staining of thin sections. *J. Biophysic. and Biochem. Cytol.*, 1961, **11**, 736.

31. Nath, V., Egg–Follicle of *Culex*, *Quart. J. Micr. Sc.*, 1924, **69**, 151.

32. Nath, V., Studies on the shape of the Golgi apparatus. I. The egg follicle of *Culex*, *Z. Zellforsch.*, 1929, **8**, 655.

33. Nicholson, A. J., The development of the ovary and ovarian egg of a mosquito, *Anopheles maculipennis*, *Quart. J. Micr. Sc.*, 1920, **65**, 395.

34. Palade, G. E., Transport in quanta across the endothelium of blood capillaries, *Anat. Rec.*, 1960, **136**, 254.

35. Palade, G. E., and P. Siekevitz, Liver microsomes. An integrated morphological and biochemical study, *J. Biophysic. and Biochem. Cytol.*, 1956, **2**, 171.

36. Parks, J. J., An anatomical and histological study of the female reproductive system and follicular development in *Aedes aegypti* L., Master of Science Thesis, University of Minnesota, 1955.

37. Peachey, L. D., Accumulation of divalent ions in mitochondrial granules of intact cells, in 5th International Congress for Electron Microscopy, Philadelphia, 1962 (S. S. Breese, Jr., editor), New York, Academic Press, Inc., 1962, **2**, OO–3.

38. Roepke, R. R., and L. D. Bushnell, A serological comparison of the phosphoproteins of the serum of the laying hen and the vitellin of the egg yolk, *J. Immunol.*, 1936, **30**, 109.

39. Roth, T. F., and K. R. Porter, Specialized sites on the cell surface for protein uptake, in 5th International Congress for Electron Microscopy, Philadelphia, 1962 (S. S. Breese, Jr., editor), New York, Academic Press, Inc., **2**, LL–4.

40. Roth, T. F., and K. R. Porter, Membrane differentiation for protein uptake, *Fed. Proc.*, 1963, **22**, No. 2, abstract.

41. Roy, D., and S. Majumdar, On mating and egg formation in *Culex fatigans* Weid, *J. Malaria Inst., India*, 1939, **2**, 243.

42. Schjeide, O. A., and M. R. Urist, Proteins and calcium in serums of estrogen treated roosters, *Science*, 1956, **124**, 1242.

43. Schjeide, O. A., and M. R. Urist, Proteins and calcium in egg yolk. *Exp. Cell Research*, 1959, **17**, 84.

44. Singh, K. R. P., and A. W. A. Brown, Nutritional requirements of *Aedes aegypti* L., *J. Insect Physiol.*, 1957, **1**, 109.

45. Smith, A. H., Follicular permeability and yolk formation. *Poultry Sc.*, 1959, **38**, 1437p.

46. Stay, B., personal communication on pits in the *Cecropia* silkworm.

47. Straus, W., Cytochemical investigation of phagosomes and related structures in cryostat sections of the kidney and liver of rats after intravenous administration of horseradish peroxidase, *Exp. Cell Research*, 1962, **27**, 80.

48. Telfer, W. H., Immunological studies of insect metamorphosis. II. The role of a sex-limited blood protein in egg formation by the *Cecropia* silkworm, *J. Gen. Physiol.*, 1954, **37**, 539.

49. Telfer, W. H., The selective accumulation of blood proteins by the oocytes of saturniid moths, *Biol. Bull.*, 1960, **118**, 338.

50. Telfer, W. H., The route of entry and localization of blood proteins in the oocytes of saturniid moths. *J. Biophysic. and Biochem. Cytol.*, 1961, **9**, 747.

51. Trembley, H. L., Mosquito culture techniques and experimental procedures. *Bull. No. 3, American Mosquito Control Association Inc.*, Berkeley, California; Lederer, Street, and Zeus Co., Inc., 1955.

52. Ward, R. T., The origin of protein and fatty yolk in *Rana pipiens*. II. Electron microscopical and cytochemical observations on young and mature oocytes, *J. Cell Biol.*, 1962, **14**, 309.

53. Wartenberg, H., Electronenmikroskopische und Histochemische Studien uber die Oogenese der Amphibieneizelle, *Z. Zellforsch.*, 1962, **58**, 427.

54. Wissig, S. L., An EM study of the permeability of capillaries in muscle, *Anat. Rec.*, 1957, **130**, 467.

The Appearance of Stable Polysomes During the Development of Chick Down Feathers*

TOM HUMPHREYS

SHELDON PENMAN

EUGENE BELL

The molecular sequence from gene to protein molecule (Brenner, *et al.*, 1961; Gros, *et al.*, 1961) presents at least two distinct alternatives for programming protein synthesis during development. Genes may be activated for extended periods to produce a continual supply of short-lived messenger-RNA (m-RNA) to translate for specific cell proteins (Scott and Bell, 1964). Alternatively, genes may function only during a brief period to program the protein synthesizing machinery with long-lived m-RNAs which act as persistent templates for the specific proteins of the differentiated cell (Bishop, *et al.*, 1961; Scott and Bell, 1964).

Experimentally these two possibilities can be distinguished either by demonstrating that development is or is not stopped by inhibition of RNA synthesis (Gross, *et al.*, 1963) or by demonstrating the presence or absence of stable m-RNA for the synthesis of cell specific proteins. The latter approach appeared possible in a tissue which passed through a developmental phase of rapid synthesis of one or a few cell specific proteins (Bell, 1964). Embryonic chick down feathers begin to synthesize very large quantities of keratins during a relatively short developmental period between 13 and 14 days of incubation which appears to be a crucial time in feather development (Bell and Thathachari, 1963; Ben-Or and Bell, 1964; Bell and Humphreys, 1964). Since functional messenger is complexed with ribosomes to form polysomes (Warner, *et al.*, 1963), any large fraction of m-RNA appearing at 13 days should be detectable in the developing feather as a new class of polysomes. Once this new species is detectable, the half life of its m-RNA can be

measured after inhibition of RNA synthesis with actinomycin D (AmD) (Penman, *et al.*, 1963).

MATERIALS AND METHODS

Back skin or back feathers from embryos incubated at 37.6°C were collected in cold, sterile Tyrode's solution (see Bell and Thathachari, 1963 for a description of the skin and feathers). The tissue was treated with AmD† *in vitro* suspended in 20 volumes of 37°C Waymouth medium in a shaker flask. Polysomes were extracted from the chick tissue by a procedure used for HeLa cells (Penman, *et al.*, 1963) except the chick tissue had to swell 15 to 60 minutes in the hypotonic buffer (RSB; 0.01 M Tris; pH 7.5, 0.01 M KCl, 0.0015 M Mg^{++}) and then be broken up by 5 to 10 quick strokes of the "loose" ball before complete disruption with the "tight" ball of the Dounce homogenizer. Sedimentation analyses were performed on 15% to 30% linear sucrose gradients in RSB centrifuged 180 minutes at 24,000 rpm at 8°C. Polysomes to be sonicated were collected from a gradient, pelleted at 38,000 rpm for 90 minutes in a Spinco SW 39 rotor, resuspended in RSB, and sonicated for 1 minute. After sonication they were layered on a second gradient and recentrifuged. Polysomal RNA was analyzed in SDS gradients (Gilbert, 1963).

Radioactive amino acids were incorporated into polysomes by a 4-minute incubation of the tissue in 37° Tyrodes solution with 2% dialyzed serum and 30 μc C^{14} algal protein hydrolysate (1 mc/mg, New England Nuclear Corporation) per ml. RNA synthesis was

* Supported by NSF grants GB-614 and GB-2021.

† Kindly supplied by Dr. Horace D. Brown, Merck, Sharp, and Dohme.

measured as TCA precipitable counts per O.D. 260 mu in phenol extracted, alcohol precipitated material (Scherrer, *et al.*, 1962) from tissue incubated 2 hours in 37°C Waymouth medium with 5 μc C¹⁴ uridine (30 μc/mM) per ml.

RESULTS

Cytoplasmic extracts from freshly isolated skin of five and one-half to 10 days and feathers of 11 to 15 days when sedimented in a sucrose gradient yielded curves of optical density at 260 mμ characteristic of the ribosomal structures of many cell types (Figs. 1a and 2a). Below the non-sedimenting material was a large 74S single ribosome peak and a series of lesser peaks with a long tail representing polysomes (polysome profile). In this tissue the polysome profile was almost constant throughout the developmental stages examined, changing only at 13 days. Before 13 days the 4 ribosome polysome peak strikingly predominated, after 13 days the 5 and 6 ribosome polysome peaks increased until by 15 days the 5's peak at least equaled the 4's peak (compare Figs. 1a and 2a). Keratinization physically prevented extraction of polysomes from later stages. This relatively constant distribution of polysome sizes is characteristic of chick skin and feathers and does not occur in other chick tissue so far examined (Scott and Bell, 1964).

Radioactive amino acids are rapidly incorporated into the polysome regions of these gradients (Figs. 1a and 2a). Treatment of these extracts with ribonuclease quickly moved most of the O.D. and radioactivity into the region of the single ribosome peak. Most of the material recovered in the polysome region of these gradients are therefore clearly polysomes. However, in tissue 13 days and younger there was a distinct optical density peak, with no associated radioactivity, which resisted the ribonuclease and persisted in the area of the four ribosome polysomes (Fig. 1b). After 13 days ribonuclease moved all optical density and radioactivity from the polysome region into the single ribosome peak (Fig. 2b).

Upon 99% inhibition of RNA synthesis (Table I) by AmD *in vitro*, the polysome profiles of 9 day skin and 11, 13, and 15 day feathers began to decay rapidly. Polysome profiles of all tissues cultured *without AmD* remained essentially unchanged for more than 24 hours. After 12 hours in AmD the polysome profile from 9 day skin and 11 and 13 day feathers consisted of a sharp, prominent peak in the 4 ribosome polysome region on an otherwise low background (Fig. 1c). This peak persisted until the tissue began to disintegrate at about 18 hours in 9 day skin and well beyond 24 hours in 11 and 13 day feathers. This persistent peak did not incorporate radioactive amino acids even when the tissue was incubated with label for 20 minutes (Fig. 1c). The ratio of optical density at 269 mu/280 mu at the persistent peak was 1.9 which is the ratio of the single ribosome peak. Sonication of the persistent peak moved it to the single ribosome peak. The RNA of the persistent peak sedimented in a sucrose gradient exactly like the RNA of single ribosomes. This persistent peak therefore appears to represent a multiple ribosomal aggregate. The polysome profile of 15 day feathers decayed much as that of 13 day

TABLE I. Percent RNA synthesis in tissue cultured *in vitro* with actinomycin D as compared with controls cultured an equal time without AmD

Time in Culture	9-Day Skin with 30 μg/ml	11-Day Feathers with 30 μg/ml	13-Day Feathers with 60 μg/ml	15-Day Feathers with 60 μg/ml
2 hours	0.8	—	9	6
6 hours	0.4	—	3	2
24 hours	0.4	1	1	0.8

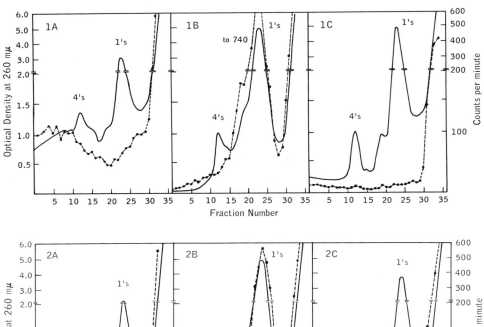

Figs. 1 and 2. Polysome profiles from zone sedimentation of radioactive amino acid labeled cytoplasmic extracts centrifuged 24.000 rpm for 3 hours at 8°C on a 15 to 30% sucrose gradient. Solid line is optical density at 260 mμ. Broken line is TCA precipitable counts per minute. Fig. 1. Extracts from 13-day feathers. Fig. 2. Extracts from 15-day feathers; (A) freshly isolated tissue; (B) extract A after treatment with 1 γ RNAase at 4°C for 30 minutes; (C) tissue treated with actinomycin D for 24 hours.

feathers except there were several peaks of larger long-lived polysomes along with the predominant peak in the 4 ribosome polysome region (Fig. 2c). Radioactive amina acids were rapidly incorporated into the long-lived 15-day polysomes (Fig. 2c).

DISCUSSION

Maturation of the down feather is completed by the rapid deposition of large quantities of the structural proteins, keratins, between 13 and 17 days of incubation. These results suggest that before 13 days, during feather growth and morphogenesis, the feather cells are preparing for this final step by producing and storing 4 ribosomal aggregates as non-functional polysomes whose m-RNA is specifically protected against ribonuclease activity. When morphogenesis is almost completed at 13 days, this store of polysomes appears to be activated to produce the proteins necessary for maturation.

This interpretation raises several interesting questions. It assumes that the non-functioning 4-ribosomal aggregates which appear before 13 days are organized around m-RNA molecules and are the direct precursors of the stable, functioning 4, 5, and 6 ribosome polysomes occurring after 13 days. The ap-

pearance of 5 and 6 ribosome stable polysomes in addition to the original 4 ribosome
polysomes may indicate random attachment
and movement of ribosomes during translation of a single species of m-RNA or may
indicate several species of m-RNA which had
been previously complexed uniformly with 4
ribosomes in the non-functioning state. Several m-RNA species would be expected since
more than one keratin protein is known for
several tissues (Mercer, 1961), but these possibilities have not been examined experimentally. Indeed, another plausible alternative is
that the appearance of functional, stable polysomes at 13 days results completely or in
part from the synthesis at that time of one or
more new species of m-RNA.

Cytological identification of these nonfunctional ribosomal aggregates with the
"clouds" of 200 to 250 A particles found in
developing down feathers (Kischer, 1962)
may be possible. These "clouds" were thought
to be related to the keratohyline granules
which build up in cells of mammalian keratinizing tissue before keratinization and then
rapidly disappear as keratinization occurs
(Brody, 1959). To our knowledge, nucleic
acid in these granules has not been studied.

The interpretation presented demands
three distinct controls which must operate in
the regulation of the synthesis of these feather
proteins. Genes must be activated early in
feather development to produce m-RNA for
the non-functioning aggregates. The preformed aggregate must be switched on, and
the functioning polysome must be stabilized to
function over the period necessary to complete deposition of sufficient protein.

REFERENCES

1. Bell, E., *National Cancer Institute Mono-graph* No. 13 (1964).
2. Bell, E., and T. Humphreys, in preparation.
3. Bell, E., and Y. T. Thathachari, *J. Cell Biol.* **16**, 215 (1963).
4. Ben-Or, S., and E. Bell, *Developmental Biol.* (1965). In press.
5. Bishop, J., G. Favelukes, R. Schweet, and E. Russel, *Nature*, **191**, 1365 (1961).
6. Brenner, S., F. Jacob, and M. Meselson, *Nature*, **190**, 576 (1961).
7. Brody, I., *J. Ultrastructure Res.*, **3**, 84 (1959).
8. Gilbert, W., *J. Mol. Biol.*, **6**, 389 (1963).
9. Gros, F., W. Gilbert, H. Hiatt, C. Kurland, R. W. Risebrough, and J. D. Watson, *Nature*, **190**, 581 (1961).
10. Gross, P. R., L. I. Malkin, and W. A. Moyer, *Proc. Natl. Acad. Sci. U. S.*, **51**, 407 (1963).
11. Kischer, C. W., *J. Ultrastructure Res.*, **8**, 305 (1963).
12. Mercer, E. H., *Keratin and Keratinization*, (Pergamon Press, New York, 1961).
13. Penman, S., K. Scherrer, Y. Becker, and J. E. Darnell, *Proc. Natl. Acad. Sci. U. S.*, **49**, 654 (1963).
14. Scherrer, K., H. Latham, and J. E. Darnell, *Proc. Natl. Acad. Sci. U. S.*, **49**, 240 (1963).
15. Scott, R. B. and E. Bell, *Science*, **145**, 711 (1964).
16. Warner, J. W., P. M. Knopf, and A. Rich, *Proc. Natl. Acad. Sci. U. S.*, **49**, 122 (1963).

11

Macromolecules as the Basis of Structure

THE DIFFERENTIATED STATE often results from the organization of subunits into a macromolecular pattern. Is the information required for the construction of the macromolecule sometimes contained in the subunit molecule itself (Edds 1961)? With collagen the question can be answered yes; collagen molecules will organize themselves into fibrils *in vitro.*

The collagen network in turn provides nucleation sites for hydroxyapatite crystals which are laid down during the process of calcification of bone (*Glimcher, Hodge, and Schmitt 1957*).* Fitton Jackson (1957) has observed the regular and periodic arrangement of the crystals in electron micrographs. A precondition for the symmetrical deposition of foci of mineralization on collagen *in vitro* is the proper concentrations of calcium and phosphate (*Glimcher, Hodge, and Schmitt 1957*).

Other facts must exist which confer morphogenetic specificity on the collagen producing cells to organize them into bone primordia of regionally characteristic shape. What these factors are so far is not known.

In many tissues heterogeneous subunits are polymerized into specialized arrays. In muscle other structural proteins in addition to actin and myosin combine to form the striated fibrils (Johnson 1963). In the feather a large number of proteins is probably involved in the formation of a structure which gives a unique x-ray diffraction pattern (Bell 1965). These are multi-phasic systems in which constituents are poorly or not yet identified. They are difficult to isolate, hence are not yet amenable to *in vitro* manipulation. Whether their organization into polymers and organelles depends only upon the presence of the subunits and small molecules or whether the organization depends also upon enzymes or other "helper" proteins (see Discussion, Introduction, Chapter 6) is still unknown.

A key question concerns the relationship of final cell shape to the structural components (protein, carbohydrate, etc.) which comprise it, in particular, the cells differentiation products like actomyosin or hemoglobin. Specifically, is cell shape determined by the organization of its subunits or do subunits polymerize in a shell whose shape is determined by other causes? The question has not yet been fully resolved in what might be one of the simplest cases to analyze: the sickle cell in which the principle protein, hemoglobin, differs from hemoglobin in the normal erythrocyte by a single amino acid substitution (Ingram 1957). It appears that sickling of the erythrocyte can be attributed to the aberrant protein because the sickle cell hemoglobin forms into tactoids which distort the cell shape (Harris 1950; Perutz and Mitchison 1951).

* Italicized references indicate articles which appear in this book.

The morphology of the fiber cell of the developing lens may be established before γ crystallin is synthesized but after other lens proteins (α and β crystallin) are present. What role they play in determining fiber-cell morphology is not known.

In plants, deposition of primary cell-wall substances occurs at the same time that cells are growing. In the primary cell wall microfibrils run in all directions within the plane of the wall. When elongation occurs the microfibrils become more oriented along a longitudinal axis (Mühlethaler 1961). In the formation of the secondary cell wall the microfibrils are at first successively less scattered and are finally arranged in a parallel texture. Both primary and secondary cell walls can be stretched and torn with new cell growth. A principal force is that of turgor determined by water uptake. It is clear that the resulting shape will depend upon the previous patterning of microfibrils (Green 1963) as well as upon regulation of water intake. Factors which determine the orderly deposition of microfibrils are unknown but they lie in the cortical cytoplasm (Preston 1961). Green (1963) proposes that cytoplasmic elements near the growing cell wall might have orienting properties. Whether microtubes recently found in the cortical cytoplasm of plant cells arranged in the long axis of the cell (Ledbetter and Porter 1963, 1964) do so has not yet been shown, although colchicine which drastically disorients the fibers of the cell wall causes the microtubules to disappear. Similarly, how control of water intake is managed is not known. That auxin stimulates water entry by a metabolic pumping device has been suggested by Thimann (1951).

The general questions of what comes first—cell shape or specialized cell product—and whether cell shape is due to the organization of the product are still open ones.

REFERENCES

1. Allen, R. D. (1961). Ameboid movement. In J. Brachet and A. Mirsky (eds.), *The Cell*, Vol. II, Academic Press, New York, pp. 135–216.

2. Bell, E. (1965). Differentiation of skin. In R. Dehaan and H. Ursprung (eds.), *Organogenesis*, Holt, Rinehart and Winston.

3. Edds, M. V. Jr. (1961), Preface. In M. V. Edds, Jr. (ed.), *Macromolecular Complexes*, Ronald Press, New York, pp. iii-iv.

4. Fitton Jackson, S. (1957). The fine structure of developing bone in the embryonic fowl. *Proc. Roy. Soc. (London)* B **146**:270–280.

5. Green, P. (1963). On mechanisms of elongation. In M. Locke (ed.), *Cytodifferentiation and Macromolecular Synthesis*, Academic Press, New York, pp. 203–234.

6. Harris, J. W. (1950). Studies on the destruction of red blood cells. VIII. Molecular orientation in sickle cell hemoglobin solutions. *Proc. Soc. Exptl. Biol. Med.* **75**:197–201.

7. Ingram, V. M. (1957). Gene mutations in human haemoglobin: the chemical difference between normal and sickle cell haemoglobin. *Nature* **180**:326–328.

8. Johnson, William (1963). Fibrous protein systems in muscle. In R. Borasky (ed.), *Ultrastructure of protein fibers*, Academic, New York, pp. 139–176.

9. Ledbetter, M. C., and K. R. Porter (1963). A "microtubule" in plant cell fine structure. *J. Cell Biol.* **19**:239–250.

10. Ledbetter, M. C., and K. R. Porter (1964). Morphology of microtubules of plant cells. *Science* **144**:872–874.

11. Mühlethaler, K. (1961). Plant cell walls. In J. Brachet and A. Mirsky (eds.), *The Cell*, Vol. II, Academic Press, New York, pp. 85–134.

12. Perutz, M. F., and J. M. Mitchison (1950). State of haemoglobin in sickle-cell anemia. *Nature* **166**:677–679.

13. Preston, R. D. (1961). Cellulose-protein complexes in plant cell walls. In M. V. Edds, Jr. (ed.), *Macromolecular Complexes*, Ronald Press, New York, pp. 229–253.

14. Thimann, K. V. (1951). "Studies on the Physiology of Cell Enlargement." The Society for the Study of Development and Growth, p. 5.

The Behavior of Collagen Units as a Model in Morphogenesis*

JEROME GROSS

Among the most intriguing problems in biology is that which deals with the formation, on supramolecular and tissue levels, of morphologically specific and repeatedly reproduced structures. On the macromolecular level, the controlled formation of highly organized fibrils, crystallites, and two dimensional sheets from solutions of collagen molecules furnishes an interesting model system for the study of such phenomena.

The reconstitution of collagen fibrils by increasing the pH or ionic strength of acid solutions of this protein is an old and familiar story (8, 29, 33). An exciting development was the revelation by electron microscopy that the reconstituted fibrils had the same precisely ordered morphology as did the native fibrils, namely the repeating axial period of about 640 A plus the detailed fine structure (1, 20, 36, 40, 49, 50). The two aspects of the problem which have engaged the attention of most investigators in this area are the characterization of the molecule and elucidation of the mechanism of *in vitro* fibrogenesis with the hope of relating it to the *in vivo* physiological process. Recent observations 16, 20, 26, 27, 46) on the production of radically different morphological forms of collagen by controlling conditions of pH and ionic strength, and by the addition of well characterized, non-collagenous substances, may bear pertinently on problems of morphogenesis in the organism.

Reprinted by permission of The Rockefeller Institute Press, from *Journal of Biophysical and Biochemical Cytology*, July 25, 1956, Vol. 2, No. 4, Supplement, 261–274.

* This is publication No. 191 of the Robert W. Lovett Memorial Laboratories for the Study of Crippling Diseases, Department of Medicine, Harvard Medical School, and the Massachusetts General Hospital.

This investigation has been supported in part by grants-in-aid from the National Institute of Arthritis and Metabolic Diseases of the National Institutes of Health, United States Public Health Service.

These may be summarized as follows:

1. An apparently homogeneous population of macromolecules may be precipitated from solution under the influence of physical chemical forces in the form of highly ordered structures, even when in the presence of a variety of other high molecular weight substances.

2. The morphological characteristics of the precipitated structures may vary so radically as to appear completely unrelated to each other, depending on readily controlled conditions in the solution. The conditions required for determining the type of structure may, in some cases, be no more than differences in concentration of the inducing agent.

3. The several different morphological forms may be readily dissolved and transformed one into another.

4. The specificity for structure formation may reside almost entirely in the reacting system, the macromolecular building blocks of collagen, while the inducing agents may be relatively non-specific.

5. Identical structural types may be precipitated from solutions ranging greatly in ionic content and properties by using different manipulations.

6. Morphologically identical end products may be produced via different intermediate stages in structure formation.

THE COLLAGEN FIBRIL AND ITS BUILDING BLOCK, TROPOCOLLAGEN

The commonest characteristic of collagen fibrils, in addition to the distinctive x-ray diffraction pattern (4) and an unusual amino acid composition (6, 35), is an axial periodicity of about 640 A with detailed intraperiod fine structure. This pattern may be observed with the electron microscope and detected by x-ray diffraction in the collagen fibers of most phyla ranging from sponges to mammals (13, 21, 32). In several instances, however, collagen which can be identified by x-ray diffraction and amino acid composition appears to be composed of unstriated fibrils; the best example being that of the earthworm cuticle (42). In addition, collagen fibrils having axial periods of 220 A have been observed in embryonic tissues and in tissue culture (39, 41). Electron microscopic analyses of several different structural forms reconstituted from solution (to be described), led to the characterization of the unit building block or molecule of collagen called *tropocollagen* (17). This particle, from electron microscope studies, was considered to be 2000 to 3000 A long and less than 50 A wide. Recent physical chemical studies by Boedtker and Doty (5) on acid solutions of fish collagen (ichthyocol) confirmed the existence of this particle in solution. The dissolved population of tropocollagen particles was remarkably monodisperse. The unit was shown to be a stiff rod 2900 A long by 14 A wide with a molecular weight of 340,000.

It was suggested that the manner in which such highly asymmetric particles lined up one with the other, gave rise to all the different structural forms of collagen described above (46, 47).

PRECIPITATION OF COLLAGEN FROM SOLUTION

Certain collagens may be rendered soluble at acid, neutral, and moderately alkaline pH without apparent degradation of the molecule (3, 9, 14, 15, 18, 23, 27, 30, 37). Electron micrographs of highly dilute solutions of collagen at pH 5.0 reveal very thin, filamentous aggregates (Fig. 1).

The simplest procedure for precipitating fibrillar collagen from acid solution requires the addition of monovalent salts or neutralization as described by Nageotte, Fauré-Fremiet, and others.

Important factors determining the kind of structures obtained are collagen concentration, the amount and kind of salt added, pH, and temperature. The way in which the salt is added is often of some consequence (20). Randall *et al.* (40) discuss the parameters influencing reconstitution and describe a series of carefully controlled experiments designed to evaluate the roles played by these various factors.

If the concentration of NaCl ranges between 0.02 and 0.2 M, the precipitate consists of fibrils all with the usual collagen axial period of about 640 A (Fig. 2) and the frequency distribution curve of periodicity is about the same as that for the native fibrils. The fine structure is also similar. There is as much variability in the number and density of the intraperiod bands in the reconstituted as in the native fibrils.

If the concentration of salt is elevated to 0.35 M, most of the fibrils formed have axial periods of about 220 A (Fig. 3). With increasing concentration (0.5 M NaCl) all the fibrils precipitated are non-striated (Fig. 4). Perhaps the occasional appearance in some tissues of non-striated fibrils or those with 220 A spacings is a result of environmental conditions—provided they can be otherwise identified as collagen. There is great variation in fibril width and form with different collagen solutions. In some instances relatively short, tactoidal fibrils are found rather than the "endless" type. Variation in width along the length of individual fibrils is often noted.

The major portion of the dissolved collagen is precipitated by salt; the reasons for frequently observed variability are as yet unknown. The question as to whether inorganic ions and non-collagenous components are incorporated into the structure in a relevant way is still unsettled.

An interesting and important feature of this phenomenon is the interconvertibility of the three forms. Precipitates of each structure type may be redissolved in acid and reprecipitated in any of the other forms by appropriately adjusting the conditions. Unfortunately, the interconvertibility of the three structural forms (640 A, 220 A and no periodicity) has not yet been studied quantitatively; it is important to know how much of the collagen can be reversibly precipitated in any of the three forms, since the question may be raised as to whether there exist several different although closely related molecular species of collagen in the same solutions. If this were so, the interplay between the different molecules could be important in the formation of structure.

It should be noted that 640 A type collagen fibrils may be precipitated from solution via several different routes. An acetic acid extract of calf corium dialyzed against near neutral salt solutions of ionic strength above 0.15 remains clear and fluid. On warming to 37°C. a rigid opaque gel composed of interlacing characteristic collagen fibrils is formed (14). Similar gels are produced by warming crude neutral salt extracts of fresh connective tissues (18).

A new and highly ordered form of collagen fibril never observed in native tissue was discovered by Highberger, Gross, and Schmitt (26) in precipitates of citrate extracts of fresh connective tissue prepared by a modification of the procedure of Orekhovitch (37). This fibril called "fibrous long spacing" or FLS had an axial period of about 2400 A with a detailed and *symmetrical* intraperiod fine structure. Occasional free individual segments of the same length were noted. This phenomenon could be duplicated in acetic acid solutions of ichthyocol or rat tail tendon by the addition of α_1 acid glycoprotein of serum to such solutions followed by dialysis against water (27) (Fig. 5). FLS was readily proven to be of collagenous origin by x-ray diffraction, hydroxyproline content, and the fact that it could be converted to fibrils with the 640 A period by dissolving in acid and dialyzing against saline. The use of smaller amounts of glycoprotein led to the formation of mixtures of FLS and 640 A type fibrils. Sometimes individual fibrils showed the presence of both types of structure, one gradually developing into the other (Fig. 6). Still lower concentrations of glycoprotein resulted in the formation of usual 640 A type fibrils only. Iodinated glycoprotein was used in an effort to determine the amounts of glycoprotein present in the washed precipitates and also to localize by electron microscopy the position of this substance in the structure. About 15

to 20 per cent was incorporated in FLS and 5 to 10 per cent in the 640 A type fibrils. The likelihood of some non-specific adsorption makes these figures only approximate. Localization of the iodine was not observed.

One of the most interesting aspects of this phenomenon from a morphogenetic point of view is that two radically different structural forms could be produced by the interaction of two molecular species simply by varying their relative concentrations.

Another new structural type of collagen was discovered in precipitates of neutral phosphate extracts of fresh connective tissue (46), in the form of short segments or crystallites of varying width having lengths averaging 2400 A. They were called "segment long spacing" or SLS and were characterized by a detailed asymmetrically banded fine structure. Because these extracts showed ultraviolet absorption maxima at about 260 $m\mu$ attempts were made to precipitate the collagen in acid solutions of ichthyocol (having no absorption peak in this range) with purine- and pyrimidine-containing compounds. RNA and DNA produced only non-striated fibrils. ATP in the acid form, however, precipitated nearly all the dissolved collagen in the form of SLS (Fig. 7) having extremely detailed and highly reproducible fine structure (Fig. 7 *a*). The particular pattern of cross-banding is even more reproducible than that of the native 640 A collagen type or that of FLS (Fig. 5 *a*) and may be an even more definitive fingerprint for collagen. There proved to be about 12 per cent ATP incorporated in the precipitate which could be gradually washed out with acid; this was accompanied by dissolution of the structure (46). Partially frayed SLS revealed the presence of parallel fibrous units the length of the segment and less than 50 A thick (17, 46). These, too, could be readily dissolved, in this case in neutral saline, and converted almost quantitatively into 640 A collagen type fibrils by dialysis against 1 per cent NaCl (17).

Two other interesting structures were precipitated from collagen solution, both of them showing large areas of two dimensional order. The first (Fig. 8) was precipitated by dialysis

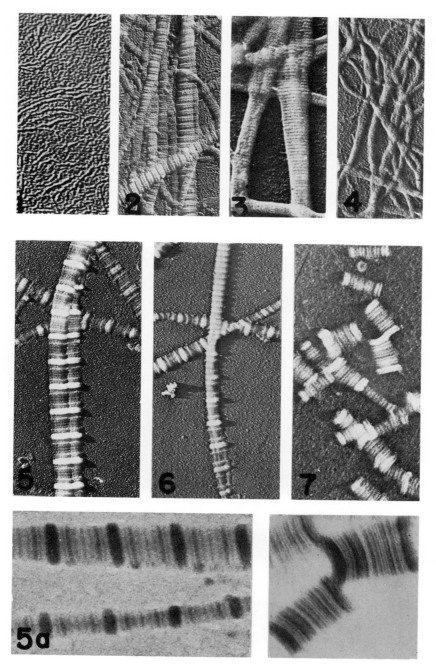

Fig. 1. Acetic acid solution of ichthyocol, pH 5.0; chromium shadowed. $\times$ 50,000. Fig. 2. Collagen fibrils precipitated from ichthyocol solution by 1 per cent NaCl. Average period 650 A. $\times$ 32,000. Fig. 3. Collagen fibrils precipitated from ichthyocol solution by 2 per cent NaCl. $\times$ 45,000. Fig. 4. Collagen fibrils precipitated from ichthyocol solution by 3 per cent NaCl. $\times$ 30,000. Fig. 5. FLS precipitated from ichthyocol solution by addition of α_1 acid glycoprotein 0.06 per cent followed by dialysis. $\times$ 30,250. Fig. 5 a. Same but stained with PTA. Note symmetrical fine structure. $\times$ 103,000. Fig. 6. Intermediate fibril type, native collagen period transforming to FLS. Induced by addition of 0.03 per cent glycoprotein. $\times$ 26,000. Fig. 7. SLS precipitated from ichthyocol solution by addition of 0.2 per cent ATP. $\times$ 38,500. Fig. 7 a. Same as Fig. 7 but stained with PTA. $\times$ 117,000.

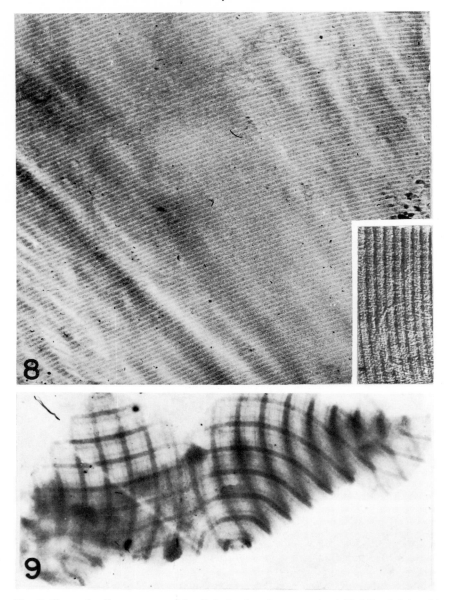

Fig. 8. Sheet of collagen prepared by dialysis of a citrate extract (pH 4.0) of 3-day-old rat corium dialyzed against water, PTA-stained. × 33,000. Insert is portion of a similar structure shadowed with chromium. Fig. 9. Sheet of FLS prepared by dialysis of ichthyocol solution containing 0.2 per cent α_1 glycoprotein. × 29,000.

from an acid citrate extract of young rat skin. Similar sheets of material were found throughout the preparation. The repeating period was somewhat lower than the usual 640 A, but in some specimens was in the usual range. Only two bands per period were observed and in shadowed preparations (insert in Fig. 8) were represented by sharply elevated ridges. In some cases the banding carried over to regions of collagen separated by apparently clear spaces. This probably is explained by the presence of an extremely thin layer of collagen in the seemingly empty spaces, too thin to provide adequate contrast.

It is interesting to note that electron micrographs of bone have revealed sheets of collagen fibrils with periods in register over large areas (43). The second two dimensional sheet was prepared by adding a relatively large quantity of acid glycoprotein to ichthyocol, followed by dialysis. Figure 9 illustrates the form of the two dimensional "long spacing" pattern occasionally obtained in this manner. Not only is the main period reproduced in two dimensions, but also some of the intraperiod fine structure. The plaid pattern may be the result of the folding over of a thin sheet of material, in a direction 45° to the banding. However, in all cases in which this phenomenon was observed similar patterns more or less askew were found.

INTERMEDIATE STAGES IN STRUCTURE FORMATION

As part of the effort to establish the nature of the building block of collagen, "time sequence" studies were made of the stages of formation of 640 A fibrils, FLS, and SLS by removing samples for electron microscopy from the reacting mixtures at short intervals of time during dialysis; in case of SLS formation, after mixing ATP and the collagen solution (17). A most interesting aspect of the development of FLS was that the identical final structural form could be obtained via the formation of two different types of intermediates. In one series of experiments after 10 to 15 minutes of dialysis, electron micrographs revealed extensive areas of densely stained (PTA) centers arranged in roughly hexagonal array from which extended thin fibrous processes. These centers were separated by 1500 to 2500 A. With time, local condensations appeared giving the appearance of clouds of dense spheroids, again packed in rough hexagonal array, from which appeared to emerge FLS fibrils as a product of further condensation (Fig. 10). Within 30 minutes the "clouds" were gone, to be replaced by broad, loosely formed FLS which became more compact and characteristic with time. Often during the "cloud-forming" stage, numerous tactoidal particles about 3000 A long

and 100 A across their centers appeared only to disappear shortly afterwards. A similar transient tactoidal stage was observed during the formation of 640 A collagen type fibrils. In another series of apparently identical experiments using solutions of ichthyocol similarly prepared, the intermediate stages of condensation from large clouds of collagen were never observed. Instead the first stages were represented by the appearance of randomly scattered dense centers or spheroids about 100 to 400 A in diameter which soon developed into very thin individual segments. These segments were about 2400 A long and less than 100 A wide; no fine structure was observed. Growth into typical FLS fibrils occurred by the process of lateral and lengthwise aggregation of tropocollagen particles (Fig. 11). The reason for these different pathways of formation is not established; they may reflect differences in collagen concentration. SLS tends to form from densely staining spheroidal centers about 500 A in diameter and grow laterally from extremely thin particles.

INDUCING AGENTS

It was evident very early that Na^+ or Cl^- ions were not specific for the precipitation of 640 A collagen fibrils from acid solutions. Similarly, in the case of the highly ordered, regularly reproducible structure of FLS and SLS the inducing agents, acid glycoprotein and ATP, were not specific. The list includes thrombin, mushroom tyrosinase, *clostridium* collagenase (inactivated), chondroitin sulfate, sulfated dextran, and gum arabic (16, 41). Curiously enough, the first three agents were even more effective and produced more perfect fibrils after they were boiled and treated with 20 per cent trichloracetic acid, the precipitate removed, the acid dialyzed out, solution lyophilized, and the dry powder used. Many other substances such as hyaluronic acid, ribo- and desoxyribonucleic acids, serum albumin and globulin, α_2 serum glycoprotein, ovomucoid, gliadin, and protamine were ineffective even in relatively high concentration. The nature of the common factor responsible

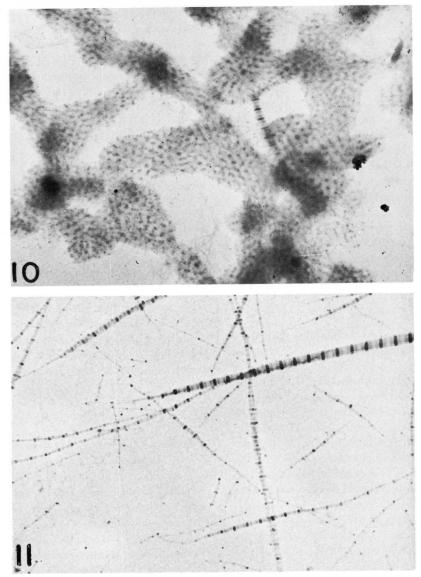

Fig. 10. Clouds of incipient FLS. Early stage in formation. PTA-stained. × 16,300.
Fig. 11. Intermediate stages in formation of FLS which differ from that shown in Fig. 10 illustrating the emergence of identical structural end products arrived at via different intermediate forms. × 21,300.

for FLS-inducing properties is still unknown. It certainly does not appear to be highly specific. Again, in the production of "segment long spacing" ATP proved not to be specific. Inosine triphosphoric acid could accomplish the same job. However, purine or pyrimidine bases, AMP, ADP, adenosine tetraphosphoric acid, and hexametaphosphoric acid were ineffective. Both nucleic acids and the mucopolysaccharides produced non-striated fibrous precipitates only. Typical SLS with the same fine structure could be produced by crude RNA, DNA, heparin, and chondroitin sulfate, if they were added to a cold solution of collagen at neutral pH (phosphate buffer) and the clear solution dialyzed against an acid buffer (pH about 3–5). These SLS were insoluble in salt solutions whereas those produced by ATP were instantly dissolved in the presence of salt.

It became evident that the specificity for FLS, SLS, or 640 A collagen formation resided in the fundamental building block of collagen in solution and not in the inducing agents (16). The dissolved collagen molecules are capable of aligning themselves in different ways so as to produce different structural forms. The inducing agent somehow makes one state of organization preferable to another, perhaps by blocking certain reactive groups on the molecule.

One might postulate that the inducing agents, be they an inorganic cation or a glycoprotein or ATP molecule, act by masking, and thereby weakening, certain reactive groups on the rigid tropocollagen particle thus permitting attractive forces of the remaining reactive groups to cause precipitation to occur in certain specific configurations depending on the positions of the particular groups remaining active. It seems less likely that the inducing agents themselves act as bonding agents between the molecules, since it is hard to visualize how ATP and chondroitin sulfate molecules could induce the formation of identical structures. An important question arises as to why giant molecules such as mucopolysaccharides, nucleic acids, or glycoproteins, if present in appreciable quantity, do not produce serious steric hindrance to the precise alignment of tropocollagen particles. Perhaps this is explained by the high water content of the precipitated structures; the large molecules may fill in space normally occupied by water.

SOME FACTORS REGULATING RATE OF FIBER FORMATION

As mentioned earlier, collagen dissolved in cold neutral salt solution will form stiff, opaque gels composed of striated collagen fibrils (640 A) when warmed to 37°C. Gelation takes longer at lower temperatures. Because the development of uniform opacity could be readily followed by light transmission in a colorimeter, this system was used in studying the influence of certain agents on fibril formation. Preliminary examination indicated that the opacity was the result of fibril formation and at pH above 6.0 gelation occurred as

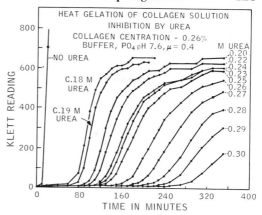

Text-fig. 1. Rate of opacitation (and gelation) in neutral phosphate solutions of collagen warmed to 37°C under the influence of increasing concentrations of urea.

opaqueness began to develop. It is evident that such methods reveal little concerning important factors such as the amount of collagen involved in the solid phase, or size of fibril as related to light transmission. However, for study of *relative* rates of opacitation related to gelation and fibril formation, the method is quite satisfactory. The preparations used in this study (14, 19) were acetic acid extracts of calf skin collagen dialyzed against phosphate buffer pH 7.6, $\Gamma/2 = 0.4$.

The development of opacity follows a sigmoid curve. The lag period increases while the level of maximum opacity and the slope of the rising portion of the curve decrease with decreasing collagen concentration.

The rate of opacitation and gelation could be significantly delayed by as little as 0.01 M of urea and 0.0005 M of arginine. Text-fig. 1 illustrates the influence of urea concentration on development of opacity. 0.3 M urea and 0.1 M arginine completely prevented gelation; however, the inhibition is reversible since removal of the agent by dialysis permits gelation to occur at the same rate as that of the control solution. The inhibitory or retarding effect of urea or arginine on gelation is reversed entirely by the addition of potassium iodide in concentrations one-tenth that of the inhibitor. Bicarbonate and thiocyanate ions are even more effective than iodide. Studies in progress indicate that a number of low molecular weight compounds have inhibitory and

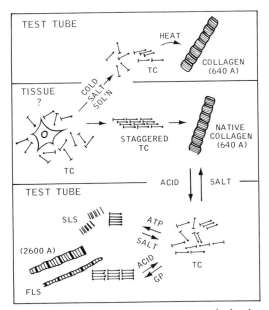

Text-fig. 2. Schematic representation of the hypothesized aggregations of tropocollagen particles in the formation of three different structural types of collagen. The central block suggests a possible way in which collagen fibrils are formed extracellularly, *in vivo*, from secreted tropocollagen. TC = tropocollagen; SLS = segment long spacing; FLS = fibrous long spacing; ATP = adenosine triphosphoric acid; GP = glycoprotein.

anti-inhibitory activity. These are being investigated for common denominators in an effort to understand the mechanism of action of such agents as well as to cast some light on the factors involved in fibril formation *in vitro* and *in vivo*. Interestingly enough, highly charged polymers such as chondroitin sulfate, heparin, hyaluronic acid, and α_1 acid glycoprotein have no measurable inhibitory or accelerating activity at $\Gamma/2 = 0.4$ or 0.14.

STATES OF AGGREGATION OF TROPOCOLLAGEN AND THE FIBROGENESIS OF COLLAGEN

A working hypothesis discussed elsewhere (47, 48) accounting for the various structural forms of collagen and suggesting in skeleton form the process of physiological fibrogenesis is described in Text-fig. 2. It hinges on the characterization of the tropocollagen particle

as a relatively rigid rod of dimensions 2000 to 3000 A long and less than 50 A in cross-section in which the internal fine structure (dependent on amino acid composition and polypeptide chain configuration) is asymmetrically distributed along its length. (The question of the helical configuration of the polypeptide chains or their number need not concern us here.) This is indicated in the diagram by the short rod with a ball at one end and a transverse bar at the other. If the tropocollagen particles (TC) when aggregated in orderly array, are all polarized in the same direction, the fine structure in the resulting fibril or segment will be polarized. If they aggregate in random or "antiparallel" array, the fine structure will be symmetrical. In the formation of SLS, the inducing agent causes aggregation in such a way that the tropocollagen particles line up in parallel with ends even with each other and all oriented in the same direction, thus leading to formation of a crystallite with polarized fine structure, approximating the length of the particle. In the formation of FLS the tropocollagen particles line up in an "antiparallel" array with random orientations in the axial direction but still not staggered. This random orientation would give rise to symmetrical intraperiod fine structure, and indeed an approximation of this fine structure can be simulated by superimposing two transparencies of an SLS unit one upon the other in reverse orientation. The formation of *fibers* of FLS may be due to interdigitations of the ends of tropocollagen particles possibly helped by the presence of a little "glue" in the form of the inducing agent. Certainly there is a heaping up of material at the ends of the periods as seen in Fig. 5. The formation of the polarized 640 A period of native fibrils is postulated to occur via the staggered ordering of tropocollagen particles all oriented in the same direction but staggered in such a way as to give rise to an axial striation of 640 A. The 220 A period could be formed in a similar way by a lesser degree of staggering and the non-striated fibril formed by a completely random lateral and linear aggregation. At concentrations of salt at about physiological ionic strength, the preferred and most stable degree of staggering is that which gives rise to the 640 A period. Thus any axial striation observed in collagen is a kind of "beat" period of a fundamental unit about 2800 A long. The intraperiod fine structure is probably just another more detailed manifestation of the same phenomenon. It will be extremely important to obtain evidence of the length of the tropocollagen particle *in the fibril* via x-ray diffraction or electron microscopy.

The center block in Text-fig. 2 suggests a highly simplified model of physiological fibrogenesis. The fibroblast secretes tropocollagen particles and these are spontaneously precipitated in the form of collagen type fibrils because of the characteristics of the ionic environment. It is possible that the earliest secreted collagen unit may require enzymatic action such as in the case of the fibrinogen-fibrin transformation; however, present information does not indicate the need for such a mechanism. The rate of fibril formation may be regulated by the concentration of some common metabolic product analogous to urea or arginine as in the *in vitro* system. The role in fibrogenesis of the non-collagenous components of the ground substance such as mucopolysaccharides, glycoproteins, etc., is unknown. Among other functions, they may provide the necessary viscous, even thixotropic, medium required to keep the precipitated fibrils localized to specific areas and arranged in a particular pattern; the fibrils might otherwise precipitate in a random tangled mass around the cells. *In vitro* systems involving fibril precipitation with agents such as chondroitin sulfate or glycoprotein constitute no evidence for their participation in *in vivo* fibrogenesis. Typical collagen fibrils may be precipitated from solution in the absence of detectable uronic acid, with only very small amounts of hexose, hexosamine, and tyrosine present (27). Conversely, a host of seemingly unrelated compounds may also precipitate characteristic collagen fibrils.

The upper block in Text-fig. 2 illustrates the extraction of precursor tropocollagen from the ground substance by cold neutral salt solutions and its precipitation as 640 A striated fibrils by warming. Gross (15) has shown that the amount of neutral salt-extractible collagen, in the case of guinea pig corium, is a direct function of growth rate, there being a precipitous drop when growth is restricted by diet.

DISCUSSION

The concept of biological crystallizations as a possible mechanism in structure formation has been discussed by Needham (34), Brachet (7), Weiss (53), among others, and more recently and specifically, by Schmitt (44, 45). It is conceivable that structures and organelles such as cell membranes, chromosomes, mitotic spindles, endoplasmic reticulum, mitochondria, etc., are formed, dissolved, and reformed by the spontaneous association of high polymer building blocks under the influence of physical chemical forces, the collagen system being a simplified example of such a process. The synthetic enzymatic mechanisms would be concerned with producing the building blocks and regulating the requisite environment of low molecular weight metabolites and electrolytes. The latter components would function in a manner analogous to the inducing agents and rate regulators in the model, *in vitro* collagen systems. The large molecular building blocks have built-in specificity and ability to associate in the form of well-ordered structures. If macromolecules with associated enzyme systems undergo intermolecular rearrangements such as described for collagen, this phenomenon would assume considerable functional significance beyond that of structure formation. A similar hypothesis concerning enzyme activities at cell interfaces was suggested by Weiss (53).

Considered from another aspect, the precipitability of collagen molecules in the form of organized fibrils and sheets with different highly ordered patterns depending on environmental factors suggests a mechanism to explain the directed movements of cells. The beautifully organized three-dimensional network of collagen in Descemet's membrane described by Jakus (31) suggests that two- and three-dimensionally ordered collagen is not just an interesting *in vitro* artifact. It is worthy of note that this structure is not entirely dissimilar to the clouds of collagen observed in the formation of FLS (Fig. 10).

Weiss (51, 52), Weiss and Garber (54), and Garber (10) have shown how the movements and even shapes of cells may be directly influenced by orientations in the extracellular matrix in tissue cultures and regenerating nerve. The "matrix" theory of morphogenesis invoking the aid of intercellular substances has been suggested periodically in the past (2, 24, 51) and in more detail recently by Grobstein (12). Quoting the latter, "A labile intercellular continuum, locally alterable in penetrability and other properties by physiological shifts, endowed with a high degree of specificity closely responsive to the genotype, able through polymerization to condense to higher levels of order thus providing boundaries and interfaces, seems to be exactly the missing piece required in many puzzles of development." Tropocollagen dispersed or loosely aggregated in the intercellular ground substance would seem to fit most of these requirements.

The number of *in vitro* systems in which highly ordered crystalline and para-crystalline arrays may be induced from solutions of large molecules is growing steadily. Perhaps the oldest known is the production of myelin forms from lipide and protein mixtures. Recently Geren (11) has demonstrated highly ordered laminated structures in preparations of pure lipide not unlike those of certain intracellular organelles. Precipitates formed from solutions of fibrinogen (22, 25), paramyosin (28), and meromyosin (38) display precise striated morphology.

If crystallizations of the type discussed here can be demonstrated to occur in tissues and to play a role in morphogenesis, studies on *in vitro* systems such as described for collagen should contribute much toward an understanding of the forces and factors involved in developmental processes.

BIBLIOGRAPHY

1. Bahr, G. F., *Exp. Cell Research*, 1950, **1**, 603.
2. Baitsell, G. A., *Quart. J. Micr. Sc.*, 1925, **69**, 571.
3. Banfield, W. G., *Anat. Rec.*, 1952, **114**, 157.
4. Bear, R. S., *Adv. Protein Chem.*, 1952, **7**, 69.
5. Boedtker, H., and P. Doty, *J. Am. Chem. Soc.*, 1955, **77**, 248.
6. Bowes, J. H., and R. H. Kenten, *Biochem. J.*, 1948, **43**, 358.
7. Brachet, J., *Chemical Embryology*, New York, Interscience Publishers, Inc., 1950.
8. Fauré-Fremiet, E., and A. Garrault, *Arch. anat. micr.*, 1937, **33**, 81.
9. Gallop, P. M., *Arch. Biochem. and Biophysic.*, 1955, **54**, 486
10. Garber, B., *Exp. Cell Research*, 1953, **5**, 132.
11. Geren (Uzman), B., *J. Biophysic. and Biochem. Cytol.*, 1956, **2**, No. 4, suppl., 219.
12. Grobstein, C., in *Aspects of Synthesis and Order in Growth* (D. Rudnick, editor), Thirteenth Symposium of the Society for the Study of Development and Growth, Princeton University Press, 1954, 233.
13. Gross, J., *Fed. Proc.*, 1954, **13**, No. 1, pt. 1, 52.
14. Gross, J., *Fed. Proc.*, 1956, **15**, No. 1, pt. 1, 82.
15. Gross, J., *J. Exp. Med.*, 1958, **107**, 247.
16. Gross, J., J. H. Highberger, and F. O. Schmitt, *Proc. Soc. Exp. Biol. and Med.*, 1952, **80**, 462.
17. Gross, J., J. H. Highberger, and F. O. Schmitt, *Proc. Nat. Acad. Sc.*, 1954, **40**, 679.
18. Gross, J., J. H. Highberger, and F. O. Schmitt, *Proc. Nat. Acad. Sc.*, 1955, **41**, 1.
19. Gross, J., and D. L. Kirk, *J. Biol. Chem.*, 1958, **233**, 355.
20. Gross, J., F. O. Schmitt, and J. H. Highberger, *Tr. 4th Josiah Macy, Jr. Conf. Metabolic Interrelations*, 1952, **4**, 32.
21. Gross, J., Z. Sokal, and M. Rougvie, *J. Histochem. and Cytochem.*, 1956, **4**, 227.
22. Hall, C. E., *J. Biol. Chem.*, 1949, **179**, 857.
23. Harkness, R. D., A. M. Marko, H. M. Muir, and A. Neuberger, *Biochem. J.*, 1954, **56**, 558.
24. Harrison, R. G., *Tr. Connecticut Acad. Arts and Sc.*, 1945, **36**, 277.
25. Hawn, C. v. Z., and K. R. Porter, *J. Exp. Med.*, 1947, **86**, 285.
26. Highberger, J. H., J. Gross, and F. O. Schmitt, *J. Am. Chem. Soc.*, 1950, **72**, 3321.
27. Highberger, J. H., J. Gross, and F. O. Schmitt, *Proc. Nat. Acad. Sc.*, 1951, **37**, 286.
28. Hodge, A., *Proc. Nat. Acad. Sc.*, 1952, **38**, 850.
29. Huzella, T., *Z. Krist.*, 1932, **83**, 89.

30. Jackson, D. S., and J. H. Fessler, *Nature*, 1955, **176**, 169.

31. Jakus, M. A., *J. Biophysic. and Biochem. Cytol.*, 1956, **2**, No. 4, suppl., 243.

32. Marks, M. H., R. S. Bear, and C. H. Blake, *J. Exp. Zool.*, 1949, **111**, 55.

33. Nageotte, J., *Compt. rend. Acad. sc.*, 1927, **184**, 115.

34. Needham, J., *Biochemistry and Morphogenesis*, Cambridge University Press, 1942.

35. Neuman, R. E., *Arch. Biochem.*, 1949, **24**, 289.

36. Noda, H., and R. W. G. Wyckoff, *Biochim. et Biophysic. Acta*, 1951, **8**, 494.

37. Orekhovitch, V. N., *Proc. 2nd Internat. Congr. Biochem., Paris*, 1952, 106.

38. Philpott, E. D., and A. G. Szent-Gyorgyi, *Biochim. et Biophysic. Acta*, 1954, **15**, 165.

39. Porter, K. R., *Tr. 2nd Josiah Macy, Jr. Conf. Connective Tissue*, 1951, 126.

40. Randall, J. R., F. Booth, R. E. Burge, S. F. Jackson, and F. C. Kelly, *Symp. Soc. Exp. Biol. (Great Britain)*, 1955, **9**, 127.

41. Randall, J. T., R. D. B. Fraser, S. Jackson, A. V. W. Martin, and A. C. T. North, *Nature*, 1952, **169**, 1029.

42. Reed, R., and R. M. Rudall, *Biochim. et Biophysic. Acta.*, 1948, **2**, 7.

43. Robinson, R. A., and M. L. Watson, *Anat. Rec.*, 1952, **114**, 383.

44. Schmitt, F. O., in *Analysis of Development*, (B. H. Willier, P. A. Weiss, and V. Hamburger, editors), Philadelphia, W. B. Saunders Co., 1955.

45. Schmitt, F. O., *Nature*, 1956, **177**, 503.

46. Schmitt, F. O., J. Gross, and J. H. Highberger, *Proc. Nat. Acad. Sc.*, 1953, **39**, 459.

47. Schmitt, F. O., J. Gross, and J. H. Highberger, *Symp. Soc. Exp. Biol. (Great Britain)*, 1955, **9**, 148.

48. Schmitt, F. O., J. Gross, and J. H. Highberger, *Exp. Cell Research*, 1955, suppl., 3, 326.

49. Schmitt, F. O., C. E. Hall, and M. A. Jakus, *J. Cell. and Comp. Physiol.*, 1942, **20**, 11.

50. Vanamee, P., and K. R. Porter, *J. Exp. Med.*, 1951, **94**, 255.

51. Weiss, P., *Am. Naturalist*, 1933, **67**, 322.

52. Weiss, P., *J. Exp. Zool.*, 1945, **100**, 353.

53. Weiss, P., *J. Embryol. and Exp. Morphol.*, 1953, **1**, 181.

54. Weiss, P., and B. Garber, *Proc. Nat. Acad. Sc.*, 1952, **38**, 264.

Macromolecular Aggregation States in Relation to Mineralization: The Collagen-Hydroxyapatite System as Studied *in Vitro*[*]

MELVIN J. GLIMCHER[†]

ALAN J. HODGE

FRANCIS O. SCHMITT

Mineralization in the tissues of living organisms, involving the deposition of substantial amounts of inorganic material in a well-defined crystalline form, serves highly important physiological and adaptive functions.

Proceedings of the National Academy of Sciences, **43**, 860–867, 1957. Reprinted with permission.

[*] These studies were aided by a research grant, E-1469 (C1) from the National Institute of Allergy and Infectious Diseases of the National Institutes of Health, United States Public Health Service.

[†] Special Postdoctoral Research Fellow of the National Heart Institute, National Institutes of Health, United States Public Health Service.

The process must also be restricted to appropriate tissues, such as tooth and the exo- and endoskeletal systems, which are differentiated for mechanical purposes; serious consequences result when, as in certain degenerative and other diseases, mineral is deposited in inappropriate tissues (such as in the cardiovascular system, skin, tendons, and ligaments). It is to be expected that, like other functions of such vital importance to the organism, mineralization will be found to be under the control of specific and very delicately balanced biochemical and biophysical mechanisms.

In any particular organism the extracellular fluid concentrations of those ions comprising the particular mineral to be deposited are at levels such that spontaneous crystallization does not occur. It follows, therefore, that in those tissues which normally become mineralized, some mechanism exists which must be capable both of inducing crystallization of the appropriate mineral and of controlling the amount, orientation, and crystal size of the deposits. It is that mechanism capable of inducing crystallization which is under consideration here. Throughout the article the term "nucleation" will be used to denote this induction of mineralization; no more precise specification is intended or possible at the present time.

It has for some time been supposed that a local factor or factors governing mineralization exist in the organic matrix. Indeed, in the case of bone and cartilage certain specific substances, such as enzymes,[1] chondroitin sulfate,[2] or chondroitin sulfate–collagen complexes[3] have been proposed as "local factors." Other investigators have felt that the degree of polymerization[4] and ion-binding characteristics[5] of the ground substance constitute the local factor.

In addition, connections have been sought between certain morphological features of the collagen fibril and the size, shape, and orientation of the inorganic crystallites as determined by X-ray diffraction and electron microscopy.[6] Furthermore, it has been shown that in embryonic bone the earliest particles identifiable as crystals occur in definite relationship to certain of the bands in the axial repeating structure of the collagen fibril.[7] However, these studies have been primarily descriptive of the anatomic relationships rather than illuminating with respect to the physical chemical mechanisms involved.

In several instances reconstituted collagens have been used to "seed" solutions metastable with respect to calcium nd phosphate. In one case, where the collagen was believed to be complexed with chondroitin sulfate, an increase in ash weight was demonstrated.[3] In another instance, using a preparation of reconstituted collagen shown by electron microscopy to be of the native 640 A type, the ratio of calcium and phosphate ions removed from the solution was found to be comparable with that of apatites.[8] In similar experiments by the same group of investigators fibrin and gelatin failed to modify the calcium and phosphate concentrations of the test solutions. However, in these studies, no direct evidence concerning the identity of the solid phase was obtained, nor was the process of mineralization related to the stereochemical configuration and aggregation state of the collagen macromolecules.

In this paper,[9] and in detailed descriptions which will be published in due course elsewhere, is given a working hypothesis of a possible physical chemical mechanism based on the stereochemistry of the major organic component. This has already been given careful study in the case of the collagen-hydroxyapatite system and may apply to the problem of biological mineralization generally. The hypothesis proposes that the mechanism of nucleation involves a specific stereochemical configuration resulting from a particular state of aggregation of collagen macromolecules. Only when the macromolecules interact to form fibrils with the configuration characteristic of the native state does this favorable and highly specific stereochemical matching of groups occur.

A brief exposition of the various patterns of interaction of collagen macromolecules will facilitate an understanding of the various experiments to be described presently.

When a connective tissue, such as rat-tail tendon or fish swim bladder, is extracted with dilute acid or with cold neutral salt solutions, a viscous solution is obtained which contains the individual elongate molecules of collagen ("tropocollagen") or linear polymers of such molecules (protofibrils). The individual macromolecules have dimensions[10] of 14×2900 A and consist of three covalent chains helically coiled about one another and strongly bound together by hydrogen bonds.[11] Solutions of such macromolecules, when appropriately treated,[12] readily aggregate to form fibrils that have the same axial repeat (about 640 A) and the same band pattern, as seen in the electron microscope, as do native fibrils. It is believed[13] that the pattern characteristic of the native state is produced when the tropocollagen macromolecules (TC) are aligned in parallel array (i.e., with like ends "pointing" in the same direction) and with ends of adjacent macromolecules staggered with respect to one another by a specific fraction of their length. The pattern of interaction of side chains of adjacent macromolecules may be altered reversibly so that the resulting fibrils represent different states of aggregation. Under certain conditions of ionic strength, the dispersed TC macromolecules aggregate so as to produce fibrils with an axial repeat of about one-third that of native fibrils (220 A); under still other conditions there may be no band pattern at all, the fibrils being structureless.[14] If certain organic substances of high negative charge, such as α-1 acid glycoprotein (GP), are added to the dispersed TC in acid solution and the pH raised by dialysis, a long-spacing modification is produced in which the axial repeat distance is about equal to the length of the TC molecules (2600–3000 A). In this artificial aggregation type called "fibrous long-spacing" or FLS, the band pattern is symmetrical (i.e., unpolarized), and the TC macromolecules are arranged in antiparallel array. When certain other substances, such as adenosine triphosphate (ATP), are added to the acid solution of TC, a different long-spacing modification is formed immediately without adjustment of pH or ionic strength. In this form the TC molecules are in parallel array, and like ends are in register, giving a band pattern which is asymmetric (i.e., polarized). The structures appear as segments rather than as fibrils, and this form is therefore called "segment long-spacing" (SLS).

Thus, from a solution of fully dispersed TC macromolecules, it is possible to pass reversibly from one aggregation type to another among the five forms already clearly established. Certain transition forms are also occasionally observed. All these various forms reflect different modes of interaction of side-chain groups in adjacent TC molecules and therefore present different surface configura-tions to the environment. This provides a unique system with which the mineralization theory proposed above may readily be tested.

The experiments necessary to test the hypothesis were carried out by exposing the collagen molecules, linear polymers of molecules, and the various TC aggregation types to solutions containing calcium and phosphate ions. These solutions, though inherently capable of forming hydroxyapatite spontaneously, were adjusted with respect to calcium and phosphate ion concentrations, ionic strength, and pH so as to form metastable solutions which did not precipitate spontaneously for periods very long (months) with respect to the duration of the experiments. In such solutions the product of the activities of Ca^{++} and HPO_4^{--} exceeds the solubility product of $CaHPO_4 \cdot 2H_2O$ but is below the point of spontaneous precipitation.[8] Such solutions, to be referred to as Ca-P solutions, are therefore in metastable equilibrium. They were checked for the presence of suspended colloidal particles by ultracentrifugation and Millipore filtration both before and after the experiments, as recommended by Levinskas.[15]

Calf and guinea-pig skin[27] was extracted at $0°–2°$ C. with dilute acetic acid and dialyzed against a buffer at pH 7.4 and ionic strength 0.45. After filtration and ultracentrifugation, such solutions contain dispersed TC macromolecules and linear polymers of TC, but no fibrils or other aggregates. No evidence of crystal formation was observed after repeated dialysis versus the appropriate Ca-P solution. However, when such solutions were warmed to $30°–37°$ C., fibrils of native type were formed which caused prompt mineral nucleation from the same solution. It is clear, therefore, that, although the individual macromolecules or protofibrils themselves are incapable of mineralization, the lateral aggregation of these molecules to form fibrils of the native type through side-chain interactions of a specific kind results in a stereochemical configuration favorable for the induction of hydroxyapatite crystallization.

Further experiments were performed as follows. The particular TC aggregation type to be tested was formed in a dialysis bag under appropriate conditions and then exposed to Ca-P solutions at constant temperature for periods ranging from 18 hours to 10 days. A small portion of the resultant material was used for electron-microscopic and electron-diffraction examination and the remainder spun down. After decanting, the matted precipitate was filtered and dried in a specially constructed Millipore filter[16] apparatus which removed about 90–95% of the solvent. Control samples which had been dialyzed against equivalent buffer solutions yielded material which showed no X-ray diffraction evidence for the presence of the major salt (NaCl) in the buffer. In view of this and because of the very low concentrations of calcium and phosphate ions relative to the sodium chloride concentration in these solutions, the possibility of error arising from the formation of apatite by evaporation of residual solvent was eliminated. Following filtration, the precipitates were further dried in a desiccator and then subjected to X-ray diffraction analysis.[17] Aliquots were also analyzed for dry weight, ash weight, calcium, and phosphorus.[18] When present, the mineral crystallites could be observed in electron micrographs both of unshadowed and of shadowed preparations. That this mineral was, in fact, an apatite was established by selected-area electron diffraction.[19]

Nucleation of mineral was observed only in preparations containing reconstituted native-type collagen fibrils. These were prepared from various types of connective tissue and precipitated in several ways. Included were collagen from normally non-calcifying connective tissues, such as rat-tail tendon, the skin of calf and guinea pig, and the ichthyocol of the fish (carp) swim bladder. The various reconstituted forms of collagen other than the native type were also produced and tested as described. All failed to induce nucleation, despite extensive dialysis against Ca-P solutions.

Although most of the diffraction patterns indexed were characteristic of hydroxyapatite, several showed additional reflections which corresponded to what has been called "octocalcium phosphate."[20] The significance of these particular diffractions ($d \cong 18.3$, 9.3, 5.5 A) is a subject of controversy at the pres-

ent time.[20, 21] The only pertinent fact to note with respect to the present hypothesis is that similar reflections have been reported from intact bone.[22]

Electron-microscopic examination revealed rather heavy deposits of crystals on the fibrils and in the background in preparations which had been exposed to the Ca-P solutions for relatively long periods of time. However, time-sequence studies are currently being undertaken, and preliminary observations on samples withdrawn after relatively short exposures support the view that mineralization is initiated at specific sites within the intraperiod band pattern characteristic of native-type collagen. In preparations containing both FLS and native-type fibrils, the FLS-type fibrils were free of crystallites, whereas those of native type were heavily calcified. Although the electron-microscope results support the present theory of mineralization, they cannot be regarded as conclusive because of the difficulty of adequate sampling and other factors at the high magnifications necessary. Definitive evidence is, however, provided by the analytical data, which revealed no significant increase in calcium or phosphorus content in any of the preparations shown by electron microscopy to be free of native-type fibrils.

In our preparations no preferred orientation of the crystallites was detected by X-ray diffraction. No orientation could be demonstrated even in those preparations in which reconstituted native-type fibrils had been successfully oriented prior to exposure to the Ca-P solutions. It is of interest to note that similar findings have been reported for embryonic and early postfetal bone.[7, 23]

In order to produce the various TC aggregation states, it was necessary to employ a wide range of ionic strengths. Under these conditions it was impossible to compare accurately the activities of calcium and phosphate ions in the various solutions, particularly in those of high ionic strength. Hence it was not possible to determine quantitatively whether the various Ca-P solutions were equally metastable. This difficulty was overcome by recourse to the following experimental device.

Freshly reconstituted native 640 A type fibrils were exposed to solutions such as were used in testing the other four fibril types (220 A, structureless, FLS, SLS). In every case the native-type fibrils initiated crystallization of apatite. The results of analogous experiments utilizing the other fibril types confirmed the conclusion that failure to initiate crystal formation is due to the unfavorable configurations of the reconstituted collagens rather than to the nature of the test solutions.

Attempts to calcify freshly dissected rat-tail tendon fibrils by similar procedures failed, even though the activities of calcium and phosphate ions were raised to the point of spontaneous precipitation. This result is supported by recent work[24] but disagrees with an earlier report.[25] No calcification occurred even when the rat-tail tendon fibers were thoroughly minced to eliminate possible diffusion barriers. It is noteworthy, however, that *reconstituted* native-type fibrils from rat-tail tendon, as mentioned earlier, were able to initiate crystallization.

So far as is known, the fibrous collagen of all connective tissues has the same molecular organization, as revealed by X-ray diffraction and electron microscopy. It is this *native* structure and only this structure which calcifies *in vitro*. However, that this is not the only determining factor in calcification *in vivo* is indicated by the obvious failure of many collagenous tissues to calcify under normal conditions. Failure to calcify, if attributed to the collagenous component, would presumably involve subtle structural differences as yet unresolved by the physical and chemical methods thus far applied. However, it seems more probable that non-collagenous components in the ground substance are responsible for the inhibition and control of calcification.[26] Although the mechanisms by which mineralization is initiated and regulated in the organism are undoubtedly far more complex, the process under consideration in the present paper—namely, the induction of crystallization by a specific stereochemical array of reactive groups as manifested by a particular macromolecular aggregation state—is probably fundamental in mineralization.

The precise manner in which the specific stereochemical configuration of the collagen causes nucleation of apatite crystals is not clear. However, it is conceivable that the binding of solute ions by groups arranged in a definite geometric array results in a modification of the interaction energies of the component ions such that formation of the crystal lattice is favored. Subsequent growth beyond a certain critical crystallite size would then be spontaneous (except, of course, for limitations of a biological character). The present state of physical chemical knowledge in relation to nucleation phenomena is rather tenuous, even in simple systems, and it must therefore be left to the future to form a clearer picture of the exact mechanisms involved.

SUMMARY

A general concept of the process of initiation of mineralization in biological structures has been put forward and illustrated by observations on the specific interrelationships between collagen and hydroxyapatite. In the type of mechanism envisaged, the nucleation of the inorganic crystals requires a precise juxtaposition of groups in the organic matrix to form a specific stereochemical array.

The nature of the specificity between collagen and hydroxyapatite has been demonstrated by experiments involving collagen reconstituted *in vitro* in a number of different forms, namely, the native-type fibrils (640 A axial repeat), 220 A period fibrils, unstructured fibrils, fibrous long-spacing, and segment long-spacing. Of these forms, only the native-type fibrils are capable of inducing the formation of hydroxyapatite crystals when exposed to otherwise stable solutions containing calcium and phosphate ions. Positive identification of the crystals was accomplished by X-ray diffraction, selected-area electron diffraction, and analytical chemical data. It has also been demonstrated that the dispersed tropocollagen macromoecules themselves and linear polymers of tropocollagen (protofibrils) are incapable of initiating mineralization.

The ability to initiate mineralization does

not appear to be specific for bone collagen, as a variety of otherwise normally uncalcified collagens can be mineralized *in vitro*. Freshly dissected collagen fibers from rat-tail tendon do not calcify under similar physical chemical conditions; yet when the collagen is extracted and reconstituted in the native configuration, it is able to mineralize. The implications of these facts are briefly discussed in relation to calcification *in vivo*.

[1] R. Robison, *Biochem. J.*, **17**, 286, 1923; A. B. Gutman and T. F. Yu, in *Transactions of the 2d Conference on Metabolic Interrelations* (New York: Josiah Macy, Jr., Foundation, 1950).

[2] A. E. Sobel and M. Burger, *Proc. Soc. Exptl. Biol. Med.*, **87**, 7, 1954.

[3] A. E. Sobel, *Ann. N.Y. Acad. Sci.*, **60**, 713, 1955.

[4] P. S. Rubin and J. E. Howard, in *Transactions of the 2d Conference on Metabolic Interrelations* (New York: Josiah Macy, Jr., Foundation, 1950); I. Gersh, in *Transactions of the 2d Conference on Connective Tissues* (New York: Josiah Macy, Jr., Foundation, 1951); M. B. Engel *et al.*, in *Transactions of the 5th Conference on Metabolic Interrelations* (New York: Josiah Macy, Jr., Foundation, 1953).

[5] E. Freudenberg and P. Gyorgy, *Biochem. Z.*, **118**, 50, 1921.

[6] D. Carlström, A. Engström, and J. B. Finean, in "Fibrous Proteins and Their Biological Significance," *Symposia Soc. Exptl. Biol.*, **9**, 85, 1955; R. A. Robinson and M. L. Watson, *Ann. N.Y. Acad. Sci.*, **60**, 596, 1955; A. Engström, in "Bone Structure and Metabolism," *Ciba Foundation Symposium*, ed. G. E. W. Wolstenholme and C. U. O'Connor (London, 1956); H. Fernandez-Moran and A. Engström, *Biochim. et Biophys. Acta*, **23**, 264, 1957.

[7] S. F. Jackson and J. T. Randall, in "Bone Structure and Metabolism," *Ciba Foundation Symposium*, ed. G. E. W. Wolstenholme and C. U. O'Connor (London, 1956).

[8] B. S. Strates, W. F. Neuman, and G. J. Levinskas, *J. Phys. Chem.*, **61**, 279, 1957.

[9] The substance of this paper was presented by one of us (M. J. G.) in Meriden, New Hampshire, at the Gordon Conference on Bone and Tooth, July 15, 1957.

[10] H. Boedtker and P. Doty, *J. Am. Chem. Soc.*, **78**, 4267, 1956.

[11] G. N. Ramachandran and G. Kartha, *Nature*, **176**, 593, 1955; A. Rich and F. H. C. Crick, *Nature*, **176**, 915, 1955; P. M. Cowan, S. McGavin, and A. C. T. North, *Nature*, **176**, 1062, 1955.

[12] F. O. Schmitt, C. E. Hall, and M. A. Jakus, *J. Cellular Comp. Physiol.*, **20**, 11, 1942; J. H. Highberger, J. Gross, and F. O. Schmitt, *Proc. N.A.S.*, **37**, 286, 1951; J. Gross, J. H. Highberger, and F. O. Schmitt, *Proc. N.A.S.* **41**, 1, 1954.

[13] J. Gross, J. H. Highberger, and F. O. Schmitt, *Proc. N.A.S.*, **40**, 679, 1954; F. O. Schmitt, J. Gross, and J. H. Highberger, *Exptl. Cell Research* (Suppl.), **3**, 326, 1955; F. O. Schmitt, J. Gross, and J. H. Highberger, in "Fibrous Proteins and Their Biological Significance," *Symposia Soc. Exptl. Biol.*, **9**, 148, 1955.

[14] J. H. Highberger, J. Gross, and F. O. Schmitt, *Proc. N.A.S.*, **37**, 286, 1951.

[15] G. J. Levinskas, Ph.D. thesis, University of Rochester, Rochester, New York, 1953.

[16] Manufactured and distributed by Millipore Filter Corporation, Watertown, Massachusetts.

[17] The X-ray diffraction was done on equipment in Professor R. S. Bear's laboratory in this department. We are very grateful to him and to Dr. Diego Carlström, Dr. Carolyn Cohen, Mr. Carol Johnson, and Mr. Lawrence Bonar, who generously made many of the diffraction patterns.

[18] We are greatly indebted to Dr. Bernard Bachra, of the Department of Biochemistry, Jewish Hospital of Brooklyn, for many of these analyses and to Dr. Albert Sobel, in whose laboratory the analyses were performed.

[19] Thanks are due to Dr. David Spiro, Department of Pathology, Massachusetts General Hospital, Boston, Massachusetts, for the use of his electron microscope in connection with certain of the electron diffraction studies.

[20] P. W. Arnold, *Trans. Faraday Soc.*, **46**, 1061, 1950.

[21] A. S. Posner and A. Perloff, *J. Research Natl. Bur. Standards*, **58**, 279, 1957; D. Carlström, *Acta Radiol.* (Suppl.), **121**, 1955.

[22] C. I. Reed and B. P. Reed, *Am. J. Physiol.*, **138**, 34, 1942; *Proc. Soc. Exptl. Biol. Med.*, **50**, 196, 1942; G. H. Bell, *J. Physiol.*, **106**, 286, 1947.

[23] S. M. Clark and J. Iball, *Nature*, **179**, 94, 1957; G. Wallgren, *Acta Paediat.* (Suppl.) **113**, 1957.

[24] G. N. Ramachandran and M. S. Santhanam, *Experientia*, **22**, 340, 1956.

[25] A. Engström, B. Engfeldt, and R. Zetterström, *Experientia*, **8**, 259, 1952.

[26] Most references in the literature (e.g., notes 2, 3, and 4 in this paper) have postulated that certain ground-substance components, in particular the chondroitin sulfates, initiate calcification rather than inhibit it. However, these experimental data may be interpreted otherwise.

[27] We are indebted to Dr. Jerome Gross, of the Massachusetts General Hospital, for generously supplying the calfskin.

12

Hormones

THERE IS MUCH EVIDENCE, particularly from studies of insect development, that hormones serve to trigger cellular changes (*Wigglesworth 1960;* * Williams 1963). Growth and differentiation of the imaginal discs commence when hormones appear at the time of pupation. The fate of imaginal discs for wing, leg, etc., is determined sometime during larval development (Bodenstein 1950). To what extent new genes are activated when discs are exposed to hormones is unknown. There is no proof that hormones directly activate genes. It is possible that they act circuitously through other metabolic routes. Certain chromosome bands in chironomus puff after administration of the hormone ecdysone to larvae (Clever 1964). The primary response is the puffing of two bands within 1 hour. A secondary response occurs over a period of several days during which additional puffs appear. Treatment of the larvae with puromycin (Clever 1964) suggests that a protein may be needed for the secondary but not the primary response.

The morphogenetic and biochemical consequences of the release of thyroxin at the time of amphibian metamorphosis have been extensively described. Changes in serum proteins, in hemoglobin, in skin and visual pigments, and in vitamin A and other factors have been correlated with the hormonal induction of metamorphosis (Kollros 1958, 1961; Frieden 1961; Wilt 1959). Recently an enzyme collagenase concerned with the remodeling of the tail at metamorphosis have been discovered (Gross, Lapiere, and Tanzer 1963). Thyroxin stimulation of collagenase activity in tadpole was demonstrated by incubation of tissue fragments on a labelled collagen substrate. Enzyme function was detected by release of C^{14} from the collagen gel. The enzyme appears to be tightly bound *in vivo* to collagen. By this device rigid control of its activity may be maintained when drastic remodeling of gut, gills, skin, and tail occur during metamorphosis. Out of control, the enzyme might destroy tissues destined to be preserved for the adult.

As *Weiss and Rossetti (1951)* have shown, thyroxin may affect targets even in the same organ differently. Whereas growth of nerve cells and mitotic activity of neural epithelium is enhanced in the tadpole brain, Mauthner's neurons atrophy. The routes to each end must be clearly different.

The mode of action of hormones which function in the maturation of gametes, in the reproductive cycle and in maintaining sex characteristics, is not at all understood at the molecular level. For example, how progesterone stimulates the growth and preparation of the uterus and prevents the fetus from aborting and how the androgens promote spermatogenesis and maintain secondary sex characteristics such as the cock's comb is poorly understood. Villee (1962) has proposed that

---

* Italicized references indicate articles which appear in this book.

estrogens increase the available supply of "biologically useful energy" by stimulating pyridine nucleotide transhydrogenase activity. However, this may not be the primary site of its action. The stimulation of enzyme activity by hormone has been alluded to in Chapter 8.

There are in addition to hormones other "small molecules" whose actions result in developmental change. CO_2 stimulates formation of resistant sporangia in Blastocladiella (Cantino 1952) and sexuality in Hydra (Loomis 1959). The ameboid Naegleria can be transformed to flagellate cell with a stiff cuticle by means of distilled water (Willmer 1963). A pH shift (as well as other factors such as light, temperature, or orientation of neighboring cells) can determine polarity in the egg of the seaweed Fucus (Whitaker and Berg 1944; Jaffe 1958).

Vitamin A has been shown to direct cells which would otherwise keratinize to secrete mucous or develop cilia (Fell and Mellanby 1953); and phenylalanine has been shown to stimulate amphibian ectodermal cells to make pigment (Wilde 1959).

Whether they be hormones or other small molecules, the use of defined compounds to study gene activation seems to hold much promise.

REFERENCES

1. Bodenstein, D. (1950). The post-embryonic development of Drosophila. In M. Demerec (ed.), *The Biology of Drosophilia*, Wiley, New York, pp. 275–367.
2. Cantino, E. C. (1952). The biochemical nature of morphogenetic patterns in Blastocladiella. *Amer. Naturalist* **86**:399–404.
3. Clever, U. (1964). Actinomycin and puromycin: effects on sequential gene activation by ecdysone. *Science* **146**:794–795.
4. Fell, H. B., and E. Mellanby (1950). Effects of hypervitaminosio A on foetal mouse bones cultivated *in vitro*; preliminary communication. *Brit. Med. J.* **2**:535–539.
5. Frieden, E. (1961). Biochemical adaptation and anuran metamorphosis. *Am. Zool.* **1**:115–149.
6. Gross, J., C. Lapiere, and M. Tanzer (1963). Organization and disorganization of extracellular substances: the collagen system. In M. Locke (ed.), *Cytodifferentiation and Macromolecular Synthesis*, Academic Press, New York, pp. 175–202.
7. Jaffe, L. (1958). Tropistic responses of zygotes of the Fucaceae to polarized light. *Exptl. Cell Res.* **15**:282–299.
8. Kollros, J. J. (1958). Hormonal control of onset of corneal reflex in the frog. *Science* **128**:1505.
9. Kollros, J. (1961). Mechanisms of amphibian metamorphosis: hormones. *Am. Zool.* **1**:107–114.
10. Loomis, W. F. (1959). Feedback control of growth and differentiation by carbon dioxide tension and related metabolic variables. In D. Rudnick (ed.), *Cell, Organism and Milieu*, Ronald Press, New York, pp. 3–42.
11. Villee, Claude A. (1962). The role of steroid hormones in the control of metabolic activity. In J. M. Allen (ed.), *The Molecular Control of Cellular Activity*, McGraw-Hill, New York, pp. 297–318.
12. Whitaker, D. M., and W. E. Berg (1944). The development of Fucus eggs in concentration gradients: A new method for establishing steep gradients across living cells. *Biol. Bull.* **86**:125–129.
13. Wilde, C. E. (1959). Differentiation in response to the biochemical environment. In D. Rudnick (ed.), *Cell, Organism and Milieu*, Ronald Press, New York, pp. 3–43.
14. Williams, C. M. (1963). Differentiation and morphogenesis in insects. In J. M. Allen (ed.), *The Nature of Biological Diversity*, McGraw-Hill, New York, pp. 243–260.
15. Willmer, E. N. (1963). Differentiation in Naegleria. In G. E. Fogg (ed.), *Symposia of the Society for Experimental Biology, Number XVII, Cell Differentiation*, The University Press, Cambridge, England, pp. 98–126.
16. Wilt, F. (1959). The organ specific action of thyroxin in visual pigment differentiation. *J. Embryol. Exp. Morph.* **7**:556–563.

Growth Responses of Opposite Sign among Different Neuron Types Exposed to Thyroid Hormone*

PAUL WEISS

FIAMMETTA ROSSETTI

INTRODUCTION

The metamorphic changes transforming the tissues of the tadpole into those of the mature frog have been shown to be under the "control" of the thyroid hormone. That is, they fail to occur, if the hormone is absent. However, it is becoming increasingly clear that "control" does not mean the determination of the specific character of the ensuing changes, but refers merely to the reactivation and further sustenance of different chains of morphogenetic events, temporarily arrested in the larval stage, then continuing in each tissue reacting according to its own characteristic properties. Hormone action does not initiate heterogeneity in homogeneous tissues; it merely leads to the realization, including visualization, of latent differences based on pre-existing heterogeneity. The mosaic of terminal hormone effects is anticipated by a corresponding latent mosaic of differential susceptibility and response among the various reacting tissues (Weiss, 1924). In brief, the morphogenetic action of a hormone is not too unlike the action of the photographic developer in bringing out the latent picture on an exposed plate.

It is less clear whether tissues react essentially as units, perhaps as a result of regional vascular or metabolic changes, or whether each cell responds separately as an individual. This problem has broad significance particularly in the case of the nervous system. Many

behavior patterns, e.g., mating behavior, are dependent on sex hormones (see Beach, 1950) much in the same way as amphibian metamorphosis depends on thyroid. The fact that metamorphosis is accompanied by profound behavioral changes makes the parallel even closer. Yet the neurological basis of these hormonal effects on behavior is still quite obscure. It is reasonable to assume that it consists of the selective and differential response to hormone of certain neuron systems, in contradistinction to others, based on innate differences among the respective neurons. The following account presents a crucial demonstration of such critical differences among neuron types in their response to the metamorphosing hormone.

THE TEST OBJECT: MAUTHNER'S CELL (M-CELL)

The hind brain of the tadpole contains, at the level of the entrance of the vestibular nerve, a single pair of giant cell bodies, so-called Mauthner's cells (hereafter referred to as "M-cells") with large descending axons generally considered to be concerned with swimming movements of tail and trunk. For further details about these cells, we may refer to two recent reviews (Stefanelli 1950, 1951). During the larval period, the M-cells can easily be told from all other neurons of the surroundings by their extreme size. After metamorphosis, evidently correlated with the loss of undulatory swimming, they undergo regression,[1] losing size until they can no longer be distinguished. Our experiments were designed to analyze the causes of this regression.

According to recent studies (summarized

Proceedings of the National Academy of Sciences, **37**, 540–556, 1951. Reprinted with permission.

* This work has been aided by the Wallace C. and Clara A. Abbott Memorial Fund of the University of Chicago and by a research grant from the National Institutes of Health, Public Health Service.

TABLE 1. Nuclear size of Mauthner's cells after unilateral transection of spinal cord

Case	Age at Operation	Stage	Days Post-operative	Nuclear Diameters of M-Cells in Units[a]	
				Experimental	Control
SA7[I]	33	V	5	9×7	9×6
SA7[II]	31	IV	5	10×7	11×6
SA8	31	IV	7	12×10	12×7
SA1	22	II	7	11×6	9×7
SA5	33	V	8	12×8	13×9
SA3[I]	43	VII	9	11×7	11×7
SA3[III]	43	VII	9	11×6	12×6
SA4	43	VII	9	12×7	10×7
SA6[III]	31	IV	11	11×6	10×9
SA5[I]	33	V	12	13×7	11×9
SA11[I]	33	V	28	11×8	15×8
SA15[II]	31	IV	28	14×7	12×7
SA12[II]	31	IV	29	10×6	10×8
			Average	11.3×7.1	11.1×7.4
				80.2	81.4

[a] 1 unit equals 1.75 μ. The final averages are given as products of the average largest and smallest diameters.

TABLE 2. Mitotic activity in normal hind brain

a	b	c	f	g	h
	Age at		Mitotic Count		Mitotic Index
Case	Fixation	Stage	Hind Brain	Spinal Cord	Hind Brain
NP2[6]	33	V	18	20	11.3
NP2[5]	33	V	12	5	7.5
NP2[9]	43	VII	20	27	11.1
NP2[10]	43	VII	17	15	9.4
NP3	64	XIII	19	—	9.0
				Average	9.7
NP4[III]	91	XXII	2	—	0.8
NP4[IV]	93	XXIII	0	—	0.0

TABLE 3. Mitotic count in hind brains with grafts of submaxillary gland

a	b	c	d	e	f	h
	Age at		Stage at	Days Post-	Mitotic	Hind Brain
Case	Operation	Stage	Fixation	operative	Count	Mitotic Index
Fresh Submaxillary						
FS1	36	V	V	3	27	16.4
FS2	36	V	V	3	10	5.9
FS3	39	VI	VI	3	10	5.8
FS4	39	VI	VI	3	10	5.8
FS5	39	VI	VI	3	14	8.2
FS6	39	VI	VI	3	12	7.0
					Average	8.2
Boiled Submaxillary						
BS1	34–36	IV–V	V	3	22	13.8
BS2	34–36	IV–V	IV–V	3	13	8.1
BS3	34–36	IV–V	IV–V	3	37	25.2
BS5	34–36	IV–V	IV–V	3	14	8.7
BS6	34–36	IV–V	IV–V	3	26	16.2
					Average	14.8
					Grand average	11.2

TABLE 4.   Mitotic count in hind brain and cord with thyroid grafts

Case	Age at Operation	Stage	Stage at Fixation	Days Post-operative	Mitotic Count Hind Brain	Mitotic Count Spinal Cord	Mitotic Index, Hind Brain
T35[2]	34	IV	V	3	107	134	67.0
T34[2]	34	IV	V	3	78	35	49.0
T33[2]	34	IV	V	3	106	104	66.1
T32[2]	34	IV	V	3	74	149	46.1
T36[2]	35	IV	V	4	91	117	56.9
T18[I]	37	V	X	4	71	58	44.0
T39	41	V	VI	3	110	44	65.0
T18[III]	43	VI	XX	5	42	40	23.5
T27[I]	44	VI	XXII	6	45	44	25.0
T27[II]	44	VI	XXI	6	36	37	20.0
T27[III]	44	VI	XXI	6	55	—	30.5
T5[II]	45	VI	XXI	7	55	69	30.0
T5[III]	45	VI	XXI	7	52	50	29.0
T41[2]	46	VII	VIII	3	133	145	76.0
T26[I]	49	VII	XXI	6	17	14	9.0
T3[III]	58	VII	XXI	15	13	15	6.3
T28[II]	60	XI	XXI	5	42	20	19.9
T25[II]	62	XI	XX	7	25	8	11.8
						Average	37.5

in Young, 1950 and Weiss, 1950a), neuronal size depends on trophic interactions with the peripheral tissues, perhaps through functional reinforcement (Hamburger and Hydén, 1945; Edds, 1950). These effects seem to operate, however, upon a background of intrinsically different growth potentials among different kinds of neurons, emphasizing the multifactorial character of size determination. M-cells, specifically, have been shown to acquire their excessive growth capacity early in development (Rossetti, 1947; Stefanelli, 1951), though remaining subject to size variation in accordance with the extent of their dendritic fields. Nothing was known, however, about the factors causing their metamorphic reduction. Considering that neurons deprived of peripheral connections atrophy (Weiss, Edds and Cavanaugh, 1945; Sanders and Young, 1946; Cavanaugh, 1951), the M-cell regression could have been ascribed to the shrinkage of their peripheral field in the course of tail resorption. Failing this explanation, the next plausible assumption would be that the M-cell body itself reacts adversely to the metamorphosing hormone. Experiments were therefore undertaken in which the effects on the M-cell of loss of tail innervation and of thyroid hormone could be tested separately, and both prior to, hence uncomplicated by, the normal metamorphosis of the test animal.

MATERIALS AND METHODS

Tadpoles of *Rana pipiens*, *Xenopus laevis* and *Pseudacris versicolor* were used. The former were staged according to Taylor and Kollros.

To test the loss of tail innervation, either tailless larvae were produced by removing the tail bud in the embryo, or the tail was later amputated and kept from regenerating by periodic reamputations, or, lastly, the spinal cord was hemisected in the second trunk segment, the anterior stump being turned upward to prevent reconnection of the longitudinal tracts containing the M-axon. The success of the operation was later checked histologically.

The effect of thyroid hormone on the nerve cells was tested by the technique developed in this laboratory by Kollros (1943), implanting a hormone source in the vicinity of the hind brain. We used either fragments of rat thyroid gland or flakes of agar *ca.* 0.5 mm. across, soaked for 20 minutes in a 1:1000 solution of thyroxin (synthetic "Roche Organon"). In control experiments, fragments of parotid gland of rats were used. The grafts were placed either into the fourth ventricle it-self or on top of the choroid plexus.

Most animals were sacrificed within the first week after the operation. They were fixed and stained either by Bodian's protargol tech-nique or, for mitotic counts, by Heidenhain's iron hematoxylin. Brain cells were measured by projecting the slides on paper under high magnification, selecting in each preparation 100 cells at random from the vicinity of the M-cells and recording their nuclear diameters in equidistant size classes, as described previ-ously for nerve fibers (Weiss, Edds and Cava-naugh, 1945; Cavanaugh, 1951). In M-cells, the longest and shortest nuclear diameters were measured, and in addition, the area of the largest cross-section of the whole M-cell body was determined by planimeter.

M-Cell Bodies after Amputation of M-Fibers

Both tail amputation and high spinal cord severance deprived the M-fibers of a major portion of their length and all the correspond-ing innervation area. Contrary to expecta-tions, this trenchant reduction of peripheral load left the size of the cell bodies essentially unaffected.

Tail Amputation

Tails (15–25 mm. in length) were ampu-tated in 6 tadpoles (28–36 mm. total length). The 12 M-cell nuclei of these animals (1, 3 and 6 days postoperative) measured 82.7 square units on an average, while 12 M-cells of normal control animals of comparable age and size (tail length 20–23 mm., total length 30–35 mm.) averaged 81.6 square units. Thy-roid treatment, as will be shown later, pro-duces its most marked effects on cell size during the first week. The fact that tail ampu-tation had no effect whatsoever during the corresponding period is therefore significant.

Spinal Cord Hemisection

Table 1 summarizes the measurements of M-cells in 13 animals preserved at various in-tervals after unilateral cord section. Of the two M-cells of each animal, one ("control")

has an intact fiber with normal peripheral dis-tribution, while the other ("experimental") has only a fiber stump. Yet both cells have remained about equal in size up to 29 days after the operation, averaging 81.4 and 80.2 square units, respectively, which is nearly the same value as in the preceding series.

In conclusion, amputation of a major por-tion of an M-fiber by either method has failed to cause regression of the cell body within the period of investigation. The Nissl pattern of the cell bodies was likewise found to have remained unaltered. These facts seem to prove that, contrary to Bodian's (1947) assumption, the mere loss of axonal substance does not of itself cause neuronal atrophy. Such atrophy, where it occurs, is rather the result of the loss of functional connections (Weiss, 1950). In the present case this would lead one to suspect that the residual collateral connections of the M-fiber stump or newly formed connections at the level of transection may have been suffi-cient to preserve the integrity of the neuron.

At any rate, these results rule out the idea that M-cells regress after metamorphosis be-cause the resorption of the tail has deprived them of innervation territory. We therefore turned to the second alternative, that of a di-rect response of the M-cell body to the meta-morphosing hormone of the thyroid.

Effect of Thyroid Grafts on Local Brain Growth

A. Mitotic Effect

During metamorphosis, brain growth takes a marked spurt accompanied by intensified mitotic activity. Mitoses are confined to the ependymal layer lining the brain ventricles, and must therefore be referred to the number of nuclei in that layer rather than to the total number of brain cells. The ependymal cells, being densely packed, cannot be counted with the desired accuracy. But since the packing is uniform, the number of cells per unit length of ependymal lining is rather constant, hence mitotic rate can be expressed, for comparative purposes, as the number of mitoses per unit length of the ventricular contour. Thyroid

TABLE 5. Mitotic Count in Hind Brain with Boiled Thyroid Grafts

a	b	c	d	e	f	g	h
	Age at		Stage at	Days Post-	Mitotic Count		Mitotic Index,
Case	Operation	Stage	Fixation	operative	Hind Brain	Spinal Cord	Hind Brain
TC42	52	IX	IX	4	30	20	19.0
TC43	55	X	XII	4	9	—	4.4
TC48	48	VIII	XI	3	36	22	18.0
TC46	48	VIII	VIII	3	7	—	3.5
TC49	58	XI	XIII	3	48	34	23.0
TC35	60	XI	XV	5	45	19	21.5
TC50	58	XI	XII	3	18	—	8.6
TC38	60	XI	XIII	5	27	32	12.8
TC32	60	XI	XV	5	15	12	7.2
TC40	60	XII	XIII	5	8	—	3.8
TC31	60	XI	XIII	5	34	10	16.2
TC30	60	XI	XIII	5	36	19	17.1
						Average	13.0

grafts accelerate the local growth of the adjacent brain parts. In comparing their mitotic rates with those of normal tadpole brains, this expansion must be taken into account. For this purpose, the normal growth curve of the inner contour of the fourth ventricle in cross-section (at the M-cell level) was secured from a series of measurements in normal samples stages (Fig. 1). From this curve the ependymal length, i.e., the denominator for the mitotic index, could then be read directly for any given age.

The mitotic data are summarized in Tables 2–5 and Fig. 2. In view of the precipitate metamorphosis of their head region, animals with thyroid grafts were staged (column d) according to head criteria. In each case all mitoses in 10 alternate sections through the hind brain (column f) and 10 alternate sections through the spinal cord about 500 μ farther caudally (column g) were recorded. The total count amounts to 2335 mitoses.

Table 2 lists mitotic activity in normal controls for the age group used in the experiments. Omitting the last two stages (XXII and XXIII), during which mitotic activity has practically ceased as a result of maturation, an average mitotic index (stages V through XIII) of 9.7 is calculated. Table 3 gives the mitotic counts in animals of comparable ages which had received implants of fresh or boiled rat parotid glands in or near

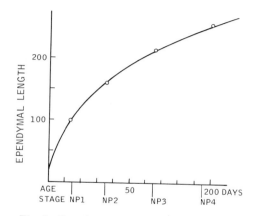

Fig. 1. Growth curve of 4th ventricle at level of M-cells. Length of the ependymal lining in cross-sections of hind brain (in arbitrary units) plotted over larval age.

the fourth ventricle, 3 days after the operation, which is the time when the mitotic effect of thyroid grafts (see below) reaches its peak. The table shows that neither the operation as such nor the presence and discharges of a foreign gland of similar consistency as thyroid have any marked effect on mitotic activity, the average index (11.2) being not much above that of unoperated controls. This average of the pooled data has been used as control base in Fig. 2 (dotted line).

By contrast, Table 4, summarizing the cases with thyroid grafts, shows a marked elevation of the mitotic index, particularly during the early days following the operation. On the third day postoperative, the mitotic index reaches an average (6 cases) of 61.5, which is about 600% of the normal and control indices. From this peak the index gradually declines (Fig. 2), until by day 15 it has returned to a normal level. Comparison of columns c and d shows that external features of the animals have advanced by several stages, indicating a regional acceleration of metamorphic events by the thyroid discharge from the grafts.

Thus by the sixth day postoperative the various heads showed characters of regular stage XXI–XXII larvae. In view of the fact that the mitotic index at such late stages would normally already be very low (less than 1; see Table 2), the average of 22.2 for the seven animals counted on days 6 and 7 postoperative is still extremely high. It is difficult, therefore, to decide how much of the decline of the curve in Fig. 2 is due to the dissipation of the hormone source as a result of the disintegra-

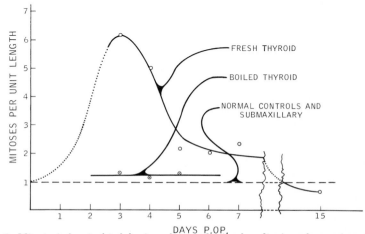

Fig. 2. Mitotic index in hind brains of controls (broken line) and experimental cases (solid lines).

tion and phagocytosis of the graft, and how much to the precipitate maturation, hence depletion of germinal cells, of the ependymal layer. But the fact that hormone delivery from the graft is of limited duration will be further supported below.

In the brains with thyroid grafts, an occasional extra-ependymal mitosis was observed, but these seem to have been true germinal cells which had simply been crowded out from their ventricular sites during division.

Table 5 gives the mitotic counts in the vicinity of grafts of boiled rat thyroid. The average index of 13.0 (Fig. 2) is only slightly higher than that of non-thyroid controls (Tables 2 and 3). Even if the five ostensibly negative cases (TC32, 40, 43, 46 and 50) are omitted, the remaining average of 18.2 is still considerably lower than the average of 51.4

calculated from Table 4 for cases with live thyroid grafts of comparable postoperative ages. Boiled thyroid thus seems to have had a perceptible, but weak, mitotic effect. Since it is generally recognized that thyroid hormone as such does not lose potency in boiling, the different effectiveness of fresh and boiled glands in our experiments must presumably be attributed to differences in the mode of release. Either the cells of the fresh gland continue to produce hormone even after grafting, or, more likely, the boiled gland has been so altered in the process of boiling and coagulation that hormone will not be as readily released, especially since the boiled cells, in contrast to live ones, will not undergo autolysis.

The mitotic effect of thyroid grafts placed near the fourth ventricle spreads far down

TABLE 6. Distribution of nuclear sizes in hind brain samples of *Rana pipiens*

Case	Age or Stage (Days)	Days Post-operative	Nuclear Diameters in Unit Classes 1	2	3	4	5	6	7	8	Mean Nuclear Diameter of M-Cells, $d_m = \sqrt{d_{max} \cdot d_{min}}$	
						Controls						
NP3[II]	64		1	6	48	25	13	7	0	0	8.8	9.8
NP2[9]	43		0	11	41	39	6	2	1	0	—	—
NP2[10]	43		0	9	52	28	9	2	0	0	9.5	9.8
NP2[5]	33		0	1	45	38	12	3	1	0	9.9	9.4
NP2[II]	33		0	2	56	32	6	4	0	0	9.4	10.0
NP2[6]	33		1	8	54	27	9	0	1	0	7.9	8.8
NP2[III]	33		0	22	55	17	6	0	0	0	—	—
NP2[IV]	33		0	11	44	36	6	3	0	0	11.4	10.8
NP2[2]	31		1	22	53	19	5	0	0	0	10.0	—
NP2[1]	31		0	14	53	27	5	1	0	0	9.9	9.2
Average 38			0.3	10.6	50.1	28.8	7.7	2.2	0.3	0	Average	9.7[b]
Total relative volume 4822 cu. units												
						Thyroid Grafts						
T39	38	3	0	1	14	35	33	12	4	1	7.3	9.4
T41	43	3	0	1	17	43	22	8	9	0	9.8	9.2
T6[I]	38	13	0	6	31	44	10	8	1	0	9.5	9.2
T8[I]	33	8	0	6	34	42	13	5	0	0	8.9	8.8
T6[II]	38	13	1	8	55	25	7	4	0	0	8.5	9.9
T7[II]	33	10	0	4	26	31	21	14	4	0	8.8	12.2
T3[II]	43	9	0	2	24	42	24	5	3	0	8.1	8.4
T18[I]	33	4	0	2	17	35	26	11	5	4	8.8	8.8
T5[II]	38	7	0	3	26	32	28	6	4	1	9.4	8.5
T36	31	4	0	1	25	40	28	5	1	0	8.0	7.8
Average 37			0.1	3.4	26.9	36.9	21.2	7.8	3.1	0.6	Average	9.0
Total relative nuclear volume 8821 cu. units												
						Thyroxin-Agar Grafts						
C5[II]	II–IV[a]	6	0	4	35	41	13	4	3	0	9.5	9.4
C5[I]	II–IV	6	0	1	22	42	24	10	1	0	8.8	9.4
C13[III]	VI–IX	7	0	4	32	35	16	9	4	0	8.1	11.4
C13[IV]	VI–IX	7	0	2	26	38	22	9	3	0	9.4	8.8
C1	V	4	0	2	24	53	18	3	0	0	8.5	7.9
C7	V	6	0	3	30	35	18	9	5	0	8.8	8.9
C12	VIII–IX	8	0	2	33	41	17	6	1	0	8.8	9.0
C3	V–VIII	6	0	3	33	42	14	6	1	0	10.5	10.5
C11[2]	V	4	0	3	36	43	16	2	0	1	10.2	7.9
C13	V–IX	4	0	3	38	40	15	4	0	0	9.9	8.9
Average			0.0	2.7	30.9	41.0	17.3	6.2	1.8	0.1	Average	9.3
Total relative nuclear volume 7650 cu. units												

[a] Indicates head stages at beginning and end of experiments.
[b] See text.

into the spinal cord. Table 4 reveals mitotic counts similar to those of the hind brain (column f) at a cord level 500 μ behind (column g). To obtain a more complete picture of the spread, two normal larvae (33 days old; stage V) and two larvae with thyroid grafts (36 days, stage V, and 46 days, stage VII), the latter 3 days after implanta-tion, were sectioned frontally, and all mitoses in alternate sections of the spinal cord were counted. The counts were, for the normal animals, 462 and 662 mitoses (average, 562), and for the ones with grafts, 1840 and 1180 (average, 1510) mitoses, revealing a two- to threefold increase above normal. Since according to Table 4 a higher increase was

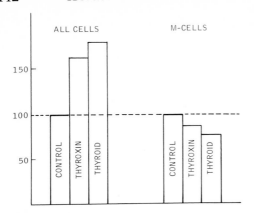

Fig. 3. Relative volumes of non-M-cells (left) and M-cells (right), with controls set at 100%. Each non-M bar represents 1000 cells.

found at a far anterior cord level, it is evident that the effect grades off anteroposteriorly within the cord. Presumably it spreads by diffusion from the ventricle through the central canal.

B. Effect on Cell Size

While the ventricular cells near thyroid grafts grew and divided, the cells of the mantle, which had lost their mitotic capacity, just grew in size. Table 6 lists 10 cases with thyroid grafts, 10 cases with thyroxin-agar implants and 10 normal controls of comparable average ages; in each case, a random sample of 100 nuclei from the vicinity of the M-cells was taken and their distribution according to diameter classes recorded (the

nuclei being nearly spherical). From these figures, the total relative volume of the 100 nuclei was calculated according to the formula: $V = M_1 + 2^3M_2 + 3^3M_3 + 4^3M_4 + \ldots + n^3M_n$; where M_1, M_2, M_3, etc., represent the numbers of nuclei recorded in size classes 1, 2, 3, etc. The mean diameter of each ellipsoid nucleus of the M-cells was determined as the square root of the product of the longest times the shortest diameters. The relative volumes of the M-nuclei are given as the cubes of the mean diameters. The resultant changes in nuclear volumes are summarized in the graph, Fig. 3, as percentages of the normal control values. The nuclei of non-M-cells have gained 59% with thyroxin-agar grafts, and 83% with thyroid grafts, while the nuclei of the M-cells of the same animals have lost 12% and 19%, respectively. It is uncertain whether the lower effectiveness of the synthetic, as compared to the natural, product is a matter of potency or merely of dosage. But it is evident that thyroid hormone in either form affects the sizes of M-cells and of non-M-cells in opposite directions.

This antagonistic response of the two neuron types suggest some fundamental difference in their constitution. On the other hand, it is equally conceivable that the growth stimulation by thyroid is merely an inverse function of cell size, reversing its sign at a critical size level above that of the largest non-M-cells, but below that of the M-cells. This possibility, however, is ruled out by the fact that all size

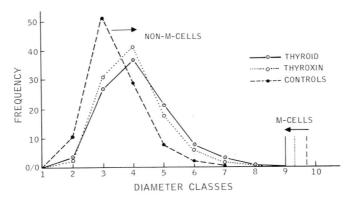

Fig. 4. Histograms of nuclear diameters in 1000 non-M-cells each of control, thyroid and thyroxin cases. Mean diameters of M-cells for corresponding series are also indicated.

Fig. 5. Histograms of M-cells (largest cross-sectional areas) in controls (--●--) and thyroid- or thyroxin-grafted cases (——⊙——) of *Rana pipiens*.

classes of non-M-cells are about equally enhanced. Figure 4 shows the histogram of nuclear diameters for the non-M-cells in the three groups of animals listed in Table 6. It can be seen that the thyroid treatment has moved the whole nuclear population up by approximately one size class; the larger size classes are, if anything, favored. The graph also gives for comparison the mean diameter values of the M-cell nuclei, showing the displacement in the reverse direction from that of the histograms of non-M-nuclei.

Histograms for the M-cells were made from planimetric measurements of the largest cross-sections of the cell bodies rather than from nuclear measurements; the greater accuracy of this method seemed indicated in view of the fact that the size of the sample of M-cells was only one-fiftieth of that of non-M-cells. Values for thyroid- and thyroxin-cases have been pooled. The resulting histograms for 24 normal (-- ● --) and 43 experimental (— ⊙ —) cells are reproduced in Fig. 5;

the size classes are on a different scale than those in Fig. 4. It is immediately evident from the graphs that thyroid treatment has affected all M-cells about equally, regardless of size, causing a shift of the whole population downward by about 3 size classes. These data prove clearly, particularly when taken in conjunction with those of Fig. 4, that the populations of M-cells and of non-M-cells react as wholes in qualitatively different fashions, and that cell size as such is not a decisive factor.

The average volumes of M-cell bodies, computed from the planimetric data, were in the thyroid series approximately 60% of those of the control series. Comparing this value with the corresponding reduction of nuclear volumes to *ca.* 80% (Fig. 3), it appears that Bok's formula (1934), according to which the volumes of cell bodies of neurons vary as the squares of their nuclear volumes, holds roughly in the present case, too. It has likewise been found to apply to the atrophy of ganglion cells following peripheral disconnection (Cavanaugh, 1951).

All experiments described in the foregoing were done in *Rana pipiens*. An additional series with grafts of rat thyroid was carried out in the faster growing South African clawed toad, *Xenopus laevis*. The results, compiled in Table 7 and Fig. 6, are quite similar to the previous ones. The thyroid hormone produced an increase in size of the non-M-cells, but reduction in the size of the M-cells (loss of M-nuclear volume: 17%). The histograms of the M-cells bodies based on the largest cross-sectional areas are given in Fig.

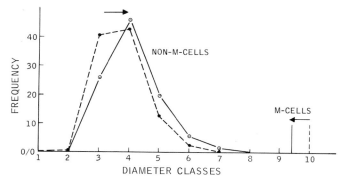

Fig. 6. Histograms of non-M-nuclei in normal (--●--) and thyroid-grafted cases (—⊙—) and record of the mean diameters of the M-nuclei (*Xenopus laevis*).

TABLE 7. Distribution of nuclear sizes in hind brain samples of *Xenopus laevis*

Case	Age at Fixation	Days Post-operative	Nuclear Diameters in Unit Classes								Mean Nuclear Diameter of M-Cells, $d_m = \sqrt{d_{max} \cdot d_{min}}$	
			1	2	3	4	5	6	7	8		
						Controls						
X1C	27		0	1	49	35	12	2	1	0	10.5	9.6
X4C	27		0	1	42	46	7	3	1	0	9.8	9.9
X1C1	27		0	1	43	42	11	3	0	0	10.5	10.5
X4C[I]	27		0	0	40	46	12	2	0	0	9.4	9.0
CX5	31		0	1	31	48	19	1	0	0	10.5	10.4
CX5–6	31		0	0	37	41	15	5	2	0	10.0	10.2
Average			0	0.66	40.3	43.0	12.6	2.6	0.6	0	Average	10.0
					Thyroid Grafts							
XII2	20	5	0	0	37	47	12	3	1	0	8.8	9.9
X4[2]	22	5	0	0	38	42	12	7	1	0	8.8	9.2
X5–7	24	8	0	0	29	41	20	7	3	0	9.4	9.9
X5–6	24	8	0	0	26	41	19	12	2	0	8.9	9.4
X1[II]	17	10	0	0	15	55	25	4	1	0	8.9	
X4[3]	22	5	0	0	21	43	28	7	1	0	9.9	10.4
X1[I]	17	10	0	0	22	54	21	1	2	0	8.8	9.2
Average			0	0	26.9	46.1	19.6	5.9	1.6	0	Average	9.4

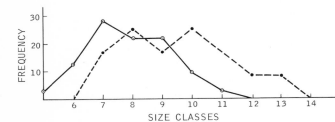

Fig. 7. Histograms of the M-cell bodies in control (--●--) and thyroid graft cases (Xenopus). Note opposite shift from that in Fig. 6.

7, showing the shift of the thyroid-treated M-cells toward the smaller size classes.

RESIDUAL EFFECTS

The observed acceleration of proliferation and cell growth naturally is reflected in dimensional changes of the whole cross-section of the hind brain. While the processes thus far discussed augment the gray matter, concomitant outgrowth and presumably caliber increase of nerve fibers from the enlarged brain parts add to the thickness of the white matter. The resulting over-all changes are summarized in the graphs, Figs. 8–10. Figure 8 represents the normal "growth curve" of the cross-section of the hind brain during the larval period, based on planimetric measurements of the total cross-section, as well as of the gray matter only, in 23 normal controls. Figure 9 shows the increase in cross-sectional area in the medullae oblongatae containing thyroid grafts. As one can readily see, growth is initially accelerated, falling off by the 6th day, in general agreement with the detailed cell events discussed above. In Fig. 10, finally, the growth curves of the thyroid cases and of normal controls of comparable ages (taken from Fig. 8) are combined. These curves show quite conclusively that the thyroid-induced growth acceleration has been only temporary. After the initial rise, the curves for the experimental animals run strictly

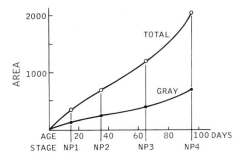

Fig. 8. Cross-sectional increase (area in arbitrary units) of hind brain and its gray matter in normal larvae up to 100 days.

parallel to those for the controls. This means that the former retain their erstwhile advance, but otherwise continue to grow at a normal rate once the thyroid source has been exhausted. The action thus is comparable to that of a single solid dose of hormone administered over a limited period, and the course of events clearly proved that the observed growth phenomena were direct, rather than secondary, consequences of the local hormone action.

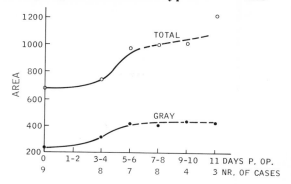

Fig. 9. Growth of cross-section of hind brain following thyroid implantation at approximately stage NP2 of Fig. 8.

DISCUSSION

The local hormone application in these experiments has but precipitated events which eventually would have taken place in the course of normal metamorphosis. In this regard, the results merely amplify earlier observations on circumscribed metamorphic changes in the vicinity of thyroid grafts (e.g., Hartwig, 1940; Kollros, 1943). In fact, Kollros, *et al.*, in a recent preliminary note (1950), report size increase in midbrain cells in response to thyroxin pellets implanted in to the cranial cavity, quite similar to the response of the non-M-cells of the hind brain in our own experiments.

The added significance of our results lies in the demonstration of the fact that different neurons of the same locality, the M-cells and the non-M-cells, respond in wholly different ways, resulting in changes of opposite sign. Again, regression of M-cells amidst growing non-M-cells would have been a normal feature

of these brains during metamorphosis anyhow; but we now have proof that while the change as such is brought on by the thyroid hormone, the pattern of the change is predetermined in the responding cells, which evidently constitute a mosaic of quite diverse cell species. Thus, both the property of M-cells to respond to thyroid by involution, and the property of non-M-cells to respond to the same agent by growth, are but attributes of the more distinctive constitutional differentials acquired by these various cell types previously in the course of embryonic differentiation. Having been dealt with comprehensively in some recent publications (Weiss, 1949, 1950), these problems need not be labored here further.

Two points, however, should be reemphasized. First, since the differently reacting cell types lie intimately intermingled, their differ-

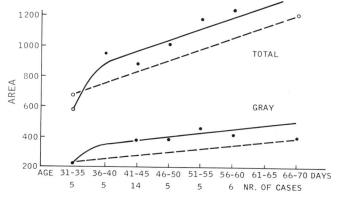

Fig. 10. Growth curves of cross-section of hind brain in normal (broken lines) and thyroid graft cases (solid lines).

ential response cannot be attributed to differential exposure to and accessibility by, the hormonal pool. Second, since the non-M-cells of all sizes have been equally enhanced in their growth (Figs. 4, 6), the degrowth of the M-cells cannot be explained simply by their large size, that is, by mere quantitative extrapolation of the positive growth effect beyond a critical upper size level. The difference between the two cell types thus is not merely one of degree, but one of kind, and the large size differential between M-cells and non-M-cells is but one of the superficial signs of much more profound constitutional, i.e., physicochemical and metabolic distinctions. It is reasonable to assume that similar distinctions exist among the non-M-cells, except that either they do not become reflected in cell size or our techniques of measurement and group assay are too crude to detect them. Indirect evidence for the qualitative differentiation ("speciation") among neurons is accumulating rapidly; numerous examples have been cited in the recent symposium on Genetic Neurology (Weiss, 1950b). The evidence pertains both to the fact that specific qualitative differences among neurons exist and to the relevance of these differences to the establishment and maintenance of functional order in the nervous system. Their relevance to the insuring of developmental order, in counterplay with the humoral milieu, is demonstrated clearly by the results of this paper. Whether this also brings us any nearer to an understanding of the relation between hormone action and patterns of behavior remains to be ascertained.

Summary

Grafts of rat thyroid or thyroxin-agar implants near the hind brain of tadpoles produce within a few days a burst of mitotic activity in the neural epithelium and marked growth of nerve cells with the exception of Mauthner's neurons, which atrophy. Evidence is presented to show that this antagonistic response, which occurs similarly in normal metamorphosis in response to the metamorphosing hormone of the thyroid, is based upon qualitative differences among the neuron types involved. The data confirm the view that hormones do not create differentials among equipotential tissue units, but merely help to realize pre-existing latent differentials. The results stress anew how relevant qualitative diversity among neurons is to the development of neural order, and perhaps suggest a clue to the mechanism of hormonal "control" of behavior.

Beach, F., *Harvey Lectures*, series 63, 254–280 (1950).

Bodian, D., *Symp. Soc. Exper. Biol.*, No. 1, 163–178 (1947).

Bok, S. T., *Psych. en Neur. Bladen*, **38**, 318–326 (1934).

Cavanaugh, M., *J. Comp. Neur.*, **94**, 181–220 (1951).

Edds, M. V., Jr., *Ibid.*, **93**, 258–276 (1950).

Hamburger, C.-A., and H. Hydén, *Acta Otolaryngol.*, **61**, 5–89 (1945).

Hartwig, H., *Biol. Zentralbl.*, **60**, 473 (1940).

Kollros, J. J., *Physiol. Zool.*, **16**, 269–279 (1943).

Kollros, J. J., V. Pepernik, R. Hill, and J. C. Kaltenbach, *Anat. Rec.*, **108**, No. 3, 77 (1950).

Rossetti, F., *Boll. Soc. ital. Biol. sper.*, **23**, f. 4, 1–2 (1947).

Sanders, F. K., and J. J. Young, *J. Exp. Biol.*, **22**, 203–212 (1946).

Stefanelli, A., In: Weiss, ed., *Genetic Neurology*, University of Chicago Press, 161–165 (1950).

Stefanelli, A., *Quart. Rev. Biol.*, **26**, 17–34 (1951).

Taylor, A. C., and J. J. Kollros, *Anat. Rec.*, **94**, 7–24 (1946).

Weiss, P., *Jahresber. f. d. ges. Physiol. f. d. Jahr 1922*, 47 (1924).

Weiss, P., In: Parpart, ed., *Chemistry and Physiology of Growth*, Princeton University Press, 35–186 (1949).

Weiss, P., *Quart. Rev. Biol.*, **25**, 177–198 (1950).

Weiss, P., In: Weiss, ed., *Genetic Neurology*, University of Chicago Press, 1–39 (1950a).

Weiss, P., ed., *Ibid.*, University of Chicago Press (1950b).

Weiss, P., M. V. Edds, Jr., and M. Cavanaugh, *Anat. Rec.*, **92**, 215–233 (1945).

Young, J. Z., In: Weiss, ed., *Genetic Neurology*, University of Chicago Press, 92–104 (1950).

A brief note that has come to our attention after this manuscript had gone to press [G. M. Baffoni and G. Catte, *Atti della Accad. Naz. dei Lincei*, 8th ser., vol. **9**, fasc. 5, pp. 282–287 (1950)] reports precipitate involution of Mauthner's cells in tadpoles kept in water with dilute thyroid extract.

Metamorphosis and Body Form

V. B. WIGGLESWORTH

William Harvey entered Gonville Hall, now Gonville and Caius College, of the University of Cambridge, in 1593. He stands foremost among the past members of our College; and it was a happy coincidence that led to our celebrating last year the tercentenary of Harvey's death in 1657 and the centenary of the birth of Charles Sherrington, another distinguished member of the College, who did for our conception of the nervous system very much what Harvey had done for our understanding of the circulation of the blood.

It will therefore come as no surprise to you to learn that I received the invitation to lecture before the Harvey Society with a quite unusual sense of pleasure.

Harvey's foremost interest was in the pursuit of his researches in physiology, and in his second great work, the *Generatione Animalium* published in 1651, he extended his interests beyond the mammals and the vertebrates and devoted much attention to the generation of insects.

We do not know to what extent Harvey's conclusions on this subject were based upon his own observations, for all his records have been lost. When Jan Swammerdam, some eighteen years later, was writing his courteous refutation of some of the opinions of "this great philosopher" he excused the mistakes of Harvey on the grounds that insects are difficult to study "unless by persons accustomed to experiments of this kind; it is no wonder that the most happy geniuses, the immortal Harvey, for example, and many others should have fallen into an error."

Harvey had developed the theory that the insect egg contains so little yolk that the embryo is forced to leave it before completing its development. It then goes through a more or less prolonged larval stage during which it stores up food reserves before resuming the

Harvey Lectures, 1958–1959, pp. 40–59, Academic Press, 1960.

egg form or pupa and completing its embryonic growth.

This theory did not start with Harvey, for Aristotle had likewise taught that the embryonic life of insects continues until the formation of the adult, the "perfect insect" or "imago." "The larva while it is yet in growth" he wrote "is a soft egg."

This idea has persisted to the present day. In current textbooks on entomology the view is commonly expressed that the origin of metamorphosis is to be sought in the immaturity of the insect at the time of hatching from the egg.

The amazing transformations of insects from the grub, to the pupa and to the butterfly have always been a source of wonder for observers of nature, and this idea of the larva as an undeveloped embryo seemed to provide a satisfying explanation. But when we look into it more closely, it is not so satisfactory. Of course, the development of the pupa has much in common with the development of the embryo. Certain parts of the body, such as the wings, grow and differentiate enormously, drawing upon reserves elsewhere in the body, just as the growing organs of the embryo draw upon the yolk. That, however, is no more than an analogy; it does not afford evidence that the insect larva really is an embryo.

But it was the miraculous element in Harvey's conception of insect "metamorphosis" which Swammerdam was out to challenge. Harvey recognized quite rightly that the substance of the full-grown larva furnished the material for the production of the adult insect; but he supposed that under the action of some mysterious influence this material suffered a "metamorphosis" and was rebuilt into an entirely new form: like wax bearing the impress of a seal, as he said.

In his *Biblia Naturae* or *Historia Generalis Insectorum* published in 1669, the Dutch naturalist strongly opposed this mysterious conception of metamorphosis (see Swammerdam, 1758). For Swammerdam "epigenesis," a gradual and natural growth, is the only way in which all animal form is fashioned. He stripped away the skin of the caterpillar before it was due to be cast off, and found the wings and other parts of the adult butterfly already in process of growth.

He inferred that every structure arises by a process of continuous growth from an existing structure; that everything is already preformed in some state, some invisible state that we are unable to appreciate, from the earliest stages of growth. As growth proceeds, the parts become visible and differentiated. Unfortunately, his followers adopted the crude and exaggerated idea that all the future structures of the body were actually "preformed" in the egg, and that all growth and development consisted in the unfolding of these structures as successive covering shells were discarded. The height of absurdity was reached when observers claimed to have seen "homunculi," diminutive outlines of the human form, within the spermatozoon! It was excesses such as these which brought the very reasonable views of Swammerdam into disrepute.

Swammerdam was trying to express ideas for which there was as yet no adequate foundation in physiology. We are in much the same case today—although, with the development of chemistry, histology, and genetics we have got a little nearer to the heart of the problem.

As was pointed out by Swammerdam the most obvious weakness in Harvey's theory of metamorphosis lies in the fact that in the more primitive insects, such as silverfish or cockroaches, the creature that emerges from the egg has the same general form as the adult. It is in the highest insects, such as the beetles, butterflies, bees, or flies, that the most striking examples of metamorphosis are to be found. And yet the eggs of these higher insects are not notably more deficient in yolk.

It can, of course, be argued that, for some unknown reason, it is only in these higher forms that the insect emerges from the egg at an early stage of embryonic development. But the resemblance of caterpillars or maggots to embryos is really only superficial. When they are looked at closely they are seen to be most complex organisms, highly adapted each for its own special mode of life.

Now it is well known that many genes affect only the characters of the larva, while others affect only the adult. There are some insects which are quite unlike in the adult state but indistinguishable as larvae, and others with almost identical adults but totally different larvae.

When an insect larva lives in conditions different from those of the adult, it will be exposed to quite different selective pressures. In other words, it will evolve in such a way that it becomes closely adapted to its special environment, while the pupal form and the adult form are evolving in quite different directions according to the special requirements of their environments. Indeed, as soon as there are differences in the mode of life of the adult insect and its larva, the characters of the two forms will tend to diverge, and such divergence may continue until we reach the extremes that separate the maggot from the fly.

All animals are more or less "polymorphic"; within a single species there are a number of recognizable forms. Perhaps the most familiar and striking are the differences between male and female; but there are any number of other inherited variations, controlled by genes. And since a single gene often has multiple effects, a single gene change may produce large differences in general form.

These genes are transmitted according to the laws established by Mendel and therefore, when the various forms are cross-mated, it should be possible to predict the probable numbers of each type that will be produced. But in practice it does not always work out that way because other factors may come in and influence the manifestation or "penetrance" of some gene effects.

To give two concrete examples: The main effect of the gene *antennaless* in the fruit fly *Drosophila* is to lead to a failure of the antennae to develop in the adult (Fig. 1, a). But if the food of the larvae is rich in riboflavin, even flies which genetically should be

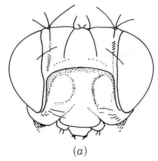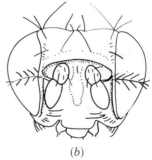

(a)   (b)

Fig. 1. Front view of head of *Drosophila* of the mutant "antennaless." (a) Reared on normal diet; antennae absent. (b) Reared on diet with abundant riboflavin; antennae developed. After Gordon and Sang (1941).

"antennaless" will develop normal antennae (Fig. 1, b) (Gordon and Sang, 1941).

There is another mutant gene in *Drosophila*, called *tetraptera*, which causes the modified hind wings, the little knobbed "halteres," to develop into wings, so that these normally two-winged flies develop two pairs of wings. But this effect is greatly influenced by temperature: at 25°C. the "penetrance" of *tetraptera* is 35 per cent, at 17°C. it is only 1 per cent (Astauroff, 1930).

Now according to the conception of metamorphosis which I have just outlined, each individual insect presents a number of divergent forms which are controlled by genes. According to this view metamorphosis is just a special example of polymorphism in which the different forms, instead of appearing in different individuals, occur at successive stages in the development of one individual.

In order to press this parallel more closely I might remind you that sex is an example of genetically controlled dimorphism, determined primarily by the balance between the actions of the sex chromosomes and autosomes within the nucleus. But the administration of steroid sex hormones to the female mammal during pregnancy results in a partial reversal of sex; and the sexual characters of mature birds can be reversed by castration or by the implantation of gonads. In the male of some Crustacea there is an "androgenic gland" which is quite separate from the gonad. When this gland is implanted into the female, both primary and secondary sexual characters become those of the male (Charniaux-Cotton, 1956). That would be a close parallel to the conception of metamorphosis as I picture it.

Sex reversal may occur also in insects. If certain solitary bees are invaded during their larval life by the strange parasitic insect *Stylops*, the male bees will develop the markings of female bees; and female bees acquire the characters of males (Smith and Hamm, 1914). Defective nutrition seems to be the immediate cause of these changes; for *Stylops* induces sex reversal only in those bees or wasps which allocate a fixed ration to their larvae. If the larva is fed by its mother according to its needs, sex reversal does not occur (Salt, 1927, 1931).

One must suppose that when the growing organs and tissues are deprived of some essential factor in nutrition, the gene balance is upset and the latent genes of the opposite sex, which would normally be suppressed, are able to exert their action.

It is worth pointing out that whereas the male *Stylops* is a well-developed winged insect, the female is a much larger, degenerate, and grublike creature, not much more than a sac of eggs. It is only the large female, with its higher food requirements, which induces sex reversal.

In other insects the whole outward form of the body may be transformed by a change in nutrition; and the transformation may be so great that the resulting insects could readily be mistaken for different species. The tiny parasitic wasp *Trichogramma semblidis* develops within the eggs of other insects. If it develops in the egg of various large moths it is a normally winged insect; but if it develops in the egg of the alder fly (*Sialis*), not only is it devoid of wings, but the form of the legs and the antennae is strikingly changed (Salt, 1937) (Fig. 2). Here again, we must suppose that some element in nutrition has influenced the "penetrance" of certain genes. It

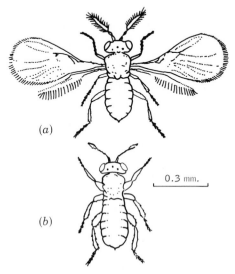

Fig. 2. Dimorphism in the male of *Trichogramma semblidis*. (a) Winged male reared in eggs of Lepidoptera. (b) Apterous male reared in egg of *Sialis*. After Salt (1937).

has indeed been claimed that the nature of the egg membranes in the *Sialis* egg leads to a deficiency in oxygen supply for the enclosed *Trichogramma* (Bouillon, 1949).

One striking example which has recently come to light concerns three species of May fly which are usually placed in three different genera: *Ephemerella*, *Torleya*, and *Chitonophora*. The adult forms are indistinguishable, but they have quite different larvae. Recent work by Verrier (1956) strongly suggests that all three belong to a single species which has a polymorphic larva, the form of which is controlled by seasonal factors and by habitat.

In these examples of polymorphism we have all the elements of a satisfactory theory of metamorphosis. We must picture the insect as having a larval, a pupal, and an adult form.

Each of these forms has evolved as an adaptation to life in a special environment, and each is controlled by its appropriate set of genes. But what controls the activation or "penetrance" of these gene sets?

Twenty-five years ago it was shown that insect metamorphosis is controlled by a small gland of internal secretion known as the corpus allatum, which lies just behind the brain. It was proved by experiment that during the larval stages the corpus allatum secretes a hormone, commonly called the juvenile hormone or "neotenin," the "youth substance." Under the influence of this hormone the larval characters are retained. When the larva is fully grown, the corpus allatum no longer secretes the hormone, the adult characters are developed, and "metamorphosis" occurs.

These facts were first established on the large South American blood-sucking bug *Rhodnius prolixus* (Wigglesworth, 1934, 1936) (Plate I), but they have been confirmed by various authors on almost all other groups of insects (Wigglesworth, 1954). Furthermore, there is much evidence to suggest that in insects such as Lepidoptera, which have a pupal stage, a large amount of hormone secretion is needed to produce the larval form, a very little is required to produce the pupa, and in the complete absence of hormone the adult form appears (Piepho, 1942).

Implantation of an active corpus allatum from a young larva into a larva that is becoming full grown, causes this to retain its larval form and to grow into a giant larva (Plate I, c). Conversely, removal of the corpus allatum from the young larva causes it to undergo precocious metamorphosis and develop into a diminutive adult.

In the mature adult of many insects the corpus allatum begins once more to secrete the juvenile hormone, which is needed for the full activity of the reproductive organs, notably for the deposition of yolk in the eggs. In at least one insect, the Cecropia silk moth of North America, this hormone accumulates, for some unknown reason, in the abdomen of the male. This has made possible the prepara-

Plate I. (Left) The last or fifth-stage larva of *Rhodnius*. (Middle) The winged adult of *Rhodnius* produced when the fifth stage molts. (Right) Giant or sixth-stage larva produced by the implantation of the corpus allatum from a young larva into a fifth-stage larva.

tion of active extracts of the hormone which will reproduce on injection all the effects previously obtained by the implantation of the corpus allatum (Williams, 1956).

When the corpus allatum is implanted, it may sometimes produce only a small localized patch of larval cuticle immediately over the implant. It clearly has a direct effect on the epidermal cells which lay down the cuticle. It is possible to abrade selected areas on the surface of the cuticle in *Rhodnius* so as to facilitate the entry of the hormone and then, by the application of the cecropia extract to produce an adult insect with one larval segment on the abdomen, with one larval wing (Plate II) or with larval genitalia (Wigglesworth, 1958).

The juvenile hormone must be a comparatively simple chemical substance, perhaps a steroid of the same general type as the steroid hormones of mammals. [Indeed, Gilbert and Schneiderman (1958) have recently obtained a sterol from the adrenal gland of cattle which reproduces the effects of the juvenile hormone when injected into the insect.] We have here a clear-cut example of a single chemical substance which determines whether the enzymes responsible for the development of larval characters shall be active or not. It is a

reasonable assumption that the production of these enzymes is under the control of the appropriate genes; but it is a moot point whether we should think of the hormone as acting upon the genes in the nucleus or upon those elements of the cytoplasm which determine the activity of particular genes.

Growth must first be set going by the growth and molting hormone "ecdysone" (Y in Fig. 3), which is secreted by the thoracic gland when activated by another secretion (X in Fig. 3) from the neurosecretory cells of the brain. But the character of the structures produced during growth are controlled by the juvenile hormone (Z in Fig. 3). When much hormone is present the gene system of the larva is active; in the absence of the hormone the gene system of the adult becomes active; and in those insects in which there is a pupal stage, there is good evidence that the pupa is formed when a very small amount of juvenile hormone is present (Wigglesworth, 1957) (Fig. 4).

In the present stage of knowledge it is impossible to say just how a simple chemical substance leads to the activation of one set of genes or of enzymes to the exclusion of another set. But the resemblance between this phenomenon and the examples of polymor-

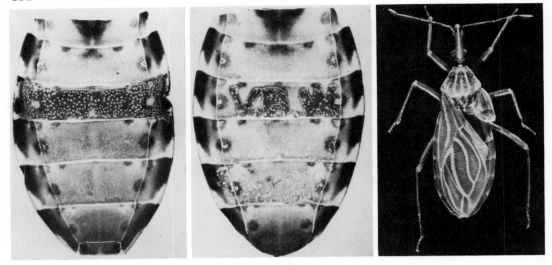

Plate II. (Left) Abdomen of adult *Rhodnius* with one larval segment produced by the local application of "juvenile hormone" in the fifth-stage larva. (Middle) Abdomen of adult *Rhodnius* with initial letters traced out in larval cuticle. (Right) Adult *Rhodnius* with one larval wing produced by local application of "juvenile hormone."

phism that we have already discussed is obvious. Hormones seem often to be token stimulators. They are, as it were, keys which will open particular doors; what is inside these doors bears no relation to the properties of the key.

We have already seen that, besides controlling metamorphosis, the juvenile hormone will control the deposition of yolk in the eggs, and doubtless other metabolic functions. It may well play a part in some of the other polymorphisms that occur in insects. In grass-

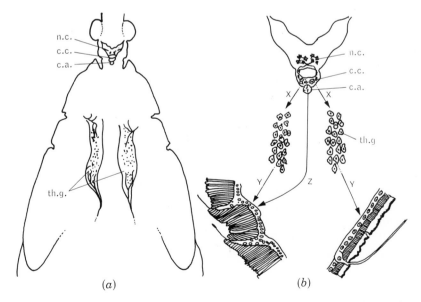

Fig. 3. (a) Fifth-stage larva of *Rhodnius* showing the location of the chief endocrine organs. (b) Schema of the endocrine system in *Rhodnius*. *c.a.*, Corpus allatum; *c.c.*, corpus cardiacum; *n.c.*, neurosecretory cells; *th.g.*, thoracic gland; *X*, activating hormone from the brain; *Y*, thoracic gland hormone (the molting hormone "ecdysone"); *Z*, corpus allatum hormone (the juvenile hormone "neotenin"). To the left in (b), larval abdominal cuticle is shown; to the right, adult abdominal cuticle.

hoppers or locusts there are often two "phases" (which at one time were regarded as separate species), a gregarious phase which builds up into destructive swarms and a solitary phase which is a harmless creature. There is evidence that some at least of the characters of the solitary phase can be produced by the implantation of corpora allata (Joly and Joly, 1953), and Kennedy (1956) has suggested that the solitary phase may perhaps be regarded as a slightly juvenile form, a neotenic form of the species.

The termites are another group of insects which show a remarkable degree of polymorphism. Here again there is evidence that the implantation of extra corpora allata into the larvae leads to the production of "soldiers," forms with powerful mandibles, which may perhaps be regarded as "superlarvae" (Lüscher, 1958).

We saw that in the case of sex it is sometimes possible for differentiation to be reversed: first one set of secondary sexual characters appears and then the other. This same reversal is possible also in metamorphosis. No one has succeeded in making whole insects revert from adult to larva. But in *Rhodnius* (Wigglesworth, 1940b) and in certain Lepidoptera (Piepho and Meyer, 1951), it has been possible to cause a restricted area of the integument of the abdomen of an adult insect to molt and to lay down again a cuticle with larval characters or partially larval characters. Clearly, in some of the cells, the enzyme system responsible for larval characters is still present and capable of reactivation in the adult after metamorphosis.

There is, therefore, a very close parallel between the "successive polymorphism" which we call "metamorphosis" and the "alternative polymorphism" in which the different characters are developed by different individuals of the species. But there is yet another type of polymorphism which is even more familiar. I refer to the "differentiation" of the parts of the body.

The body begins its life as a single cell, the fertilized egg cell. The nucleus of this cell contains the system of genes necessary for the production of all the varied parts of the body of the full-grown animal. This single nucleus

divides and subdivides to form the multifarious organs. The process of cell division by mitosis is so devised as to ensure an exact sharing of all the genetic material in the chromosomes among the daughter nuclei. It is therefore generally assumed that all the cells in the body have the same genetic constitution.

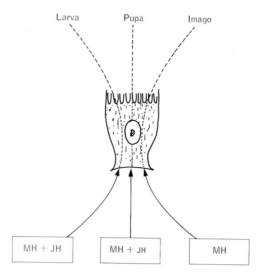

Fig. 4. Hormonal control of metamorphosis; *MH*, growth and molting hormone; *JH*, juvenile hormone. Explanation in text.

But very soon after the egg cell has begun to divide, the daughter cells become "differentiated." Some are already destined to form the head, others the limbs, the eyes, or the tail. We have here the most striking "polymorphism" of all. And since the nuclei appear to be genetically uniform throughout the body, it is generally assumed that "differentiation" resides in the cytoplasm of the cells and that different cytoplasms activate the different nuclei in such a way that different elements in the gene system can exert their effects.

In the developing nervous system of the grasshopper each neuroblast divides to give rise to another neuroblast and a ganglion cell. In the well-known work of Carlson (1952), it was shown that if the spindle of the dividing neuroblast is rotated with a needle through 180°, so that the cytoplasm of the ganglion cell receives chromosomes that should have gone to the neuroblast, this makes no difference to the result: it is the cytoplasm and not the chromosomes which determine the type of cell produced.

The differences in the different cytoplasms are presumably chemical in nature; they probably exert their effect on the gene system in the nucleus by chemical means. We have, therefore, a very close parallel here with the other types of polymorphism that we have been considering. We pictured these widespread changes in form, whether of sex or of metamorphic characters, as due to nutritional factors or hormones acting upon the cells in all parts of the body. In the case of differentiation we may picture a similar relationship, except that the factors responsible for bringing about the different modifications in the cytoplasm do not spread freely throughout the body, but are tied to particular areas known as morphogenetic "fields." The developing embryo becomes divided into these zones or "fields" in which the cytoplasm is committed or "determined" to form particular elements in the pattern of the body.

We do not know how the various cytoplasmic "fields" become different from one another. It would not be difficult to suggest a number of hypothetical mechanisms. One suggestion that was put forward many years ago (Wigglesworth, 1940a) to explain differentiation in the epidermis of *Rhodnius* may be mentioned here. The epidermis of an insect consists of a single layer of cells which secrete the "cuticle." The horny cuticle is the only part of the insect which is visible in everyday life. The form of the insect is in fact the form of the cuticle, and this is entirely controlled by the activity of the epidermal cells below.

In the larva of *Rhodnius* the epidermal cells retain a certain capacity to differentiate and give rise to other organs: special secreting cells or oenocytes (*a*, Fig. 5), which probably contribute lipoproteins to the cuticle; dermal glands (*b*); and sense organs (*c*, Fig. 5). The little tactile sense organs (*c*) are distributed at more or less regular intervals over the surface of the abdomen. Each consists of

an innervated hair arising from a socket that lies at the center of a little dome or plaque of smooth cuticle.

The essential parts of this sense organ are formed by four cells which are the daughter cells of a single epidermal cell. One of these daughter cells (the tormogen) forms the socket, one (the trichogen) forms the hair, one forms the sense cell and axon filament, and one becomes the so-called neurilemma cell which provides a sheath for the sense cell and its axon. The sense cell which arises from the epidermis in this way becomes a true part of the nervous system. It gives off one filament which is connected to the hair and is stimulated when the hair is moved, and one filament or axon which grows inward, joins the nearest nerve that it chances to meet, and accompanies this until it finally arrives at the ganglia of the central nervous system (Wigglesworth, 1953).

These small sense organs appear at more or less regular intervals in the epidermis. It is very rare to find two of them close together; and if there is a wide space without a sense organ, a new one is sure to appear there at the next molt when a new cuticle is formed. If the epidermis is killed by applying a hot needle to a certain area of the abdomen, the surrounding cells multiply and grow inward to repair the injury. The next time the larva molts, this new epidermis lays down a cuticle without sense organs. But at the following molt new sense organs are developed; and they appear at the proper distance one from another.

What controls this regular distribution of sense organs? The suggestion was made (Wigglesworth, 1940a) that some chemical substance is necessary to induce an epidermal cell to give rise to a four-celled sense organ. It was further suggested that this substance is in limited supply, so that a developing sense organ drains it away from the surrounding cells and thus prevents the appearance of another sense organ in the immediate vicinity. But beyond a certain distance there will be sufficient of this hypothetical substance to induce another cell to start differentiating

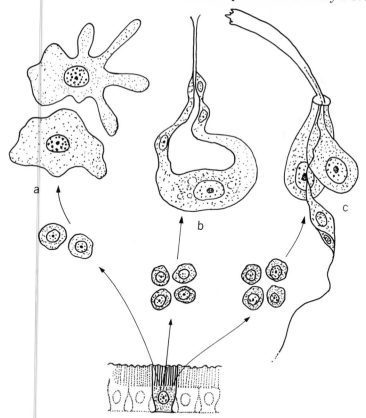

Fig. 5. Schema showing the differentiation of an ordinary epidermal cell in *Rhodnius* to form a pair of oenocytes (*a*); a dermal gland (*b*); a tactile sense organ (*c*).

into a sense organ and then draining the cells immediately around it (Fig. 6).

At the moment this is just a hypothesis, a tool for thought, a way of thinking about the problem. But it is worth pointing out that a similar process is going on around us continually in human society, and that the distribution of human institutions is controlled in a similar fashion. An essential ingredient for the formation of a university, for example, is a supply of students. When a university is established it will drain off these students and will thereby inhibit the appearance of another university in the immediate neighborhood.

Besides being able to differentiate into four-celled sense organs, the epidermal cells can give rise to dermal glands whose function it is to secrete a thin protective covering over the outer surface of the cuticle. These

glands likewise are made up of four cells, and there is some evidence that sense organs and dermal glands are closely related or homologous organs; for under certain conditions it is possible to obtain structures intermediate between the two.

In normal development, however, the two organs are quite distinct. Both arise from the four daughter cells of a single epidermal cell, but whereas in the sense organ these cells form, respectively, the hair, the socket, the sense cell with its axon, and the ensheathing neurilemma cell, the four cells of the dermal gland comprise a large secreting cell and the cells which form the duct to the exterior.

We saw that where the epidermis is destroyed by burning and a new epidermis and cuticle are regenerated, sensory hairs fail to appear at the first molt. But dermal glands *are* formed, and they make their appearance,

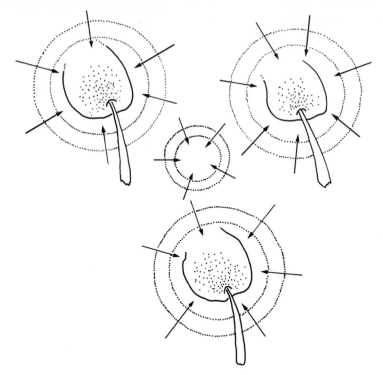

Fig. 6. Theory of determination of sensory hairs in epidermis of *Rhodnius*. Explanation in text.

evenly distributed throughout the epidermis, at their normal intervals (Wigglesworth, 1953).

These observations led to an extension of our hypothesis. For it is possible to suppose that a single essential substance is needed for the formation of sense organs and dermal glands, but that a larger amount is required for a sense organ—just as a large amount of juvenile hormone leads to the formation of a larva and a very small amount, to the formation of a pupa.

This idea is even more speculative, and it leaves us with no explanation of how the four cells in the group that is going to form a sense organ become so completely different from one another. But the interest of this system of dermal glands and sense organs in the integument of *Rhodnius* lies in its simplicity. It provides a model system for the differentiation of the body in general. According to the conception we have developed, an area of undifferentiated substrate absorbs

some substance, an "inductor" or "modifier." The plasma thereby becomes determined for some particular type of development, and at the same time, by draining the inductor substance from the surrounding region, it inhibits a like determination in its vicinity. It is immaterial to the argument whether the modified plasma is divided into nucleated cells or whether it forms a nonnucleated continuum.

This change is illustrated in diagrammatic form in Fig. 7. The zone *A* is the determined "field." This then proceeds to grow, and within it the same type of change occurs, leading to a new and more specialized "field" of determination, *B*. And this in turn leads to the new field, *C*. And so the process proceeds, with the uptake by an active center of the materials necessary for a particular determination and the consequent inhibition in the surrounding zones of centers with the same potential activities.

These potential centers are suppressed because they are deprived of their essential raw material. There is thus not only a limitation of potencies in the activated center, there is also a positive evocation of faculties hitherto dormant—the two conditions postulated by Hans Spemann as necessary for any satisfactory theory of differentiation.

If the hypothesis that I have outlined here bears any relation to the truth, it is clear that differentiation, polymorphism, and metamorphosis may all be regarded as different aspects of a single phenomenon: the activation of specific gene systems latent in the nuclei, by appropriate chemical stimuli furnished by hormones, inductors, or specific nutritional factors.

In conclusion, I should like to quote once more the words which Sir Thomas Browne wrote in his *Religio Medici* in 1635 when William Harvey was at the height of his powers: "Those strange and mystical transmigrations that I have observed in Silkworms, turned my Philosophy into Divinity . . . Ruder heads stand amazed at those prodigious pieces of Nature, Whales, Elephants, Dromidaries and Camels; . . . but in these narrow Engines there is more curious Mathematics.

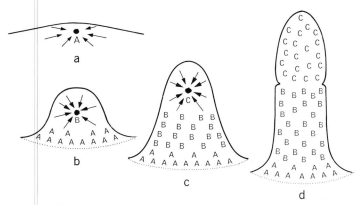

Fig. 7. Stages in the progressive determination in an appendage according to the hypothesis put forward. Explanation in the text.

Who . . . wonders not at the operation of two Souls in those little Bodies?"

The purpose of this lecture has been to show how we are still groping for a description of this duality in scientific terms.

REFERENCES

Aristotle. *Generation of Animals*, II, i; III, ix.
Astauroff, B. L. (1930). *Z. induktive Abstammungs- u. Vererbungslehre* **55**, 183–262.
Bouillon, A. (1949). *Cellule rec. cytol. histol.* **53**, 35–95.
Carlson, J. G. (1952). *Chromosoma* **5**, 199–220.
Charniaux-Cotton, H. (1956). *Ann. sci. nat. Zool. et biol. animale* [11] **18**, 305–310.
Gilbert, L. I., and H. A. Schneiderman (1958). *Science* **128**, 844.
Gordon, C., and J. H. Sang (1941). *Proc. Roy. Soc.* **B130**, 151.
Harvey, W. (1651). *Generatione Animalium*, exercitationes XLV and L. Amsterdam.
Joly, P., and L. Joly (1953). *Ann. sci. nat. Zool. et biol. animale* [11] **15**, 331–345.
Kennedy, J. S. (1956). *Biol. Revs. Cambridge Phil. Soc.* **31**, 349–370.
Lüscher, M. (1958). *Naturwissenschaften* **45**, 69–70.
Piepho, H. (1942). *Wilhelm Roux' Arch. Entwicklungsmech. Organ.* **141**, 500–583.
Piepho, H., and H. Meyer (1951). *Biol. Zentr.* **70**, 252–260.
Salt, G. (1927). *J. Exptl. Zool.* **48**, 223–331.
Salt, G. (1931). *J. Exptl. Zool.* **59**, 133–166.
Salt, G. (1937). *Parasitology* **29**, 539–553.
Smith, G., and A. H. Hamm (1914). *Quart. J. Microscop. Sci.* **60**, 435–461.
Swammerdam, J. (1758). *The Book of Nature: or the History of Insects.* London.
Verrier, M. L. (1956). *La Biologie des Éphémères.* Paris.
Wigglesworth, V. B. (1934). *Quart. J. Microscop. Sci.* **77**, 191–222.
Wigglesworth, V. B. (1936). *Quart. J. Microscop. Sci.* **79**, 91–121.
Wigglesworth, V. B. (1940a). *J. Exptl. Biol.* **17**, 180–200.
Wigglesworth, V. B. (1940b). *J. Exptl. Biol.* **17**, 201–222.

Wigglesworth, V. B. (1953). *Quart. J. Microscop. Sci.* **94,** 93–112.

Wigglesworth, V. B. (1954). *The Physiology of Insect Metamorphosis*, Monographs in Exptl. Biol., No. 1. Cambridge Univ. Press, London and New York.

Wigglesworth, V. B. (1957). *Symposia Soc. Exptl. Biol.* **11,** 203–227.

Wigglesworth, V. B. (1958). *J. Insect Physiol.* **2,** 73–84.

Williams, C. M. (1956). *Nature* **178,** 212–213.

13

Growth Substances

GROWTH SUBSTANCES in plants have been shown to be relatively simple compounds, for example, indole acetic acid and kinetin (6-furfuryl amino purine). Although their general physiological actions have been extensively described (*Skoog and Miller 1957*),* their metabolic or genetic consequences are not yet understood. How indole acetic acid results in cell growth and how kinetin stimulates cell division are unanswered questions.

In animal cells endogeneous compounds which have turned out to be proteins have been shown to exert specific growth-promoting influences on various embryonic target tissues assayed *in vivo* and *in vitro*. Strong evidence that the nerve growth factor (*Levi-Montalcini 1964*) which has been found in the mouse salivary gland functions during normal development comes from experiments in which antibodies are made against the growth-promoting substance. When these antibodies are presented to a chick embryo *in ovo*, normal development of sympathetic ganglia does not occur; in fact, development of the sympathetic nervous system is nearly completely inhibited. The nerve growth-promoting factor has been shown to be present normally in sympathetic ganglion cells, in the blood, and in the body fluids of a variety of vertebrates.

Precocious opening of eyelids and eruption of teeth in the mouse or the rat is produced by administration of an epidermal growth-promoting factor to the fetus (*Cohen 1964*).

Isolation and characterization of both the nerve growth-promoting substance and the epidermal growth factor are major achievements. Recently, Cohen has found that the epidermal stimulating protein can be made radioactive by treatment with labeled acetic anhydride. The preparation does not lose its biological activity. Now that the factor can be tagged, its metabolic pathway and its ultimate site of action in the cell may be traced. Further purification of nerve growth factor has yielded two components which have biological activity only when combined (Schenkein and Bueker 1964).

Both plant and animal growth substances stimulate metabolic processes. The epidermal growth factor promotes incorporation of precursors into both RNA and protein (*Cohen 1964*) and both indole acetic acid and kinetin induce considerable RNA synthesis in tuber tissue of the Jerusalem artichoke (Setterfield 1963).

Like the hormones, the growth substances may provide tools for probing mechanisms of gene activation and for examining the means by which the synthetic machinery and the cell can be stimulated.

* Italicized references indicate articles which appear in this book.

REFERENCES

1. Schenkein, I., and E. Bueker (1964). The nerve growth factor as two essential components. *Ann. N.Y. Acad. Sci.* 118:171–182.
2. Setterfield, G. (1963). Growth regulation in excised slices of Jerusalem artichoke tuber tissue. In G. E. Fogg (ed.), *Symposia of the Society for Experimental Biology, Number XVII, Cell Differentiation,* The University Press, Cambridge, England, pp. 98–126.

Isolation and Biological Effects of an Epidermal Growth-Stimulating Protein [1, 2, 3]

STANLEY COHEN [4]

It has long been recognized that the growth and differentiation of certain specific cells are regulated by specific chemical substances produced in the organism. The extent to which the organism may rely on this mechanism has not, perhaps, been fully appreciated.

Two hitherto unsuspected growth-regulating factors have been studied in recent years in our laboratories: the "nerve growth factor" (NGF) and an "epidermal growth factor" (EGF). The discovery, isolation, and biological effects of this latter factor are reviewed here.

During our investigations on the nerve growth-promoting protein of the submaxillary gland of the mouse (1, 2), we noted that the daily injection of partially purified extracts of the salivary gland into newborn mice resulted in some gross anatomical changes, in addition to the previously reported effects on the nerve cells: (a) precocious opening of the eyelids, as early as 7 days instead of the usual 12 to 14 days; (b) precocious erup-tion of the incisors, at 6 to 7 days instead of the normal 8 to 10 days; and (c) a marked stunting of the animals with an inhibition of hair growth.

With a biological assay based on the precocious opening of the eyelids in newborn mice, the purification and identification of the factor were attempted. The isolation of the factor was reported in 1962 (3), and it was found to be a heat-stable, nondialyzable, antigenic protein, whose most distinctive chemical characteristic was the absence of phenylalanine and lysine.

The isolation procedure involved standard methods of protein fractionation and included, in the final purification steps, chromatography on carboxymethylcellulose and diethylamino-ethylcellulose and gel filtration with Sephadex G-75. From 22 g wet weight of submaxillary glands derived from 150 adult male mice, 5 to 7 mg of the pure protein was obtained. This represented a yield of approximately 20 percent, with a purification of about 150-fold, based on protein content.

GROSS ANATOMICAL EFFECTS

The effects of graded dosages of the purified protein injected into newborn mice are shown in Table 1. A demonstrable biological effect was produced by the injection of 0.5 μg per 1.5 g of body weight per day, and with higher doses, there was precocious separation of the eyelids as early as 6 days after birth compared to the 12 to 13 days required in control

Symposium: Metabolic Control Mechanisms. National Cancer Institute Monograph No. 13: 13–37, 1964. Government Printing Office, Washington, D.C.

[1] Presented at the Symposium on Metabolic Control Mechanisms in Animal Cells, Boston, Mass., May 27–30, 1963.

[2] This investigation was supported in part by research grant RG-6638 from the National Institutes of Health, Public Health Service, and from an institutional grant of the American Cancer Society, Inc., to Vanderbilt University.

[3] Part of this research was carried out in the Istituto Superiore di Sanità, Rome, Italy.

[4] Research Career Development Awardee of the U.S. Public Health Service.

TABLE 1. Effect of injection of purified epidermal factor into newborn mice*

Dosage (μg/1.5 g/Day)	Animal Number	Eyelids Open (Day)	Incisors Erupt (Day)	Weight on Day 10 (g)
8	A–1	6	6	5.5
8	A–2	6	6	5.6
4	A–3	7	7	6.5
4	A–4	7	7	6.8
Control	A–5	12	10	7.2
Control	A–6	13	10	7.5
4	B–1	7	7	5.4
4	B–2	8	7	5.0
2	B–3	8	7	6.0
2	B–4	8	8	5.6
2	B–5	9	8	6.0
1	B–6	9	9	6.2
1	B–7	9	9	6.0
Control	B–8	12	10	6.4
Control	B–9	12	10	6.1
1	C–1	9	10	5.1
1	C–2	10	10	5.6
0.5	C–3	10	10	5.6
0.5	C–4	10	10	5.6
Control	C–5	12	10	5.5
Control	C–6	12	10	5.7

* Newborn mice were given daily injections of 0.025 ml per 1.5 g body weight. Controls did not receive injections. Effects on litters A, B, and C are recorded.
From *J Biol Chem* 237:1555–1562, 1962.

animals. The effect of the factor on tooth eruption in newborn mice and rats is illustrated in Fig. 1.

PROPERTIES OF THE GROWTH FACTOR

The purity and properties of the isolated material were studied and the results are outlined. The details of the procedures have appeared in a previous publication (3).

Only a single component, having a sedimentation constant of $125S_{20,w}$ was detectable when the material was examined in a Spinco analytical ultracentrifuge (Fig. 2).

The ultraviolet absorption spectrum showed a maximum at 277 to 278 mμ and a trough at 249 to 250 mμ. The ratio of A_{280} to A_{260} was 1.6.

The protein may be chromatographed on paper with the following solvent systems: propanol-water-ammonia and butanol-water-acetic acid. After being stained with bromo-

phenol blue only one spot could be detected, with some tailing in the basic solvent (Fig. 3). The protein band could be eluted from companion strips, and on injection into newborn mice, the lid separation and tooth eruption effects were elicited.

The results of a paper electrophoretic examination of the material are shown in Fig. 4. Again, only a single major component was detectable (protein stain), with some tailing in the more acid buffers. From a companion strip at pH 6.5, the protein band was eluted and was biologically active. From the relative positions of the glucose (Fig. 4) the apparent corrected mobilities were calculated, and the results indicated that the factor had an isoelectric point at pH 4.2.

The factor is antigenic. Upon examination of the protein by electrophoresis and immunoelectrophoresis with cellulose acetate strips, it was found that only one electrophoretic and only one precipitating band could be demonstrated (Fig. 5).

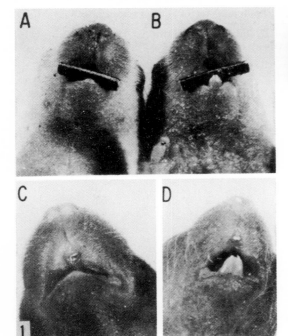

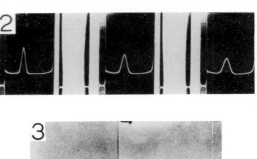

Fig. 1. Photographs showing extent of incisor eruption in control and treated 8-day-old mice and rats. *A*, control mouse; *B*, mouse given daily injections of 2 μg per 1.5 g body weight of the epidermal growth factor; *C*, control rat; and *D*, rat given daily injections of 1 μg per 1.5 g body weight of the factor. (Reprinted from the *J Biol Chem* 237: 1555–1562, 1962.)

The amino acid composition of the protein after acid hydrolysis was examined, both qualitatively by two-dimensional paper chromatography and quantitatively with a Beckman automatic amino acid analyzer. All the common amino acids were present except phenylalanine and lysine. Their absence may also be considered as a criterion of purity, since it might have been expected that contaminating polypeptides would contain these amino acids. The results of the analysis are shown in Table 2. The minimal molecular weight, as determined from the amino acid ratios with the assumption of 1 alanine residue per molecule, was 14,638.

That the biological activity of the factor is associated with its protein structure is also supported by the fact that this activity is destroyed by incubation with crystalline chymotrypsin or bacterial proteinase and par-

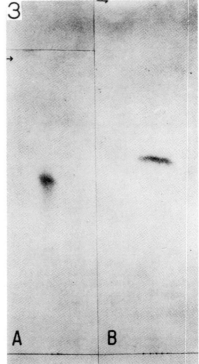

Fig. 2. Ultracentrifugation pattern of the epidermal growth factor at a concentration of 4 mg per ml in 0.15 M NaCl, 0.1 M Tris buffer, and 0.001 M Versene, adjusted to pH 7.86. The pictures were recorded at 8-minute intervals at 59.780 rpm in a valve-type synthetic-boundary cell. Fig. 3. Ascending paper chromatography of the epidermal growth factor; *A*, propanol-water-ammonia; *B*, butanol-water-acetic acid. *Line* indicates starting position and *arrow* the solvent front. (Reprinted from the *J Biol Chem* 237: 1555–1562, 1962.)

tially inactivated with trypsin. The biological activity is stable to boiling in distilled water for 30 minutes but is destroyed when heated in 0.1 N NaOH for 1 hour or in 0.2 N HCl for 2 hours in a boiling water bath.

Finally, an antiserum against the protein may be obtained by injecting the protein together with Freund's complete adjuvant into rabbits. Incubation of the antiserum with the protein formed a precipitate and the biological activity was inhibited. The precipitate, when washed and suspended in isotonic sodium chloride, showed no biological activity when injected into newborn animals. However, when a duplicate suspension was boiled for 5 minutes to denature the antibody, between 25 and 50 percent of the original activity was recovered. These exploratory experiments indicate that the observed inhibition of biological activity was due to the presence in the antiserum of normal precipitating antibodies.

Thus it is clear that the isolated factor is a protein and that the same protein is responsible for the precocious separation of the eyelids and the eruption of the incisors. There is some evidence for the existence in salivary gland extracts of minor chromatographically separable peaks with a similar biological activity, but their nature has not been ascertained. Although the injection of relatively high concentrations of the purified protein into newborn mice leads to some inhibition in weight gain and hair growth, the marked toxicity and growth-inhibiting effects (relative to the lid-tooth effects) of the crude salivary gland extracts are absent.

EPIDERMAL GROWTH RESPONSE IN VIVO

At this point in the investigation, the mechanisms by which the factor elicited such diverse effects were not understood. A histological study was then undertaken with Dr. George Elliott in an attempt to clarify the process. A short report of the results was published in 1963 (4), which provided histological evidence that the observed eyelid separation is a consequence of a more generalized biological effect, i.e., an enhancement of epidermal keratinization and an increase in the over-all thickness of the epidermis.

In the first series of these experiments the protein was injected subcutaneously into newborn mice and rats for varying lengths of time. Littermates receiving injections of distilled water were used as controls. At the termination of the injection period, desired

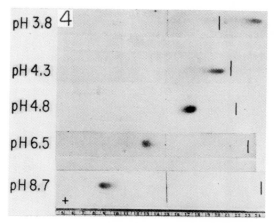

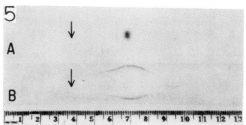

Fig. 4. Paper electrophoresis of the epidermal growth factor. The specimens were applied at *center* line. All runs were for 16 hours at a field strength of 9 volts per cm in buffers in 0.1 ionic strength, except the barbital buffer which had an ionic strength of 0.07. Sodium acetate-acetic acid mixtures were used to prepare buffers of *p*H 3.8, 4.3, and 4.8. KH_2PO_4 for *p*H 6.5, and barbital-sodium barbital for *p*H 8.7. The electroosmotic flow is indicated by *line* representing the glucose spot, visualized in parallel strips by being sprayed with aniline hydrogen phthalate. Fig. 5. Electrophoretic (*A*) and immunoelectrophoretic (*B*) patterns of the factor. Cellulose acetate strips 16 × 2.5 cm were used, with a 0.07 ionic strength barbital-sodium buffer, *p*H 8.6. The sample (20 μg of protein) was applied approximately one fourth the distance from the anode end, as indicated by *arrow*. The run was performed at room temperature for 3.5 hours at 0.5 ma per cm width of the strip. In the immunoelectrophoretic run, the diffusion under oil was allowed to proceed for 20 hours. Ponceau S was used to stain the protein. (Reprinted from the *J Biol Chem* 237: 1555–1562, 1962.)

specimens were removed, fixed, and embedded by standard procedures. Tissue sections were stained with hematoxylin and eosin.

Typical cross sections of the eyelid area from experimental and control 8-day-old rats are shown in Figs. 6a and 6b. In the control animal the epidermis connecting the eyelids

TABLE 2. Amino acid composition of the epidermal factor*

Amino Acid	Residues per Molecule	
	Calculated	Assumed
Aspartic acid	17.30	18
Threonine	5.06	5
Serine	11.47	12
Glutamic acid	10.28	10
Proline	5.18	5
Glycine	14.57	15
Alanine	1.04	1
Cystine	5.81	6
Valine	5.16	5
Methionine	1.68	2
Isoleucine	4.96	5
Leucine	10.00	10
Tyrosine	11.07	11
Phenylalanine	<0.02	0
Lysine	<0.02	0
Histidine	2.11	2
Ammonia	14.30	14
Arginine	8.98	9
Tryptophan	4.61	5
Cysteic acid	Trace	
Methionine sulfoxides	Trace	
Total		121
Estimated molecular weight		14,638

* Tryptophan was determined spectrophotometrically. The values recorded were calculated on the basis of 10 leucine residues per mole. No corrections were applied for possible destruction of serine or threonine, or for any increased ammonia formation due to destruction of amino acids.
From *J Biol Chem* 237:1555–1562, 1962.

had just started to keratinize, whereas in the experimental animal the keratinization process was considerably advanced and the eyelids had begun to separate. Sections prepared from 8-day-old mice showed an almost identical histological picture.

Whether these keratinizing changes were limited to the eyelid area or were more general was then examined. Figures 7a and 7b illustrate typical sections of back skin (epidermal portion) from 12-day-old experimental and control rats. It can be seen that in the skin of the experimental animal the thickness of both the keratin and cellular layers of the epidermis had increased. Middorsal skin sections prepared from 12-day-old mice indicated that their skin also responds to the injection of the active protein.

In a second set of experiments 12 normal mice ranging in age from 12 to 20 days received daily injections of a partially purified preparation of the factor; littermates were used as controls. After 3 to 4 weeks of injections, gross observation of the mice revealed a clearly visible increase in the diameter of the tail in all the experimental animals. Figures 8a and 8b illustrate typical sections of the epidermis of the tail in these animals. There is a marked increase in the thickness of the epidermal layers. Sections taken from the plantar surface of the hind feet of these animals showed a similar histological picture. However, in contrast to the newborn animals, no differences were noted in sections of the skin of the back from these older control and experimental animals.

Preliminary data indicate that the epithelium of the oral cavity, esophagus, and stomach of the mouse and rat can respond to the injection of the factor.

We have confirmed the histological picture by making a number of chemical measurements of pure epidermis obtained by trypsinization of standard areas of skin from 5-day-old control and experimental rats. The ratios of the average values for the experimental animals to those for the control animals were: dry weight, 1.7; total nitrogen, 1.7; deoxyribonucleic acid content, 1.3; ribonucleic acid content, 1.3; histidase activity, 1.8; and acid phosphatase activity, 1.7 (unpublished data, Angeletti, P., Salvi, M. L., Chesanow, R., and Cohen, S.).

EPIDERMAL GROWTH RESPONSE IN ORGAN CULTURE

Among the many unresolved problems presented by these data was whether the factor acts directly on the epidermis or indirectly by way of some other systemic (hormonal?) process. The techniques of tissue and organ culture seemed ideally suited for resolving this problem. The study of this aspect has been carried out at the Biochemical Section of the Instituto Superiore de Sanità in Rome in collaboration with Dr. Rita Levi-Montalcini and Dr. Domenica Attardi. Dr. Levi-Montalcini devised the first experiments to demonstrate clearly a direct *in vitro* growth-promoting effect of the "epidermal growth factor" on embryonic chick skin.

In the following experiments we made use of a rather simple technique. Dorsal skin was dissected out from 7-day chick embryos, and fragments 1 to 2 mm in diameter were incubated in 1.2 ml of a completely synthetic medium (Eagle's basal medium) in small Falcon plastic dishes. To the experimental cultures was added 12 μg of the growth factor [Sephadex G-75, fraction as described in (3)]. The cultures were then placed in a humidified incubator kept at 37° C and flushed with a 4 percent CO_2-air mixture. At desired intervals the tissue was removed, fixed in Susa's fluid, and embedded by standard

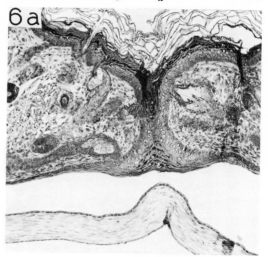

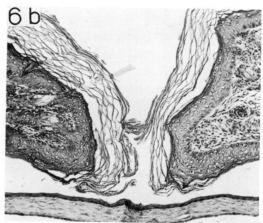

Figs. 6a and 6b. Cross sections of the eyelid area from control, *6a*, and experimental, *6b*, 8-day-old rats. Experimental animal had received daily injections (1 μg per 1 g body weight) of the epidermal growth factor. $\times$ 100. (Reprinted from the *J Investigative Dermatol* 40: 1–5, 1963.)

procedures. Tissue sections were stained with hematoxylin and eosin.

Figures 9a and 9b show sections of the control and experimental fragments of skin after cultivation for 48 hours. The epidermis of the control cultures remained almost unchanged in appearance during the period of cultivation, whereas it can be seen that a marked proliferation of the epidermal layers had occurred in the experimental culture. Photographs of a duplicate set of cultures under higher magnification are shown in Figs. 10a

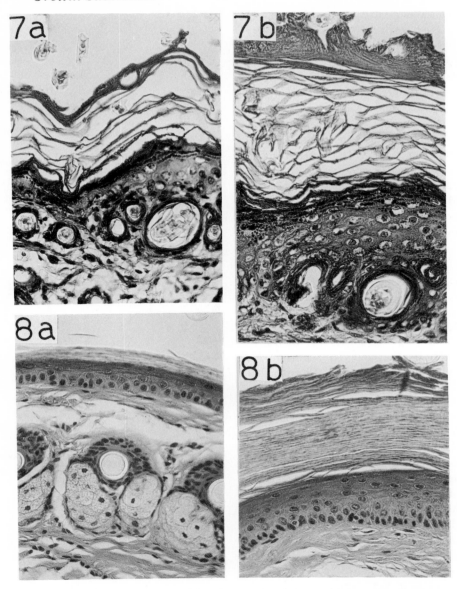

Figs. 7a and 7b. Sections of middorsal back skin (epidermis) from control, *7a*, and experimental, *7b*, 12-day-old rats. Experimental animal had received daily injections (0.5 μg per 1 g body weight) of the active protein. × 200. Figs. 8a and 8b. Sections of epidermis of the tails of control, *8a*, and experimental, *8b*, 45-day-old mice. Experimental animal had received daily injections (8 μg per 1 g body weight) of a partially purified fraction [Sephadex G-75 fraction as described in (*3*)]. Injections were started when the animals were 13-days old. × 200. (Reprinted from the *J Investigative Dermatol* 40: 1–5, 1963.)

and 10b. Although a concentration of the growth factor of 10 μg per ml was routinely used in these experiments, easily observable biological effects were produced by concentrations of 0.1 μg per ml.

If the cultures are allowed to grow for 5 days, the control cultures continue to remain practically unchanged; the experimental cultures appear to keratinize (Figs. 11a and 11b).

We were greatly aided in the interpretation

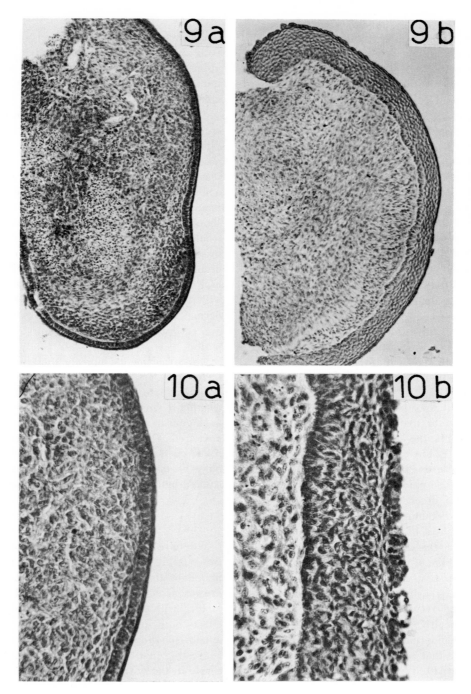

Figs. 9a and 9b. Control, *9a,* and experimental, *9b,* explants of 7-day chick embryo skin after 48-hour incubation. × 150. Figs. 10a and 10b. Control, *10a,* and experimental, *10b,* explants of 7-day chick embryo skin after 48-hour incubation. × 300.

of our results by the studies of Dr. Wessells on the cultivation of chick embryo skin (5). He reported that skin of 8- and 10-day embryos failed to develop in synthetic medium. Our control cultures confirm his results. The development and cornification of skin derived from 12-day chick embryos in synthetic medium were clearly demonstrated by Wessells. Our results with eyelid skin derived from the 12-day chick embryo, to be published in detail elsewhere, confirm these results and also show that in the presence of the growth factor the multiplication of the epidermal cells is more rapid and the thickness of the final cornified layer is greater.

It thus seems clear that the EGF acts directly on the skin and that its action does not necessarily involve other systemic or hormonal influences. The growth factor stimulates the division of the epidermal cells and their subsequent keratinization. Preliminary experiments have shown that the EGF can also act directly on skin explanted from the mouse embryo.

We next considered whether the dermis was necessary for the epidermal effects. In these experiments, the epidermis of the eyelid area of 11- to 12-day chick embryos was separated from the dermis by trypsinization into a sheet of cells. The epidermal sheets were then cultivated as described previously, except that Eagle's minimum essential medium was used and the sheet of cells was placed on a fiber glass disc, the cells thus being covered only by a thin film of medium.

Figures 12a, 12b, 13a, and 13b illustrate typical sections prepared from control and experimental trypsin-separated epidermis after 48-hour cultivation. The appearance of the control epidermal cultures again was very similar to that reported by Wessells in an experiment with synthetic medium (6) in that ". . . the basal layer was no longer columnar and could not be identified, and as a result all epidermal cells tended to look alike in gross morphology." The absence of layering was also noted. In contrast, our experimental cultures (Figs. 12b and 13b) were markedly different. Layering and the formation of pearl-like structures were clearly observed together with areas containing cells apparently undergoing keratinization. Similar results were obtained with epidermis derived from 7-day chick embryos.

This rapid apparent differentiation in pure epidermal sheets resembles the much slower differentiation observed by McLoughlin who used a very complex medium containing plasma and a chick embryo extract (7), which may contain traces of a specific growth factor similar to the one described here. It should be recalled that the keratinization of whole skin from very young embryos occurs in similar complex media (8, 9). In our experiments the growth-stimulating effects of EGF are still marked in media supplemented with 15 percent calf serum, although the epidermal cells of the control cultures have begun to divide during the 48-hour incubation period.

Our experiments indicate that the growth factor can act directly on epidermal cells. Whether there is a stimulation of mitosis and whether the morphological changes are, in fact, analogous to normal keratinization remain unanswered. The contributions of mesenchymal tissue on the maintenance of oriented columnar cells, mitosis, and keratinization have been studied by McLoughlin (8) and Wessells (6).

DISCUSSION

We have thus isolated and characterized two specific "growth factors" from the submaxillary gland of the male mouse, the "nerve growth factor" and the "epidermal growth factor" with demonstrable specific biological effects both in the intact animal and on isolated tissue *in vitro*. Although there is evidence suggesting that the nerve growth factor plays a role in the normal life of sensory and sympathetic nerve cells, we have as yet no direct evidence that the EGF acts similarly in the normal development of the epidermis.

It is also not yet established whether these factors are synthesized in the salivary gland or elsewhere and merely stored in these organs. I have reported the failure to detect

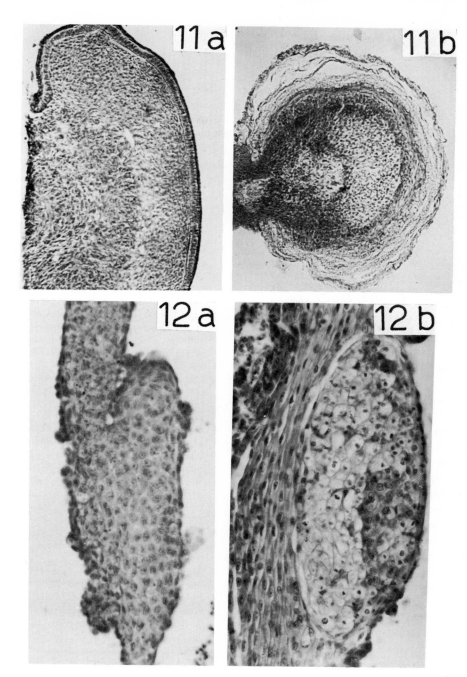

Figs. 11a and 11b. Control, *11a* and experimental, *11b*, explants of 7-day chick embryo skin after 5-day incubation. × 150.   Figs. 12a and 12b. Control, *12a*, and experimental, *12b*, explants of trypsin-separated epidermal sheets from eyelid skin of 11-day chick embryos after 48-hour incubation. × 390.

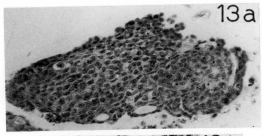

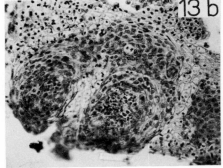

Figs. 13a and 13b. Control, *13a*, and experimental, *13b*, explants of trypsin-separated epidermal sheets from eyelid skin of 12-day chick embryos after 48-hour incubation. × 360.

the EGF in the salivary glands of female mice and of other species and in extracts of a variety of mouse tissues (*3*). However, the *in vivo* assay was used in these experiments, and low concentrations of the active material would escape detection. In fact, preliminary tissue culture experiments indicate that serum may stimulate epidermal growth in tissue culture. Argyris and Argyris (*10*) and Patterson (*11*) have reported the *in vivo* growth stimulation by certain tumors on adjacent epithelial tissue. The nature of these effects must be studied further.

The effects of a number of vitamins and hormones, such as vitamin A and estrogens, on epidermal structures have been reviewed recently by Bern and Lawrence (*12*) and Laschet (*13*). The influence of hydrocortisone and vitamin A on explants of chick skin has been described by Fell (*9*), and a stimulating effect by thyroxine on such explants has been described by Wessells (*14*). The mechanisms by which these various substances, including the EGF, exert their influence on the epidermis, as well as their interrelationships, are obscure.

SUMMARY

The isolation and characterization of an epidermal growth-promoting protein from the salivary glands of mice are reviewed. The biological effects of the protein *in vivo*, on the epidermis of the mouse and rat, are described. Evidence is presented that the growth factor can act directly not only on explants of chick embryo skin, but also on dermis-free epidermal sheets.

REFERENCES

1. Cohen, S.: Purification and metabolic effects of a nerve growth-promoting protein from the mouse salivary gland and its neurocytotoxic antiserum. *Proc Nat Acad Sci USA* 46: 302–311, 1960.
2. Levi-Montalcini, R., and S. Cohen: Effects of the extract of the mouse submaxillary salivary glands on the sympathetic system of mammals. *Ann NY Acad Sci* 85: 324–341, 1960.
3. Cohen, S.: Isolation of a mouse submaxillary gland protein accelerating incisor eruption and eyelid opening in the newborn animal. *J Biol Chem* 237: 1555–1562, 1962.
4. Cohen, S., and G. A. Elliott: The stimulation of epidermal keratinization by a protein isolated from the submaxillary gland of the mouse. *J Invest Derm* 40: 1–5, 1963.
5. Wessells, N. K.: An analysis of chick epidermal differentiation *in situ* and *in vitro* in chemically defined media. *Develop Biol* 3: 355–389, 1961.
6. ———: Tissue interactions during skin histodifferentiation. *Develop Biol* 4: 87–107, 1962.
7. McLoughlin, C. B.: The importance of mesenchymal factors in the differentiation of chick epidermis. I. The differentiation in culture of the isolated epidermis of the embryonic chick and its response to excess vitamin A. *J Embryol Exp Morph* 9: 370–384, 1961.
8. ———: II. Modification of epidermal differentiation by contact with different types of mesenchyme. *J Embryol Exp Morph* 9: 385–409, 1961.
9. Fell, H. B.: The influence of hydrocortisone on the metaplastic action of vitamin A on the epidermis of embryonic chicken skin in organ culture. *J Embryol Exp Morph* 10: 389–409, 1962.
10. Argyris, T. S., and B. F. Argyris: Differential response of skin epithelium to growth-promoting effects of subcutaneously transplanted tumor. *Cancer Res* 22: 73–77, 1962.

11. Patterson, W. B.: Induction of normal cell proliferation by tumor cells. In *Biological Interactions in Normal and Neoplastic Growth* (Brennan, M. J., and Simpson, W. L., eds.). Boston, Little, Brown & Co., 1962, pp. 247–252.

12. Bern, H. A., and D. J. Lawrence: Influence of vitamin A on keratinization. In *Fundamentals of Keratinization* (Butcher, E. O., and Sognnaes, R. F., eds.). Washington,

D.C., Publ #70 Amer Ass Adv Sci, 1962, pp. 95–112.

13. Laschet, U.: Die Wirkung von Vitaminen und Hormonen auf das Epithel. *Z Vitamin Hormon Fermentforsch* 12: 1–14, 1961.

14. Wessells, N. K.: Thyroxine initiation of epidermal differentiation as studied *in vitro* in chemically defined medium. *Exp Cell Res* 24: 131–142, 1961.

Growth Control of Nerve Cells by a Protein Factor and Its Antiserum

RITA LEVI-MONTALCINI

Discovery of this factor may provide new leads to understanding of some neurogenetic processes.

Long before the possibility of experimentally modifying the developing nervous system was conceived, it was realized that end organs play an all-important role on the associated nerve structures. For it is the very nature of nerve cells to establish contact with other cells such as muscle fibers, glandular tissue or other nerve cells. Such close morphological and functional connections could hardly be conceived without a bondage which would interlock the life of the two partners: both would be severely affected if such links were broken. While the mutual dependency of nerve cells and associated structures was clearly documented in the adult organism, it remained for the study of the embryo to bring into focus, in a deceptively clear and persuasive way, the role of such end organs in the growth, differentiation, and maintenance of nerve cells.

The great experimental embryologist, R. G. Harrison, first realized the advantages offered by the embryo as the object of study of the differentiating nerve centers, and it was the nervous system of the amphibian larva which

was first challenged to solve problems it had never faced, such as providing for the innervation of organs and limb rudiments borrowed from larvae belonging to species of different size. In thrusting his glass needle into the soft body of the larva and in performing heteroplastic transplantations, the embryologist wanted to test the capacity of the developing nervous system to establish functional connections with foreign tissues. Even more, he wanted to see how the nerve centers and the growing nerve fibers would adjust to the different geometrical dimensions and structural configuration of the foreign organs. The results indicated a remarkable flexibility on the part of the developing nervous system which readily adapts to a new situation even to the point of accelerating the growth rate of its nerve fibers to keep pace with the fast-growing limb rudiments of a smaller species (*1*).

These results also proved that the embryonic nervous system is highly receptive to influences exerted by tissues which supply the peripheral field to the outgrowing nerve fibers. That this influence is not species specific is documented by the growth response called forth by organs or limb rudiments of a different species. Such experiments and others dealing with heterotopic transplantations proved that peripheral fields are interchangeable, provided that some of the basic rules are respected: motor and sensory nerve fibers

Reprinted from *Science*, January 10, 1964, Vol. 143, No. 3602, pages 105–110. Copyright © 1964 by the American Association for the Advancement of Science.

have their own fields of innervation; deprivation of one given sector of its motor or sensory nerve contingent does not favor invasion by the other. The same holds true with respect to somato-motor and somato-visceral fibers. The somato-motor fibers end in the voluntary striated muscles while the somato-visceral make synaptic contact with nonstriated muscles, heart, and glandular tissues. Hence embryonic nerve fibers, as well as mature nerve fibers, have no access to peripheral end organs which belong to a category different from their own. In one instance only were embryonic nerve fibers of a given type seen to make functional connections with tissues of an entirely different type from that with which they normally connect. This was the case when intrinsic nerve fibers from the exposed stump of a sectioned neural tube wandered into the surrounding tissues and established functional connections with muscles (2).

When Harrison presented in the Harvey lecture the results of the experimental analysis of the developing nervous system in the amphibian larvae, the report, although impressive for the ingenuity of the experiments and the talent displayed in the analysis of the response of nerve centers to all possible changes inflicted to their peripheral fields of innervation, may have raised some doubt as to the information one could gain in this way on the factors which control growth and differentiation in the nervous system. The concluding sentence in the lecture pointed to a sideline of these investigations which seemed to Harrison even more promising than the main object of the research. "By ablation and transplantation of parts of the embryo it is possible to fashion almost any kind of nervous system desired and subsequently to study its function without the disturbing effects of trauma. This is one of the most promising lines of investigation leading off from the field covered in the present lecture" (1).

Almost thirty years later, one must admit that these predictions did not materialize, while instead some valuable information was gained by pursuing the main line of research opened by Harrison and his students, and by

carrying further the inquiry into the control mechanisms of the developing nervous system.

Considerable progress was achieved by replacing the amphibian larva with the chick embryo. It was V. Hamburger who conceived and contributed most of the work on the effects of the peripheral field of innervation on sensory and motor spinal systems in the chick embryo (3–5). Even though these same nerve structures were also the object of experimental analysis in the amphibian larvae, a considerable amount of work had centered on the causal analysis of brain structures and associated sense organs; for the vertebrate brain, with all its structural and functional complexity, holds such a fascination for man that it is difficult for him to resist the temptation of exploring it in the hope of learning more about his own brain.

Compared to the brain, the spinal cord appears to be of almost diagrammatic simplicity. How deceptive in fact this is, was to be learned through long and laborious attempts to explore the mechanisms which control the growth and differentiation of the spinal cord and of the sensory ganglia. The chick embryo proved to be particularly suited for this analysis. Its nervous system is more complex, but it lends itself better than the amphibian nervous system to the analysis, for its nerve centers are more clearly segregated and defined and their strong affinity for silver permits a visualization of the nerve structures far superior to that in amphibians. But it was a new approach to the problem which brought a significant contribution to our admittedly still very rudimentary knowledge of neurogenesis. Most of the previous work had focused on the study of the end effects of early surgical interventions on the developing nervous system. The results of heteroplastic and heterotopic organ transplantations were in fact explored in the fully developed larvae, long after the problem of adjusting to the new situation had been solved by the nerve centers and contact had been firmly established between the growing nerve fibers and the new periphery. It now became clear that this static approach would leave unanswered the main question:

how does the nervous system solve the problem with which it is confronted? It is, in fact, the mechanics of developmental processes rather than their final completion that are of primary interest to the student of neurogenesis. This realization prompted a detailed analysis of the nervous system of the chick embryo from the stage of 38 hours of incubation, when the first wave of differentiation starts in the rostral part of the neural tube, to the time of hatching. The study of normal embryos was rewarding. It made clear the composite nature of apparently simple neurogenetic processes and, in so doing, brought into focus some basic problems which lent themselves to the experimental approach.

In this article I will briefly outline some of the developmental neurogenetic processes which were the objects of investigation in recent years.

At the time of its early formation, that is during the first week of incubation, the nervous system of the chick embryo (and the same is true for all vertebrates) is the stage for massive cell movements, segregation of cell groups, and degeneration of other cell populations. Migration of neuroblasts, that is, nerve cells at an early stage of their differentiation, occurs throughout the entire length of the neural tube from its apical to its caudal end. Migrating nerve cells move in the same orderly fashion as ant or termite armies and, like them, they keep in close reciprocal contact during the long journey which takes place in the dense matrix of the brain vesicles and in the spinal cord. Closely timed inspection of the developing nervous system, hour after hour and day after day, revealed the complexity and extension of these active cell displacements which may take several days to be completed (6, 7). At the same time as these migratory movements occur, other nerve cell populations undergo disintegration and death and are wiped out, in a matter of a few hours, by intervening macrophages. Finally other populations form and achieve their differentiation without undergoing either degenerative or migratory processes. Thus the final product, the differentiated nervous system with its motor, sensory, and associative centers

well segregated from each other and interconnected through hundreds of fiber tracts, is greatly different from the embryonic nervous system. The developmental history of each nerve center should therefore be traced back to its early inception in order to know how such a center attains its final size and position. Differentiation itself, in the central nervous system, does not seem to obey the rules which operate in other systems. Some nerve cells show all marks of morphological and functional differentiation at an early developmental stage, while others retain the characteristics of immature cells till the end of the incubation period and then suddenly transform into fully differentiated neurons. Differences in apparently homogeneous cell populations become manifest as differentiation progresses and hitherto similar cells diverge from each other in their growth rate, structure, and end connections. These differences become even more apparent under experimental conditions. Of the experimental work performed on the developing nervous system of the chick embryo, I will briefly mention here only some of the results of experiments aimed at the analysis of spinal ganglia confronted with a larger peripheral field or, conversely, deprived of their field of innervation. The main contribution of these experiments was not so much to stress the all-important role of the periphery on associated sensory centers, as to reveal the extent of these effects on the different developmental aspects which we are used to refer to with the rather general and vague term of "differentiation." The closely timed study of the response of these ganglia to the extirpation of the limb bud in two-day chick embryos, gave evidence of a sharp decrease in the mitotic activity of ganglia destined to innervate the amputated limb rudiment. Since dividing cells lack any differentiative mark and have no fiber connection with the periphery, these effects were designated with the noncommittal term of "field effects" or remote rather than direct effects (5). If the adverse effects on the mitotic activity already reduce the size of the sensory cell population, the same populations are even more severely affected by a destructive process which attacks cells in early differentiative stages in the same ganglia. About half of these cells undergo sudden death between the fourth and the fifth day of incubation. Dead cells are removed in a few hours by intervening macrophages, while the surviving cells undergo slow regressive changes but survive till the end of the incubation period. The striking similarity between this massive cell disintegration and the physiological disintegrative processes already mentioned raises the question of whether in both instances, death might not follow the depletion of some agent essential to growth and differentiation of these nerve cells. Other instances of massive cell degeneration will be considered subsequently.

Thus the severe atrophy of ganglia deprived of their peripheral field of innervation is the end result of a number of detrimental effects. Why some cells should undergo sudden death while others, also deprived of their end organs, should suffer only regressive changes compatible with life is one of the many questions still unanswered (5). Equally extensive and complex is the growth response of the same ganglia confronted with the task of providing the innervation of an additional limb bud. The mitotic activity sharply increases in these ganglia, and all subsequent developmental steps from early to advanced differentiative processes are likewise enhanced. While suggesting that the periphery releases some agents which control the mitotic activity as well as differentiation in the sensory nerve cells associated with these end organs, the results gave no clue concerning the nature of these agents and we would today have progressed no further than stating the problem, were it not for a fortuitous discovery which led to the identification and isolation of one of such factors.

GROWTH RESPONSE OF NERVE CELLS TO A TUMOR FACTOR

When in 1947 E. Bueker implanted a fragment of mouse sarcoma 180 into the body wall of a 2-day chick embryo, he had in mind to test the capacity of sensory and motor nerve fibers of the host to innervate a fast-growing tissue. Since the tumor, at variance with a limb bud or other embryonic organs, is homogeneous in structure, the experiment was also expected to answer the question of whether the tumor would admit all or only a given type of nerve fibers. In his 1948 paper (8) Bueker reported that nerve fibers from the adjacent sensory ganglia had gained access to the tumor and that these ganglia underwent what seemed to be a moderate increase in size of the same order of magnitude as that resulting from the implantation of an additional limb bud. The author saw in these results a confirmation of the hypothesis that the final size attained by the sensory ganglia is dependent upon the extension of their peripheral field of innervation. The fact that sensory but not motor fibers branched into the tumor confirmed the hypothesis of a selective affinity of nerve fibers for peripheral end organs. Finally, the observation that only sensory ganglia connected through nerve fibers with the tumor increased in size seemed to emphasize the similarity between these effects and the effects elicited by an additional limb rudiment and to give support to the hypothesis that nerve fibers are instrumental in channeling the effects of the periphery on the associated nerve centers. Viewed in this light, the results of the tumor implantation conformed to the results of limb or organ transplantation. Fifteen years had to elapse before the impact of this ingenious experiment on the classic and somewhat ill-defined concepts of "peripheral field effects" was fully realized.

Of the extensive work performed during the last twelve years, I shall consider here only that not fitting into previous schemes, thus paving the way to new experiments and to the revision of old concepts. A reinvestigation of the tumor effects (9) led to the discovery of new facets of the phenomenon. It was found that the growth response of the sensory ganglia contributing fibers to the tumor far exceeds the response called forth by an additional limb bud implanted in the embryo at the same developmental stage, that is, at 3 days of incubation. Whereas sensory ganglia supplying nerve fibers to an additional limb undergo a size increase ranging between 20 and 40 percent in excess of the controls, the tumor evokes an increase in volume of the same ganglia two to three times their normal size. Nerve fibers branching into the tumor make no attempt to establish synaptic contact with the neoplastic cells, but wander around in tortuous circuits, and build a dense fibrillar net around and between the cells. If the size increase of the sensory ganglia and the peripheral branching of their fibers departed already to a considerable extent from the effects evoked by an additional limb, the growth response of the sympathetic ganglia adjacent to the tumor had no precedent in any previously observed effects. These ganglia appeared in fact to be five to six times larger than controls. In addition, atypical accessory ganglionic agglomerates were partly imbedded in the tumor and partly irregularly scattered on the fringe of the neoplastic mass. Normal and atypical sympathetic ganglia sent large fiber bundles into the tumor where they intermingled with the sensory fibers and, together with them, took possession of that bizarre "peripheral field" which mimicked like a caricature the effects of normal peripheral end organs on associated nerve centers. The viscera of the embryo, which normally lack a sympathetic innervation up to the end of the third week of incubation, were now flooded with sympathetic nerve fibers from the end of the first week of incubation.

In some organs like the mesonephros, which during its short life cycle is deprived of sympathetic innervation, the density of nerve fibers was such as to force the tubules apart. All the available space in this and other organs like the ovary, the spleen, and the thyroid was filled with large nerve bundles of such size and density that the characteristic structures of the invaded organs were overshadowed.

These most unusual findings led me to propose a different interpretation of this extraordinary growth response. The observed effects could in fact be better explained by assuming that the tumor harbors a growth factor which selectively enhances the nerve fiber outgrowth from the sensory and sympathetic ganglia of the host (*10*). This hypothesis received

full confirmation from experiments of extraembryonic tumor transplantation. Fragments of sarcoma 180 or sarcoma 37 (both elicit the same effects) were grafted onto the chorioallantoic membrane of 4- to 6-day embryos. In such a position the tumors and the embryos share the circulation, but no direct contact is established between the embryonic and the neoplastic tissues. The effects compared in all respects with the effects of intra-embryonic tumor transplants, thus giving decisive evidence for the release into the blood stream of a "nerve growth factor" (NFG) produced by the neoplastic cells. In intra- as well as in extra-embryonic tumor transplantations, thick nerve bundles were also found in the lumen of large and small veins. Some vessels were in fact filled with dense nerve agglomerates to the point that the blood circulation was greatly obstructed (*10, 11*).

These discoveries, while giving new support to the hypothesis that the tumor harbors a nerve growth factor, also suggested a different experimental approach to the problem. In order to isolate and identify the active agent, a less complex system than the developing embryo was needed. The tissue-culture technique seemed to offer considerable advantages over the embryo by making it possible to test the effects of the tumor directly on isolated sensory and sympathetic ganglia. These experiments were first performed at the Biophysics Institute of Rio de Janeiro in association with H. Meyer. Sensory and sympathetic ganglia of 7- to 9-day chick embryos were confronted *in vitro* with fragments of sarcoma 180 or sarcoma 37.

In control cultures the same ganglia were combined with tissue fragments explanted from chick or mouse embryos. The culture medium consisted of a drop of chicken plasma and a drop of embryonic extract, later replaced with a similar amount of amino acid solution. The cultures were incubated at 37°C and examined at 6-hour intervals. The results confirmed the expectations. As early as 5 hours after the beginning of incubation, ganglia combined with a fragment of sarcoma 180 or sarcoma 37 showed striking differences from controls. While these controls produced only few and sparse nerve fibers, ganglia adjacent to a tumor fragment were surrounded by a dense halo of nerve filters which increased in density and length during the following 24 hours (*12*). Once decisive evidence was obtained that this *in vitro* effect was invoked by the same neoplastic factor which enhances sensory and sympathetic nerve fiber outgrowth *in vivo*, the tissue-culture method replaced almost entirely the laborious and time-consuming technique of implanting the tumor in the chick embryo and analyzing the effects 2 to 3 weeks later. These results marked the turning point of the investigation. As a result, some of the picturesque and esthetically attractive features of the embryological research were lost, but the investigation itself gained in precision and depth, since for the first time the chemical approach to the problem was made possible.

While biochemists consulted earlier had refrained from the too difficult task of identifying the tumor factor which evokes the growth effects in the embryo, the same problem presented in the simplified version of identifying the factor which promotes the nerve fiber outgrowth *in vitro* now seemed accessible to analysis. The biochemist, S. Cohen, agreed to join our group and undertake the task of identifying the agent. Ever since this *in vitro* technique was first devised in 1953, it has become the method of choice for the test of nerve growth factors in our laboratory as well as in other laboratories which are also engaged in the study of the same problem (*13*). It was only after the nerve growth factor became available in a purified form and in large quantities, that it was possible to assay its effects in the living organism. The embryos and the newborn animals then resumed their roles as the major objects of this investigation.

THE NERVE GROWTH FACTOR: ITS NATURE, BIOLOGICAL SOURCES, AND EFFECTS

It is the rule rather than the exception in research that new leads should come from accidental findings and that these leads, when followed, would channel the main investigation into a new direction. Of all sciences, biological sciences still remain the most dependent upon such fortuitous leads to unravel some of the intricate mechanisms of life. The discovery of a potent nerve growth factor in snake venom and in the mouse salivary glands which occurred shortly after the discovery of the tumor nerve growth factor, and the recognition that both agents have many properties in common with the tumor factor, can well be listed among such fortuitous events. In 1954, Cohen had succeeded in isolating a nucleoprotein from sarcomas 180 and 37, endowed with the growth-promoting properties of the tumors and of their extracts (*14*). It was now of interest to establish whether the activity resided in the intact nucleoprotein fraction or if the nucleic acids or the proteinic component of such fraction elicited the growth effects. In this connection, snake venom was used by Cohen because of its phosphodiesterase content. Its addition to the culture medium in minute amounts was aimed at the degradation of the nucleic acid component of the active fraction. The unexpected and startling outcome of these experiments was the finding that the snake venom itself harbors a nerve growth factor. In fact ganglia cultured in a medium containing the purified venom at a concentration of 0.05 μg per ml developed an exceedingly dense halo of nerve fibers. This observation prompted a search for the venom effects in the living embryo. The results gave additional evidence for the striking similarity between the tumor and the venom effects. Daily injections of 0.5 μg of the purified venom into the yolk of embryos between the 6th and 9th day of incubation, evoked the same nerve growth effects as intra-embryonic or extra-embryonic tumor transplantation (*15*). It now became clear why the injection of the tumor extract had failed to produce any growth effect. The specific activity of the venom is in fact about 1000 times higher than the same activity in the tumor homogenate. The intact tumor evokes the growth effects, in spite of its relatively low content of the NGF, through continuous release of this factor by living and actively dividing cells. Both the tumor and the snake venom factors are heat labile, nondialyzable, destroyed by acid (0.1N HCl), stable to alkali (0.1N NaOH), and to 6N urea. The chemical analysis of the venom factor was pursued farther than had been possible with the tumor factor. Upon acid hydrolysis and two-dimensional paper chromatography, the amino acid pattern was qualitatively identical to the chromatogram of crystalline bovine albumin. The activity is destroyed upon incubation with proteolytic enzymes and upon incubation with anti-serum to the snake venom. The estimated molecular weight as determined with the Spinco analytical ultracentrifuge is of the order of 20,000 (*16*).

While the discovery of the growth-promoting factor in snake venom could not possibly have been anticipated, the finding of a similar factor in the submaxillary salivary glands of the mouse was the result of a planned search. The occurrence of two agents with nearly identical biological properties in mouse tumors and in the snake venom suggested the existence of other possible sources of this agent. The mouse salivary glands, being in many respects homologous to the snake venom glands, were thought of by Cohen as another possible source of a NGF factor. Experiments *in vitro* fully confirmed the guess (*17*). The submaxillary salivary glands of the adult male mouse harbor a factor endowed with the same nerve growth promoting activity as the sarcomas and the snake venom (Figs. 1 and 2). Its specific activity is of the order of 6000 to 10,000 times higher than the specific activity of tumors and about ten times higher than that of the snake venom. Its effects *in vitro* and *in vivo* on sensory and sympathetic ganglia of the chick embryo are qualitatively identical with the effects of the two other factors. The active agent was identified by Cohen in a protein particle that is heat labile, destroyed by acid, resistant to alkali, and nondialyzable. Like the NGF isolated from the snake venom, it is destroyed by proteolytic enzymes. Its molecular weight is of the order of 44,000 (*18*).

The high specific activity of the salivary NGF which *in vitro* evokes the halo effect

at a molar concentration of 1×10^{-9}, suggested a test of its effects in mammals. Daily injections of the NGF into newborn mice in the amount of 0.5 μg per gram of body weight, evoked a striking increase of the sympathetic ganglia, already well apparent 48 hours after the first two injections. In 2- to 3-week old mice injected daily, beginning at birth, the same ganglia are four to six times larger than controls, while no changes are apparent in the parasympathetic and sensory ganglia nor in any other nerve cell population (Figs. 3 and 4). Cell measurements and cell counts show that the NGF calls forth an increase in cell number as well as increase in size of individual nerve cells (Figs. 7 and 8). When the mitotic activity comes to an end at 9 days after birth, the NGF evokes cell hypertrophy but no increase in cell number. In adult mice, sympathetic neurons attain a size two times larger than controls (*17*). The universality of the NGF effects was verified by *in vitro* experiments on ganglia of several species, man included. Ganglia explanted from human fetuses which became available from surgical abortions, show the same growth response to the NGF as ganglia of birds and rodents. The essential role of this protein in the life of the NGF effects was verified by *in vitro* experiments on sensory and sympathetic nerve cells dissociated through trypsinization and explanted in liquid media. Nearly all of these cells disintegrate in the first 24 hours in a medium consisting of the Eagle solution alone or supplemented with 10 percent horse serum. The same nerve cells survive up to the third week in this medium when the NGF is added at a concentration of 0.05 μg per milliliter of solution (*19*).

ANTISERUM TO THE NERVE GROWTH FACTOR

An antiserum to the NGF was prepared by S. Cohen by injecting the purified NGF protein into the pads of rabbits together with Freund adjuvant. The antibody titer was first assayed *in vitro*. When it was found that its addition to the NGF solution at progressively higher dilutions inactivated the growth effects of the NGF *in vitro,* the antiserum was injected into newborn mice and the injection was repeated daily for the first week after birth. Three weeks later, treated and control mice of the same litter were killed. On macroscopic inspection, the sympathetic chain ganglia of the injected mice were virtually absent. Upon microscopic analysis, the diminutive ganglia consisted of satellites and a few neurons amounting to 3 to 5 percent of the normal cell population (Figs. 5, 6, and 9). Similar results were obtained with newborn rats, rabbits, and kittens. The injection of the antiserum in adult animals produces less drastic but still severe detrimental effects, while no adverse effects are apparent in other nerve cell populations or in other cell types [20].

Ever since these results were first reported in 1960, hundreds of mice and rats were injected with the antiserum in this and other laboratories. The nearly total atrophy of the sympathetic chain ganglia was in all instances ascertained by microscopic inspection up to two years after the treatment. Of interest is the observation that the lack of any sympathetic control is compatible with a normal life, at least under the sheltered conditions of the laboratory. The treated animals are comparable to controls in growth and in other respects. They are now the object of extensive physiological, pharmacological, and behavioral investigations.

Reevaluation of Control Mechanisms of Nerve Cells by Extrinsic Agents

One may ask whether the identification and isolation of specific nerve growth factors in some mouse sarcomas, in the snake venom, and in the mouse salivary glands, has any bearing upon the problem which promoted this search, namely the control mechanism of the end organs on the associated nerve structures. At the time of the discovery of the growth effects elicited by chorioallantoic tumor transplantations on the sympathetic system of the embryo, this response appeared quite different from the growth response evoked by additional limb buds or sense organs on the nervous system of the host. It differed from it not only in the magnitude of the effects but also in many other respects. The massive invasion of the embryonic viscera by large sympathetic nerve bundles and the penetration of these nerve fibers into the lumen of blood vessels indicated such a profound deviation from normality as to raise the question of whether the sympathetic nerve cells had not undergone a radical transformation into malignant cells. Such a hypothesis was readily dismissed but still we were not prepared to see any similarity between the effects elicited by the tumor and the effects evoked by normal embryonic tissues. The discovery of the nerve growth factor in the snake venom and in the mouse salivary glands proved that the production of the NGF is not the prerogative of neoplastic cells. A number of experiments devised and performed together with P. U. Angeletti proved that granuloma tissue, experimentally produced in a variety of mammals, releases the NGF [21]. The same factor was detected in the sympathetic ganglia and in the serum of mammals, man included [22]. Its presence was likewise ascertained in embryonic tissues [13]. Hence we came to the conclusion that the nerve growth promoting protein is a normal constituent of the sympathetic cells and is normally present in the blood and body fluids of birds and mammals. Leaving open the long debated and still unanswered question of its main source of production in the organism, all evidence seems to us to favor the hypothesis that this protein which we designated as the "nerve growth factor" plays a most important role in the life cycle of the sympathetic nerve cells. As for the sensory cells, we have evidence that the same protein is required during their early developmental stages. Why the mature sensory neurons should become refractory to the NGF is one of the many unsolved aspects of this problem.

The identification of the NGF in a protein which is normally present in the developing and in the mature organism, raises the question of whether the end organs might not af-

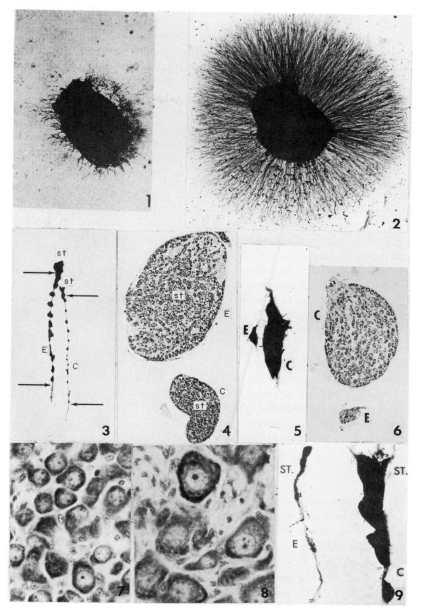

Figs. 1 and 2. Photomicrographs of 7-day sensory ganglia of chick embryo after 24 hours of culture *in vitro*. Fig. 1. Ganglion in a control medium. Fig. 2. Ganglion in a medium supplemented with the salivary NGF at a concentration of 0.01 micrograms per ml. Silver impregnation. Fig. 3. Whole mounts of the sympathetic thoracic chain ganglia of experimental (E) and control (C) mice 19 days old. Experimental mouse injected daily with salivary NGF from birth. *ST*, stellate ganglia. Fig. 4. Transverse sections of stellate ganglia (*ST*) in experimental (E) and control (C) ganglia of Fig. 3. Sections through levels indicated by arrows in both chains in Fig. 3. Fig. 5. Whole mounts of control (C) and experimental (E) superior cervical ganglia of 3-month-old mice injected for a week after birth with the antiserum to the salivary NGF. Fig. 6. Transverse sections through the superior cervical ganglia of control (C) and experimental (E) 9-month-old mice. Experimental mouse injected for three consecutive days after birth with the antiserum to the salivary NGF. Figs. 7 and 8. Comparison of cell size in control (Fig. 7) and experimental (Fig. 8) stellate ganglia represented in Figs. 3 and 4. Fig. 9. Whole mounts of stellate ganglia of control (C) and experimental (E) 9-month-old mice. Experimental mouse injected for three consecutive days with the antiserum to the salivary NGF.

fect the growth and differentiative processes of associated nerve centers through the release of specific growth factors. In this way one could explain the mitotic effects and the excessive branching and altered peripheral distribution of nerve fibers subsequent to the implantation of additional organs or limb rudiments, which could not be otherwise explained. In contrast to the tumor and the purified nerve growth factors, end organs have a very restricted field of action. End organs affect only the growth of nerve centers which provide their innervation. Such differences could be of a quantitative rather than a qualitative order and could be correlated with differences in the production and release of growth factors in the two sets of experiments. Production and discharge may in fact be very limited in cases of implantation of limbs or additional organs.

In suggesting that peripheral structures and the NGF might in the final analysis operate in a similar way, we do not imply that the released growth factors should be the same. On the contrary, there is reason to believe that each nerve cell type might be receptive to only one specific factor.

SUMMARY

Evidence is presented that sympathetic nerve cells of birds and mammals are receptive to the growth promoting effects of a protein (NGF) which was isolated from some mouse sarcomas, snake venom and mouse salivary glands. This same protein is a normal constituent of the sympathetic cells and is present in the blood and body fluids of a variety of vertebrates, man included. An antiserum to the NGF selectively destroys the sympathetic nerve cells of newborn animals without affecting other nerve cells or organs. The "immuno-sympathectomized" animals are comparable to controls in growth and viability.

These results give evidence for the essential role of this particular protein in the growth, differentiation, and maintenance of sympathetic nerve cells. They also suggest that other nerve cells might also depend upon specific factors for their differentiation and growth. These results are discussed in the general framework of neurogenetic problems.

REFERENCES AND NOTES

1. R. G. Harrison, *Proc. Roy. Soc. London Ser. B* **118**, 155 (1935).
2. P. Weiss, *J. Exptl. Zool.* **113**, 397 (1950).
3. V. Hamburger, *ibid.* **68**, 449 (1934).
4. ———, *Physiol. Zool.* **12**, 268 (1939).
5. ——— and R. Levi-Montalcini, *J. Exptl. Zool.* **111**, 457 (1949).
6. R. Levi-Montalcini, *J. Morphol.* **86**, 253 (1950).
7. ———, in *Nature of Biological Diversity*, J. Allen, Ed. (McGraw-Hill, New York, 1963), pp. 261–295.
8. E. D. Bueker, *Anat. Record* **102**, 369 (1948).
9. R. Levi-Montalcini and V. Hamburger, *J. Exptl. Zool.* **116**, 321 (1951).
10. R. Levi-Montalcini, *Ann. N.Y. Acad. Sci.* **55**, 330 (1952).
11. ——— and V. Hamburger, *J. Exptl. Zool.* **123**, 233 (1953).
12. R. Levi-Montalcini, R. Meyer, V. Hamburger, *Cancer Res.* **14**, 49 (1954).
13. E. D. Bueker, I. Schenkein, J. L. Bane, *ibid.* **20**, 1220 (1960).
14. S. Cohen, R. Levi-Montalcini, V. Hamburger, *Proc. Natl. Acad. Sci. U.S.* **40**, 1014 (1954).
15. R. Levi-Montalcini and S. Cohen, *ibid.* **42**, 695 (1956).
16. S. Cohen and R. Levi-Montalcini, *ibid.*, p. 571.
17. R. Levi-Montalcini and B. Booker, *ibid.* **46**, 373 (1960).
18. S. Cohen, *ibid.*, p. 302.
19. R. Levi-Montalcini and P. U. Angeletti, *Develop. Biol.* **7**, 653 (1963).
20. R. Levi-Montalcini and S. Cohen, *Ann. N.Y. Acad. Sci.* **85**, 324 (1960).
21. R. Levi-Montalcini and P. U. Angeletti, in *Regional Neurochemistry*, S. S. Kety and J. Elkes, Eds. (Pergamon, New York, 1960), p. 362.
22. ———, *Quart. Rev. Biol.* **36**, 99 (1961).

Chemical Regulation of Growth and Organ Formation in Plant Tissues Cultured *in Vitro*

FOLKE SKOOG

CARLOS O. MILLER

I. INTRODUCTION

The vast domain of morphogenesis has been explored for a long time from different points of view and staked out into separate fields of highly specialized disciplines. Each of these which has been intensively studied has yielded its share of information for the development of such general concepts and understanding of growth as we now have. In the context of the symposium this report is to deal with the biological action of growth substances as revealed in organ formation, especially bud formation in plant tissues cultured *in vitro*. This emphasis on technique may give the impression that we are dealing with a concise, rigidly defined subject, perhaps even too technical and artificial to be of general biological interest or usefulness. Actually the problems of growth encountered in studies of tissue and organ cultures are essentially as complex as in those of intact organisms, but a brief consideration of the experimental approach itself as well as of the results is called for.

The "Formal" Biochemical Approach

In dealing with biochemical aspects of morphogenesis, Needham has distinguished between (1) morphogenetic substratum, (2) morphogenetic stimuli and (3) morphogenetic mechanisms. The validity of such categories, especially the existence of the third as set apart from the first two, is debatable; and if this third category is at all logically justifiable, it must be as a very temporary scaffold for the elaboration of the others. Nevertheless, arbitrary as this classification may be, these first two categories at least serve to draw attention to distinctions between problems of raw materials and energy supplies for growth

Symposia of the Society for Experimental Biology, 11, 118–131, 1957. Reprinted with permission.

on the one hand, and the finer regulation of rates and co-ordination of component processes on the other. At the present time major emphasis seems to be on aspects of the former of these categories, i.e., metabolism. Especially intermediary carbohydrate metabolism is being studied extensively and scrutinized intensively for possible clues to the secret of growth. From this line of approach come reports in which differences between normal development and uncontrolled growth of cancer are considered as being due merely to the funneling of the energy-providing substrate into alternative aerobic or anaerobic, that is, respiratory, fermentative or otherwise grossly different pathways of degradation. Somewhat more subtle and now extremely popular are working hypotheses based on the assumption that the relative quantitative activities of key enzyme systems in the general respiratory chain are decisive in the regulation of growth. When it is considered, however, that complete cessation of growth may be achieved, at least in plants, by lowering the total respiratory rate by as little as 10–20% through the intervention of various inhibitors, it would appear that the energy-supplying mechanism as such, although it is a prerequisite for growth, can hardly act as a sensitive governor of the processes involved in normal differentiation and development. It seems rather that biochemistry in its preoccupation with metabolic cycles has revealed the general nature of the energy-furnishing machinery but not yet the finer points of its operation. This is said, not to detract from the great achievements in this field, but to emphasize the necessity, in analyses of growth, of working also at higher levels of structural organization, i.e., of using more complex systems than it has been possible to handle effectively so far with chemical tools exclusively.

The Physiological Approach with Plants

(a) *General Physiological Analyses.* From the more physiological approach to the analysis of growth, students of plants early postulated separate factors for the regulation of successive phases of development. Sachs spoke of specific organ-forming substances. At the cellular level a sharp distinction was made between increase in size and numbers. Much effort has been spent in studies of cell elongation and cell division as processes separate and distinct from one another, and in attempts to determine the additive contributions and interactions of the two in tissue differentiation and in organ formation, especially as observed in regeneration phenomena.

(b) *Search for Growth Hormones.* A natural consequence of this reasoning has been a deliberate search for a specific chemical regulator of cell elongation and a specific regulator of cell division as well as, of course, the continuing search for specific organ-forming substances. It is said that he who seeks shall find. We now have the auxins, the very definition of which is based on physiological activity (hormone action) leading to cell enlargement. Also for a long time there has been good indirect evidence for a cell-division hormone (Haberlandt, 1921), and recently the term kinin has been proposed as a generic name for substances with physiological activity promoting cell division in plant tissues under certain specified conditions (Miller, Skoog, Okumura, von Saltza and Strong, 1956; Strong, Okumura, von Saltza, Miller and Skoog, unpublished). Further investigations into the manner in which the known growth regulators exert their specific effects in cell elongation and division respectively have led to a blank wall. Instead of finding their intimate and unique nature, we have found that they are involved indirectly in a wide variety of biochemical activities or physiological functions and lead to most heterogeneous histological and morphological end results. For example, under appropriate conditions auxins have been shown on the one hand to promote root formation and even cell division in the cambium (Snow, 1935); and, on the other hand, to inhibit root elongation and bud development. Thus we do not yet know the specific organ-forming substances, but instead evidence is accumulating against their existence; although various claims and specifications for calines (in the sense of Went's proposal, 1951), for rhizocaline (Bouillenne, 1950), florigens, vernalins, etc., are still being made.

(c) *In Vitro Studies of Nutrient and Growth-Factor Relationships.* The complexity and variability in growth responses indicated above obviously mean that the interaction of many factors must be considered, and that some of these perhaps might be revealed in studies of the simplest possible material capable of "multiple growth responses" and grown under as rigidly standardized conditions as reasonably could be attained. The present experimental approach utilizing stem segments, pith and callus tissues grown on inorganic nutrient media with added organic substrates and various growth factors was intended to eliminate some of the extraneous features and variables which are difficult to control in intact plants. Because valid comparisons and integration of results obtained with different tissue-culture methods and materials are still very difficult, if not impossible, the present discussion will be confined mainly to work carried out in our laboratory, with only brief consideration given to pertinent work in other laboratories. Details of the methodology, media, etc., have been reported (Skoog and Tsui, 1948; Miller and Skoog, 1953; Jablonski and Skoog, 1954). It is hoped that the evidence to be presented will convincingly demonstrate that this approach does in fact permit a closer examination of individual factors and their interaction in various growth processes than has been possible so far with intact plants. For a more general review of the tissue-culture approach in studies of growth see Gautheret (1955).

II. GENERAL RESULTS

The present work was started in an attempt to account for the dual, stimulatory and inhibitory, action of auxin (IAA) as exemplified in its promotion of growth of the terminal shoot and inhibition of lateral buds. A study particularly of the latter process led to the recognition of a parallel function of auxin in the initial formation of organ primordia and in the subsequent development of buds.

Interaction of IAA, Adenine and other Factors in Bud Formation

Experiments with tobacco callus and stem tissues cultured *in vitro* have shown that a delicate, quantitative balance between IAA and adenine and between these and other factors will determine the types of growth and organ formation which occur (Skoog and Tsui, 1951; Miller and Skoog, 1953; Skoog, 1954a). For example, with reference to the induction of bud formation in tobacco-stem segment cultures, the addition of 5 µg./l. IAA to the medium was enough to prevent completely spontaneous bud formation in control segments, and about 40 mg. of adenine must be supplied to restore bud formation to the same level as in controls. Computations on the basis of numerous experiments of this type indicated that under the conditions used about 15,000 molecules of adenine were required to counterbalance 1 molecule of IAA. Furthermore, by the use of purine-type inhibitors such as 2,6-diaminopurine and the reversal of their effects (Miller, 1953), it could be clearly shown that adenine as well as auxin is required for each of the several types of growth tested, including cell elongation. The interaction of adenine with IAA, therefore, can hardly be one of competitive inhibition. Also other naturally occurring purines and pyrimidines may enhance or modify the effect of adenine in bud formation (Skoog, 1954b).

Isolation of Kinetin; Kinins

In view of the above, a search was made for possible reaction products or complexes of IAA and adenine within the tobacco tissues. In this connexion it was found that excised pith tissue responds differently to IAA in the absence and presence of vascular tissue; in the former case there is only cell enlargement,

whereas in the latter case some cell division and eventually root formation occur as well. The presence of a factor in the vascular tissue which induces division in the pith cells (especially in the presence of added auxin) was demonstrated and was shown to be present also in various natural products (Jablonski and Skoog, 1954). Later a crystalline substance with properties of this type was isolated from commercial DNA preparations, identified as 6-(furfurylamino) purine, and synthesized (Miller *et al.* 1956). The structural formula is given in Text-fig. 1. Because of its

6-furfurylaminopurine, I:

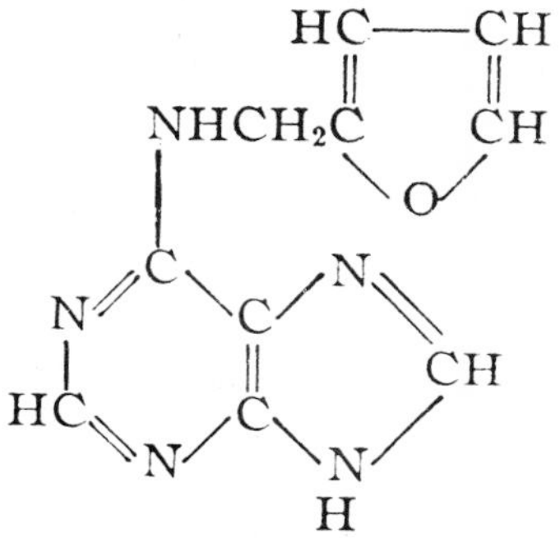

Kinetin, I

Text-fig. 1. Structural formula of kinetin.

activity in promoting cell division, it was named kinetin. More than twenty analogues (all adenine derivatives) have since been found to possess similar activity to varying degrees, but none has been markedly more active than the furfuryladenine (Okumura, von Saltza, Strong, Miller and Skoog, 1955). The following are among the more active derivatives (active in tobacco callus or pith cultures in concentrations of 1–10 µg./l.): benzyl-, phenyl-, 2-thenyl-, butyl-, amyl-, hexyl-. Of the alkyl derivatives ethyl- and heptyl- were slightly active, but methyl-, octyl- and decyl- were not active in our tests. Substitutions of polar groups in the side chain has led to inactivation. Substitutions in the purine nucleus almost invariably has led to complete loss in activity, but in the case of —NH₂ sub-

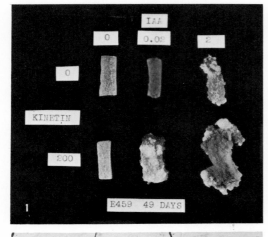

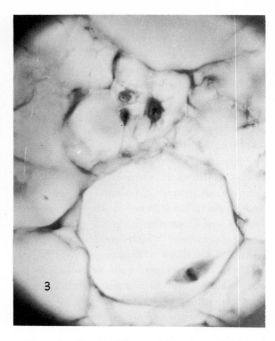

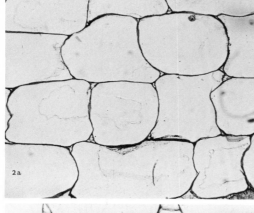

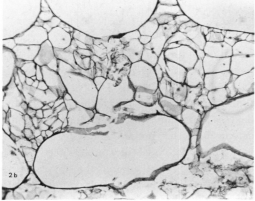

Plate 1. Fig. 1. Effects of kinetin and IAA on growth of excised tobacco pith tissue cultures on modified White's nutrient agar. Age of cultures, 49 days. Fig. 2. Sections through pith tissue cultured on modified White's nutrient agar. *a*, control. *b*, with 0.2 mg./l. kinetin and 2.0 mg./l. IAA added to medium. Fig. 3. Early stage of cell division in tobacco pith tissue culture on modified White's nutrient agar with 0.2 mg./l. kinetin and 2.0 mg./l. IAA added. Age of culture, 10 days. Section stained with Harris's haematoxylin showing metaphase, presumably leading to first division, in large cell, and divided adjacent cells (Das, Patau and Skoog, 1956).

Kinetin-IAA Interactions in Growth of Cells

The requirement for both IAA and kinetin in the growth of excised pith tissue is demonstrated in Pl. 1, Fig. 1. The effect on cell division may be seen by comparison of Pl. 1, Fig. 2*a* and *b*. Detailed studies of cytological effects of kinetin in tobacco pith have been carried out by Drs. Patau and Das in cooperation with the writer. Early stages in the division of cells are shown in Pl. 1, Fig. 3, and summaries of counts of mitosis and of newly formed cells plotted as functions of concentration and length of kinetin treatments in the presence of IAA, are shown in Text-fig. 2*a* and *b* respectively. A diagram (Text-fig.

stituted in the 2 position some activity was retained. Further details will be published by Strong *et al.* As mentioned, these substances with physiological activity similar to that of kinetin have been named kinins. This generic term may also include structurally different substances of the type reported by Shantz and Steward (1955*a, b*).

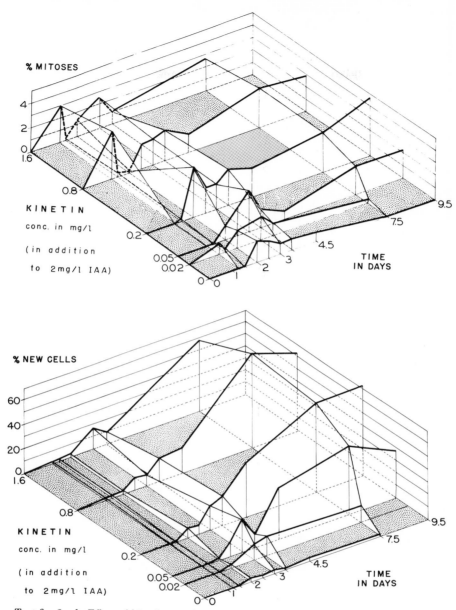

Text-fig. 2*a*, *b*. Effect of kinetin as a function of concentration and time of treatment on: (*a*) the rate of cell division (percentage mitosis), and (*b*) the number of new cells formed in tobacco pith sections cultured on modified White's nutrient agar media with 2.0 mg./1. IAA added (Das, Patau and Skoog, 1956).

3) illustrating the interaction of kinin and auxin (kinetin and IAA) in DNA* increase, mitosis and cytokinesis, has been prepared by Dr. Patau. It shows that some DNA formation

* DNA measured spectrophotometrically on large numbers of individual, Feulgen-stained nuclei.

may be induced by kinetin in the absence of added IAA, and vice versa that some mitoses may be induced (Naylor, Sander and Skoog, 1954), and also a few cell divisions may be induced by IAA in the absence of added kinetin, whereas no cell division or mitosis

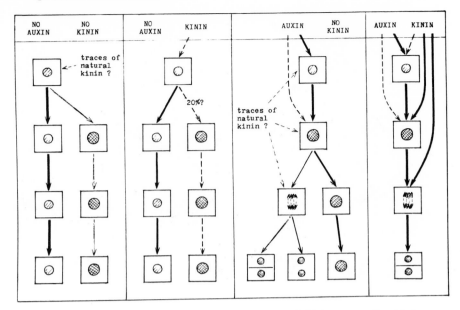

Text-fig. 3. Diagram representing action of kinetin and IAA, separately and in combination, on DNA synthesis, mitosis and cell division in tobacco pith tissue (Patau and Das, unpublished).

is found in the controls. These slight effects of the treatments with only one substance undoubtedly depend on the presence of small endogenous contents of the other. In general it can be stated that both substances are required for active DNA synthesis, mitosis and cell division to proceed continuously.

Kinetin-IAA Interactions in Organ Formation

Perhaps we may think of these definite and rather quantitative effects of IAA and kinetin on cells as primary manifestations of their growth regulatory action. However this may be, the morphogenetic influences of the substances are numerous and "pliable," that is, subject to modification by a variety of factors and/or conditions. They are, nevertheless, consistently reproducible, and distinct to the visual observer to a degree that can only be poorly reflected in black and white photographs, weights or dimensional measurements of various types.

(*a*) *Effects of Concentration.* A most striking morphogenetic effect of kinetin is in the initiation and development of buds, as observed in tobacco callus or stem-tissue cultures

(Pl. 2). This effect is greatly dependent on the concentration and on the presence of other factors, especially the auxin level in the nutrient medium. The influence of a high phosphate level must also be noted. In Pl. 3 is shown the effect of increasing kinetin concentrations on first generation subcultures of stem segments grown on modified White's medium (Miller and Skoog, 1953) with a constant 2 mg./l. level of IAA. Some growth, mainly cell enlargement and the formation of a few short roots, is seen to have occurred in controls. The effect of 0.02 mg./l. is mainly on undifferentiated callus growth, whereas that of 0.5 and 1.0 mg./l. is mainly on bud formation and development with a repression of root formation. Still higher concentrations of kinetin tend to inhibit growth under the conditions of this experiment, but are not very toxic, so that cultures with high kinetin levels actually will remain alive for months longer than the control or low-level kinetin cultures. The interaction of kinetin at two levels (0.2 and 1.0 mg./l.) with increasing concentrations of IAA from 0 to 3.0 mg./l. are compared with each other and with controls in Pl. 4, and the same experiment with the addition of 3 g./l. casein

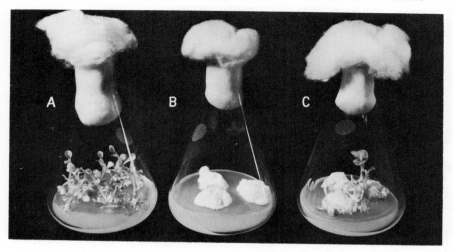

Plate 2. Bud formation in tobacco callus. Callus (fifth subculture of tobacco stem) on modified White's medium. A, with kinetin 0.2 mg./1.; B, with kinetin 0.2 mg./1. plus IAA 2mg./1.; C, with kinetin 0.2 mg./1., IAA 2 mg./1. and in addition KH_2PO_4 400 mg./1. Age of cultures, c. 45 days.

hydrolysate in the medium is represented in Pl. 5. The actual appearance of the cultures in Pls. 4 and 5 receiving 1.0 mg./1. kinetin may be better judged perhaps from the photographs shown in Pl. 6A and B respectively. Points to be noted are: (1) Very little growth occurred without addition of either kinetin or IAA. (2) in the presence of 0.2–3.0 mg./1. IAA these callus tissues subcultured from stem segments, as expected, underwent considerable enlargement associated with some cell division and root development from the cambial or phloem derivatives. (3) 0.2 mg./1. kinetin alone permitted sufficient growth to produce a bud or two per piece of tissue. (4) With increasing IAA concentrations growth increased, but bud formation was repressed by the higher IAA levels. (5) 1.0 mg./1. kinetin was more effective than was 0.2 mg./1. in promoting growth, especially bud development, but with increasing IAA concentration growth increased and again bud formation was gradually repressed in favour of callus growth. (6) The apparently greater increase in size of callus with high IAA levels and 0.2 mg./1. as compared with 1.0 mg./1. kinetin is misleading. It reflects "watery" tissues with a large proportion of loosely packed cells as compared with very firm tissues consisting of numerous small "meriste-

matic" cells. (7) Finally, it should be mentioned that both kinetin levels used in this experiment were too high for promotion of root growth (cf. Pl. 3).

(*b*) *Casein Hydrolysate and Amino-Acid Effects on Growth.* Stimulatory effects of casein hydrolysate and amino-acid mixtures have been reported in studies of cell division of carrot tissues (see Steward and Shantz, 1954). Recent claims that suitable mixtures of known amino acids will replace the requirement for the coconut factor in cell division (Paris and Duhamet, 1953) seem not to be generally true, but this may be so in specific cases. In the present experiments (Pls. 4, 5 and 6) the effect of casein hydrolysate was a marked general promotion of growth, but only in the presence of added IAA or kinetin. In the presence of high auxin levels the development of roots was favoured; the inhibiting action of IAA on root elongation was counteracted. In the presence of kinetin, especially at the higher (1.0 mg./1.) level, bud development was enhanced, and again the inhibiting action of IAA was counteracted.

Tests of the influence of individual amino acids have shown that the beneficial role of the casein hydrolysate in promoting bud development in this case can be explained, even if not entirely accounted for, by the effect of

Plate 3. Effect of kinetin concentration (in 0-10 mg./l. range) on growth and organ formation of tobacco callus cultured on modified White's nutrient agar with 2.0 mg./l. IAA added. Age of cultures, 44 days (Skoog *et al.*).

tyrosine, as is shown in Pl. 7. Phenylalanine by comparison only had a small effect, and tryptophane, which under these conditions is oxidatively deaminated to give a high level of IAA, as expected, did not promote bud formation. A large number of roots may be seen to be present in the tyrosine-treated tissues. These, however, have arisen from the stems after the buds were formed, and in the early stages only buds were observed. It would seem that the effect of tyrosine was exerted especially on stem and leaf development. However, it appears from the results already presented that no sharp distinction except in a quantitative sense can be made between growth-factor requirements for buds and roots.

The difficulty in the past of obtaining root formation directly in tobacco callus seems to be eliminated by the use of suitable proportions of kinetin and IAA. Still there is evidence of other factors which strongly favor

the expression of root formation in these cultures. Nevertheless, it would seem that the two-factor control of lateral root formation explored by Torrey (1950, 1955) and Geissbühler (1953) may be largely a kinin-auxin phenomenon. Although kinetin in minute concentrations favours the development of seedling root systems, in higher amounts it strikingly inhibits elongation and branching of roots and instead promotes growth in thickness of the primary root (Pl. 8, Fig. 1). In fact, in a certain kinetin concentration range, the roots formed in tobacco callus cultures may even develop nodules superficially similar to those on legumes (Pl. 8, Fig. 2). Similarly in cuttings, low kinetin levels favor and high levels inhibit root formation.

c) *Variability in the Response by Different Tissues or Strains of Callus.* In experiments with stem segment cultures (Pl. 9) kinetin, supplied alone tended to retard rather than to promote bud formation in the early stages,

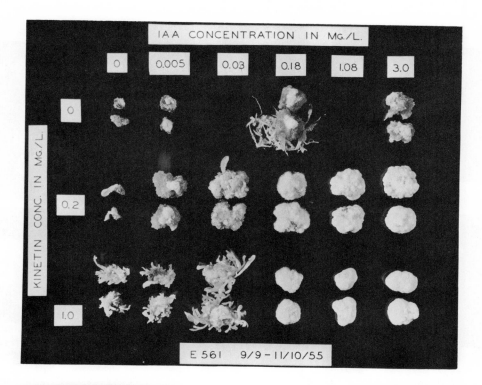

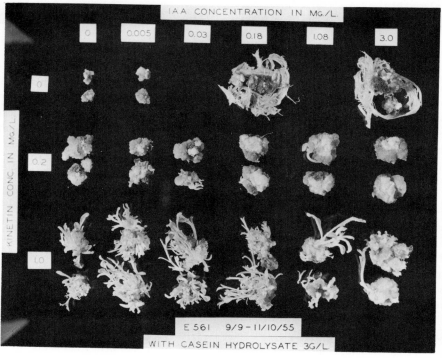

Plates 4 and 5. Effect of increasing IAA concentration at different kinetin levels on the growth and organ formation of tobacco callus cultured on modified White's nutrient agar; (Plate 4) without, and (Plate 5) with, 3 g./l. casein hydrolysate added. Age of cultures, 62 days (Skoog *et al.*).

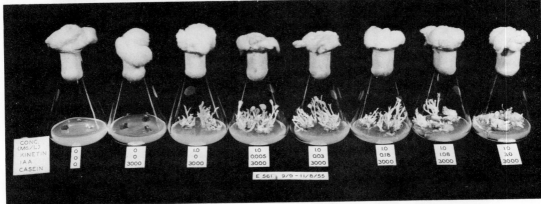

Plate 6. A and B. Representative flasks from treatments with 1.0 mg./l. kinetin, in lower rows of Pls. 4 and 5 respectively (Skoog *et al.*).

although in later stages more buds were found on the kinetin-treated segments than on controls. Furthermore, these buds, in contrast with the control ones, continued to elongate in the absence of root formation.* Note, however, the relatively tremendous growth and organ-forming activity induced by combinations of adenine and kinetin. It may be seen that the phenyl derivative which is less active than kinetin, possibly for this very reason, has given a marked boost to growth, including bud formation of the segments, but in combination with adenine it was less effective than kinetin.

Differences in response of tissues derived originally from the same parent stock can be demonstrated also in callus strains derived from the internal phloem, cambium or pith of the stem, but probably are due to differences in capacities acquired in the course of sub-

culturing and without reference to the parent type of tissue. In part they may be merely quantitative in nature. In this connection, Dr. Tryon's work with strains of cultures of Turkish tobacco of common origin is of special interest (Tryon, 1955, 1956). She has developed certain strains which, when subcultured on modified White's medium, grow as undifferentiated masses, others which continuously form buds, and still others which exhibit continuous and profuse root formation. By suitable additions of IAA and kinetin under favourable P and N nutrient conditions, she has been able to repress bud formation or root formation respectively. In the case of a "non-differentiating" strain of Wis. no. 38 tobacco she recently has obtained bud formation, by combined treatments with kinetin, adenine and tyrosine, whereas with either of the latter two substances alone no buds were obtained. These results further illustrate the variable and multiple nature of growth-factor requirements for organ formation.

Interactions of kinetin and IAA very com-

* Thus kinetin in this instance (and especially kinetin plus tyrosine) fills the specifications for the effect if not the properties of a caulocaline (cf. Went, 1951; Skoog, 1954*a*; Howell and Skoog, 1955).

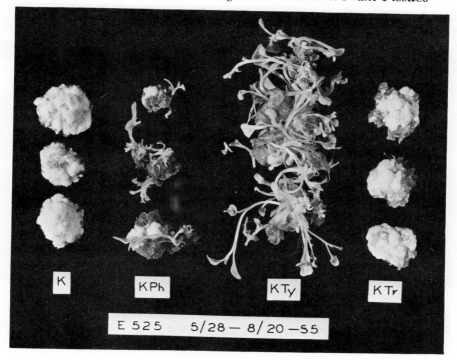

Plate 7. Effect of individual amino acids on the growth and organ formation in tobacco callus cultured on modified White's nutrient medium with 2 mg./1. IAA, 0.2 mg./1. kinetin and additions. K, none; KPh, DL-phenylalanine 150 mg./1.; KTy, DL-tyrosine 210 mg./1.; and KTr, DL-tryptophan 60 mg./1. Age of cultures, 84 days.

parable to those reported here have also been observed in the growth and differentiation of moss cultures by Eakin and Gorton (private communication, see also Skinner and Shive, 1955). Rather different are the effects of kinetin in promoting germination of lettuce seed and rapid development of hypocotyls and cotyledons in the dark as well as in promoting expansion of leaf disks in the dark (Miller, 1956). The latter effect has also been observed by Liverman *et al.* (private communication). In these cases, in which the primary effect of kinetin is on cell enlargement rather than cell division, the substance may be said to replace the well-known "morphogenetic" action of light, but its effect is not identical with that of light in all particulars.

III. Discussion and Conclusions

The evidence we have obtained points to a uniformity in growth-factor requirements and regulatory mechanisms for all types of growth. Definite parallelisms in these respects are found in cell elongation and cell division of tissues, in the initiation of roots and buds, and in the subsequent development of these organs. Interactions between IAA and kinetin and between these and other factors appear to exert decisive influences in each case. Both types of chemical seem to be required for growth. Low levels of one with high levels of the other and vice versa lead to opposite morphological end results. The same holds true in cuttings. For example, bean stems dipped into auxin solution and planted with their basal ends in water or nutrient solution will show increased root formation and decreased lateral bud development as compared with untreated controls. Cuttings dipped in a kinetin solution, on the other hand, will show enhanced bud development and no or markedly retarded development of adventitious roots. Thus, all the evidence reported here points to quantitative interactions rather than qualitative action of growth factors in the regulation of growth. This general conclu-

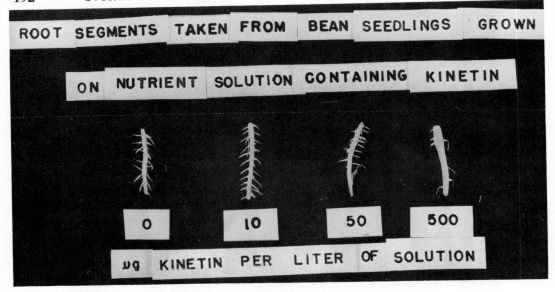

ROOT SEGMENTS TAKEN FROM BEAN SEEDLINGS GROWN

ON NUTRIENT SOLUTION CONTAINING KINETIN

0   10   50   500

µg KINETIN PER LITER OF SOLUTION

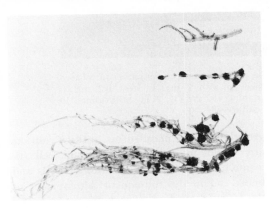

Plate 8. Fig. 1. Effect of kinetin concentration on lateral root development in seedling root of bean. Fig. 2. Nodule-like proliferations appearing in place of lateral rootlets on a tobacco root system formed on callus culture *in vitro*. Sample from control culture to left. Samples from low kinetin treatments to right.

sion is, of course, directly opposite to concepts of specific organ-forming substances (as advocated by Bouillenne (1950) or Gautheret (1950)). It tends to minimize the significance of slight structural modifications found in plants or in cultured tissues, because these, even when consistently reproducible, often must reflect only slight differences in growth-factor contents. The results obtained also are sharply in conflict with the concept of "determination," i.e., irreversible loss in regenerative capacities of cells and tissues, in ontogeny.

On the other hand, in drawing attention to the complexities and levels of chemical interactions in the regulation of growth, they suggest the futility of attempts to interpret growth phenomena on the basis of very precise computations of the interaction between only two factors in a multifactor system, as in the determinations of so-called auxin-antiauxin competitions (cf. McRae, Foster and Bonner, 1953; Bonner and Foster, 1956). Even though they exist, as experimentally determined, they can have meaning only in a general sense. At the other extreme are schemes postulating interaction of fields or "gradients" which are too general or non-specific to be meaningful, as, for example, Wardlaw's (1955) discussion based on Turing's (1952) proposal. Clearly actual control mechanisms must be too heterogeneous both in detailed structure and in location (dispersion) within the cells and tissues to be amenable to such treatments. In a recent discussion of our work, Thimann (1956) points to certain similarities in the structure of adenine, kinetin and IAA, as well as of biotin. It must be considered, however,

Plate 9. Effect of adenine and kinetin or 6-(phenylamino) purine (phenyladenine) singly and in combination on growth and bud formation in tobacco stem segments. Stem segments cultured on modified White's medium with additions. *O*, none; *A*, adenine 54 mg./1.; *K*, kinetin 0.86 mg./1.; *AK*, *A* + *K*; *P*, 6-(phenylamino) purine 0.8 mg./1.; *AP*, *A* + *P*. Age of cultures, 38 days. (All treatments with *K* or *P* are 4×10^{-6}M and with adenine 4×10^{-4}M.)

that his structural formulae are purposely sketched in a suggestive manner with disregard for exact geometric relationships demanded by atomic considerations. We rather feel that the evidence we now have for the combined action of IAA and adenine or kinetin, or both, in processes varying from nucleic acid synthesis, cell division and cell elongation to the regulation of organ formation, would preclude an interpretaton of the action of these substances merely on speculative considerations of competitive interaction between them.

As regards the pertinence of the present results to ontogeny, more work is needed. We do know that both kinins, of as yet unknown chemical nature, and auxins are present in leaf and stem tissues. It may be logically assumed that they participate in meristematic activity, differentiation and organ development in the intact plant in the same manner as in tissue cultures. It would appear, therefore, that the results reported here go a long way towards answering the original question of the dual action of auxin on growth and in

inhibition of buds. The exact chemical nature of the interaction of IAA and kinetin remains to be determined, but there can be little doubt that both are involved in nucleic acid metabolism, including nucleic acid synthesis. It is possible to visualize, therefore, an essentially nuclear mechanism of growth regulation which possesses recognized means for interaction with the cytoplasm and which also is considered to be represented rather directly in the synthesis of large molecular structural units of the cell walls.

We are approaching the stage, therefore, where sharp distinctions between stimuli, "energy-furnishing" metabolites and structural units are disappearing, as these can be seen to grade into each other in integrated biosynthetic systems which function in all types of growth, and which would account for the remarkable uniformity of the regulatory mechanisms in the different phases of growth and morphogenesis that we have observed. The present results suggest that numerous potential possibilities exist for the regulation of growth by chemical manipulations of the media at such different levels as 1 μg./l. hormone and 400 mg./l. inorganic phosphate. The reason for this must be that cellular constituents of all types, including growth factors, are so closely interlocked that a change in one affects many others. For the understanding of the detailed function or biological action of any one growth substance, therefore, we must also learn a great deal about many others.

SUMMARY

Approaches to studies of chemical regulation of growth are considered.

General results are presented of growth-factor investigations in plant tissue cultures, etc. These tend to show that quantitative interactions between growth factors, especially between IAA and kinetin (auxin and kinins) and between these and other factors, provide a common mechanism for the regulation of all types of growth investigated from cell enlargement to organ formation.

The bearing of these results on current concepts of plant morphogenesis is discussed.

Much of the work covered in this report was supported in part by the Research Committee of the Graduate School with funds from the Alumni Research Foundation and by a Research Grant (Proj. BO-19 to F. Skoog) from the American Cancer Society upon recommendation of the Committee on Growth of the National Research Council. The authors are grateful to the graduate students and colleagues in the Department of Botany who have participated in this work, and especially to Prof. F. M. Strong and his students in the Department of Biochemistry for collaboration in the isolation and chemical investigations of cell-division factors.

REFERENCES

Bonner, J., and R. J. Foster (1956). In *The Chemistry and Mode of Action of Plant Growth Substances*, p. 295. Ed. Wain, R. L. and Weightman, F. London: Butterworth's Scientific Publications.

Bouillenne, A. (1950). *Année biol.* **54**, 597.

Das, N. K., K. Patau, and F. Skoog (1956). *Physiol. Plant.* **9**, 640.

Gautheret, R. J. (1950). *Année biol.* **54**, 719.

Gautheret, R. J. (1955). *Ann. Rev. Pl. Physiol.* **6**, 433.

Geissbühler, H. (1953). *Ber. schweiz. bot. Ges.* **63**, 27.

Haberlandt, G. (1921). *Beitr. allg. Bot.* **2**, 1.

Howell, R. W., and F. Skoog (1955). *Amer. J. Bot.* **42**, 356.

Jablonski, J. R., and F. Skoog (1954). *Physiol. Plant.* **7**, 16.

McRae, D. H., R. J. Foster, and J. Bonner (1953). *Plant Physiol.* **28**, 343.

Miller, C. O. (1953). *Proc. Soc. Exp. Biol., N.Y.*, **83**, 561.

Miller, C. O. (1956). *Plant Physiol.* **31**, 318.

Miller, C. O., and F. Skoog, (1953). *Amer. J. Bot.* **40**, 768.

Miller, C. O., F. Skoog, F. S. Okumura, M. H. von Saltza, and F. M. Strong (1956). *J. Amer. Chem. Soc.* **78**, 1375.

Naylor, J., G. Sander, and F. Skoog (1954). *Physiol. Plant.* **7**, 25.

Okumura, F. S., M. H. von Saltza, F. M. Strong, C. O. Miller, and F. Skoog (1955). 28th Meeting Amer. Chem. Soc. Minneapolis, Minn.

Paris, D., and L. Duhamet (1953). *C.R. Acad. Sci., Paris*, **236**, 1690.

Shantz, E. M., and F. C. Steward (1955a). *J. Amer. Chem. Soc.* **77**, 6351.

Shantz, E. M., and F. C. Steward (1955b). *Pl. Physiol.* Suppl. **30**, 35.

Skinner, C. G., and W. Shive (1955). *J. Amer. Chem. Soc.* **77**, 6692.

Skoog, F. (1954a). In *Dynamics of Growth Processes*, p. 148. Ed. Boell, E. G. Princeton, N.J.: Princeton University Press.

Skoog, F. (1954b). In *Abnormal and Pathological Growth, Brookhaven Symposia in Biol.*, **6** (BNL 258 (c–19)).

Skoog, F., and C. Tsui (1948). *Amer. J. Bot.* **35**, 782.

Skoog, F., and C. Tsui (1951). In *Plant Growth Substances*, p. 263. Madison: University of Wisconsin Press.

Snow, R. (1935). *New Phytol.* **34**, 347.

Steward, F. C., and E. M. Shantz (1954). *Année biol.* **30**, 139.

Thimann, K. V. (1956). *Amer. Nat.* **40**, 145.

Torrey, J. G. (1950). *Amer. J. Bot.* **37**, 257.

Torrey, J. G. (1956). *Ann. Rev. Pl. Physiol.* **7**, 237.

Tryon, K. (1955). *Amer. J. Bot.* **42**, 604.

Tryon, K. (1956). *Science*, **123**, 590.

Turing, A. M. (1952). *Proc. Roy. Soc. B*, **237**, 37.

Wardlaw, C. W. (1955). *Embryogenesis in Plants*. London: Methuen and Co. Ltd.

Went, F. W. (1951). In *Plant Growth Substances*, p. 287. Ed. Skoog, F. Madison: University of Wisconsin Press.

☆ 14 ☆

Cell-Virus Interaction

THE ASPECT of cell-virus interactions which is of particular interest to students of development is that concerned with the morphological transformation of the host cell (*Temin and Rubin 1958;** Temin 1960; *Marcus 1962;* and Vogt and Dulbecco 1962). Several viruses, for example, the Rous sarcoma virus, the myxovirus (NDV), and the polyoma virus, alter the properties of the cell surface.

Associated with changes in cell shape is first the deposition of viral antigen at the cell membrane which has been demonstrated immunologically. Shortly after this, pieces of membrane and cellular processes become detached from the infected cell resulting in altered cell shape. This process typifies the transformation of a cell from a flat stretched fibroblast to a round sarcoma cell by Rous virus (Vogt and Rubin, 1962). Similar observations of budding off of cell surface villi or filopodia have been reported by *Marcus (1962)*.

The alteration may involve antigens coded for by the host or by the viral genome. These possibilities so far can not be distinguished operationally. A host cell protein induced by virus may become associated with it so that antiserum against "pure" virus is not really virus specific. The alternative would be that the antigen is synthesized on a template from the viral code.

It has been suggested (Dulbecco 1962) that there may be a connection between contact inhibition and regulation of cell division, and that cell division is kept under a kind of control by paralysis due to maintenance of cell contact.

The appearance of new antigens in other regions of cells transformed by viruses, as well as in plasma membranes, and tumors produced by viruses, are also subjects which are germaine to the study of differentiation (Klein and Klein 1962). Elucidation of cell modifications by virus may direct attention to processes which can account for change during normal development.

* Italicized references indicate articles which appear in this book.

REFERENCES

1. Dulbecco, R. (1962). Basic mechanisms in the biology of animal viruses. *Cold Spring Harbor Symposia on Quantitative Biology,* Vol. XXVII, pp. 519–525, The Biological Laboratory, Cold Spring Harbor, New York.
2. Klein, G., and E. Klein (1962). Antigenic properties of other experimental tumors. *Cold Spring Harbor Symposia on Quantitative Biology,* Vol. XXVII, pp. 463–470, The Biologi-

cal Laboratory, Cold Spring Harbor, New York.
3. Temin, H. M. (1960). The control of cellular morphology in embryonic cells infected with Rous sarcoma virus *in vitro. Virology* 10:182–197.
4. Vogt, M., and R. Dulbecco (1962). Properties of cells transformed by polyoma virus. *Cold Spring Harbor Symposia on Quantitative Biology,* Vol. XXVII, pp. 367–374, The Bio-

logical Laboratory, Cold Spring Harbor, New York.

5. Vogt, P., and H. Rubin (1962). The cytology of Rous sarcoma virus infection. *Cold Spring*

Harbor Symposia on Quantitative Biology, Vol. XXVII, pp. 395–405, The Biological Laboratory, Cold Spring Harbor, New York.

Characteristics of an Assay for Rous Sarcoma Virus and Rous Sarcoma Cells in Tissue Culture[1]

HOWARD M. TEMIN[2]

HARRY RUBIN

An accurate tissue culture assay for Rous sarcoma virus (RSV) and Rous sarcoma cells is described. The Rous sarcoma virus changes a chick fibroblast into a morphologically new and stable cell type with the same chromosomal complement as ordinary chick embryo cells. One virus particle is enough to change one cell, but at any one time 90% of the cells in a culture are not affected by RSV. The cellular resistance is the same in a clonal population. The physiological state of the cell is of some importance in deciding whether or not it is competent to be infected by RSV, but so far attempts to infect all the cells in a chick embryo culture by altering the physiological condition have failed.

INTRODUCTION

The customary technique for assaying the Rous sarcoma virus (RSV) has been the production of tumors in chickens (Rous, 1911; Bryan, 1946). More recently, the virus has been assayed by infecting the chorioallantoic membrane of the developing chicken embryo (Keogh, 1938; Rubin, 1955; Prince, 1957). Although these techniques are satisfactory for many experiments, they do not provide the accuracy nor the ease of manipulation re-

quired for a diversified study of virus-host interactions at the level of the individual cell. An assay technique comparable to the methods used for assaying bacteriophages and cytopathogenic animal viruses has now been developed and is described in the present paper. The assay depends upon the morphological change caused by RSV in chick embryo cells.

The first clear demonstration that chick embryo cells grown in tissue culture were changed into Rous sarcoma cells by infection with RSV was given by Halberstaedter *et al.* (1941), who exposed chick fibroblast cultures to pieces of intensely irradiated Rous sarcoma cultures and observed gross changes in the culture and cytological changes similar to those present in cultures of Rous sarcoma cells derived from a chicken sarcoma. Lo and associates (1955) succeeded in changing fibroblasts *in vitro* with partially purified RSV. They also showed that the culture containing changed cells produced virus for several months. By following this lead Manaker and Groupé (1956) succeeded in producing discrete foci of changed cells upon treatment of monolayer cultures of chick embryo cells with RSV. In the range tested the number of foci per culture was proportional to the concentration of virus added.

In the assay method to be described here an agar overlay has been introduced to decrease the chance of formation of additional foci by virus liberated from infected cells and by detachment and reattachment of infected cells. In addition, a technique will be described for determining the number of infected cells in a

Virology 6, 669–688 (1958). Reprinted with permission.

[1] Supported by grants from the American Cancer Society and the United States Public Health Service, grant E 1531.

[2] United States Public Health Service predoctoral fellow.

mixed population. The properties and nature of the changed cells are also discussed.

MATERIALS AND METHODS

Solutions and Media

"Standard medium":

8 parts Eagle's medium (Eagle, 1955) with double concentration of amino acids and vitamins and 4.2 g $NaHCO_3$ per liter

1 part Difco Bacto-Tryptose phosphate

1 part serum (usually 0.8 calf and 0.2 chicken serum)

Trypsin:

0.25% Bacto-Trypsin in tris buffer

Eagle's minus:

Eagle's medium in which the salts of Ca^{++} and Mg^{++} have been omitted

Incubation

All cultures were made in petri dishes. They were incubated at 37° in a water-saturated atmosphere. The pH was regulated at about 7.3 by a bicarbonate buffer controlled by CO_2 injected into the incubator.

Examination of Cultures

Cultures were examined at 25- and 100-fold magnifications of a Zeiss plankton (inverted) microscope.

Chick Embryo Cultures

Primary cultures of 9- to 13-day-old chicken embryo cells were made by the method of Dulbecco as modified by Rubin (1957). Four million cells in 10 ml of standard medium were placed in a 100-mm petri dish. After 3–5 days of incubation secondary cultures were made. The primary cultures were washed twice with Eagle's minus, and 2 ml of 0.05% trypsin in Eagle's minus were added. After 15 minutes incubation 2 ml of standard medium were added to stop the action of the trypsin. The cells were pipetted twice and centrifuged at 1500 rpm for 1 minute. The pellet was resuspended in standard medium and the cells counted. Two or three hundred thousand cells in 3 or 5 ml of standard medium were placed in 50-mm petri dishes. After incubation overnight these plates were used for the assay of Rous sarcoma virus and Rous sarcoma cells. The cultures consisted chiefly of fibroblasts.

Assay for Virus

The secondary culture was washed once with Eagle's medium and then virus in a volume varying from 0.1 to 0.8 ml was added. After an adsorption period of from 10 minutes to 1 hour 5 ml of standard medium containing 0.6% agar was added. (The concentration of agar is not critical for focus development.) Three days later the culture was fed by adding 2 ml of agar medium on top of the first agar layer. Five to seven days after infection 3 ml of a 1/20,000 solution of neutral red in Eagle's medium was added to allow easier counting of the Rous sarcoma foci. After 2 hours incubation the neutral red was removed and the plate was placed on a piece of glass with a rectangular grid of 2-mm squares and was scanned for foci at a 25-fold magnification of the inverted microscope.

Assay for Rous Sarcoma Cells or Foci Formers

The cells to be assayed were trypsinized, counted, diluted, and added to a secondary plate. After incubation for 8–16 hours to allow attachment of the cells, the medium was removed and standard medium with 0.6% agar was added. Three days later the culture was fed by adding 2 ml of agar medium on top of the first agar layer. After 5–7 days 3 ml of a 1/20,000 solution of neutral red in Eagle's medium was added and the plate scanned for foci at a 25-fold magnification.

Virus Stocks

The original virus used in this work was generously supplied by Dr. Bryan of the National Cancer Institute. This preparation contained about 2×10^6 focus-forming units (FFU) per milliliter and was derived from tumors in chickens. Tissue culture virus was obtained by infecting secondary chick embryo cultures with 10^5 FFU of RSV and growing the cultures in standard medium without chicken serum for 2 weeks with four transfers. The supernatants were then collected. They contained between 10^5 and 10^6 FFU per milliliter.

Chromosome Counts

Cells were transferred to dishes containing sterile 22×22-mm No. 0 cover slips and incubated in standard medium. Eighteen hours later the cover slips were put through the following modification of the procedure of Hsu and co-workers (1957):

1 part Eagle's : 9 parts	
distilled water	15 minutes
Dry rapidly under blower	
100% Methyl alcohol	1 hour
Aceto-orcein	2 hours
Ethyl alcohol (absolute)	Rinse
Ethyl alcohol (absolute)	10 minutes
Mount in Euparal	

Drawings of well-spread chromosome figures were made with a camera lucida at 1350 magnification. The actual counts were made from the camera lucida drawings.

Cloning Technique

Cells were cloned by the feeder layer technique of Puck *et al.* (1957). Twenty-four hours before cloning cultures containing 5×10^4 HeLa cells or chick fibroblasts were X-rayed with a dose of 5000 r. The cells to be cloned were dispersed with trypsin, counted, and 2×10^3 cells added to each plate. At sixteen hours 5 ml of standard medium containing 0.3% agar was added. At 8 days and every 4 days thereafter the cultures were fed by adding agar medium on top of the first agar layer. When the clones were large enough to be picked, the agar was removed and trypsin added. Under a dissecting microscope the clones were picked with a micropipette and transferred to a new dish.

X-Irradiation

Cultures were X-irradiated from a Machlett OEG.60 tube with tungsten target and beryllium end window operated at 50 kilovolts and 30 milliamperes. The outlet of the tube was covered with a 0.38-mm Al filter. The irradiation of the cells was carried out at a distance of 6.6 cm from the target in a covered petri dish at an intensity of 2640 roentgens per minute.

Ultraviolet Irradiation

Ultraviolet irradiation was given from a Westinghouse germicidal lamp. The virus was in 1 ml of medium, $11\frac{3}{4}$ inches from the lamp.

Abbreviations

RSV—Rous sarcoma virus
FFU—Focus-forming unit

EXPERIMENTAL

Morphological Changes in Chick Embryo Cells Following Infection with Rous Sarcoma Virus

One or two days after addition of Rous sarcoma virus to a chick embryo culture rounded refractile cells appear. As single cells these can be confused with cells in mitosis. However, these cells and their progeny retain their changed appearance throughout interphase, giving rise after 2 or 3 days to groups of rounded refractile cells. These groups or foci can easily be distinguished from the background of fibroblasts (Plate I, Fig. A). The cells differ markedly in their colonial characteristics from the fibroblasts. They grow in a grapelike cluster only loosely attached to one another and to the glass. Often a focus becomes multilayered and the rounded cells migrate out on top of the other cells (Plate I, Fig. B). The cell sheet may also tear and retract in the region of a focus leaving a hole surrounded by the round, refractile cells (Plate I, Fig. C). As long as the culture is fed every 3 days, the number of cells in a focus doubles about every 18 hours (Fig. 1). If the culture is not fed, the cells in a focus lose their refractility and become difficult to distinguish from the background of fibro-

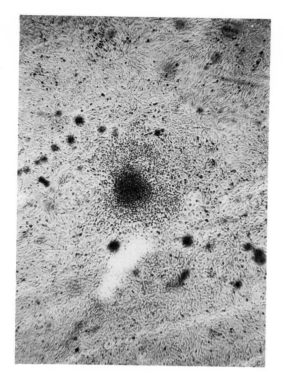

Plate I. Fig. A. Focus on Rous sarcoma cells formed on a secondary chick embryo culture. Unstained; magnification: $\times$ 80.

blasts. Upon addition of fresh medium the cells in a focus may regain their refractility.

Mechanism of Growth of a Focus

There are two processes which could be concerned in the growth of a focus: division of the cells in a focus; and infection of normal cells by the virus released from cells in the focus. Several experiments were carried out to determine whether both of these processes actually occur. Cells which had been infected more than 2 days before with RSV were plated in the following ways:

1. The cells were plated as described under methods for assay of Rous sarcoma cells.
2. The cells were plated as in (1) but on a secondary culture of cells $\frac{1}{40}$ as sensitive to virus infection as the strain regularly used.
3. The cells were plated as in (1), but the secondary culture was X-rayed previously.

4. The cells were X-rayed to prevent their multiplication and plated as in (1).

Under (1) both reinfection and division can occur. Under (2) reinfection is $\frac{1}{40}$ as likely and under (3) impossible. (Previous work had shown that X-rayed fibroblasts cannot be infected by RSV.) Under (4) infection would be necessary for initiation of a focus.

The relative number of foci resulting from the four methods of plating are presented in Table 1. The table shows that the number of foci was the same in all cases. It is concluded that a focus can be formed by dividing Rous sarcoma cells in the absence of reinfection but that nondividing Rous sarcoma cells can initiate formation of a focus, showing that virus released from a cell on the glass can infect the surrounding cells. Since there was little difference in the size of the foci obtained in the different ways even when reinfection was impossible, (3), the major role in the development of the foci must be assigned to division of changed cells.

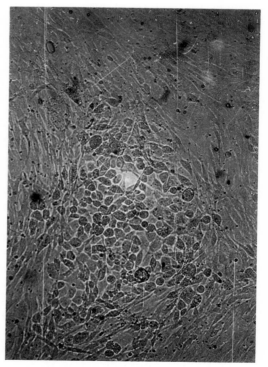

Plate I. Fig. B. Focus of Rous sarcoma cells formed on a secondary chick embryo culture. Lightly stained with neutral red; magnification: $\times$ 20.

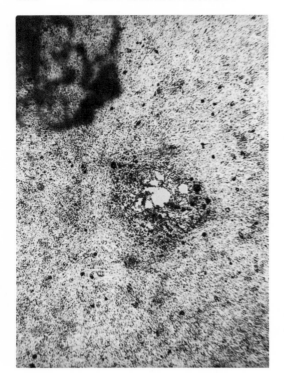

Plate I. Fig. C. Focus of Rous sarcoma cells formed on a secondary chick embryo culture. Heavily stained with neutral red; magnification: × 20.

Properties and Nature of Rous Sarcoma Cells

After the agar overlay is removed from an infected culture, the cells can be transferred and grown in fluid medium. Chick serum is omitted to allow further infection. After 2 weeks the culture becomes composed chiefly of round, refractile cells. These cells are producing RSV. They resemble the basophilic, round cells of Doljanski and Tenenbaum (1943).

The Rous sarcoma cell is a stable cell type which can be grown in pure culture. Rous sarcoma cells were cloned and grown for twenty generations in the absence of ordinary chick embryo cells. After more prolonged culture the cells became giant and diverse in appearance.

To check whether or not the morphological change was associated with a gross change in the chromosome complement, chromosome counts were done on Rous sarcoma cells and on chick embryo fibroblasts. The number of chromosomes found in less than 1-month-old Rous sarcoma cells and in normal fibroblasts was the same (Fig. 2). The mode was in the middle seventies for both types of cells and the spread was similar. After more prolonged culture of the Rous sarcoma cells at a time when many giants were present, over half of the cells were polyploid.

The nature of the chick embryo cell which is changed by RSV to a Rous sarcoma cell has been controversial since Carrel's claim that only macrophages could be infected (Carrel, 1924, 1925). Several workers have disputed this contention, claiming the fibroblast as the cell of origin of the Rous sarcoma cell (quoted in Lo et al., 1955). To determine unequivocally whether the fibroblast, which is the major cell type of the secondary chick embryo culture, is indeed the cell which is changed by infection with RSV, clonal lines

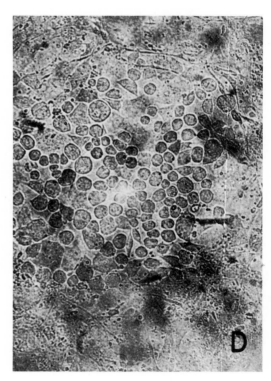

Plate I. Fig. D. Focus of Rous sarcoma cells formed on a clonal population of chick embryo fibroblasts. Unstained; magnification: × 80.

TABLE 1. Initiation of a focus[a]

Number of Foci after Standard Plating of Cells (1)	Treatment	Number of Foci after Designated Treatment
105	2	111
23, 44, 79	3	40, 46, 66
197, 212	4	180, 204

[a] Rous sarcoma cells were plated in the following ways: (1) The cells were plated on a secondary plate as described under methods for assaying Rous sarcoma cells. (2) The cells were plated on a secondary plate composed of chick embryo cells ⅟40 as sensitive to RSV as the strain usually used. (3) The cells were plated on a X-rayed feeder layer. (4) The Rous sarcoma cells were X-rayed and then plated as in (1). The number of foci resulting by each procedure are given in relation to (1).

of fibroblasts were exposed to the virus. The foci which resulted were similar in number and appearance to those found on the usual assay plates (Plate I, D).

Quantitative Features of the Assay

Adsorption Volume. The following experiment was carried out to determine the relative efficiency of virus adsorption as a function of the volume of virus inoculum placed on the secondary culture. Virus was diluted in Eagle's medium. A constant amount of virus was suspended in different volumes of fluid and placed on separate assay plates. After 30 minutes the supernatant was removed and an agar overlay added. The results are in Table 2. The number of foci per plate for the same amount of virus doubles as the volume of

TABLE 2. Adsorption volume[a]

Volume of Original Virus Suspension	Volume of Inoculum	Number of Foci
1/ 5,000 ml	0.1 ml	177
	.2	200
	.4	135
	.8	55
1/20,000	.1	41
	.2	40
	.4	23
	.8	11
1/80,000	.1	11
	.2	9
	.4	6
	.8	3

[a] Virus was diluted in Eagle's medium. A constant amount of virus was suspended in different volumes of fluid and placed on separate assay plates. After 30 minutes the supernatant was removed and an agar overlay added.

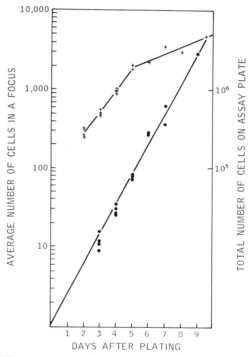

Fig. 1. Increase in number of cells in a focus. Rous cells were plated on assay plates. Twenty hours later agar was added to the plates. Every day the number of cells in 10–20 foci was counted. The total number of cells on the plate was also counted; first, by directly counting a fraction of the cells on the plate; and after the third day, by removing the agar, trypsinizing the cells, and counting in a hemocytometer. • = Average number of cells in a focus. + = Number of cells on an assay plate.

the inoculum was lowered from 0.8 ml to 0.4 ml and from 0.4 ml to 0.2 ml. No difference was found between 0.2 ml and 0.1 ml. Two-tenths of a milliliter is therefore used as a standard inoculum.

Kinetics of Adsorption. An inoculum of

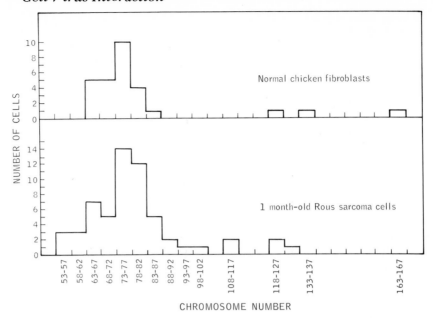

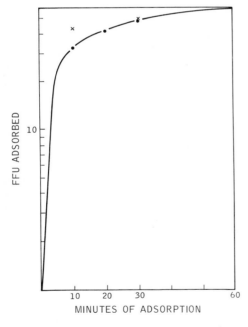

Fig. 2. Chromosome number of Rous sarcoma cells and of fibroblasts. Rous cells or normal cells were transferred to cover slips and fixed and stained by a modification of the procedure of Hsu. Drawings of well-spread chromosome figures were made with a camera lucida at 1350 magnifications, and counts were made from the drawings.

Fig. 3. Kinetics of adsorption. An inoculum of virus containing 50 FFU in 0.2 ml was added to each of several secondary cultures. After adsorption for varying lengths of time the supernatant was removed and an agar overlay added. Two separate experiments are shown. Each point is the average of two assay plates.

virus containing 50 FFU in 0.2 ml was added to each of several cultures. After adsorption for varying lengths of time the supernatant was removed and an agar overlay added. The number of foci per plate is plotted as a function of the time of adsorption (Fig. 3). For practical reasons 30 minutes has been used as a standard adsorption time.

Relationship between Virus Concentration and Number of Foci. A series of twofold dilutions between 1/80 and 1/2560 of a virus stock containing 3.5×10^5 FFU/ml were placed on secondary culture for 30 minutes and agar added. The number of foci per plate was found to be proportional to the virus concentration over a thousand-fold range (Fig. 4). This linear dose response confirms earlier results, using *in vivo* assay techniques, which showed that one virus particle is sufficient to cause an infection (Keogh, 1938; Rubin, 1955; Prince, 1957).

Relationship between Virus Concentration and Number of Infected Cells. A series of twofold dilutions from undiluted virus to 1/512 of a virus stock containing 10^5 FFU/ml were placed on secondary cultures for 30 minutes. The cultures were washed, trypsinized, and various dilutions of the infected cell suspension were placed on each of two secondary cultures. Sixteen hours later agar was added. The number of foci per plate on the sixth day is plotted in Fig. 5. The number of Rous sarcoma cells per plate was a linear function of virus concentration until 0.5% of the cells were infected. Further increases in virus concentration failed to increase the fraction of cells infected. In other experiments the maximal fraction of cells infected usually varied from 1.0 to 10%.

The efficiency of the technique for detecting the number of infected cells by plating them in suspension as focus-formers was tested in the following manner. Three plates were infected with 100–600 FFU of RSV. After a 30-minute adsorption period the plates were washed. Agar was added to two plates and they were incubated as in the standard virus assay. The number of foci showed the number of cells infected. The cells on the third

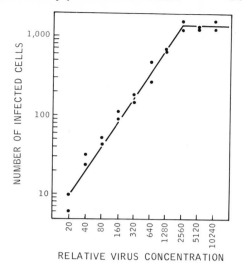

Fig. 5. Relationship between virus concentration and number of infected cells. Virus dilutions from undiluted to 1/512 of a stock containing 10^5 FFU/ml were placed on secondary cultures for 30 minutes. The cultures were washed, trypsinized, and various dilutions of the infected cell suspension were placed on each of two secondary cultures. Sixteen hours later agar was added. The plates were counted on the sixth day after infection.

plate were suspended with trypsin and plated on secondary cultures. The results of several experiments are presented in Table 3. The efficiency of the technique to determine the number of infected cells by plating them in suspension varied between 10 and 100% when compared with the number of foci in the direct assay. This variation in efficiency of plating is partly responsible for the fluctuation in the maximum fraction of cells infected measured above, but does not explain why no more than 10% of the cells can be infected in *any* experiment.

Factors Limiting the Fraction of Cells Which Can Be Infected at Any Given Time. There are several possibilities to explain the restriction in the proportion of cells infected at a given time by RSV. The culture may be heterogeneous with regard to the genetic or embryological origin of the cells; with regard to their physiological state, either in general or in reference to the division cycle; or there may be interfering substances, such as an inactive virus, in the inoculum. Investi-

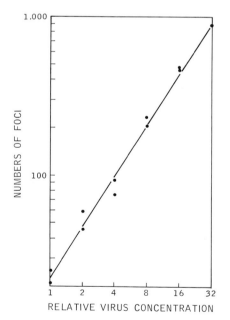

Fig. 4. Relationship between virus concentration and number of foci. A series of twofold virus dilutions between 1/80 and 1/2560 of a virus stock containing 7×10^5 FFU/ml were placed on secondary cultures for 30 minutes and agar added. To enable counting of as many as 100 foci per plate the cultures were counted on the fifth day after infection.

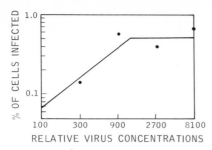

Fig. 6. Relationship between virus concentration and number of infected cells in a cloned population. Cultures of 2×10^5 were made from a clonal line of chick embryo fibroblasts. They were infected with serial threefold dilutions at high virus concentrations and the number of infected cells determined.

gation of these possibilities was carried out.

1. Variation in genetic or embryological origin of the cells: Two lines of clonal fibroblasts were obtained. They were infected with serial three-fold dilutions at high virus concentrations and the number of infected cells determined as above. The results of such an experiment are presented in Fig. 6. A plateau in the number of infected cells was found at the same level as was found with secondary chick embryo cultures of varied cell origin. Since the clonal population was from a single cell, the plateau could not be due to heterogeneity in the origin of the cell.

2. Variation in physiological susceptibility: The fraction of infectible cells on secondary cultures was determined under different conditions as a function of the time which had elapsed since the plates were made. One group of cultures was kept in standard conditions; a second was placed in Eagle's medium without glutamine or glucose for 24 hours (Vogt, personal communication); a third group was kept at 14° for 24 hours in an attempt at obtaining synchronization (Chevremont *et al.*, 1957). At 3-hour intervals after the cells were returned to standard conditions, different cultures were infected with 10^5 FFU of RSV and the number of infected cells determined as above. The results presented in Fig. 7 show there is a considerable fluctuation in the fraction of susceptible cells in a culture with time and under different environmental conditions.

3. Interference: The possible occurrence of interference by inactive virus particles was tested by the following experiment. Stock virus was killed by irradiation with ultraviolet-light or by incubation at 37°. Two-tenths milliliter of killed virus was placed on a secondary plate. After 30 minutes the supernatant was removed and live virus added as in the direct assay. The results presented in Table 4 indicate that such killed virus preparations interfere with infection by live virus.

Since the standard virus stocks would be expected to contain significant amounts of 37°-inactivated virus, such virus could cause autointerference and restrict the number of cells infected. To minimize the amount of inactivated virus, fluid was collected from a

Fig. 7. Physiological state and per cent cells infected. Secondary cultures were made at time 0. One group of cultures was incubated in the usual manner; a second group was placed in Eagle's medium without glucose or glutamine for 24 hours and then standard medium was replaced; a third group in sealed dishes was placed at 14° for 24 hours and then returned to 37°. At the indicated times the cultures were infected with a high concentration of virus. After adsorption they were trypsinized, the cells counted, and 10^4 cells placed on each of two secondary cultures. Each point represents an average of two plates. • = Control; X = starved for 24 hours; △ = 14° for 24 hours.

TABLE 3. Efficiency of plating infected cells in suspension[a]

Number of Foci Resulting		Efficiency of Plating Infected Cells in Suspension (%)
From Direct Assay	From Plating of Infected Cell in Suspensions	
555	48, 54	9.2
280, 210	80	33
135, 123	55, 75	50
855, 815	645, 510	69
101, 102	84, 104	93
595, 610	653, 662	109

[a] Three plates were infected with from 100 to 600 FFU of RSV. After a 30-minute adsorption period the plates were washed. Agar was added to two plates and they were incubated as in the standard virus assay. The number of foci showed the number of cells infected. The cells on the third plate were suspended with trypsin and plated at a dilution of 1/1 to 1/4. A number of different experiments are listed.

TABLE 4. Interference[a]

Treatment	Untreated Virus	Treated Virus (Diluted 1:10)	Treated Virus (Undiluted) Followed by Untreated
UV 10 minutes	533	11	121, 120
37° 72 hours	1005, 1100	0, 1	85, 110

[a] Stock virus was inactivated by UV irradiation or by prolonged incubation at 37°C. The undiluted inactivated virus was placed on secondary cultures for thirty minutes. The supernatants were then removed and live virus at a concentration of about $\frac{1}{500}$ was added.

TABLE 5. Infection with 6-hour virus[a]

Virus Stock (Hours after Washing)	Titer (FFU/ml)	Per Cent Cells Infected
6	5×10^5	8.5
48	2.5×10^5	5.6

[a] Fluid was collected from a culture of Rous sarcoma cells 6 hours after washing. Secondary cultures were infected with this virus stock. The percentage of cells infected is compared with the percentage of cells infected using a standard virus stock.

culture of Rous sarcoma cells 6 hours after washing. The maximum number of infectible cells, using this virus stock for infection, was only slightly higher than when standard virus was used for infection (Table 5). This finding indicates that autointerference by 37°-inactivated virus plays a minor role in limiting the number of cells infected.

4. Repeated infection with RSV: The results in the previous sections suggest that the physiological condition of the cells is an important factor in limiting their susceptibility to infection. An experiment was carried out to determine whether or not the physiological variation of chick embryo cells to RSV infection was due to a transient period of competence in individual cells. Several cultures were infected with a saturating dose (10^5 FFU) of RSV for 1 hour. Supernatants were removed from the cultures and medium added. Each hour thereafter for 4 hours, virus was added to a different culture for 1 hour to determine whether any more cells had become susceptible in the interval. One culture was not reexposed to virus. At the end of 5 hours the number of infected cells in each culture was determined. The results of two such experiments are given in Fig. 8. The number of infected cells in a culture could be increased beyond the usual plateau level by re-

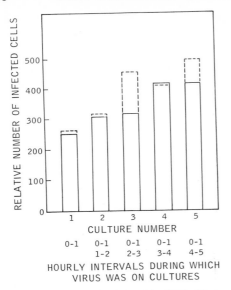

Fig. 8. Repeated infection with RSV. Five cultures were infected with 10^5 FFU of RSV for 1 hour. Supernatants were removed from the cultures and medium added. Each hour thereafter for 4 hours virus was added to one culture for 1 hour. One culture was not re-treated. At the end of 5 hours the number of infected cells in each culture was determined. Each line is the average of two plates. Two separate experiments are shown.

exposing the cells to virus at a time after the initial exposure. The maximum increase was obtained when the interval between the first and second inocula was 2–3 hours; longer intervals did not increase it further, suggesting that cells undergo a 2–3-hour transient period of competence.

Relative Efficiency of in Vitro Assay and Chorioallantoic Membrane Assay. Comparative titrations of a virus stock sent by Bryan were carried out on the chorioallantoic membrane of the developing chick embryo and by the standard tissue culture technique. The titer on various occasions varied from 1 to 4×10^6 FFU/ml in both assays.

DISCUSSION

Use of the tissue culture assay for RSV which has been described here has shown that at a given time over 90% of the cells in a chick embryo culture are not susceptible to being infected by RSV. This resistance is not due to the diverse genetic or embryological

nature of the cells. There is some interference by material in the virus stock which influences the number of infectible cells but does not appear to be the major limiting factor. The physiological state of the cells does affect their susceptibility and experiments with repeated infection suggest that the cells pass through a transient state of competence to infection and change, similar to that described by Hotchkiss (1954) for transformation of pneumococci. Among temperate phage, the physiological condition of the cells has also been shown to play an important role in determining the proportion of cells which will undergo the lysogenic cycle (Bertani, 1957). Attempts to synchronize cultures of chick embryo cells with prolonged starvation has given results indicative of cyclical changes in competence (Temin, unpublished). At the time of maximum competence, however, 90% of the cells still are not infected.

It is possible that methods of synchronization which require less drastic treatment of the cells will enable all cells to be infected with RSV simultaneously.

REFERENCES

Bertani, L. E. (1957). The effect of the inhibition of protein synthesis on the establishment of lysogeny. *Virology* **4**, 53–71.

Bryan, W. R. (1946). Quantitative studies on the latent period of tumors induced with subcutaneous injections of the agent of chicken tumor. I. 1. Curve relating dosage of agent and chicken response. *J. Natl. Cancer Inst.* **6**, 225–237.

Carrel, A. (1924). Action de l'extrait filtre du sarcome de Rous sur les macrophages du sang. *Compt. rend. soc. biol.* **91**, 1069–1071.

Carrel, A. (1925). Effets de l'extrait de sarcomes fusocellulaires sur des cultures pures de fibroblastes. *Compt. rend. soc. biol.* **92**, 477–479.

Chèvremont, S., Firket, H., Chèvremont, M., and Frederic, J. (1957). Contribution à l'étude de la préparation à la mitose. *Acta Anat.* **30**, 175–193.

Doljanski, L., and Tenenbaum, E. (1943). Studies on Rous sarcoma cells cultivated *in vitro*. 2. Morphologic properties of Rous cells. *Cancer Research* **3**, 585–603.

Eagle, H. (1955). The specific amino acid requirements of a human carcinoma (cell strain HeLa) in tissue culture. *J. Exptl. Med.* **102**, 37–48.

Halberstaedter, L. Doljanski, L., and Tenenbaum, E. (1941). Experiments on the cancerization of cells *in vitro* by means of Rous sarcoma agent. *Brit. J. Exptl. Pathol.* **22**, 179–187.

Hotchkiss, R. D. (1954). Cyclical behaviour in pneumococcal growth and transformability occasioned by environmental changes. *Proc. Natl. Acad. Sci. U.S.* **40**, 49–54.

Hsu, T. C., Pomerat, C. M., and Moorhead, P. S. (1957). Mammalian chromosomes *in vitro*. VIII. Heteroploid transformation in the human cell strain Majes. *J. Natl. Cancer Inst.* **19**, 867–872.

Keogh, E. V. (1938). Ectodermal lesions produced by the virus of Rous sarcoma. *Brit. J. Exptl. Pathol.* **19**, 1–8.

Lo, W. H. Y., Gey, G. O., and Shapras, P. (1955). The cytopathogenic effect of the Rous sarcoma virus on chicken fibroblasts in tissue cultures. *Bull. Johns Hopkins Hosp.* **97**, 248–256.

Manaker, R. A., and Groupé, V. (1956). Discrete foci of altered chicken embryo cells associated with Rous sarcoma virus in tissue culture. *Virology* **2**, 838–840.

Prince, A. M. (1957). Quantitative studies in Rous sarcoma virus. I. The titration of Rous sarcoma virus on the chorioallantoic membrane of the chick embryo. *J. Natl. Cancer Inst.* **20**, 147–158.

Puck, T. T., Cieciura, S. J., and Fisher, H. W. (1957). Clonal growth *in vitro* of human cells with fibroblastic morphology. *J. Exptl. Med.* **106**, 145–158.

Rous, P. (1911). A sarcoma of the fowl transmissible by an agent separable from the tumor cells. *J. Exptl. Med.* **13**, 397–411.

Rubin, H. (1955). Quantitative relations between causative virus and cell in the Rous No. 1 chicken sarcoma. *Virology* **1**, 445–473.

Rubin, H. (1957). Interactions between Newcastle disease virus (NDV), antibody and cell. *Virology* **4**, 533–562.

Dynamics of Surface Modification in Myxovirus-Infected Cells

PHILIP I. MARCUS

INTRODUCTION

Research concerning the sites of synthesis, routes of transport, areas of accumulation, and ultimate distribution of viral specific protein in animal cells is currently the subject of extensive investigations utilizing techniques that provide an almost continuous spectrum of resolution. None of the methods reported, however, provides the resolution required to score individual virus particles simultaneously with a means for monitoring the entire surface of the *living* cell for newly acquired viral induced modifications. By careful application of the hemadsorption technique of Vogel and Shelokov (1957) to single myxovirus-infected cells, it is possible to obtain this degree of resolution under conditions that do not adversely affect viability of individual cells or

Cold Spring Harbor Symposia on Quantitative Biology, **312**, 351–365, 1962. Reprinted with permission.

preclude their isolation by standard cloning procedures. This report will describe the dynamic behavior of the surface of cells infected with myxovirus and will demonstrate the strikingly uniform pattern associated with the sequential events and movements occurring at the cell surface, as revealed by hemadsorption studies on single cells.

When monodisperse suspensions of cells are exposed to virus as in the HeLa cell-Newcastle disease virus system, the infecting virus initiates synthesis of several new molecular species. One of these, hemagglutinin, can be detected readily in a living system by the specific adsorption of red blood cells to the host cell surface. The methods described below have been developed to score the first appearance of viral hemagglutinin under conditions where binding of a single erythrocyte to an isolated host cell is significant. By this means, specific binding of individual erythrocytes to the host cell is used to tag hemagglutinin. Thus, as will be shown, it is possible to score by morphologic means with the light microscope the initial point of appearance, active transport, and final distribution of newly incorporated molecules on the cell surface. In addition, the distribution in time and rate of acquisition of the hemadsorption character can be quantitated by counting the number of red blood cells bound to each infected host cell as a function of time following infection.

The highly regular patterns and sequence of events found to occur on the surface of myxovirus-infected cells form the basis of a model of cell dynamics that is consistent with the several surface phenomena reported here, and with the generally accepted mode of fabrication of myxovirus at the cell surface; they also allow certain testable predictions concerning the behavior of normal, uninfected cells—the cell as first invaded by the virus.

THE HEMADSORPTION REACTION ON SINGLE CELLS

Large populations of monodisperse clonal line HeLa cells are infected with Newcastle disease virus (NDV) under conditions which preserve the colony-forming integrity of each isolated cell and permit an accurate determination of virus multiplicity. The dual temperature-dilution sequence (Marcus, 1959) in which virus-cell complexes formed at $0°C$ are simultaneously diluted and brought to $37°C$ for virus penetration is used to prepare large populations of singly dispersed infected host cells. At time zero infected cells in concentrations that preclude cross-infection or cell-to-cell interaction are seeded into plastic Petri dishes containing nonvirucidal growth medium (Marcus and Puck, 1958). The hemadsorption technique is designed to provide optimal conditions for red blood cell (RBC)-hemagglutinin interaction resulting in firm binding, and to minimize physical shearing forces and the enzymatic activity associated with receptor site destruction so as to obviate loss or elution of erythrocytes from the surface of infected host cells. At the time of testing,

all growth medium is removed from the Petri dish and is replaced with a suspension of erythrocytes kept at $4°C$ and in appropriate concentration to present a uniform, essentially continuous monolayer when the red blood cells have completely settled by gravity. Fifteen to thirty minutes at $4°C$ suffices to permit firm binding of erythrocyte to infected host cell. Subsequent gentle washing with copious amounts of cold saline buffered with phosphate to $pH = 6$ to minimize elution (Sagik and Levine, 1957) maintains RBC-host binding and produces a zero background so that the attachment of even a single erythrocyte is significant. Hemadsorption positive (HAD+) cells are examined in the living state at $4°C$ or after fixation with OsO_4 by a recently developed technique that maintains normal phase contrast relationships to a high degree of fidelity (Robbins, 1961).

Chicken and bovine red blood cells have been used throughout this investigation. As a size reference it should be recorded that the elliptically-shaped nucleated chicken erythrocyte measures about $15\ \mu$ on its long axis. The circular appearing bovine red blood cells present a mean diameter of about $6\ \mu$.

"GROWTH CURVE" OF ERYTHROCYTE BINDING CAPACITY OF NDV-INFECTED HeLa CELLS

RBC Binding to Single HeLa Cells

Following the end of the latent period and primary appearance of the hemadsorption reaction, the red blood cell binding capacity of the host cell surface increases in a uniform manner characterized by the "growth curve" shown in Fig. 1, and finally reaches saturation after 11 to 12 hr. At the low multiplicity used in this experiment, with a high probability, all infected cells have attached only one virus particle. Note that multiplicity is expressed in terms of hemadsorption producing particles (m_{HAD}), since it has been found that attachment of a single NDV particle suffices to initiate the hemadsorption reaction (Marcus, in preparation). It is a simple matter to calculate m_{HAD} from the fraction of HAD⁻ cells determined routinely at the end of an experiment. The hemadsorption-producing particle titer of active preparations of NDV strain *Calif.* is equal to the plaque forming- and cell-killing-particle assay.

The specific binding of a single RBC to the infected host cell as illustrated in Fig. 2, marks the end of the latent period. In the two experiments averaged in Fig. 1, early points in the "growth curve" were not determined. However, in more detailed studies concerned with the effect of multiplicity on the duration of the latent period, a minimum delay of approximately 4½ hr was recorded for single particle infections which decreased markedly with increased multiplicity in a similar manner to that described by Cooper (1958) for vesicular stomatitis virus. Detailed studies on shortened latency will be published separately.

The RBC binding capacity of NDV-infected HeLa cells rises at an exponential rate with an

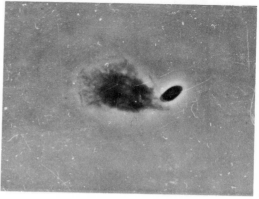

Fig. 2. Attachment of a single RBC to an NDV-infected HeLa cell. HeLa cells were infected at a low multiplicity and tested for hemadsorption with chicken RBC after 4½ hr incubation.

average doubling time, as observed in Fig. 1, equivalent to the rate of plaque forming particle liberation previously reported (Marcus, 1962). The rate of doubling of the binding capacity starts to decrease between 9 and 10 hr, and the surface of the infected cell reaches saturation with respect to hemadsorption shortly thereafter, at about 12 hr. As seen in Fig. 1, approximately 30 chicken red blood cells may be accommodated on the surface of an infected HeLa cell spread on plastic. The binding capacity remains maximal between 12 and 25 hr. Beyond about 25 hr, cytopathic effects distort and generally reduce RBC binding.

Although it should be possible to perform successive hemadsorption tests on the *same* cell in order to determine the time of doubling of the binding capacity for individual cells, to date such experiments have not been carried out.

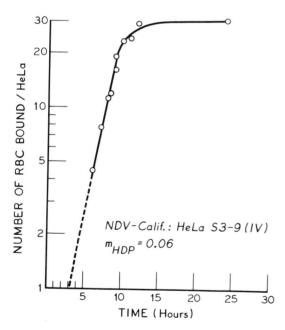

Fig. 1. Erythrocyte binding capacity of NDV-infected HeLa cells as a function of time. HeLa cells infected with an adsorbed multiplicity of 0.06 hemadsorption producing particle were tested for hemadsorption at various times and the number of chicken RBC attached per cell determined by microscopic examination. Each point represents the average count from ≧50 HAD+ HeLa cells.

A Photomicrographic Record of the Hemadsorption-Scored, "Growth Curve"

HeLa Cell as Host

Our original studies of hemadsorption on single cells involved analysis of thousands of individual HeLa cells infected at a multiplicity of 0.03 to 0.06. The characteristic manner and sequence in which the RBC

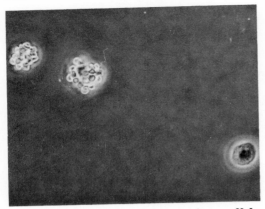

Fig. 3. Hemadsorption tests on monodisperse HeLa cells infected with NDV. Infected HeLa cells were incubated for 10 hr at 37°C and tested for hemadsorption with bovine erythrocytes. The HeLa cells in this preparation are stretched out to a lesser degree than usual. Note the "raspberry" appearance of the two HAD⁺ cells, and the smooth surface of the HAD⁻ cell.

binding capacity of NDV-infected cells progresses was recorded through a series of photomicrographs, and although scores of micrographs are available to document the sequence of events described here, only typical examples of each stage are presented for illustrative purposes. Furthermore, since the hemadsorption events recorded for HeLa cells are duplicated precisely when X-ray induced giant HeLa cells are substituted as hosts, and because the latter system provides an effective increase in resolution, our word description of hemadsorption events in time will be documented, in the majority of examples, with a series of photomicrographs shown below which depict giant- rather than normal-size HeLa cells as hosts.

Figure 2 shows a typical hemadsorption positive cell that has attached only one RBC. In view of the accepted mode of fabrication of myxovirus at the cell surface, the initial point of erythrocyte attachment to the infected cell represents the first area on the cell surface appropriately modified to release new virus. With striking regularity the initial point of attachment is always at the *circumference* of the spread host cell, i.e., where the cell periphery makes contact with the plastic or glass surface. If the spread cell is biped or tripedal

in appearance, red blood cell binding invariably occurs first at the extremities of the cell projections. Following the appearance of a positive spot on the cell circumference, the binding of RBC occurs next on the cell circumference immediately bilaterally adjacent to the initial HAD⁺ spot, and spreads radially around the cell circumference. Following saturation of the circumferential region of the cell surface, the hemadsorption positive areas broaden centripetally and fill in toward the center of the spread cell. The area immediately over the nucleus is the last region on the cell surface to display the HAD⁺ property. Thus, the hemadsorption reaction finally reaches a stage following infection in which apparently the entire cell surface manifests the capacity to bind erythrocytes. Saturated hemadsorption of bovine erythrocytes on single HeLa cells is illustrated in Fig. 3. These cells are typical of those seen 10 to 12 hr post-infection. An HAD⁻ cell may also be observed in this figure.

Chick Embryo Cell as Host

Second generation NDV-infected chick embryo cells plated as singly dispersed elements appear to display in order and in kind, the same sequence of events that characterizes development of the hemadsorption property on the surface of NDV-infected HeLa cells. Bipolar hemadsorption, described below, seems equally prominent in chick embryo cells although total number of cells sampled to date is much smaller than in the NDV-HeLa system.

GIANT HELA CELLS AS HOSTS IN THE HEMADSORPTION REACTION

In an attempt to increase the resolving power of these techniques, two approaches were considered: first, to decrease the size of the adsorbing red blood cell and, second, to increase the size of the host cell. A search of the literature revealed that erythrocytes of the smallest known ruminant, the chevrotain, are only 2 μ in diameter. To date, a search for this animal as a subject available for experimental use has proved unsuccessful. Bovine red blood cells with a mean diameter of 5.9 μ have provided a satisfactory compromise and are currently employed routinely. The production of giant HeLa cells following X-irradiation was a logical means to obtain host cells of enormously increased size. Large populations of giant HeLa cells were prepared as previously described (Puck and Marcus, 1956; Tolmach and Marcus, 1960a). Giant HeLa cells respond to infection with NDV exactly as predicted for a normal size HeLa enlarged in all its dimensions, component parts, and functional capacity (Tolmach and Marcus, 1960b).

When hemadsorption studies were carried out with individual giant HeLa cells as hosts, and bovine or chicken erythrocytes as the hemadsorbing agents, unequivocal confirmation was obtained of the highly regular pattern and sequence of events seen to occur at the surface of nonirradiated HeLa cells infected with myxovirus. The series of photomicrographs presented in Figs. 4–9 illustrate this point. As described above for normal-size HeLa, they demonstrate the circumferential location of early hemadsorption (Figs. 4–5) and progressive centripetal conversion of the cell surface (Figs. 6 and 7) until near-saturation (Fig. 8), and, finally, complete-saturation (Fig. 9) is reached.

HOST CELL BIPOLARITY AND THE HEMADSORPTION REACTION

A totally unexpected manifestation of host cell behavior became apparent from our very earliest studies of the hemadsorption reaction on single cells. It was noted repeatedly that a significant proportion of HAD$^+$ HeLa cells from the early period of the "growth curve" displayed a distinctly bipolar response in the binding of RBC, i.e., the two opposite extremities of a stretched biped HeLa were both HAD$^+$, while all other regions of the cell surface were HAD$^-$.

This strangely ordered display of surface alteration has proved to be an entirely predictable feature of the morphologically categorized biped cell. Two examples of this characteristic manifestation of the hemadsorption reaction are illustrated in Figs. 10 and 11. Bipolar hemadsorption is observed in cells infected with very low multiplicities where only one virus particle infects the cell. The cell pictured in Fig. 10 is from a population infected with an average $m_{HAD} = 0.03$. Figure 11 is unique in that infection of HeLa cells was initiated with a high input multiplicity of PR-8 *influenza virus*. To judge from the fraction of HAD$^+$ cells in this latter preparation the effective infecting multiplicity was actually very low, but produced a HAD$^+$ bipolar cell.

The bipolar manifestation of hemadsorption displayed by biped HeLa cells is not restricted to that singular morphological type. In fact, cells which show a near-perfect circular cross-section regularly display hemadsorption bipolarity. This reaction has been documented with X-ray induced giant HeLa cells as host, a large proportion of which normally produce a regular circular cross-section when spread on plastic or glass. Bipolar hemadsorption in giant cells is a very striking feature. At a very early stage in infection only opposite "ends" of the cell may bind red blood cells (Figs. 6 and 12).

We are led to conclude that regardless of size and shape HeLa cells and, with a lesser degree of certainty, chick embryo cells innately display a preferential bipolar pattern in the early phase of the sequence whereby the surface of the myxovirus-infected cell is converted from an HAD$^-$ to an HAD$^+$ condition. This conclusion is further strengthened by our findings with giant HeLa cells, described above.

HEMADSORPTION IN CRESCENT-SHAPED CELLS

In addition to the bi-, tri- and, less frequently, multi-ped stretched HeLa cells observed, there is another unique morphologic

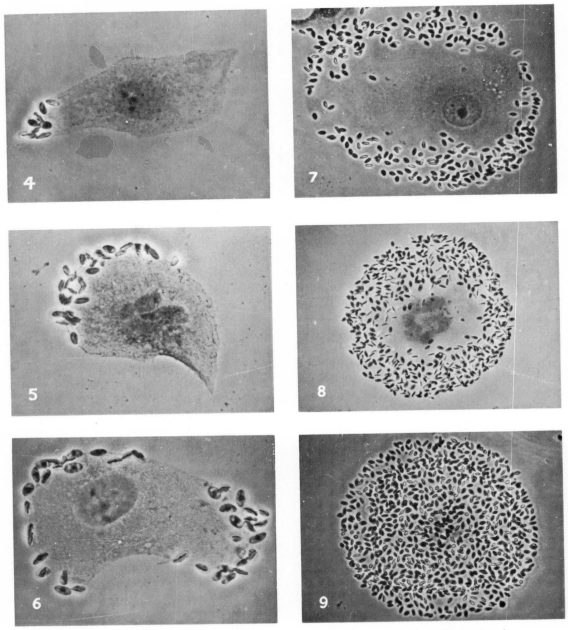

Figs. 4–9. Hemadsorption on giant HeLa cells. Figs. 4–6, and 7–8, show cells incubated for 5, and 6½ hr, respectively, after infection. The cell illustrated in Fig. 9 was from a series of plates incubated for 7½ hr. Chicken erythrocytes were used for hemadsorption in this series.

class of cells, the "crescent." The pattern of hemadsorption in crescent cells is extremely regular in its initiation and progression. Early hemadsorption arises either at one or both of the cell extremities (see Fig. 13)

and progresses circumferentially on the *convex* perimeter of the cell, never on the *concave* side harboring the nucleus (Fig. 14). The significance of this pattern of behavior will be discussed shortly.

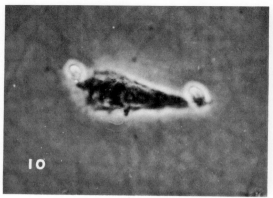

Figs. 10–11. Bipolar hemadsorption. The HeLa cell in Fig. 10 is from a population infected at $m_{HAD} = 0.03$ and tested after 5 hr incubation. One bovine RBC is attached to each "foot" of the biped. The biped cell shown in Fig. 11 was subjected to a high multiplicity of influenza virus strain PR8, and incubated 10 hr before testing with chicken RBC. Note that both "feet" have adsorbed several RBC.

SURFACE MODIFICATION IN HAD$^+$ CELLS NEUTRALIZED WITH VIRAL SPECIFIC ANTIBODY

From the experiments considered above it seems clear that the first area on the cell surface to incorporate new molecules of viral origin and specificity is located at one or two (occasionally >2) points on the circumference of the cell where it makes contact with the plastic surface. As the cell surface reaches saturation "new" and "old" hemadsorption areas cannot be distinguished and, consequently, changes at the cell surface cannot be monitored in dynamic terms. The following experiment was designed to determine whether the same pattern and sequence of events in hemadsorption dynamics operates in cells already demonstrating maximal RBC binding capacity. Giant HeLa cells infected at a high multiplicity were incubated sufficiently long to reach saturated hemadsorption (6 hr for the cells shown in Fig. 15), and then exposed for 15 min at 37°C to an appropriate concentration of specific NDV antiserum that would reduce the infectious titer of an active NDV preparation to 0.01 survivors in 5 min. Cells were washed free of antibody and tested immediately for hemadsorption

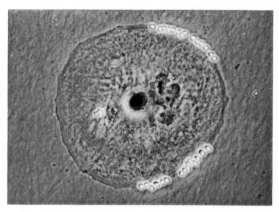

Fig. 12. Bipolar hemadsorption in a circular giant HeLa cell. Five hr after infection with NDV the giant HeLa cell pictured here was tested for hemadsorption with bovine RBC. The bipolar reaction illustrated is typical of many seen. Note the adsorption of 2 RBC near the center of the cell. This latter reaction is observed occasionally.

at 4°C. All cells in the plate were completely hemadsorption negative. A representative microscope field is illustrated in Fig. 16. The HAD$^+$ cells rendered HAD$^-$ by treatment with antiserum, thoroughly washed free of non-adsorbed antibody, were returned to the incubator at 37°C. Two possible subsequent changes in the cell surface may be considered. First, if cell surface activity diminishes and becomes essentially *static* once a saturated HAD$^+$ state is attained, the neutralized cells should remain

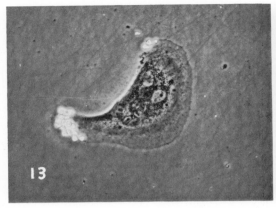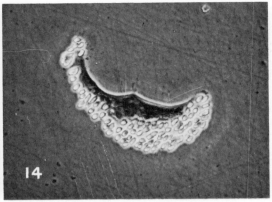

Figs. 13–14. Hemadsorption in crescent-shaped giant HeLa cells. In Fig. 13 hemadsorption tests with bovine erythrocytes were carried out 4 hr after infection with a high multiplicity of NDV. Note RBC adsorption to both extremities of the cell, and that one extremity of the cell shows a more advanced HAD⁺ response than the other. The cell in Fig. 14 was incubated 8 hr and illustrates typical adsorption on the convex side of the cell.

HAD⁻ for the remainder of the viral growth cycle (assuming stability of the antigen-antibody complex). From the work of Mandel (1962) it would seem reasonable to conclude that destruction or dissociation of antibody-viral antigen complexes at the cell surface under physiologic conditions is very unlikely. Aternatively, the infected host cell may manifest *dynamic* changes of the type observed in the very early stages of surface modification. The photomicrographs (Figs. 17–19) taken of antibody neutralized HAD⁺ cells incubated for 7

min at 37°C demonstrate clearly that such cells rapidly develop HAD⁺ areas and display the exact pattern of circumferential adsorption characteristic of an early hemadsorption reaction. The relatively uniform response observed from cell-to-cell is especially noticeable in the low magnification photomicrograph shown in Fig. 17. This apparent synchrony may reflect the fact that all cells have reached maximum synthesis of viral antigen by 6 hr, and have accumulated a large pool of hemagglutinin as evidenced by immunofluorescent studies (see below).

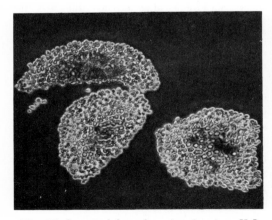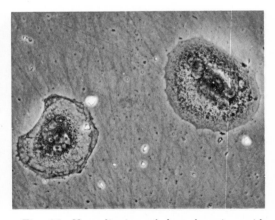

Fig. 15. Saturated hemadsorption in giant HeLa cells. NDV-infected giant HeLa cells were incubated for 6 hr and tested for hemadsorption with bovine erythrocytes (cf. Fig. 9).

Fig. 16. Neutralization of hemadsorption with specific NDV antiserum. Aliquot plates containing HAD⁺ cells as shown in Fig. 15 were exposed to NDV antiserum, washed, and tested for hemadsorption with bovine RBC. This treatment produced the HAD⁻ cells illustrated here.

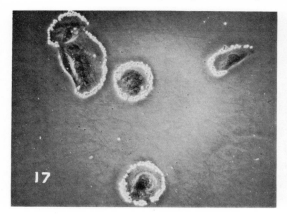

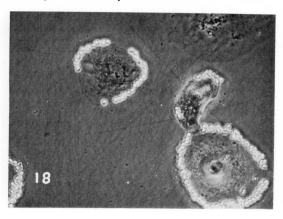

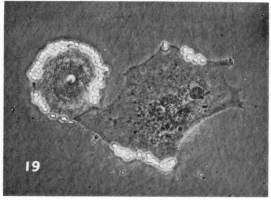

Figs. 17–19. Reappearance of hemadsorption after incubation of antibody neutralized-HAD+ cells. HAD+ cells (Fig. 15) were neutralized with NDV antiserum (Fig. 16), washed, and incubated for 7 min at 37°C, and hemadsorption tests run using bovine RBC. Figs. 17–19 illustrate typical results. The central areas remain HAD− because of antibody blocked sites of adsorption. Figs. 18 and 19 show bipolar hemadsorption patterns in several of the cells.

Note also that bipolar hemadsorption is especially prevalent in HAD+-antibody treated cells incubated only 7 min (Figs. 18 and 19).

Incubation of neutralized HAD+ cells for an additional 1½ hr reveals the typical pattern of centripetal accumulation of RBC binding sites and a concomitant reduction of the HAD− areas, with the region immediately overlying the nucleus the last to regain the HAD+ property (cf. Fig. 8). After 2 to 3 hr incubation the neutralized cells display saturated hemadsorption, indistinguishable from that shown in Figs. 9 and 15.

The Transport of Attached Erythrocytes on the Surface of Infected Cells

Although it is evident that progressive conversion of the cell surface from HAD− to HAD+ proceeds centripetally toward the nucleus, it is not clear whether this results from (1) conversion of successive, more centripetally located regions, or (2) a continuous conversion restricted to the circumferential region of the cell surface with a concomitant centripetal *movement* of the converted areas. The following experiment was designed to distinguish between these two possibilities. The surface of HAD+ saturated giant cells was rendered HAD− by neutralization with antibody, washed free of excess antibody, and incubated at 37°C to produce the characteristic circumferential ring of HAD+ response as shown in Fig. 17. Plates with cells containing these adsorbed rings of erythrocytes were returned to the 37°C incubator. If situation (1) above were operative the ring of attached RBC would remain *stationary* and more centripetally-located regions would be converted to HAD+. However, if situation (2) pertains then the RBC ring would be *transported* centripetally toward the nucleus. The photomicrographs shown in Figs. 20 and

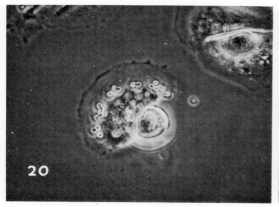
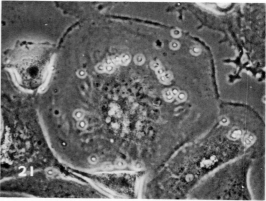

Figs. 20–21. Active transport of bovine RBC on surface of NDV-infected giant HeLa cells. HAD+-saturated cells (Fig. 15) were neutralized with NDV antiserum (Fig. 16), washed, incubated for 7 min at 37°C, and bovine RBC were added to establish circumferential hemadsorption (Figs. 17–19). Finally, the cells were incubated for 1½ hr. Note that during this period the circumferentially located RBC (cf. Figs. 17–19) have moved from the cell periphery to a position about halfway to the center of the cell.

21 are representative of many taken from cells incubated for 1½ hr after the ring of adsorbed cells had been established. There is little doubt that the attached RBC have been actively transported centripetally on the cell surface, and in many instances in unison, thus providing direct evidence that situation (2) represents the dynamic manner in which the cell surface is converted from the HAD⁻ to the HAD⁺ state.

It should be noted that only about 15–20% of the infected cells retained erythrocytes long enough to record their movement on the surface. They may represent a class of cells in which elution enzymatic activity is minimal. Whether this condition reflects a property of the infecting virus, or the invaded host remains unanswered. All other cells show complete elution of erythrocytes.

CHARACTERISTICS OF RBC-HOST CELL SURFACE BINDING

Some Biochemical and Physical Properties of Binding

Temperature. Specific attachment of erythrocytes to HAD⁺ cells is independent of temperature and may be carried out at 0°

to 37°C. However, the relatively rapid elution experienced at 37°C precludes this temperature for routine use.

Ionic Environment. Hemadsorption tests carried out with 0.3 M sucrose substituted for phosphate buffered saline result in a marked reduction in RBC-host cell binding. The addition of 0.05 M NaCl to the sucrose system restores hemadsorption to an essentially normal level.

Receptor Destroying Enzyme (Neuraminidase). NDV-infected cells grown in the presence of RDE at a concentration high enough to render uninfected cells refractory to infection by high multiplicities of NDV display a normal HAD⁺ response throughout the virus "growth curve" when washed free of enzyme and tested in the usual manner. We conclude from this experiment that the HAD⁺ areas on the cell surface are not responsive to the action of the enzyme and, consequently, would not appear to represent adsorption of virus or viral antigen onto cellular receptors. These latter structures are presumably accessible to destruction by the enzyme and their loss would result in virus elution (Rubin and Franklin, 1957).

Versene and Trypsin. When HAD⁺ saturated giant cells are removed from the plastic growth surface with versene or trypsin, and the cell-free plates subjected to a standard hemadsorption test, the rather surprising effect illustrated in Fig. 22 was observed. The bovine erythrocytes became attached to the cell-free plastic surface over areas previously occupied by host cells. About 80% of the cells left residues that produced "footprints" of the ring-type hemadsorption pattern seen in Fig. 22, while remaining "footprints" showed complete saturation and only close examination revealed the absence of a cell beneath the erythrocytes.

These observations demonstrate the lack of effect of versene or trypsin on the hemadsorption reaction. More significantly, they provide evidence that the under side, i.e., substrate oriented surface of the cell, may mirror exactly the changes observed on the top side of the cell.

In connection with the relative physical accessibility of the top and under sides of cells to the surrounding milieu, it is a simple matter to test whether viral antiserum penetrates beneath plastic-attached HAD+ cells. HAD+ saturated giant cells were rendered HAD− by exposure to specific antibody, washed free of excess antibody, trypsinized, and the plastic plates subjected to an HAD test for the presence of "footprints." The observed complete absence of "footprints" attests to the accessibility of the under side of stretched cells to the antibody molecule.

MORPHOLOGICAL ASPECTS OF ERYTHROCYTE-HOST CELL SURFACE INTERACTION: BINDING TO MICROVILLI

Our earliest microscopic observations on living preparations of HAD+ cells showed that one outstanding feature of the system was the high degree of mobility afforded each individual erythrocyte at its point of attachment to the host cell. When strong currents were deliberately created in the saline solution bathing the cells, all of the erythrocytes were seen to execute gyrations and oriented movements consistent with

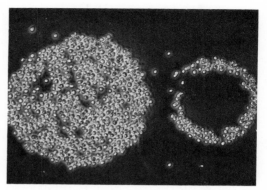

Fig. 22. Hemadsorption-positive "footprints" produced by removal of spread cells by versene. Spread HAD+ cells were removed from the plastic plate by treatment with versene, and a standard hemadsorption test was performed on the treated *plate*. The typical "footprints" observed are illustrated here.

an attachment to the cell by an extremely flexible, thin thread. This effect is documented in Figs. 23 and 24 which show hemadsorption in a living system under phase contrast microscopy. In Fig. 23 the fluid bathing the cells was not disturbed, and the bovine red blood cells display their usual circular cross-section. Figure 24 is a photomicrograph of the same cell taken while a stream of air, in the direction shown by the arrow, was directed over the surface of the fluid bathing the cells. Note that *all* of the bound erythrocytes are stretched and oriented in the direction of flow of the currents set up over the cell. If the direction of the current is shifted 90° the red blood cells respond in unison with a corresponding shift in their axis of orientation. When the saline bathing the cells comes to rest, the bovine erythrocytes resume their original circular cross-section and are identical in appearance to the cells in Fig. 23.

When a strong flow of fluid is directed across adsorbed bovine erythrocytes—as may be obtained when OsO_4 fixative is poured into a petri dish from one edge—the RBC become oriented and highly stretched, a condition readily appreciated by observing OsO_4-fixed HAD+ "footprints" at high magnification. It is apparent from Fig. 25 that the bovine erythrocytes are being held firmly to the plastic surface through a small num-

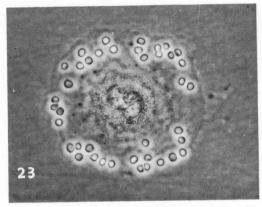 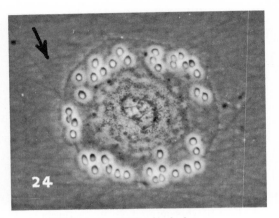

Figs. 23 and 24. Stress-oriented gyrations of attached RBC. Bovine RBC adsorbed to an NCV-infected giant cell were photographed immediately after hemadsorption while the fluid bathing the cells was in a quiescent state (Fig. 23), and then while a steady stream of air was inducing current flow in the bathing fluid (Fig. 24). The direction of fluid flow is indicated by the arrow. Comparison of identical erythrocytes in the two figures will show the oriented stretched configuration of RBC under unidirectional flow stress.

ber of attachment points. These points are clearly visible and countable in this figure, where the normally spherical and rather flexible bovine erythrocytes are seen greatly distorted. An erythrocyte may be attached at one point and produce a streamlined teardrop configuration when subjected to unidirectional forces transmitted through the fluid, or at as many as five independent

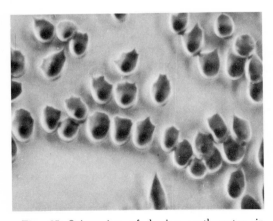

Fig. 25. Orientation of bovine erythrocytes in OsO_4-fixed "footprints." "Footprints" resulting from versene treatment of HAD+ giant cells (Fig. 22) were fixed with OsO_4 by directing a stream of fixative in one direction over the cells. Note the markedly stretched and unidirectional orientation of the RBC. Oil immersion phase contrast optics reveal finger-like projections on the RBC at the point of attachment to plastic.

points, producing a multi-fingered distorted sphere.

Close examination of individual HAD+ HeLa cells reveals exactly the same type of uni- or multi-point attachment between erythrocyte and host cells; furthermore, it is possible, with the light microscope, to resolve the structures binding the erythrocyte to the infected cell and identify them as microvilli, commonly described as a surface component on most cell types. The photomicrographs in Figs. 26–28 show RBC binding to host cells by means of microvilli. A striking characteristic of this type of binding becomes apparent upon close examination of Fig. 28. The extreme edge of the cell is outlined by a series of small arrows—all pointed in the direction of flow of the OsO_4 solution at the time of fixation. The microvilli on the leading edge of the cell normally project radially from the cell and lie along the plastic surface. The high resistance to flow presented by the relatively large RBC produces a condition in which those microvilli with attached RBC are whipped back over the cell surface by the flow of fixative. They may be observed on the cell surface connected to an RBC. Microvilli without RBC attached still remain projected radially from the cell surface.

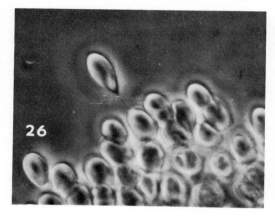

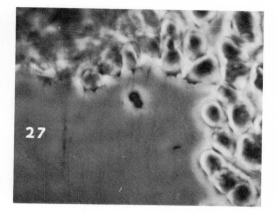

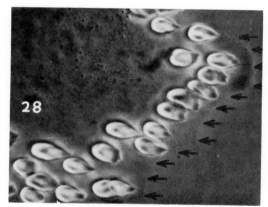

Figs. 26–28. Microvillus-erythrocyte binding in HAD+ cells. Oil immersion phase contrast photomicrographs of bovine RBC attached to NDV-infected giant cells are shown. Attachment of a single RBC to the apex of a microvillus is shown in Fig. 26. The distorted shape of the RBC results from a flow stress produced when fixative was added to the cells. In Fig. 27 several microvilli are visible at the point of contact with the red blood cell surface. In Fig. 28 the edge of the host cell is outlined by a series of arrows pointing in the direction fixative was added to the cells. The RBC are seen attached to the microvilli and displaced from the edge of the cell by the length of the microvillus. The RBC have been whipped back onto the surface of the cell.

The maximum number of microvilli to which an RBC may bind, as evidenced by the number of projections visible on erythrocytes under unidirectional flow stress, is about the same seen for RBC binding in "footprints," i.e., five. An average number of microvillus binding contacts per RBC appears to be about three or four. If a bovine RBC settling by gravity onto a HAD+ cell encounters about three or four microvilli, and the microvilli are relatively evenly distributed about the cell, we can make a reasonable estimate of the total number of potential binding sites on the cell. Thus, a normal-size HeLa cell that binds about 30–40 bovine RBC on its top surface at saturated hemadsorption and as many on the bottom surface ("footprints") may contain about 200–400 microvilli.

These numbers are consistent with values obtained by calculating how many microvilli could exist in a regular array on the surface of a spread HeLa cell (area *ca.* 1600 μ^2; Puck, Marcus, and Cieciura, 1956) when separated approximately 2 to 4 microns center-to-center as observed on several infected and non-infected cells.

Although binding of red blood cells to the host cell surface by other than attachment to a HAD+ microvillus has not been ruled out completely, no evidence has been obtained for its existence during the early stages in the virus growth cycle under consideration. The uniform distribution of viral antigen over the cell surface as shown so clearly by Morgan *et al.* (1962) through the use of ferritin-conjugated viral antiserum, and the cytohemadsorption involving large contiguous areas of the cell surface plainly revealed by the work of Hotchin *et al.* (1958) may reflect saturation of the cell surface in the relatively late stages of infection examined by these investigators.

Further insight into the morphological nature of the RBC-HAD+ cell bond is gleaned from observations on crescent-shaped cells by oil immersion dark field microscopy during early infection. The *convex* perimeter and apexes of the cell are abundant with microvilli in both infected and non-infected cells. In strong contrast, the *concave* perimeter of crescent cells is free of microvilli and presents a remarkably smooth contour. As mentioned above, and illustrated in Fig. 14, only the *convex* perimeter of crescent cells manifest a HAD+ reaction. Thus, the areas on the cell surface without microvilli remain HAD−.

Preliminary electron microscopy of HAD+ saturated cells, carried out in collaboration with Dr. Elliott Robbins, substantiates the conclusion that virtually all early RBC-host cell binding is mediated through the microvillus. Some microvilli are seen to contain at their tip an essentially mature virus particle, whereas other microvilli, active in binding, have less well-defined structures at the apex.

We conclude that in the early stages of infection specific adsorption of a single RBC to a myxovirus-infected host cell as observed by the light microscope directly reflects the presence of a single mature virion or some advanced stage in the maturation of a solitary virus particle.

A Model for Surface Modification in Myxovirus-Infected Cells

Normal Cell Behavior

A model concerned with the dynamics of surface modification in virus infected cells must consider the behavior of the normal uninfected cell. The following aspects of normal cell function deserve particular attention: (1) activities of the *cell surface*, (a) associated with the phenomenon of budding-off of fragments of the cytoplasmic membrane from the microvilli and, (b) concerned with contact-inhibition and, (2) reactions involved with the *intracellular* synthesis, accumulation, and transport to the surface of normal and special macromolecules.

Cell Surface-Associated Events. Several investigators have clearly established budding-off at the apical portion of the microvillus as a regular feature of normal cells. For example, Hoyle (1962) has demonstrated this phenomenon through exquisite use of dark-field microscopy, and Morgan *et al.* (1962) by equally superb electron microscopic studies. These and other investigators have stressed the existence of a normal cell process that produces end products, i.e., cytoplasmic buds similar in many morphological features to the mature virus particle.

In addition, the phenomenon of contact-inhibition as described by Abercrombie (1962) appears primarily to involve cell surface interactions. Vogt and Dulbecco (1962) have invoked loss of contact-inhibition as a likely explanation for the haphazard three-dimensional growth patterns which accompany transformation of normal cells by tumorigenic viruses.

Intracellular Events. The consideration of intracellular activities will be restricted to those events concerned with the synthesis of a hypothetical protein molecule in the interior of the cell and its conveyance to the surface for deposition in the cell membrane. Based on Palade's concept (Palade, 1956) of the endoplasmic reticulum as an essentially continuous network of membrane-bound cavities permeating the entire cytoplasm from nucleus to the cell membrane, one can picture a logical sequence of events to integrate in morphologic terms, the areas of protein synthesis and accumulation, to transport of cell-membrane destined protein molecules to the cell surface. Moreover, following Bennett's scheme for membrane flow (Bennett, 1956), and Watson's demonstration that the inner and outer nuclear membrane are continuous at the edge of the nuclear membrane pores (Watson, 1955), it is tempting to assume transport of normal cell messenger RNA from the cell nucleus to the ribosome-studded reticulum where synthesis of the hypothetical protein molecule would occur. The smooth membrane system of the Golgi complex, apparently continuous with the endoplasmic reticulum (Palade, 1956), would then accumulate and concentrate the protein prior to its movement to the cell surface. Evidence is available for direct movement of protein granules to the exterior of the cell by means of the Golgi system (Scharrer and Brown, 1961).

We will consider below how these defined functions and capacities of the uninfected cell may be recruited to perform similar tasks involving the modified molecular elements whose formation is dictated by the genome of the invading virus.

Behavior of Virus-Infected Cells

Investigations in the field of bacterial and animal virology present little evidence to suggest that newly infected host cells necessarily turn to new means of coding nucleic acids, revised pathways of synthesis, or different morphologic structures to encode, synthesize, and transport, respectively, viral specific molecules. In light of this, we consider as a basic premise that modification of the cell surface in the early phase of infection takes place by mechanisms and means normally available and operating in uninfected cells.

First, it is necessary, in the case of myxovirus infection, to examine the accumulation and movement of hemagglutinin *inside* the cell in order to correlate its intracellular behavior with its transport and ultimate incorporation into the cell membrane. One outstanding feature of many virus infections is the accumulation, as judged by the intensity of staining with immunofluorescent techniques, of large amounts of viral antigen in a juxtanuclear region of the host cell. The intracellular localization of NDV hemagglutinin follows this same pattern. Specific virus antigen is visible first as a barely discernible pattern of diffuse fluorescence adjacent to one side of the nucleus in a perinuclear position which, in time, increases in intensity and its degree of localization in discrete granules. In clonal lines of HeLa cells infected with NDV this localization is extremely precise

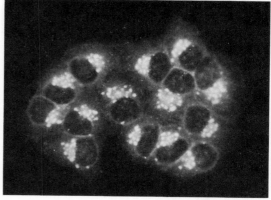

Fig. 29. Specific immunofluorescence in NDV-infected HeLa cells. Normal-size HeLa cells were infected at high multiplicity with NDV, incubated 6½ hr, and stained with fluorescein-tagged antibody specific for NDV. The clone of 14 cells pictured here illustrated the uniform staining response seen from cell to cell, and clearly demonstrated the juxtanuclear location of the viral antigen. Occasionally, a few fluorescent granules are seen in a perinuclear position more remote from the main mass of fluorescence. This photomicrograph was taken from a series of experiments done in collaboration with Morton Freiman.

and in early infection restricted to granules contained within the perinuclear region. Figure 29 illustrates this pattern of fluorescence in a clone of 14 cells after 6½ hr infection at relatively high multiplicity. Hemadsorption tests performed on infected cells after the same incubation period indicate near-saturation of RBC binding. Spontaneously formed giant cells in these preparations present the same pattern of fluorescence. The well-documented studies of Wheelock and Tamm (1961) reveal a similar pattern of fluorescence in non-clonal lines of HeLa infected with NDV. In many instances the granules appear to encircle the nucleus.

Prolonged exposure of uninfected HeLa cells to osmium tetroxide reveals the Golgi complex as illustrated in Fig. 30. All the fluorescent granules of infected cells (Fig. 29) appear to be located within that area of the cytoplasm darkened by prolonged exposure to OsO_4 and generally recognized as the Golgi region (DeRobertis, Nowinski, and Saez, 1960). Thus, we conclude that viral hemagglutinin destined to appear on the cell

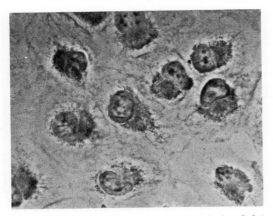

Fig. 30. Osmium tetroxide staining of the Golgi complex in HeLa cells. Normal-size, uninfected HeLa cells were stained by prolonged exposure to OsO_4. The oriented juxtanuclear position of the Golgi complex is evident. Some portions of the darkly stained Golgi region are seen to encircle the nucleus.

surface can be found in the specific region of the cytoplasm that contains the smooth membrane and vesicle system of the Golgi complex. The very likely continuous association between the nuclear membrane, endoplasmic reticulum, smooth membrane system of the Golgi complex, and the cell's exterior, referred to above, provides a logical means for the transport of hemagglutinin from its intracellular site(s) of synthesis to the cell surface. Localization of hemagglutinin in the Golgi region may reflect its accumulation in a transport area with insufficient capacity to discharge its traffic during times of peak synthetic activity, or when the rate of hemagglutinin production is not subject to feed-back control—as seems likely in virus-infected cells.

Other investigators have considered hyperfunctioning of the Golgi region in virus infected cells in a different light. Notable among these are Adams and Prince (1959) who worked with NDV-infected Ehrlich ascites tumor cells, and Love (1959) who examined several virus-cell systems. These two groups of workers envisioned the Golgi system as a type of intracellular defense mechanism.

The Golgi complex has been considered in detail here for a second reason, namely,

it provides a plausible explanation for one of the most puzzling questions raised by these studies, i.e., what special feature or organoid of the cell is associated with bipolar hemadsorption? In many specialized secretory cells the Golgi complex itself displays a significant degree of polarity within the cytoplasm (DeRobertis, Nowinski, and Saez, 1960). Polarization of the Golgi region is readily discernible both in osmium tetroxide-stained uninfected HeLa cells (Fig. 30) and the immunofluorescent NDV-infected cells (Fig. 29). In the typical biped elongated HeLa cell (Figs. 10 and 11) the Golgi complex occupies a position on one side of the nucleus and is oriented about the major axis of the cell. Two features recommend the Golgi complex as the orienting principle in hemadsorption bipolarity: (1) it is present in all cells in a definitely oriented position in the cytoplasm, independent of the cells' cross-sectional shape and, (2) it is part of the continuous chain of structures that extend from the nuclear membrane to the exterior of the cell. Although correlative studies are still in progress comparing orientation of bipolar hemadsorption in circular spread giant cells to polarity of the Golgi complex, preliminary results suggest a positive relationship.

Thus, the Golgi system would appear to qualify as an intracellular oriented organoid that may satisfy the requirements for a polarized structure in the path from nucleus to cell surface. If the smooth membrane elements actually terminate at, or near, the cell surface in an area dictated by orientation of the Golgi complex, then the transport of hemagglutinin to the cell surface may be directed to the areas of most active microvillus formation in a manner consistent with the demonstrated dynamic behavior of these structures in converting HAD^- cells to the HAD^+ state. From the results reported here, there seems little question that formation of new microvilli is restricted to one or two definite areas on the cell perimeter at the point of juncture of cell and plastic surface. Hemagglutinin is included in the outer surface of the double-membered cell membrane, and is first detected at these areas of active microvillus formation. Once formed, the HAD+ microvilli move away from their point of emergence on the cell surface and spread radially in a bilateral fashion until the entire cell circumference is positive. The hemagglutinin-laden microvilli then move centripetally toward the area overlying the nucleus. During this period of active migration the apexes of microvilli pinch off and release membrane bound structures into the surrounding medium. There is some suggestion that the formation of new microvilli and the budding-off process may represent an equilibrium state that acts to maintain a constant number of microvilli on the cell surface. Thus, although the surface of the cell appears to contain a relatively constant number of microvilli, the latter are turned over in a dynamic manner through loss (budding-off) and replacement (formation). Also, there is evidence that the equilibrium of these cell-surface structures is affected by another cell-surface phenomenon—that of contact-inhibition. Several examples were found in which the formation of HAD+ microvilli was mutually inhibited by contact between adjacent cells. Figures 18 and 19 illustrate this effect.

These considerations suggest, as a working hypothesis, that the rate of budding-off of the microvillus is the rate-limiting reaction for the release of virus from the cell. This hypothesis predicts that differences in the rate of virus liberation would be greater between various kinds of host cells than between different surface-maturing viruses in the same host cell. In this connection it is of particular interest that although increases in virus multiplicity may markedly affect the duration of the latent period as discussed above, no effect on the rate of virus liberation seems to have been reported. This hypothesis is subject to critical evaluation by measuring the rate of liberation of a normal cell surface component from uninfected cells. These experiments are in progress.

Finally, a scheme is presented (p. 524) to indicate the possible relationship of surface and intracellular reactions to events in the normal and in the infected cell.

CONCLUSION

Modification of the surface of myxovirus-infected cells in the early stages of infection is viewed as a continuous alteration brought about by the incorporation of a new molecular species into the cell membrane at active polar regions on the circumference of spread cells by a process normally operative in the cell. Newly incorporated hemagglutinin is contained in microvilli produced in these regions. The active migration of hemadsorption-positive microvilli on the surface of cells, as demonstrated here, serves to emphasize the dynamic nature of these cell surface-associated events. A model is presented to integrate certain aspects of surface modification in virus-infected cells with morphological features and activities of the cell that may logically account for the behavior observed. The sequential events proposed to explain these dynamic changes in the cell membrane by no means constitute proof of their functional existence in virus infection; however, it is hoped that this model may stimulate further experimentation to this end.

ACKNOWLEDGEMENTS

This investigation was supported by Grant No. E-3619 from the United States Public Health Service, during the author's tenure as a Research Career Development Awardee (GM-K3-15, 461-C1). The author wishes to thank Jacqueline Bergman and Aylene Kovensky for valuable technical assistance in these experiments.

REFERENCES

Abercrombie, M. 1962. Contact-dependent behavior of normal cells and the possible significance of surface changes in virus-induced transformation. *Cold Spring Harbor Symp. on Quant. Biol.*, **27**: 427–432.

Adams, W. R., and A. M. Prince. 1959. Cellular changes associated with infection of the Ehrlich ascites tumor with Newcastle disease virus. *Annals N.Y. Acad. Sci.*, **81**: 89–100.

Bennett, H. S. 1956. The concepts of membrane

NORMAL CELLULAR EVENT   VIRAL EVENT

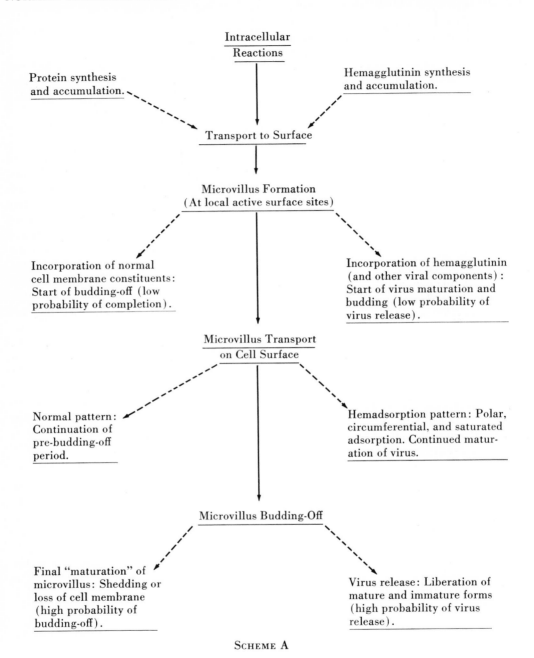

Intracellular
Reactions

Protein synthesis
and accumulation.

Hemagglutinin synthesis
and accumulation.

Transport to Surface

Microvillus Formation
(At local active surface sites)

Incorporation of normal
cell membrane constituents:
Start of budding-off (low
probability of completion).

Incorporation of hemagglutinin
(and other viral components):
Start of virus maturation and
budding (low probability of
virus release).

Microvillus Transport
on Cell Surface

Normal pattern:
Continuation of
pre-budding-off
period.

Hemadsorption pattern: Polar,
circumferential, and saturated
adsorption. Continued maturation of virus.

Microvillus Budding-Off

Final "maturation" of
microvillus: Shedding or
loss of cell membrane
(high probability of
budding-off).

Virus release: Liberation of
mature and immature forms
(high probability of virus
release).

SCHEME A

flow and membrane vesiculation as mechanisms
for active transport and ion pumping. *J. Biophys. Biochem. Cytol.*, **2** (4) Suppl. 99–103.
Cooper, P. D. 1958. Shortened latency as a result
of multiple infection by vesicular stomatitis
virus in chick cell culture. *J. Genl. Microbiol.*,
19: 340–349.

DeRobertis, E., W. W. Nowinski, and F. A. Saez.
1960. *General Cytology*, 3rd Ed., W. B. Saunders Co. Publ., Phila., Chap. 6.
Hotchin, J. E., S. M. Cohen, H. Ruska, and C.
Ruska. 1958. Electron microscopical aspects
of hemadsorption in tissue cultures infected
with influenza virus. *Virology*, **6**: 689–701.

Hoyle, L. 1962. The entry of Myxoviruses into the cell. *Cold Spring Harbor Symp. on Quant. Biol.*, **27**: 113–122.

Love, R. 1959. Cytopathology of virus-infected tumor cells. *Annals N.Y. Acad Sci.*, **81**: 101–117.

Mandel, B. 1962. Early stages of virus-cell interaction as studied by using antibody. *Cold Spring Harbor Symp. on Quant. Biol.*, **27**: 123–136.

Marcus, P. I. 1959. Host-cell interaction of animal viruses. II. Cell-killing particle enumeration: Survival curves at low multiplicities. *Virology*, **9**: 546–563.

———. 1962. Hemadsorption studies on single cells. *Bacteriol. Proc.*, p. 131.

Marcus, P. I., and T. T. Puck. 1958. Host-cell interaction of animal viruses. I. Titration of cell-killing by viruses. *Virology*, **6**: 405–423.

Morgan, C., R. A. Rifkind and H. M. Rose. 1962. The use of ferritin-conjugated antibody in electron-microscopic studies of influenza and vaccinia viruses. *Cold Spring Harbor Symp. on Quant. Biol.*, **27**: 57–66.

Palade, G. E. 1956. The endoplasmic reticulum. *J. Biophys. Biochem. Cytol.*, **2** (4), Suppl. 85–98.

Puck, T. T., and P. I. Marcus. 1956. Action of x-rays on mammalian cells. *J. Exptl. Med.*, **104**: 615–628.

Puck, T. T., P. I. Marcus, and S. J. Cieciura. 1956. Clonal growth of mammalian cells *in vitro*. Growth characteristics of colonies from single HeLa cells with and without a "feeder" layer. *J. Exptl. Med.*, **103**: 653–666.

Robbins, E. 1961. Some theoretical aspects of osmium tetroxide fixation with special reference to the metaphase chromosomes of cell cultures. *J. Biophys. Biochem. Cytol.*, **11** (2): 449–455.

Rubin, H., and R. M. Franklin. 1957. On the mechanism of Newcastle disease virus neutralization by immune serum. *Virology*, **3**: 84–95.

Sagik, B. P., and S. Levine. 1957. The interaction of Newcastle disease virus (NDV) with chicken erythrocytes: Attachment, elution, and hemolysis. *Virology*, **3**: 401–416.

Scharrer, E., and S. Brown. 1961. Neurosecretion. XII. The formation of neurosecretory granules in the earthworm, *Lumbricus terrestris* L. *Zeitz. F. Zellforchung*, **54**: 530–540.

Tolmach, L. J., and P. I. Marcus. 1960a. Development of x-ray induced giant HeLa cells. *Exptl. Cell Res.*, **20**: 350–360.

———, ———. 1960b. Newcastle disease virus (NDV) interaction with x-ray induced giant HeLa cells. *Bacteriol. Proc.*, p. 91.

Vogel, J., and A. Shelokov. 1957. Adsorption-hemagglutination test for influenza virus in monkey kidney tissue cultures. *Science*, **126**: 358–359.

Vogt, M., and R. Dulbecco. 1962. Properties of cells transformed by polyoma virus. *Cold Spring Harbor Symp. on Quant. Biol.*, **27**: 367–374.

Watson, M. L. 1955. The nuclear envelope. Its structure and relation to cytoplasmic membranes. *J. Biophys. Biochem. Cytol.*, **1**: 257–270.

Wheelock, E. F., and I. Tamm. 1961. Effect of multiplicity of infection on Newcastle disease virus-HeLa cell interaction. *J. Exptl. Med.*, **113**: 317.